NCSBN

National Council of State Boards of Nursing

The First 25 Years

1978 – 2003

Corinne F. Dorsey, M.S., RN

Joyce M. Schowalter, M.Ed., RN

ISBN #0-9796795-3-2

Table of **Contents**

ABOUT THE AUTHORS

Corinne F. Dorsey is a former nursing consultant, member of the Virginia Board of Nursing (1969–1979), and executive director for the Virginia Board of Nursing (1981–1995). Dorsey followed with keen interest and support the work of the Special Task Force—State Boards of Nursing that led to the organization of the National Council of State Boards of Nursing, Inc. (NCSBN®) in 1978. During her employment with the Virginia Board, Dorsey volunteered for appointment to committees of NCSBN and served on or chaired a committee from 1982 until her retirement in 1995, beginning with six years on the Bylaws Committee, first as a member and then as chair for five years. During that time she also chaired the special Bylaws Committee that completed the first revision of the NCSBN Bylaws. Other committee work included chairing the Subcommittee to Study the Regulation of Advanced Nursing Practice and serving as a member of the Practical/Vocational Nurse Competencies Subcommittee of the Nursing Practice and Education Committee and as a member of the Executive Director Orientation Program Task Force. With Richard Morrison she wrote an article in *Issues* entitled "Virginia Studies Access and Barriers to the Services of Nurse Practitioners" and she authored *A History of the Virginia Board of Nursing 1903-2003*. She has been honored by NCSBN with the R. Louise McManus Award, by the Virginia Nurses Association with its prestigious Nancy Vance Award, by the Medical College of Virginia Alumni Association of Virginia Commonwealth University (MCVAA of VCU) with its Hodges-Kay Service Award, and by the Nursing Division of the MCVAA of VCU with an Outstanding Nursing Alumnus Award. Dorsey has applied her avid interest in nursing history as well as her knowledge and experience to the endeavor of coauthoring this history with her friend and colleague, Joyce Schowalter.

Joyce M. Schowalter is the former executive director of the Minnesota Board of Nursing (1973–1999) and served on the American Nurses Association Council of State Boards of Nursing representing Minnesota until NCSBN was established. As a member of Area II she participated in the early planning that resulted in the establishment of the Special Task Force—State Boards of Nursing. Upon the formation of NCSBN she was elected to the board of directors and served the maximum six years in the offices of Area II director, vice president, and president. Throughout the years she chaired the Bylaws Committee, served on a test service evaluation committee and an ad hoc test security investigation team, and was part of several test service negotiating teams. She was also a member of the 1990 Executive Director Search Committee and chaired the Executive Directors' Network Planning Group (1994–1996). With Eileen McQuaid Dvorak, she wrote a chapter on the role of NCSBN in consumer protection for the second edition of *Current Issues in Nursing*, published by Blackwell Scientific Publishers, Inc. in 1985. Two relevant speaking engagements include a presentation of viewpoints on visions for the regulatory system at the December 1995 conference jointly sponsored by NCSBN and the Citizen Advocacy Center as well as the provision of a historical perspective and genesis of nursing regulation during the last 100 years as part of NCSBN's Institute of Regulatory Excellence in January 2004. A recipient of the R. Louise McManus Award, Schowalter brought a wealth of information and experience to the compilation of this book as she assisted the primary author, Corinne Dorsey.

FOREWORD

We were asked to write a review of the first 25 years of the National Council of State Boards of Nursing, Inc. (NCSBN®) soon after the celebration of its 25th anniversary. That anniversary coincided with the centennial observation of the 1903 enactment of the first four state laws to regulate nurses in the United States. Although the work is focused on the establishment of NCSBN in 1978 and events during the ensuing 25 years, we decided to include general information from the 75 preceding years to provide an overview of the history of regulation in nursing. *The American Journal of Nursing (AJN)*, from the first issue in 1900 through December 1978, provided the major source of information for the first two chapters. The editorials, articles, and proceedings of national meetings found in these publications were invaluable resources. We selected significant quotations from this source to introduce many of the chapters or to add interest within the chapters as appropriate to the topic under discussion.

Chapter 3 presents information from meetings of the American Nurses Association (ANA) Council of State Boards of Nursing and the papers of the Special Task Force—State Boards of Nursing. The latter was created in 1977 to plan for a free-standing organization that became NCSBN. Papers presented to NCSBN by Frances Waddle, Mildred Schmidt, Helen (Pat) Keefe, Sharon Weisenbeck, Sidney Willig, and others were reviewed and used to expand our background. The booklets published by NCSBN on the occasion of the celebration of the 5th, 10th, 20th, and 25th anniversaries provided insights into the work of the Special Task Force along with copies of correspondence from the members that were used in preparing these booklets. We also viewed videos of interviews with Elaine Ellibee and Mildred Schmidt. All available minutes of meetings of the NCSBN Board of Directors and the NCSBN Delegate Assembly; the *Book of Reports and Business Book*; *Issues*, *The Council Connector*, *Insight*, and the many issues of the *Newsletter to the Member Boards* served as the primary NCSBN resources for the information in Chapters 4 through 15. In addition, we reviewed NCSBN position papers, concept papers, monographs, reports of research, and the NCSBN Web site. Unfortunately the minutes of the meetings of the board of directors between the meeting of June 12, 1981, and the meeting of March 8 and 10, 1982, could not be located. While uncertain as to what may have been included that was not identified in other resources, we believe that the decision to change the name of the licensing examination was made during this time. We have also relied on our personal notes, files, and recollections as well as the files of the boards of nursing at which we each formerly worked, Virginia for Corinne and Minnesota for Joyce.

Throughout this history we used the terms state board of nursing or board of nursing consistent with the NCSBN definition of a state board of nursing as found in the 2003 NCSBN Bylaws. That definition is the following: "A state board of nursing is the governmental agency empowered to license and regulate nursing practice in any state, territory or political subdivision of the United States of America." Although we have used abbreviations extensively throughout, we have tried to define each at its first usage in each chapter and have included a List of Abbreviations at the beginning of the book.

Many persons assisted us during the past several years as we gathered material for this history. Kathy Apple, chief executive officer of NCSBN, frequently responded to questions and provided a continuing interest and support to us. Dawn Kappel, director of Marketing and Communications for NCSBN, has been our primary contact. We are grateful for her response to our many questions, her assistance in locating information, and her work in helping to finalize this publication. Several other current and former NCSBN staff members, our colleagues—both current and former executive officers of the member boards—have assisted us as well. We also wish to acknowledge the assistance of Jodi Koste, associate professor and archivist at the Tompkins-McCaw Library at Virginia Commonwealth University in Richmond, Virginia. She facilitated our review of the bound volumes of the *AJN* from 1900 to 1978 and other references housed at Tompkins-McCaw Library. Koste also provided a CD-ROM containing the illustrations from the *AJN* that are found in Chapters 1 and 2. We also acknowledge the cooperation of the ANA as the owner of the volumes of the *AJN* that were the source of these pictures.

We conclude the introduction with an expression of sincere gratitude to the intrepid women who served on the Special Task Force—State Boards of Nursing from 1977 to 1978. Gertrude (Trudy) Malone, Area I, Elaine Ellibee, Area II, Helen (Pat) Keefe, Area III, and Mildred Schmidt, Area I, committed their abilities and time to prepare the information and structure necessary for the members of the ANA Council of State Boards of Nursing to meet in June 1978 and cast the vote that created NCSBN. They obtained wise legal counsel from David Grams and were ably advised by parliamentarian Henrietta Marjan. These women built on efforts of the past, but planned for an organization designed in the public interest that would preserve the legacy of nursing regulation. They knew how to obtain necessary finances and they understood the art of negotiation. Those who have followed them as officers, directors, and members of the committees of NCSBN walk in their footsteps.

Corinne F. Dorsey and Joyce M. Schowalter
2008

The following is a list of abbreviations used throughout this work.

List of Abbreviations

AACN	American Association of Colleges of Nursing
AANP	American Association of Nurse Practitioners
ACHA	American Health Care Association
ACT	American College Testing Incorporated
ADA	Americans with Disabilities Act
AEC	Administration of Examination Committee
AHA	American Hospital Association
AIDS	Acquired Immune Deficiency Syndrome
AIM	Administrators in Medicine
AJN	*American Journal of Nursing*
AMA	American Medical Association
ANA	American Nurses Association
ANC	Army Nurse Corps
ANCC	American Nurses Credentialing Center
ANF	American Nurses Foundation
AP	advanced practice
APN	advanced practice nurse
AONE	American Organization of Nurse Executives
APRN	advanced practice registered nurse
ASAE	American Society of Association Executives
ASI	Assessment Systems Inc.
BC	board certified
CAC	Citizen's Advocacy Center
CAG	Compact Administrators Group
CAT	computerized adaptive testing
CCNE	Commission on Collegiate Nursing Education
CDC	Centers for Disease Control
CEPN-LTC	Certification Examination for Practical Nurses in Long Term Care
CGFNS	Commission on Graduates of Foreign Nursing Schools
CGI	Chauncey Group International
CLEAR	Council on Licensure, Enforcement and Regulation
CNA	certified nurse aide
CNATS	Canadian Nurses Association Testing Service Examination
CNM	certified nurse-midwife
CNS	clinical nurse specialist
CORE	Commitment to Ongoing Regulatory Excellence
CRNA	Certified Registered Nurse Anesthetist
CRNE	Canadian Registered Nurse Examination
CST®	clinical simulation testing
CTB	California Testing Bureau or California Testing Bureau/McGraw-Hill
DDB	Disciplinary Data Bank
DEA	Drug Enforcement Administration
DRG	diagnosis related group
ELVIS	Electronic Licensure Verification Information System
ETS	Educational Test Service
FANEL	Federation for Accessible Nursing Education and Licensure
FARB	Federation of Associations of Regulatory Boards
FNP	family nurse practitioner

FTC	Federal Trade Commission
GNAV	Graduate Nurses Association of Virginia
HCFA	Health Care Financing Administration
HHS	United States Department of Health and Human Services
HIPDB	Healthcare Integrity and Protection Data Bank
HIV	Human Immunodeficiency Virus
HRSA	Health Resources and Service Administration
ICAG	Interim Compact Administrators Group
ICONS	Interagency Conference on Nursing Statistics
INS	Immigration and Naturalization Service
IOM	Institute of Medicine
JCAHO	Joint Commission on the Accreditation of Healthcare Organizations
JONA	*Journal of Nursing Administration*
LRPTF	Long Range Planning Task Force
LRPC	Long Range Planning Committee
LPN	licensed practical nurse
LPN/VN	licensed practical/vocational nurse
LVN	licensed vocational nurse
MAIN	Midwest Alliance in Nursing
MBOS	Member Board Office Software
MNAR	*NCSBN Model Nursing Administrative Rules* (published)
MNPA	model nursing practice act (in development)
MNPA	*NCSBN Model Nursing Practice Act* (published)
MNRR	model nursing rules and regulations (in development)
MNRR	*NCSBN Model Nursing Rules and Regulations* (published)
MOS	military occupational specialty
MSR	multistate regulation
NACEP	Nurse Aide Competency Evaluation Program
NACNS	National Association of Clinical Nurse Specialists
NAFTA	North American Free Trade Agreement
NAPNAP	National Association of Pediatric Nurse Associates and Practitioners
NAPNES	National Association for Practical Nurse Education and Service
NASD	National Association of Securities Dealers
NBME	National Board of Medical Examiners
NCBPNP/N	National Certification Board of Pediatric Nurse Practitioners and Nurses
NCC	National Certification Corporation
NCCA	National Commission for Certifying Agencies
NCCMERP	National Coordinating Council for Medication Error Reporting and Prevention
NCLEX®	National Council Licensure Examination
NCLEX-PN®	National Council Licensure Examination for practical/vocational nurses
NCLEX-RN®	National Council Licensure Examination for registered nurses
NCNET	National Council Network
NCNIP	National Commission on Nursing Implementation Project
NCOA	National Change of Address
NCS	National Computer Systems, Inc.
NCSBN®	National Council of State Boards of Nursing, Inc.
NFLPN	National Federation of Licensed Practical Nurses
NHRA	Nursing Home Reform Act
NIRS	Nurse Information Retrieval System
NIS	Nurse Information System
NLCA	Nurse Licensure Compact Administrators

NLN	National League for Nursing
NLNAC	National League for Nursing Accrediting Commission
NLNE	National League of Nursing Education
NNAAP™	National Nurse Aide Assessment Program
NNIS	National Nursing Information System
NNLDB	National Nursing Licensee Data Base
NPDB	National Practitioners' Data Bank
N-PEC	Nursing Practice Education Consortium
NOADN	National Organization for Associate Degree Nursing
NOCA	National Organization for Competency Assurance
NOPHN	National Organization of Public Health Nurses
NP	nurse practitioner
NP&E	Nursing Practice and Education
NP&S	Nursing Practice and Standards
Nur*sys*®	Nurse System
OBRA 87	Omnibus Budget Reconciliation Act of 1987
OSHA	Occupational Safety and Health Act
PERC	Practice, Education and Regulation Congruence
PIN	provider identification number
PN/VN	practical/vocational nurse
PR&E	Practice, Regulation and Education
RCT	registered care technologist
RFP	request for proposal
RN	registered nurse
SBTP	State Board Test Pool
SBTPE	State Board Test Pool Examination
SNA	state nurses association
SNLQ	*State Nursing Legislative Quarterly*
SSD	Special Services Division
STR	Strategic Technology Research
TERCAP	Taxonomy of Error Reporting Root Cause Analysis and Practice Responsibility
TPC	The Psychological Corporation
UAP	unlicensed assistive personnel
USPHS	United States Public Health Service
VA	Veterans Administration
VN	vocational nurse
VUE	Virtual University Enterprises
YWCA	Young Women's Christian Association

CHAPTER ONE
EARLY REGULATION

It is the opinion of this International Congress of Nursing, in general meeting assembled, that it is the duty of the nursing profession of every country to work for suitable legislative enactment of regulating the education of nurses, and protecting the interests of the public by securing state examination and public registration, with the proper penalties for enforcing the same.

Resolution adopted at the International Congress of Nursing
New York, 1901[1]

THE YEAR 2003 marked the 25th anniversary of the establishment of the National Council of State Boards of Nursing, Inc. (NCSBN®) and was also, coincidentally, the year of the centennial of the first laws to regulate nurses in the United States. As a prelude to a history of the first 25 years of NCSBN, it is important to consider the events and the contributions of individuals and groups that surrounded the enactment of these first laws.

The Discussion Begins

History tells us that the earliest efforts for the legal regulation of nursing occurred in England. Ethel Gordon Fenwick founded the British Nurses' Association and the *British Journal of Nursing*, serving as its editor for many years. She also founded the International Council of Nursing in 1899, serving as its first president and then as its honorary president for many years. She was tireless in her efforts to obtain registration for nurses in England and in other countries.[2] However, England did not achieve a registration law until 1919, and the first such law was enacted in Cape Town, South Africa in 1891. Another was enacted in New Zealand in 1901.[3] These laws are believed to be the first such laws in any nation.

Early public discussion of regulation of nursing in the United States took place at a meeting of the Nurses Section of the Congress of Hospitals and Dispensaries. Held during the Chicago World's Fair in 1893, it was the first general meeting of nurses in this country. Ethel Fenwick spoke at this meeting, which was chaired by Isabel Hampton Robb. Robb was the superintendent of the Johns Hopkins Hospital in Baltimore, Maryland and later was the first president of the Nurses' Associated Alumnae of the United States and Canada. Two major organizations were formed following the 1893 congress meeting. The first, the American Society of Superintendents of Training Schools, was formed in 1894. This organization later became the National League of Nursing Education (NLNE) and in 1952 merged with other groups to become the National League for Nursing (NLN). The second was the Nurses' Associated Alumnae of the United States and Canada, organized in 1896.[4] The name of this organization was changed by the deletion of the words "and Canada" when the Canadian association withdrew in 1901 so that the organization could be incorporated in the United States, and in 1912 the name was changed again to the American Nurses Association (ANA).

Sophia F. Palmer, editor of the *American Journal of Nursing (AJN)*, called for the regulation of nursing at the New York State Federation of Women's Clubs in 1899:

> The greatest need of the nursing profession today is a law that shall place training schools under the supervision of the University of the State of New York. Such a law would require every training school to bring its standards up to a given point…[and] would require every woman who wished to practice nursing to obtain a diploma from a training school recognized by the University, to pass a Regent's examination, and to register her license to practice. It is of vital importance that examination boards be selected from among nurses in practically the same manner that medical boards are chosen from physicians [and] pharmacists, dentists and teachers are examined, each by members of their own profession.[5]

The first issue of the *AJN* was published in October 1900, and the *AJN* was the official publication for many years of the two organizations named above. The pages of the *AJN* through the first 20 years are a valuable resource in the history of the early laws regulating nursing in the United States and of the boards that administered these laws. Sophia Palmer, in addition to editing the magazine from its beginning until 1920, was also the first president of the New York Board of Nurse Examiners. She was actively involved in the national nursing organizations and played an important part in the organization of the New York State Nurses Association. Throughout her time with the magazine she continued to include information about the developing laws in her editorials, many of which were titled "Progress of State Registration." In addition, she included the full text of most of the laws as they were enacted by each state. For a number of years, the *AJN* published the entire proceedings of the annual conventions of the ANA and substantial reports of the conventions of the NLN, which have also proved to be valuable sources of historical information.

In an editorial in the *AJN* in September 1901, Palmer described the powerful results of the first general meeting of nurses:

> The congress in Chicago, held only seven short years ago, produced a complete revolution in the relations of training-schools and nurses. Movements for the higher education of the nurse in training date from that time, and our national and international fellowships and affiliations with other bodies of women are the direct offspring of that occasion.[6]

Influence of Nursing Organizations

There are many references that attest to the fact that one of the major aims of the early nursing organizations was to seek state legislation. Minnie Goodnow, in *Outlines of Nursing History*, said that such legislation would:

> classify nurses: (1) for their own protection, so that the better grades may not be confused with the poorer; and (2) for the protection of the public, so that they may be able to distinguish between the

qualities to be expected in a fully and properly trained nurse, and those in an untrained, partially trained, or imperfectly trained nurse.[7]

Palmer also called for state legislation in the proceedings of the Third Annual Convention of the Nurses' Associated Alumnae in May 1900, during a discussion about state associations:

When we come to organize a State society, the principal motive being to influence legislation, we take an entirely new departure from the motives actuating us in the organization of our associations for educational and social purposes. We go before the Legislature as citizens of the State, not as graduates of any one particular school.[8]

In the president's report at that same meeting, Isabel Hampton Robb said, in part,

As many of us know, the question of registration for trained nurses has been long in our minds, but we were also aware that to advocate legislation for nurses eight or ten years ago would have been to "put the cart before the horse." At that time, no *esprit de corps* existed among the leaders in our schools. Nothing much in the way of systematized teaching was recognized; certainly there was no uniformity in curriculum and not even an attempt at a general education and ethical standards. Among the nurses there was no professional feeling, not even among the graduates of the same school; there was simply nothing organized or professional about us. Collectively we could neither qualify as a profession, a calling, or a trade. For to be a member of a profession implies more responsibility, more serious duties, a higher skill, and work demanding a more thorough education than is required in many other vocations in life. But two things more are needful, organization and legislation.

But with the completion of the chain, the fullness of time brings us face to face with the vital question of registration for nurses, the foundation for which was laid just seven years ago. State registration is certainly the next and most important step towards achieving a fixed professional standard. According to the Constitution of the United States, an act authorizing registration for the whole profession and country cannot be passed by Congress at Washington, but each State must make its own laws for its own nurses. New York with its local and State associations will become sufficiently representative to ask for legal recognition for trained nurses within its domains. It is only fitting that this State [New York] should take the initiative. Its educational institutions are controlled by the University of the State of New York, which will not allow members of any profession to practice in the State until they show proper proofs that they have graduated from some recognized qualified school, and have also passed certain prescribed examinations in the studies taught in these schools. Only to those who satisfy these requirements is a license granted by the Regents of this University. If then, similar requirements had to be met by trained nurses, nursing would at once be established on a distinct educational plane.[9]

Palmer reported on the meeting in an editorial in 1900, bringing the call for state associations to a wider audience:

A few nurses, interested in forming a state association, met in the spring of 1900 in New York City. The focus of the meeting was on educational standards, "better trained women at the head of all schools," and concern about the caliber of "nurses" and their abilities from varied and different levels of training. The question asked at the meeting was "Do we desire to make it so that those who bear the name of nurse shall be so not in name only, but in deed and in truth?" "If so, a state association is necessary which can work for state registration and a uniform system of education." A committee was formed to discuss the questions and take action toward the organization.[10]

The first state nurses association was organized in New York in 1901. Virginia and Illinois nurses organized state associations the same year. New Jersey and North Carolina state associations followed in 1902.[11] As debate began in relation to legislation for nursing, the advocates claimed that registration was the best way of protecting nurses and the public against members of the profession they considered inferior. Opponents held that nursing is a matter of personality rather than training and examinations cannot demonstrate personal qualities. Florence Nightingale actively opposed registration. She was quoted by Sir Edward Cook in his biography, *Life of Florence Nightingale*, as having written the following in 1890,

The tendency is now to make a formula of nursing, a sort of literary expression. Now, no living thing can less lend itself to a formula than nursing. It cannot be tested by public examinations, though it may be tested by current supervision.

Cook went on to write of Nightingale,

She held that, consciously or unconsciously, the Registrationists had lost the essential truth about nursing…. Her objection was not to taking precautions against impostors, but to the misleading nature of the precautions; not to the tests, but to their inadequacy. She maintained that the number of beds in a hospital, the length of time spent in a school and the ability to write the answers to questions would not furnish a guarantee that the nurse is capable of caring for a sick person.[12]

Nurses in the United States concluded that the registration of nurses was necessary, although some cautioned that enforcement and diligence would be vital to making it work. Lavinia Dock, in the lead article in the first issue of the *AJN*, wrote,

Many laws, especially such as are meant to regulate the conditions of labor of, let us say, women and children, fail entirely to effect the desired changes because they have been so constructed that the method of enforcing the penalty has been left out. This point needs emphasis; so many people imagine that law is like an automatically working machine; that once passed it will keep on going of its own accord, protecting the good and restraining the bad. On the contrary, unless some one is enough interested to be responsible for seeing that it is obeyed, it will stand on the books forever as harmlessly as a verse from "Mother Goose." Who then is responsible for seeing that law is obeyed? Whoever is injuriously affected by its being disobeyed must see to it. If the State is injured, the State will see to it. But if we make laws for our benefit, the State will not concern itself further than by providing courts of justice. Thus we find that in the best medical laws, the county medical societies are designated as being the bodies who shall bring prosecution for violations of law, and the expenses they incur are to be repaid from the fines.

We, if we wish to secure laws, will have to do the same. The only alternative would be to allow some other body of persons to take this trouble off our hands, in return for which service we would place ourselves under their control. This would be slavery, of which not even the shadow can be tolerated.

So it comes down to this: not, What can we expect from the law? but, What can we expect from ourselves and from the people all about us? They will not willingly allow us an advantage which they think will disadvantage themselves, and we may not disregard their interests in considering our own, but should rather seek to safeguard both, and so go amicably on together.

What, then, do we want to do? To establish a recognized standard of professional education. There will be a disappointment here to many, for we cannot establish by law our highest professional standards, only the medium, only the fair general average, at any rate, at first. The secretary of the University of the State of New York writes: "It would be wise, in a movement for licensing trained nurses, to establish a State society and then to determine minimum qualifications to be exacted in preliminary and professional training. The object of the law will be defeated if the requirements are fixed too high at first."

Restrictive legislation affecting the professions, then, is not to be gained once and forever; this is another point for us to remember. It does not mean just one effort, but continuous efforts for the rest of time.[13]

This last paragraph has been quoted time and again throughout the years, as a reminder that the nurse practice acts will continue to be amended as the profession and society change.

In another editorial in the *AJN*, Sophia Palmer discussed women "who call themselves nurses," who come from schools:

where the institution is poor or where it has been established for commercial purposes, the nurse is worked to the limit of her capacity, while the systematic, practical and theoretical instruction is disproportionately small—compared to those from the better schools. The remedy for this state of affairs will only come through the efforts of the nurses themselves. Registration with its two great principles, must bring the needed protection, first in giving a better training to the nurse of the future, followed by protection to the public and the regular graduate against those same "rejected probationers," "laundresses," etc., who are now free to masquerade in a nurse's uniform.

She concluded with the following: "It may be to some a hackneyed subject, but until registration and the principles involved become a reality, it will be the *alpha* and *omega* of our text."[14]

Movement Toward Legislation

The International Congress of Nursing was held in Buffalo, New York in 1901. Representatives from the American Society of Superintendents of Training Schools, the Nurses' Associated Alumnae of the United States and Canada, and the International Council of Nursing, including its president, Ethel Fenwick, attended this meeting. The December 1901 issue of the *AJN* included an editorial by Fenwick titled "International Unity on State Registration," which had previously appeared in the October 26 issue of *Nursing Record*, a British publication. The following is an excerpt from this editorial, which reported on the recent congress:

Without doubt the most important feature of the recent International Nurses' Congress was the unanimity of the American matrons present and of upwards of five hundred trained-nurse members and delegates on the question of the fundamental need for State Registration of Nurses. We give below the resolution which was passed enthusiastically and unanimously by the Congress standing:

Whereas, The nursing of the sick is a matter closely affecting all classes of the community in every land;

Whereas, To be efficient workers nurses should be carefully educated in the important duties which are now allotted to them;

Whereas, At the present time there is no generally accepted term or standard of training, nor system of education, nor examination for nurses in any country;

Whereas, There is no method, except in South Africa, of enabling the public to discriminate between trained nurses and ignorant people who assume that title; and

Whereas, There is a fruitful source of injury to the sick and of discredit to the nursing profession;

[Therefore, be it resolved that] It is the opinion of this International Congress of Nursing, in general meeting assembled, that it is the duty of the nursing profession of every country to work for suitable legislative enactment of regulating the education of nurses, and protecting the interests of the public by securing state examination and public registration, with the proper penalties for enforcing the same.[15]

In their book, *Nursing Illuminations: A Book of Days*, P. T. VanBetten and M. Moriarity quote Carolyn E. Gray, who served on a board of nursing and was perhaps best known as one of the authors of *Anatomy and Physiology for Nurses* and who wrote in 1917,

Every bill introduced by nurses in every one of the states that has nursing laws has had for its purpose:

1. Improvement of the care of the sick.

2. Better education for the nurse so as to fit her to give this care.

3. Protection of the public by making it possible for them to differentiate between the nurses who have qualified themselves and those who have not.

She went on to argue that bringing the public to the realization that the legislation for which the nurses were working was for the benefit of the patient more than for that of the nurses was essential to overcoming opposition to the proposed laws. She concluded, "So that each one does her share to educate public opinion, we shall find we have more friends than we need."[16]

In the references cited above, there is great emphasis on the need to improve the education of nurses and to standardize this education. However, there is also a consistent focus on the protection of the public that would occur as the result of the enactment of laws to regulate nursing, and public protection was the justification for standardizing the education of nurses and improving the training schools. In their 1976 book, *Nursing Practice and the Law*, Milton J. Lesnik and Bernice E. Anderson reminded the reader that the regulation of professions and occupations is part of the police power of the state, but that the power of the state is not unlimited. It is restricted by the limits of both state constitutions and the Constitution of the United States. They stated that "in a democracy, the welfare of society is always paramount to that of the individual." Further, "when restraints and burdens are laid upon individuals, by laws enacted under the police power, they are required to be beneficial to society." Lesnik and Anderson went on to say that such laws must meet certain tests to determine public benefit. For example, "such law must operate equally on all persons within the controlled activity in the same circumstances" and "the means adopted to exercise control must be reasonable and related to the objects which the law seeks to accomplish."[17] Therefore, public protection has been recognized as the justification for laws to regulate nursing since the beginning of the movement in the late years of the 19th century through the 20th century and remains the justification for these laws to this day.

By the end of 1901, the national organizations were in place, a few state associations were organized, and the *AJN* provided a means of communication. Members of the state associations worked to develop proposed legislation to be enacted in the states. A reminder to put nursing history into the broader perspective of societal events was given by Susan B. Anthony, an outstanding proponent of suffrage for women. She spoke at a meeting of the New York State Nurses Association in 1902. In her presentation, as reported in an *AJN* editorial,

she referred to the great power of women's organizations, and she emphasized the point that if the thirty thousand graduate nurses in this country had the right to vote they would obtain what they desire much more easily. She closed her address with an earnest appeal to the nurses to remember their power and the influence of their work, and to improve it to the utmost.[18]

First Laws Enacted

By any measure, the achievement of these groups of remarkable women who could not vote is one of the proudest moments in the history of nursing. The year 1903 marked the passage of the first four laws to regulate the practice of nursing in the United States. The first of these to be enacted was signed into law on March 3 by the governor of North Carolina. The New Jersey law was passed on April 17 and another in New York on April 20. The governor of the Commonwealth of Virginia signed the law on May 13. Palmer, in an editorial in the *AJN*, said that the General Assembly of Illinois adopted a bill for nurse registration on April 17 but the governor vetoed it.[19] The newly appointed members of the boards of nurse examiners in three of these states were leaders in the efforts within their individual states to obtain these new laws. They included Mary Lewis Wyche, the first secretary-treasurer of the North Carolina Board, Sophia Palmer, the first president of the board in New York, and Sadie Heath Cabaniss, the first president of the Virginia Board. All three have been inducted into the American Nurses Association Hall of Fame. *(see fig. 1-A)*

There were similarities among these four acts and there were great differences. They did not require that all who practice nursing must be licensed but did protect the titles by requiring that individuals who called themselves nurses must be licensed. The New Jersey law made no provision for a board, the New York Board members were appointed by the regents of the University of the State of New York, and in North Carolina the law provided for three nurse members and two physician members of the board. The regents registered the schools of nursing in New York while the boards in North Carolina and Virginia approved the schools. The Virginia act provided for five nurse members and authorized payment for services of the secretary-treasurer and for the expenses of board members with excess revenues to be placed in a special fund to meet other expenses of the board.

All of these laws made provision for the protection of titles, including "registered nurse (RN)," examination of graduates from the training schools, and recognition of those persons currently practicing as nurses (now known as grandfathering). Absent from the early laws were definitions of practice. The New York legislature was the first to define the scope of nursing practice when it adopted landmark amendments to the law in 1938.[20] An article headed "A Crusade for Safer Nursing" by Emily J. Hicks, RN, includes a telling subtitle: "How New York's New Nurse Practice Law Was Won." The article goes on to say that New York's was the first law in the country to require that all who nurse for hire must be licensed. Although it took several years for the law to be fully implemented because of changes in society, including World War II and the subsequent high demand for nurses, the provisions of this new law, recorded by Hicks, included the following:

- A definition of the practice of nursing—everyone who offers or undertakes to nurse for compensation or for personal profit will have to be licensed.

- Two classes of licenses—registered professional nurse and practical nurse.

- Specific lists of violations, which are classed as misdemeanors with a provision whereby a license can be suspended or revoked for just cause.[21]

Other States Follow

In 1904, the Maryland legislature enacted a law for the registration of nurses. As the state associations continued to organize, the nurses in each state began their efforts to obtain state registration laws. These efforts were often difficult and frustrating. Palmer made reference to the role of politics in the registration of physicians in Pennsylvania and she suggested that nurses should plan for "political interference supported by the pernicious and malicious group of quack nursing schools, of which there are a great number in Pennsylvania."[22] A number of references were reviewed to determine the order in which the various states enacted what eventually came to be known as nurse practice acts. Louis C. Boyd's *State Registration for Nurses*[23] and Sophia Palmer's "Progress of State Registration" articles from 1903 to 1920[24] were chosen because they were written at the time the laws were being enacted. An NCSBN publication titled *1978–2003: 25 Years of the National Council of State Boards of Nursing: Honoring Our Past to Create Our Future*[25] was selected because it provided information consistent with other sources for later actions.

In 1913, 10 years after the first laws were enacted, 36 states and the District of Columbia had nurse practice acts in effect. The most successful year was 1909 when the legislatures in 9 states and the District of Columbia acted affirmatively on bills for nurse registration. These states were Delaware, Michigan, Missouri, Nebraska, Oklahoma, Pennsylvania, Washington, Wyoming, and Texas. While still a United States territory, the Philippines was the first of the territories to gain a nurse practice act in 1915; the next was Puerto Rico in 1930. All states and territories whose member boards comprised NCSBN at the end of its first 25 years had nurse practice acts by the early 1950s except American Samoa and the Northern Mariana Islands where such acts were passed in 1961 and 1982, respectively.

There were many disappointments and frustrations along the way as the newly organized state nurses' associations struggled to achieve their major goal: the passage of legislation to regulate nursing and nursing education in all jurisdictions. In an editorial in the *AJN* in 1901, Palmer reported that Kentucky was the first state to seek legislation, but the proposed bill was defeated. Palmer stated, "but the nurses are not discouraged by this failure."[26] A British publication, *Medical Record*, in an article critical of the recently enacted legislation in the United States, cited the following from the North Carolina law, which was included by Palmer in a 1903 *AJN* article: "That nothing shall in any manner whatever curtail or abridge the right and privilege of any person to pursue the vocation of a nurse, whether trained or untrained." The article pointed out that none of the acts made sufficient provision for enforcement and expressed concern about the differences in the requirements for training.[27]

In January 1904, Palmer began what became a frequent plea to the nurses to plan carefully for legislation and to secure support before presenting their proposal to a legislator for introduction.[28] Her concern stemmed from a series of failures to get state bills signed. In 1903, the Illinois nurses had legislation prepared and introduced, the legislature passed the bill in April of that year, but the governor vetoed the bill. Another bill was vetoed in Illinois in 1905 and it wasn't until 1907 that a bill was passed that the governor agreed to and signed. One of the problems encountered in a number of states was that the state constitutions prohibited women from holding office, and the nurses argued that their boards should be composed of nurses.[29] In Ohio in 1904, the proposed bill was determined to be unconstitutional for two reasons: (a) it would limit the appointing power of the governor, and (b) no woman could hold office for the state.[30] Ohio did not have a nurse practice act until 1915.

In March 1904, Palmer commented in an editorial on action taken by the nurses association in Iowa, which she felt had made unacceptable compromises in their bill in order to get it passed quickly. She included a copy of the bill for registration that had been adopted and then stated,

---

The Iowa communication possibly may not be authentic, but if it is true that the nurses of that state have drafted, considered for two days, and adopted the bill for registration that accompanied the report, then we can only say that the nurses of Iowa have been culpably disloyal to the profession.

She closed this editorial with "Iowa will hardly expect reciprocity with those 'sister states' which she has so dishonored."[31] In April, Palmer again referred to Iowa in an editorial, noting that she had heard from the president of the Graduate Nurses' Association of Iowa who resented the "needless harsh" criticisms found in the March issue of the *AJN*. The president stated that while the membership as a whole was in favor of a board made up of nurses, the Legislative Committee "saw fit to change the language to delete the board of nurse examiners and substitute the board of medical examiners" on advice of attorneys. Palmer responded with the following: "Better to be ten years in getting a good bill than to have to accept one like that of Iowa…The bill remains a most unfortunate measure."[32] An improved bill was finally enacted in Iowa in 1907.

In 1904, the nurses in Massachusetts began a lengthy struggle to obtain a law for the registration of nurses in that state. Palmer, writing editorially in the *AJN* in both the February and March issues, expounded on a Dr. Worcester as an opponent of registration in Massachusetts. She referred to him as a "self-appointed Czar of professional nursing."[33] The bill in that state was once again withdrawn. Speaking again in an editorial in January 1906, Palmer said "There is no state in the Union which needs registration more than Massachusetts. Both medical quackery and nursing quackery seem entirely unrestrained."[34] She also said "We send greetings to the Massachusetts Nurses and say: Hold fast to your standards." Again the proposed legislation was withdrawn in 1906. In 1908, a bill passed the House in Massachusetts, but was defeated in the Senate, "mainly by the treachery of a nurse who had always seemed to be a good friend."[35] The nurses continued to meet opposition, primarily from physicians. In 1909, Palmer noted that "No group of nurses in their efforts for registration had had to meet such bitter opposition from physicians of high calling."[36] At last, in June, 1910, Palmer was able to report, "All will rejoice with the nurses of Massachusetts in that after such a long and lengthy struggle, they have at last succeeded in obtaining state registration."[37] Mary M. Riddle, the nurse who led the struggle in Massachusetts said, in 1907,

Each form of life and work demands a standard by which to estimate its usefulness and test its power; it follows as a natural sequence that there should be an established rule by which the education of nurses may be measured…. [State registration for nurses] will set a standard of excellence and nursing education so that the professional nurse will be the registered nurse. It will give a dignity and legal status to a profession, it will be the "hallmark of distinction," so to speak, or, if you please, the state's approval will set upon the nurse a stamp by which she is known to the world as "sterling."[38]

When the Pennsylvania state association was organized in 1903, Sophia Palmer, in an editorial in the *AJN*, urged that the Pennsylvania nurses would achieve success if they would take the time to educate the public on the idea that the benefit of legislation was first to the public and secondarily to nurses.[39] Although there was a bill ready for introduction in 1904 in Pennsylvania, the law was not enacted until 1909. In 1904, an *AJN* editorial stated that the Pennsylvania bill was defeated "through the influence of medical men who have private interests of a commercial character at stake."[40] Another editorial in 1908 showed that the Pennsylvania nurses continued to be frustrated in obtaining state registration. The Pennsylvania State Committee on Nursing worked vigorously to oppose the bill, but the "state medical society promised its support to the nurses."[41]

In the Editorial Comment section of the October 1909 *AJN*, Palmer further confirmed the opposition to early efforts to obtain legislation for the registration of nurses. In an article titled "Organized Opposition to Nursing Progress," she referred to a group that had opposed the bill for registration of nurses in Pennsylvania for years and had now organized a "so-called national association which has as its object the control of the nursing profession and is now publishing a little magazine." She quoted from the opening paragraph in the second issue of this magazine as follows:

Every physician knows, and every nurse ought to know that the business of nursing was created by the medical profession. The physicians have opened the door of this opportunity and put the nurses in the way of acquiring the necessary knowledge and skill.

Other quotations from the magazine, described by Palmer in her editorial, speak volumes about the views of those responsible for its content:

Pleasing the doctors is the surest way to add jam to your bread and butter.

These valiant guardians of the public heath (state examining boards) evidently judged it unsafe to permit any one to nurse who was not equipped and inclined to encroach largely upon the physician's definite province.

Nurses of the state registration type would change that title (Angel of Mercy) to "officious meddler" or "grasping commercialist," but the rank and file of the working nurse repudiate the selfish leadership of those self-seekers and will cling to the old ideals with loyalty to physician and devotion to the patient.[42]

In California, a nurse registration law was passed in 1905, but it was not put into effect. In 1910, in the Editorial Comment section of the *AJN*, under "Progress of State Registration," Palmer noted that 37 states had enacted laws, "although in one, California, the law is a dead letter, never having been put into operation."[43] Subsequently a new law was enacted in that state in 1913 and most references show that year as the original date of the nurse practice act in California. In the Editorial Comment section of the March 1913 issue of the *AJN*, under the title, "After Ten Years," Palmer summarized the progress made toward state registration thus far and urged nurses to continue to work together:

It is now ten years since the first bills for state registration were passed. When the pioneers in such movements began they had before them no precedents in this country to follow. We were not as closely united or as perfectly organized as at the present time and it was with difficulty that members of working committees could reach nurses in every legislative district of the state. Now we find all of this changed. It is perfectly possible for the chairman of a legislative committee to know almost to a man the sentiment of every member of a legislature. She can reach the nurses of the state quickly and having been selected for this peculiarly trying office because of her broad knowledge of the nursing affairs of the state, she can be in almost personal touch day by day with her associates in every legislative district. If the members of every degree stand shoulder to shoulder, ready to co-operate with her in a manner made possible through this closer organization, there should not be the prolonged struggle in securing new laws or amendments that was universally the case during the earlier years of the registration movement.

Palmer suggested that "destructive criticism on the part of great numbers of nurses" continued to be a problem to the movement. She asked that they make their criticism constructive and suggest alternatives that they would be willing to pursue. She closed with these words:

For the comfort of those who do their best, and whose reward is criticism, we repeat a remark made to us once upon a time by a prominent business man and philanthropist: "Show me a person who has never been criticized, and I will prove him to be a nobody."[44]

Several sources consulted included unusual reports of activities related to obtaining nursing laws in the states. One such statement was found in a report of a meeting of state representatives, recorded in the proceedings of the Ninth Annual Convention of the Nurses Associated Alumni of the United States. In this report, a member from Rhode Island is quoted as saying, "Our Association is struggling. Our bill was downed by the influence of the insane hospitals, and the man who was to present the bill in the legislature for us died. We hope to get it in next year."[45]

In her 1914 report on the Kentucky legislature's enactment of a nurse practice act that the governor had signed, Palmer described a moment of poetic justice for the nurses:

One of the men, who had avowed his opposition to the bill was Mr. Samuel Turley, a representative from Mt. Sterling. The very day when he had expressed his opposition, he had an attack of acute indigestion, while in the Capitol building, and fell in a faint. Among the first to reach his side were two trained nurses, Mary Alexander and Emma Hunt. They assisted in reviving him; and when he regained consciousness, and saw the nurses ministering to him, he said "God bless you ladies; I am for your bill now." Miss Hunt went to the hotel with Mr. Turley, and spent the entire afternoon and evening with him till he died. Several times he repeated his intention to work and vote for the bill. The incident had, doubtless, a profound effect on the legislature. One representative made a speech for it, and alluded to the incident. The bill passed the House with only three negative votes.[46]

At the Annual Convention of the American Nurses Association in 1915, during the session for representatives of boards of examiners, several papers were presented, including "General Legislation Pertaining to Nurses and Nursing," by Louise Perrin, RN. She spoke of several interesting acts that were outside of the nurse practice acts. In one, a law passed in Arkansas in 1899, there was a stipulation that no trained nurses shall be compelled to disclose any information about her patients. Perrin found that in California there was an "eight-hour law that applies to nurses in training." This was a reference to an eight-hour day. In Wyoming, each new graduate from a state hospital was to receive a school pin not to exceed the cost on $15.[47] In an editorial, Palmer reported on another such bill that demonstrated the attitudes of some in the South at the time. When the Alabama legislature passed a nurse practice act in 1915, it also enacted another bill at the same time that "prohibited white female nurses from nursing in wards or rooms of hospitals, public or private, in which Negro men are placed for treatment." The Alabama State Nurses' Association opposed this bill and asked for an amendment "which would have given white supervision over colored nurses and orderlies" but the amendment was defeated. Palmer wrote,

To those of us who have cared for colored patients in hospital wards, this seems a very arbitrary ruling. The reason given for such legislation was that the colored wards in some of the southern hospitals are not respectable places for white women, but the legislators seem to be blind to the fact that the fault for such conditions lies in the administration of the institution and is not the fault of either the white nurses or the colored patients.[48]

Challenges and Changes to the Nursing Practice Acts

As the various states moved forward with implementing the nurse practice acts and additional acts were passed, individuals and groups dissatisfied with the laws began to exert efforts to amend the existing acts. The following is an excerpt from the minutes of a meeting of the Virginia State Board of Nurse Examiners in 1904:

During the Session of the House, the past winter, we have been threatened with amendments. Doctors, with limited knowledge of the law, and of the nursing profession; lawyers, whose practice you could scarcely discover with a compound microscope, yet with a commendable energy, judging by the reams of foolscap they have written, have interested themselves in behalf of a few nurses who care nothing for the good of all and who have thought to intimidate the leaders in the movement by seeking such influence. But, by the true legal wisdom of our counsel, Mr. Glasgow, who has so kindly befriended us, and by the tact and diplomacy of our President, Miss Cabaniss, we have steered clear of the political public and our law stands intact.[49]

In 1906, Palmer reported in the *AJN* on the introduction of a similarly adversarial bill in the New York legislature that called for the repeal of the 1903 law. In this proposal, a commission to regulate nursing practice would be established. This commission would be composed of three "medical gentlemen drawing modest salaries of $7500, $4500, and $4000 respectively" with an additional five-member board of examiners also composed of physicians. The duties of the commission and the board included inspection of training schools, supervision of training, regulation of hours, processing of complaints regarding the training schools, development of curricula, creation of rules and regulations for examination of students, awarding of diplomas, and conducting of examinations for license.[50] This proposal was defeated.

As time passed, articles, editorials, papers presented at meetings, and textbooks made many references to compulsory laws, or laws that required any person who practiced nursing in a state to be licensed. Very few of the early laws had this as a requirement, or if it was included, it was often negated by exceptions included elsewhere in the same law. The need to make provisions in the laws for the inspections of schools of nursing was another concern frequently mentioned. Reciprocity, or the granting of licenses in a state to a nurse licensed in another state, also arose often as a point of discussion. All of these items were included in proposed amendments to nurse practice acts over the years. By 1912 the New Jersey legislature had amended the law in that state to provide for a board composed of nurses, something omitted in the original law.[51] Speaking editorially in an in the *AJN* in December 1913, Palmer said, "It is to be remembered that every law outlives its usefulness after a time and has to be amended in order that there may be progress."[52]

In order to determine what amendments were necessary, questionnaires were sent to boards in the states, and partial data was received from 26 boards. At the ANA Convention in 1915, Mary C. Wheeler, chair, presented the results in the Second Annual Report of the National Bureau of Legislation and Information. One interesting response showed that the range for the number of nurses registered by the board prior to January 1, 1914, was from 0 to 5,863. California had registered an additional 5,002 nurses between January 1 and December 31, 1914, even though the registration process in that state did not begin until the nurse practice act was passed in 1913. Another interesting response in this report had to do with what the boards considered the weak points in their laws. Some of the weak points identified by Wheeler are summarized as follows: four states listed the fact that their laws were not compulsory and four had questions about educational standards; three states listed no provision for inspection of the training schools; two states listed the terms of the waiver, inadequate registration fees, and inadequate salary for the secretary; and individual states listed other weaknesses including: that nurses associated with the training schools were prohibited from serving on boards, that physicians were allowed to serve on boards, that no provision for reciprocity had been made, and that the reasons to withhold a certificate were not the same as the reasons to revoke a certificate.[53]

Marietta B. Squire, a member of the New Jersey Board of Nurse Examiners, wrote, in an article in the *AJN* in 1913, on compulsory versus permissive laws,

---

If after…statistics are available, it can be shown that the existing [permissive] laws in the majority of states, having been lived up to in their fullest and best sense, still fail in accomplishing the purpose for which they were enacted, or that their greater efficiency depends on their being made compulsory—then in order that the benefits registration was intended to confer may be enjoyed by all desiring them, and protected against the harmful interference of the indifferent or unworthy— all nurses must be compelled to seek registration or other fields of work.[54]

It would be 60 years before almost all states had "compulsory" laws that required nurses to be licensed in order to practice.

Education and Regulation of Assistive Personnel

At the ANA Convention in 1912, Grace E. Allison presented a paper titled "Shall Attendants be Trained and Registered?" She began with a reference to the "old-time neighbor nurse" or "practical nurse" and said that:

to-day the appreciation of this so-called practical nurse is somewhat deteriorating, and we find the public grasping for some one professing more intelligence in nursing procedures, and offering a compensation to her proportionally greater than that of the old-time neighbor nurse.

Referring to a course for attendants offered by the Young Women's Christian Association (YWCA) in New York, Allison concluded,

But until we have that protection when NO ONE shall assume the title of *nurse* except those who are properly qualified and registered, it does seem that we should struggle onward, maintaining the standards established by those gone before us, rather than encouraging and legally recognizing the partially trained attendant.[55]

When the nurse registration act was passed in Florida in 1913, it had a provision for the licensing of attendants. The New York law was amended about the same time to provide for the training and licensing of attendants. Several other states followed in the next few years. References indicate that the support for attendants and their registration was motivated by a need for their assistance in the care of the chronically ill or for those patients less able to pay for the services of the caregiver. In the July 1918 *AJN*, Palmer wrote an editorial, "Virginia Leads in the Training and Licensing of Attendants," in which she points out that after discussion for more than a year, the Graduate Nurses Association of Virginia, through its legislative committee and working with the Board of Nurse Examiners, had a bill to train and license attendants passed by the legislature. The purpose of the act was to alleviate the serious shortage of nurses resulting from the demands of the World War I.[56] The law remained in effect until 1946 when the nurse practice act in Virginia was repealed and reenacted to provide for the education and licensure of practical nurses. Soon after that, an opinion of the Attorney General of Virginia led to the grandfathering of the licensed attendants as licensed practical nurses (LPNs).

Articles in journals and other sources indicate that there were other categories of caregivers regulated by the early boards of nursing in addition to RNs and attendants. These included individuals prepared in the psychiatric hospitals to give care to patients in those facilities and those trained specifically to care for patients with tuberculosis in sanitoria in several states. In the February 1926 issue of the *AJN*, in the State News section, under the title "Virginia," the following was stated: "The status of the tuberculosis nurse was the subject for a special called meeting of the GNAV [Graduate Nurses Association of Virginia] in Richmond." A decision was reached not to amend the existing law. Instead, certificates were to be issued entitling the holders to do the work of their specialty in the state.[57] Records of the Virginia Board of Nursing show that the board, by regulation without a change in the law, began examining graduates of two-year educational programs conducted in the state tuberculosis hospitals and issued certificates to those who passed, allowing them to practice as "certified tuberculosis nurses."

Efforts to determine which jurisdiction was the first to license practical nurses have been unsuccessful. As stated above, Florida and New York licensed attendants first and a number of other states did so over the next 20 years. There are a large number of references that show that there were ongoing concerns about the "subsidiary worker" expressed in discussions at meetings and in journal articles into the 1940s. In the 1930s, some of these began to use the term "practical nurse" differently than in the past. Former references used the term to describe an untrained or partially trained woman who assisted with care for neighbors and friends. The following excerpt from a resolution adopted at the ANA Convention in 1936 illustrates some of the actions taken by that organization regarding the subsidiary worker:

Resolved, That we urge the cooperation of the medical profession and community organizations in placing the care of seriously ill patients in their homes, in the hands of professionally trained nurses to the end that the care of the sick in their homes may be properly safeguarded.

Resolved, That subsidiary workers be used only for such duties, in the care of the sick, as are outlined for these workers in the *Manual of the Essentials of a Good Hospital Nursing Service* and for similar duties in the home.[58]

An editorial in the *AJN* titled "The Subsidiary Worker" cited a report given at the ANA Convention in 1936 that stated there had been an increase in the number of calls to the registries for "non-professional registrants." The majority of these requests were for nursing service rather than "housekeeping duties." The editor stated,

It is futile to set up courses and to prepare more "junior" nurses or "practical" nurses, or "attendant" nurses and to turn them out into the community "*without first providing the means for the control of their practice.*" Consistent with this opinion, the NLNE Board of Directors in January 1935 approved "the principle that all persons who give nursing service for hire be licensed," and opposed the development of schools "for training of subsidiary workers unless there is control of their practice in the state." Further, in 1936 the Joint Boards of the ANA, NLNE and NOPHN [National Organization of Public Health Nurses] agreed "that in their opinion it is the responsibility of the nursing profession to outline the principles and policies for the control of the subsidiary worker in the care of the sick."

The editorial continued with the following report of actions taken on the subject by the ANA Board of Directors in January 1937:

1. That in order to ensure complete nursing service for the public, the use of the service of graduate registered nurses should be promoted in every possible way.

2. That no formal courses for the preparation of subsidiary workers should be approved until such time as a method for the control of the practice of subsidiary workers is devised. In the meantime it is further believed that workers of this type should be prepared on the job for the specific tasks only that they are to perform in connection with that particular job.

3. That when it seemed expedient for nurses to serve on committees which have to do with the preparation of subsidiary workers, they should serve as individuals, and not representatives of organized nursing. Instances in which they would so serve should be governed by the local situation and by the practice which has heretofore existed in the community with regard to the question of nurses serving on committees for the discussion of problems which have community implications.[59]

Education and Regulation of Licensed Practical Nurses

An impetus for the development of programs to educate attendants or practical nurses was the Smith-Hughes Act, first passed by the United States Congress in 1917 and followed for many years. During the Great Depression of the 1930s, money from this act was available for expanding the offerings for preparation for work in the public schools under vocational education programs. Isabel Stewart at the

NLNE Convention in 1938 urged "that plans be worked out for the active cooperation of state leagues with state departments of vocational education which are conducting training programs for subsidiary workers.[60] As the number of educational programs increased, the need for regulation of these workers became even more important to the nursing organizations.

Dorothy Deming, writing in 1946, stated that the beginning of the education of practical nurses and when they were first licensed had been hard to pinpoint. She said, "We do not know where the first practical nurse was trained, although we think of the Brattleboro, Vermont Mutual Aid Association (1907) as the pioneer school with a formal training course for practical nurses under graduate nurse supervision."[61] This location was verified in most of the textbooks used in schools of practical nursing.

Two organizations were established in the 1940s that brought focus to the use of the title "LPN," assisted with the development of sound educational programs for LPNs, developed a definition of the role of the LPN, and provided further emphasis on regulation. The first was the National Association for Practical Nurse Education, founded in 1941 and later known as the National Association for Practical Nurse Education and Service (NAPNES). Membership in NAPNES was open to anyone interested in the education and practice of LPNs and NAPNES subsequently developed an accreditation program for schools of practical nursing. In 1946, the board of directors of NAPNES defined a practical nurse as:

a person trained to care for subacute, convalescent, and chronic patients in their own homes or in institutions, who works under the direction of a licensed physician or registered professional nurse and who is prepared to give household assistance when necessary. A practical nurse may be employed by hospitals, custodial homes, public health agencies, and industries or by the lay public.[62]

In 1949, the National Federation of Licensed Practical Nurses (NFLPN) came into existence as the membership organization for LPNs.

Shortly after the NLNE was reorganized as the NLN in 1952, the Department of Practical Nursing Programs was organized. In 1962, the NLN announced that it had "a new council of member agencies composed of educational programs in practical nursing." Soon after that, an accreditation program for schools of practical nursing was developed under the aegis of the NLN.[63]

A report from the ANA in January 1944 stated that 15 states had provision for licensing attendants or practical nurses, using a variety of titles. One title listed for Missouri was "obstetrical nurse." In Georgia, the title selected was "trained graduate nurse." Seven state laws provided authority for the approval of the educational programs.[64] Those present at the conference of representatives of state boards of nursing in 1944 adopted a recommendation asking the ANA to urge state nurses associations to initiate legislative programs leading to the licensure of attendants and practical nurses.[65] By 1953, 43 jurisdictions including Alaska, Hawaii, Puerto Rico, and the Virgin Islands used the title practical or licensed practical nurse and 2 (California and Texas) used licensed vocational nurse (LVN). Those jurisdictions without such legislation were Colorado, Delaware, the District of Columbia, Mississippi, Nebraska, Ohio, West Virginia, and Wyoming.[66] The District of Columbia was the last of these jurisdictions to obtain a practical nursing licensing act when the United States Congress passed the bill in 1960.[67] *(see fig. 1-B)*

Regulation of Nurses in Advanced Practice

As early as 1944, descriptions of the role of the RN in advanced practice appeared in print. For example,

The clinical nursing specialist has been described as a graduate professional nurse who is an expert practitioner because she has broader knowledge, deeper insight and appreciations and greater skills than those that can be acquired in a basic nursing course of generally accepted standards. She is, therefore, better able to analyze, explore, and cope with nursing situations in a specific clinical field and, in addition, to cooperate with other specialists in the improvement of service to the patient.[68]

The question of the need to address the regulation of nurses in advanced practice surfaced in the early 1970s with the advent of the education of nurses as clinical specialists and nurse practitioners. In 1971, Idaho was the first state to codify diagnosis and treatment as part of the scope of practice of advanced practice nurses. While a landmark action, the amendment was viewed as somewhat restrictive in that it required that each act of diagnosis and treatment be authorized by regulations jointly promulgated by the Idaho State Board of Nursing and the Idaho State Board of Medicine. Further, the regulations required that every institution employing nurse practitioners must develop guidelines and policies applicable to the practice in those settings.[69] Another early amendment to a state nurse practice act occurred in Arizona in 1972 when the following was added to the law elaborating on acts considered to be a part of the practice of the RN:

> The performance of such additional acts under emergency or other conditions requiring education and training and which are recognized by the medical and nursing professions as proper to be performed by a professional nurse under such conditions and which are authorized by the board of nursing through its rules and regulations.

The purpose of the amendment to the law was to counter an opinion issued by the state attorney general the previous year that stated that the pediatric nurse associate program at Good Samaritan Hospital in Phoenix was illegal. Later the same year, through its rules and regulations, the Arizona Board of Nursing recognized nursing in an extended role in two fields—that of the nurse-midwife and that of the pediatric nurse practitioner.[70]

Efforts to Amend the Early Laws

In the editorial section of the April, 1923 issue of the *AJN*, Mary Roberts noted that it had been just 20 years since the first registration acts were passed and that there were now 47 such laws, with 7 providing for the registration or licensing of attendants. She stated that the laws were "far from uniform," that some were very weak or inadequate. She continued,

> Where then is the achievement? Those women animated by the flame of heroic purpose who have struggled to obtain the laws can best answer the question. Only the women who have sacrificed their own feelings to appear before legislative committees, who have given up hours of needed leisure, and who have worked in season and out, can really evaluate the effort expended. Something has been accomplished in influencing public opinion, in overcoming the inertia of indifference to nursing standards that for so long characterized those not in immediate need of nursing service. More, very much more, could stand to our credit if every registered nurse really accepted the obligations that go with the title, to make the "R.N." a known and honored symbol.
>
> …The achievements of twenty years are infinitely less than the pioneers in securing nursing legislation hoped. None the less we have moved forward as rapidly as our own limitations and an inert public would permit. State registration is now one of the pillars upon which our professional structure rests. It behooves every nurse to make the most of it instead of supinely taking advantage of it.[71]

Articles, editorials, and reports of meetings in the years after most jurisdictions had nurse practice acts in place speak to continuing efforts to amend these acts. In the early years the efforts were directed primarily at providing for standardization of and the inspection of the educational programs. The next big thrust that continued into the 1970s was to provide for mandatory licensure for all who practice. In the 1940s and 1950s the emphasis was on defining nursing and the licensure of practical nurses. Beginning in the 1970s there were efforts to amend the nurse practice acts to authorize the advanced practice of nursing as the numbers of nurses educated as clinical specialists and nurse practitioners increased.

Conclusion

It seems appropriate to close this chapter on the beginnings of the laws to regulate the nursing in the United States for the purpose of public protection with a quotation from an article, "State Registration," by Lizzie M. Cox of Indiana. In the article, Cox gives an excellent history of the movement for registration at home and abroad. She closed with this broad outlook:

We must all remember that state registration is not a question that merely affects nurses. It is a part of a movement toward the betterment in general education. It is part of the movement to elevate women by fitting them for the better performance of their duties. It is a part of the effort to develop the human race and bring it to a nobler type. It is not only a nurses' affair, it is a question of the age, an educational question, a question for women, for the public, and a part of human advancement.[72]

Nurses everywhere should pause periodically to reflect on the achievements of a group of women who were not allowed to vote in 1903 but were united in their efforts to persuade the members of the legislative bodies in New York, New Jersey, North Carolina, and Virginia to enact the first nursing practice acts. These leaders were ready to continue their cooperative efforts to come together to fulfill the responsibilities inherent in these new laws.

CHAPTER TWO
COMING TOGETHER

Might we not by our earnestness and esprit de corps stand so closely together as to form a solid wall upon which may lean those State societies that find arrayed against them and their efforts an extremely conservative public, an antagonistic medical profession, and an indifferent nursing body. Let us hope that each and every such society is represented here today by a good, live delegate who shall gather inspiration for a most active home missionary service upon her return.

Mary M. Riddle, 1905[1]

MARY RIDDLE'S WORDS, taken from her president's address at the Eighth Annual Convention of the Nurses' Associated Alumnae of the United States, reminded those present that the state associations were developed by the national group. In the same address, she declared, "Who shall say that that very sympathy and moral support may not have been a real source of strength to the pioneers in obtaining registration and the recognition of our profession by the States?"[2] Riddle called attention to the importance of cooperation and unity. Her words provide a basis for discussing the efforts undertaken to bring together the representatives of boards of nursing.

Joint Meetings: 1903–1913

From the beginning, the leaders in the registration movement benefited from meeting together, as reflected in Riddle's comments. It was not long after the newly created boards of nurse examiners began to assume their responsibilities for the regulation of the practice of nursing that the members saw the advantage of meeting together. It was clear to many of them that the opportunity to assemble together within the structure of existing organizations would strengthen their mission to protect the health, safety, and welfare of the public. The following is an excerpt from the transcript of a conversation between Riddle and Sophia Palmer, president of the New York Board of Nurse Examiners, which took place at the business meeting of the 1905 Convention of the Nurses' Associated Alumnae:

Miss Palmer: It seems to me that it would be a very great help if when all of the members of the State associations come together at these annual meetings there could be a sort of an informal meeting or conference and discussion by the members of the board [of examiners of nurses] and the State officers who might be present. I am sure there are a great many questions we should like to settle at once and talk over in an informal way, and it would send us all home very much better informed and make it possible for us to work on more uniform lines. There are a great many points that in our relations with boards, trustees or the Board of Regents or State Officials can be discussed privately, but not publicly; they are what you might call family affairs, and we ought to get together and talk them over and find out what course has been taken in one State that might be of benefit to another. We might have a secretary or a chairman to call the members together and have an hour's talk during these Conventions, when we might have just this kind of an informal conversation.

President Riddle: I think that point is most excellently made, and possibly Miss Palmer will call such a meeting at the end of this session, when all the delegates of the State societies, I am sure will respond. An opportunity will be given now.

Miss Palmer: I make that call now. If, after this meeting is over, the delegates from the State societies will come over to this corner of the room we will have a little talk.[3]

Thus, we have what may well have been the first meeting together of representatives of the boards of nurse examiners from the various states with members of the state societies in attendance at the convention. At the previous convention in May 1904, several papers on the subject of state registration had been presented. Bowen (first name not available) from Massachusetts set the stage for the subsequent papers when she discussed the history of the movement toward registration and emphasized the danger of haste in trying to get legislation passed.[4] Sophia Palmer gave a paper titled "The Effect of Registration Upon the Educational Standards of Training Schools as Shown by Results in New York State." She reported that there had been "excellent compliance" with the standards set by the board, but that it was too early to know what the outcomes would be.[5] Sadie Heath Cabaniss, president of the Virginia Board of Nurse Examiners, presented her paper titled "The Justice of an Examining Board Composed of Nurses." She began with the following statement: "To raise a question as to the justice of the examining board for nurses applying for state registration being composed of nurses seems quite like endeavoring to add more truth to an axiom by the addition of superlatives."[6]

M. Adelaide Nutting, from the Johns Hopkins Hospital Alumnae Association, presented the final and lengthiest paper, titled "State Reciprocity." The term "reciprocity" refers to reciprocal agreements to facilitate the movement of nurses between states. Nutting indicated that she did not see an immediate need to resolve the question of reciprocity as registration laws had been passed in only five states. She continued by noting that lawyers and teachers found it difficult to meet the requirements of a new state and "that the restrictions of the law in this respect extend into occupations as well as professions, and are felt by many to be annoying or oppressive." Nutting added that "such conditions not being entirely compatible with the ideals of freedom which this country is believed to cherish, it is probable that efforts towards reciprocal relations in most of these matters have been made." She further suggested that some sort of compromise may have been developed in these other professions. The paper then continued with the following:

Nurses are the wandering spirits of the Earth; their training teaches them to be ready to march, like a soldier, at a moment's notice; they seldom become deeply rooted in one place, seldom accumulate cumbersome belongings; they divest themselves of everything which may impede flight, and a change of residence becomes about as easy for them as for an Arab.... With this in mind, it seems not unnatural to conclude that reciprocity may have even a deeper meaning for us; its establishment may be more essential to our general welfare than to those whose tendency it is to remain settled and known in one place.

In her concluding paragraph, Nutting called for continued effort to strengthen and improve nursing education and speculated on the potential for development of a "Central Examining Board, Advisory Board or Board of Control." She said that as the state associations worked together more effectively, such a central group "may arise naturally." Finally she said,

> One thing we must realize—that is, the ideals which inspire the growth of any educational work must change from year to year; they cannot remain fixed and unalterable; they must grow, and we must grow with them if we wish to be worthy of our responsibilities and really great opportunities.[7]

This fairly lengthy report of several papers presented in 1904 is included to demonstrate that, from the beginning, farsighted leaders were identifying the issues that boards of nursing would pursue in the years to come. These included the compliance with regulatory standards for nursing education by the schools of nursing, the membership of the boards, and the appropriate level for standards set by law and by the boards in regulations. Nutting, who spoke of several issues, including interstate mobility for nurses and how to best meet the needs of the nurses as they moved from one place to another, seemed to be proposing a national body that would bring together the boards of all jurisdictions.[8]

At that same convention in 1905, M. E. Cameron from New York City presented a paper titled "Examining Boards of Nurses and Their Powers." In this paper, she cited a 1903 report from the United States Bureau of Education that showed there were 522 schools training nurses and the pupils in those schools numbered 13,779. She also stressed the need for an inspector of training schools for each board. She said that it was not easy to get approval for the position of inspector and that it was difficult to locate someone to fill the position, but perhaps the greater challenge was to insure that the inspector was a nurse. Another challenge Cameron identified was that of allowing the board of nurse examiners to have the power to withdraw the "certificate of registration of any registered school" when the board determined that it did not meet the standards established by the board.[9]

In the early years, the two nursing organizations, the American Society of Superintendents of Training Schools and the Nurses' Associated Alumnae of the United States, held their annual meetings within a week of each other. In a short time, these two organizations and the National Organization of Public Health Nurses (NOPHN) began to meet in the same city with several overlapping sessions. In the June 1907 issue of the *American Journal of Nursing* (*AJN*), Sophia Palmer discussed this overlap in an editorial titled "The Action of the National Societies on the Three Years' Course." She described how the American Society of Superintendents met in Philadelphia from May 8 through 10, 1907, and adopted a resolution in support of a three-year course for nurses, condemning a return to a two-year course. A week later, at the meeting of the Associated Alumnae in Richmond, Palmer reported that the same resolution was to have been considered, but was "overlooked in the pressure of business." The members embarked on a trip down the James River from Richmond to Norfolk, with a stop at Jamestown. En route, someone realized the oversight and "at the request of the president, Miss Damer, the members were called to the deck of the steamer as it approached Jamestown Island, and the resolution unanimously carried."[10]

Also at the 1907 Convention of the Nurses' Associated Alumnae, President Annie Damer, in her address, looked back over the past 10 years of the association. She reminded attendees that in addition to the officers present at the association's first meeting in Baltimore in 1897, there were eight delegates in attendance. She also provided some historical information when she called attention to the fact that the settlers at Jamestown arrived "this week" 300 years ago and that there was a hospital in Henrico County in Virginia in 1612, "long before the Pilgrims reached Plymouth Rock." Virginia was chosen as the site of the convention in 1907 because of the observance of the tercentennial of the founding of Jamestown in 1607. Three papers presented at this meeting were related to registration acts. Maud McCaskie presented a paper titled "Registration for Nurses in Colorado" and Sara E. Parsons and Edith Baldwin Lockwood presented on registration in Maryland and Connecticut, their respective states.[11]

Beginning with the October 1907 issue, the *AJN* began publishing an official directory, which Sophia Palmer described as a list of the names and addresses of the officers of the state associations and of the examining boards "as far as we have been able to secure them." The list below includes the 10 states listed in the first official directory and the names of the president and secretary of each board, with the exception of New Hampshire where only the secretary is listed.

State	President	Secretary
Colorado	Maud McClaskie	Mary B. Eyre
Connecticut	Emma L. Stowe	R. Inde Albaugh
District of Columbia	Lily Kanely	Katherine Douglass
Indiana	Isabella Gerhart	Edna Humphrey
Maryland	Georgia A. Cross	Mary C. Packard
Minnesota	Edith Rommel	Helen Wadsworth
New Hampshire	none listed	Augusta Robertson
New York	Sophia F. Palmer	Mary J. Elizabeth Hitchcock
North Carolina	Constance E. Pfohl	Mary L. Wyche
Virginia	S. H. Cabaniss	Mrs. S. T. Hanger

The information contained in this directory and those published subsequently provided a good resource for information about both boards of nursing and the national nursing organizations.[12]

In 1909, the entire September issue of the *AJN* was devoted to the proceedings of the Twelfth Annual Convention of the Nurses' Associated Alumnae of the United States, which was held in Minneapolis on June 10 and 11 of that year. Anna L. Alline, RN, the inspector of nurse training schools, presented a lengthy paper describing the role of the New York Board of Regents in relation to the nursing education programs and the processes involved in the inspection of and correspondence with these schools. During the discussion that followed, representatives from the various states talked about the activities of the boards of nurse examiners in their states. In a session identified as a "Board of Examiners Conference," the president called for short reports from the state boards "as to the details of their work…something that will be helpful to other state boards." Representatives from the following boards spoke: Illinois, Indiana, Maryland, Missouri, Montana, New Hampshire, New York, North Carolina, Washington, and West Virginia. Several speakers addressed the problems associated with reciprocity.[13]

In 1911, Sophia Palmer commented editorially that in eight short years, 21 states had enacted registration laws and thousands of nurses were appending the title RN to their names. She emphasized the importance of appointing the best qualified nurses to boards, requiring that provision for inspections of the training schools be added to laws where it was not included, and paying executive officers of the boards. She also spoke of the need for recognition of these public officials and urged that all nurses give them their confidence, loyalty, and support. Palmer also asked for:

such liberal compensation to inspectors and secretaries, that as they go about in the performance of duty, they may be able to stay at the best hotels, to travel first class, to dress properly, and in other words to afford the outward manifestations that custom calls for in a person occupying a dignified official position.[14]

In 1911, the name of the Nurses' Associated Alumnae of the United States was changed to the American Nurses Association (ANA), and in 1912, the name of the American Society of Superintendents of Training Schools was changed to the National League of Nursing Education (NLNE). Sophia Palmer commented in her editorial for July 1911, that groups had expressed the need to meet together at the national meetings and that one of these groups was composed of representatives of the boards of nurse examiners. Palmer asked the readers of the *AJN* to express their opinion about such meetings.[15]

At the Fifteenth Annual Convention of the ANA in Chicago, held from June 5 to 7, 1912, a session cosponsored by the ANA and the NLNE and titled "The Special Conference on State Registration" met, with Mary C. Wheeler presiding. The following resolutions were drafted and the ANA was requested to adopt them:

1. *Resolved,* That this conference recommend that the training schools for nurses require as a minimum preparation a grammar school certificate, and also require an entrance examination on the subjects of English, spelling, elementary physiology, hygiene, history, and arithmetic.

2. *Resolved,* That a committee be appointed to determine what would be a minimum unit of practical experience in the different departments of nursing work required in the professional education of a nurse.

3. *Resolved,* That state inspection is absolutely essential and therefore that in those states where inspection has not been provide for by law, the state nurses' associations in those states should assume the responsibility for such inspection.

At the same meeting, the "Special Conference" representatives adopted the following motion: "That a committee be appointed by the chair for the purpose of arranging for this conference to take definite form." It was decided that this committee would meet at the time of the ANA Convention. Thus, the year 1912 is generally recognized as the time of the official organization of a group designed to bring together the representatives of the boards of nurse examiners. This group became known as the Legislative Committee of the ANA.[16]

A Common Purpose: 1914–1923

At several meetings over a number of years, and in editorials and articles in the *AJN*, the subject of a federation, or a national organization of boards of nursing, continued to arise. Several of these references are presented here and others will be found later in this chapter. In the Editorial Comment section of the *AJN* in January 1914, Sophia Palmer spoke to the work of boards of nurse examiners and the similarity in the work of the boards among the states. She suggested several actions:

We believe the time has come when, following the lead of the medical profession, whose boards of examiners are organized, there should be a regularly organized federation of state boards of nurse examiners with an affiliation with the American Nurses' Association.... Provision would then be made for special sessions during the week of the national meetings.

Palmer spoke of the possibility that an affiliation of boards could lead to standardizing the examinations. She stated that "we should like to have a department in this *Journal* devoted to the work of the boards, where reports from the different states would have a recognized place month by month, and where common problems could be discussed."[17]

The representatives from the boards of nursing at the 1915 ANA Convention in San Francisco discussed various topics including the clerical work of boards of examiners, headquarters, office equipment, and other related items. Mary Riddle from Massachusetts said that the secretary for the Board of Registration and Medicine, who was a physician, was also a member of the Massachusetts Nursing Board. She stated that the system in place for medicine facilitated the system for nursing. The office was in the State House, there was a "nice" library in place, and there was a head clerk who worked with both boards and two clerks assigned to the nursing board. Examinations were given three times a year. Other items of discussion included the value of the practical examination, the location of examination sites and office space, and payment for both of these. A representative from the Ohio board moved that a "definite bureau be decided upon" to keep the reports and other information about the boards. Anna Jamme of California advised that this motion should be acted upon at a general session on legislation.[18]

At the session on legislation, during a joint session of the ANA and the NLNE, Chair Jamme presided and invited all representatives of boards of examiners to the platform. In her introduction, she asked members to consider the work ahead, assuming a joint sense of mission:

> It is now fourteen years since registration in the United States was born. As we know it was born at our International meeting held in Buffalo, the only one that has been held in this country. Now that forty-two states have registration laws on their statute books, it seems a fitting time for us to consider the machinery that is operating our laws and to ask ourselves: "Has our machinery [had] the constructive force that we had thought it was going to have? Have we realized our aims and our expectations in obtaining registration?" We know what an education registration has been to us. We know the heartbreaks that it has brought to us; we know what it means to be measured by a legislator and by a legislature. We have been able to see ourselves in the eyes of the legislature in a way that is often not very complimentary to us. We all know the scalding tears and the bitter disappointments we have had in this fight for our registration, for our local status; and now I think it is fitting time, after fourteen years of hard work, to quietly sit down and think over what we have [and] whether it is giving us the constructive up building that we want. No doubt there is hardly a state but feels that its registration law could be improved.[19]

At the 1916 ANA Convention, Jamme presented a report of a survey of all the states with registration laws. The purpose of the survey was to identify the requirements for accredited training schools, and 32 states responded to it. The following recommendations for consideration by the states were among those included in the report:

> • The superintendent of the school must be a registered nurse (RN).
>
> • At least two years of high school must be required for admission.
>
> • Boards of nurse examiners must establish a minimum amount of experience in all subjects.
>
> • Boards of nurse examiners should move toward uniformity in the subjects included in the examinations and the passing grade should be the same in all states to "give strength to reciprocity."[20]

In 1916, Palmer wrote in an editorial, "A National Board of Medical Examiners," about the establishment of this board, its objectives, and its structure. For Palmer, the existence of this board further supported the need for a similar board for nurses:

> The special sessions, with round table discussions, devoted to the work of the Boards of Nurse Examiners, at our conventions, are leading toward the establishing of a similar board for the examination of nurses. As more and more groups of people are coming to realize that the efforts nurses are making for the advancement of their profession lead ultimately to better nursing care of the sick, we believe we will obtain financial support from one of the great educational foundations such as has been provided to the medical profession by the Carnegie Foundation."[21]

At the 1917 ANA Convention, Dr. Matson of the Ohio Nursing Board suggested that a federation of state boards of nurse examiners be organized.[22]

The Legislative Committee met at this same convention, with Anna Jamme presiding. She gave a follow-up report to that given at the 1916 meeting and stated that several of the recommendations from that meeting had been achieved. In her report, she included a definition of reciprocity and its implications for education:

> *Basis of reciprocity.* The basis of reciprocity has been founded in the wording of the laws "requirements equivalent to." The laws of twenty-five states demand equivalent requirements. The interpretation of equivalent requirements should mean equivalent preliminary educational entrance requirements and equivalent minimum course of instruction in the training school. It is the opinion of this committee that upon the above interpretation only can a rational basis of reciprocity be established. It is therefore, the desire of this committee that the adoption of preliminary educational entrance requirements and a standard of minimum theoretical and practical instruction be made at this meeting.

The committee also reported on the "essential points of registration laws" with particular attention to the "administrative machinery" and to the "duties and powers of the Board," in what appears to be a beginning for what would later be recognized as a model nurse practice act.[23]

At another session of the 1917 ANA Convention, there was a roundtable on legislation. Boards of nurse examiners were present from 16 states. Following discussion, the participants reached agreement on details of various topics related to legislation as follows:

- Reciprocity should be based on a national standard for the schools.
- The registration fee should be $10.
- Boards of examiners should inspect all training schools.
- Members of the boards should be paid per day and expenses.
- The date of graduation should be the date the student finishes her course in a hospital.
- The time for student experience in the care of children should be at least two months.[24]

These items bear close resemblance to some of the items included in later administrative rules or regulations developed by boards of nursing.

The ANA changed from annual to biennial conventions in 1918. Subsequently the meeting was referred to as the American Nurses Association Biennial Convention or the Biennial. The NLNE and the NOPHN continued to meet in convention annually. In the years when all three met, the groups continued to assemble in the same location over approximately a week, with some joint sessions.[25] The representatives of boards of nursing continued to meet annually and in some years held additional meetings. Reports of these conferences and meetings from 1903 through to the 1970s often listed topics presented by speakers or discussed by the members present. The following is a list of topics that were often considered, and in some instances continued to be addressed, when representatives of boards of nursing met one hundred years after the first nurse practice acts were passed:

- Standards for nursing education
- Interstate mobility for nurses (reciprocity and endorsement)
- Objective type examinations
- Development of a model law that could be used by the individual states
- Nurse practice act amendments to provide for licensure of attendants or practical nurses (PNs)

- Standards for education and licensing of PNs
- Status of nurses educated in other countries and their registration
- Centralization of regulatory groups versus independent boards of nursing
- Improving public relations and relationships with other groups

---

At the business session during the ANA Convention in 1918, the Legislative Section (formerly the Legislative Committee) composed of the board of nursing representatives met to discuss the "difficulty of holding our laws for registration during the present crisis" (World War I) and, as a consequence, the need to interpret existing laws. The Legislative Section decided to establish a large working committee composed of one member from each state board of examiners. Each state was to nominate its member, who would subsequently be appointed to this committee by the chair. The purpose of this working committee was to keep in close touch with activities in each state so that the information obtained could be shared with the entire group through the *AJN*.[26]

In her report to the entire convention, Anna Jamme presented the work of the Committee on Recommended Minimum Requirements for Boards of Examiners and requested action to accept the standards developed by the committee. She stated that they would give guidance for standardizing requirements in the various states in order to facilitate reciprocity. A lengthy paper entitled "Minimum Requirements for Accredited Schools of Nursing as Approved by the Board of Directors of the American Nurses' Association on May 9, 1918," was included in the proceedings of the convention and printed in the August 1918 issue of the *AJN*.[27]

In July 1921, a six-day program titled "Institute for State Inspectors and for Nurse Examiners" was held at Teachers College, Columbia University. The announcement invited all individuals who were engaged in the work of boards of nurse examiners "to attend the institute without fee, and to take part in the discussions and conferences."[28] Representatives from 12 states and 2 Canadian provinces attended and participated in a series of lectures by "specialists in education" and by "nurses with wide experience in the inspection of nursing schools." Each day there were informal meetings to provide opportunities to discuss "all kinds of practical problems."[29] As the organization for representatives of state boards of nurse examiners evolved, conferences of two or more days, for the purpose of strengthening the process of school visits, were scheduled frequently for board and staff members. These conferences were often sponsored by the NLNE, the ANA, or occasionally by a college or university.

The Legislative Section meeting, held during the 1922 ANA Biennial Convention, included information about changes in the laws in New York and Missouri to provide for the licensing of attendants. The Legislative Section adopted bylaws at this meeting, which stated that the object of the section was "to provide opportunity for the consideration of problems of interstate relations of nursing organizations, registration by reciprocity, national minimum standards and new legislation." The membership of the section was limited to ANA members with one of the following qualifications: membership on a state or national legislative committee; membership on a state board of examiners of nurses; experience in presenting or supporting nursing bills (approved by the ANA) before state or national legislators; or approval by the ANA Board of Directors, judging them "qualified and adapted for legislative organization, movements or propaganda."[30] The adoption of bylaws by the Legislative Section provided structure and authority for future meetings and actions. The bylaws also demonstrated an effort to define the role of the section within the structure of the ANA.

Tightening Bonds: 1924–1933

The nurses of the United States agreed that a study of the nursing schools was essential for the future and raised $115,000 over a five-year period to provide partial funding. In 1925, a national study was begun—one that would have significant implications for state boards of nurse examiners. May Ayres Burgess, PhD, was named director for this study on the grading of nursing schools. Representatives from the NLNE, the ANA, the NOPHN, the American Medical Association (AMA), the American Hospital Association, the American Public Health Association, educators, and the general public served on the Committee on the Grading of Nursing Schools, headed by Burgess. It was estimated that the grading of the schools would take five years and would cost a large amount of money but would be a "constructive service to the schools."[31] Under the direction of Burgess, the committee accomplished its goals to grade schools, study the work of nurses, define the duties that fell within the scope of nursing, and determine the supply and demand for nursing services. The work of this committee lasted about seven years and its findings were published in three reports: *Nurses, Patients, and Pocketbooks; An Activity Analysis of Nursing; and Nursing Schools Today and Tomorrow.*[32]

At the 1926 meeting of the Legislative Section, the group in attendance heard a paper, "The National Board of Medical Examiners and Medical Licensure," presented by Everett S. Elwood, managing director of the National Board of Medical Examiners. He reported that this national board was "first presented" in 1916 and states gradually amended state laws in order to allow the licensing authority to accept the national board certificate in lieu of the state examination. He said that 33 states were currently accepting the certificate. He then closed with a reminder of the significant place state boards still held:

In seeking their cooperation we have endeavored to make it clear to the various state boards that the National Board is not a licensing body and never will be. It functions solely by determining through its examinations, the qualification of physicians about to enter the practice of medicine. The high type of examination given by the National Board, with the fact that its cost must be greater than that imposed by the state boards, will necessarily limit the number of candidates who apply for the National examination and will therefore leave a good proportion of applicants for the State Board examinations. Furthermore, there will always be a great need of state boards to administer and execute the medical practice acts. State examining boards should not be allowed to conclude that they will ever be supplanted by a national board.[33]

Elwood's paper appeared in the October 1926 issue of the *AJN*. In that same issue, Mary Roberts, editor of the journal, commented as follows:

The question of a national registration has arisen sporadically ever since the majority of states have had nurse practice acts. Doctor Ellwood's [*sic*] discussion of the problem, from a medical point of view, is illuminating as it brings out the points that licensing can be done only by the states, that a national examination must of necessity be a difficult one, and that it is an expensive procedure. None of these factors, however, will deter nurses from again following in the steps of medicine when a sufficient number of nurses really desire a national examination.

Roberts also pointed out that the discussion of a national board was timely because of dissatisfaction with the lack of reciprocity between states. She proposed that amending the laws to make them more consistent would be a better option than creating a national board of nurse examiners. Roberts concluded, "The idea of a National Board of Nurse Examiners need not be permanently shelved, but the time is not ripe for it. It is, however, overripe for an improvement in existing laws."[34]

In the president's address at the opening session of the Thirty-fifth Annual Convention of the NLNE in June 1929, Elizabeth C. Burgess read a paper titled "Advancement of Education through Legislation." In speaking of the study of schools that was underway and about the work of the Grading Committee, she stated that with the grading of schools in progress, the NLNE should have continuing concern about the laws which govern the practice of nursing. Burgess acknowledged the roles of both the ANA and the NLNE in support of obtaining the nurse practice acts as important to the improvement of nursing education and the movement toward a "uniform curriculum or universal standard of training." She continued,

Our legal standards of nursing of 1903 should not be those of 1929, nor should those of 1929 be unchanged in 1940–50. Education must raise the standards to meet the changing needs, public opinion will demand better nurses and nursing legislation must be obtained which will help maintain them.

She went on to say,

The laws controlling nursing practice presumably voice our ideas of what the minimum professional education should be which can fittingly prepare women as nurses. However, if one were to judge by these laws it would appear that the needs of the sick must vary in accordance with the state in which they live.

Burgess then discussed the differences among the states in educational requirements for admission to schools and the variety of persons serving on boards. She continued by stating that 28 states had boards composed entirely of nurses, while in 5 states the majority of members were physicians and in 1 state all were physicians. Only 1 state had a lay member. Other differences were the requirements for the number of beds or patients in hospitals where students gain experience. She reminded those present at the convention that there had been no definite steps toward a national examining board such as the AMA took in 1915. "Such a Board would not only assist to clarify the standards of nursing education in this country and help solve the reciprocity question but would also be a first step toward reciprocal relations with other countries." Burgess concluded with a convincing argument for working together:

Is the matter of legislation one solely for the ANA to solve? Is it not one of the great problems in nursing education in which the ANA, the NOPHN and the NLNE should join forces in a constructive program for elevation of standards in the states, for compulsory licensing and for a national examining board?[35] *(See fig. 2-A)*

The Legislative Section conducted two sessions at the ANA Biennial Convention in 1930. During one session, Mary M. Roberts presented a paper titled "The Effect of Grading of Schools upon the Accrediting of Schools." She said that all professions go through three stages of professional progress—organization, legislation, and standardization—and that nursing was about to enter the third stage. She argued that state boards should strengthen their existing programs by using the findings of the Grading Committee. Roberts also said that she believed the profession would soon find it necessary "to set up standardizing machinery" that all states would be able to recognize. This would enable the graduates of accredited schools to be eligible for examination by a national board of nurse examiners "whose findings would be acceptable to all states and thus abolish the problem of reciprocity for graduates of schools in this upper level."[36]

Adda Eldredge of Wisconsin, speaking at the same meeting, said that "state laws deal, first, with individuals and second, with schools." She stressed the importance of consulting with the attorney general of the state for legal interpretations "as the basis for board regulations." There was also a closed luncheon for state board members that provided an opportunity for "intimate discussion of problems."[37]

In an article in the April 1931 issue of the *AJN* on the effect of standardization programs such as those of the American College of Surgeons, the AMA, the Grading Committee and the state boards of nurse examiners, Adda Eldredge said the following:

Nursing has grown hand in hand with medicine. The state boards of examiners, in the twenty-seven years since the appointment of the first board, have done an almost miraculous piece of work. There have been flaws, mistakes, errors in judgment on the part of the members of these boards, due many times to a lack of education and experience for the particular piece of work they had been called upon to do. At times they have been handicapped by suspicion and opposition, both of hospitals and medical boards, and even of the general public. In spite of all these conditions, in spite of the very inadequacy of many of the laws, the condition of nursing schools today is far above what we would have a right to expect, and the foundation was laid by these boards of examiners. Think of how easy it is to establish a school of nursing, and how difficult to hold it to a standard. Take the mere matter of education and see how in spite of the above-mentioned opposition the desire of the governing boards to accept anyone and everyone who would help to do the work of the hospitals with the least possible cost to the hospital—in spite of all these the standards of nursing have been going gradually up, and, as an effect of standardization, the report of the Grading Committee, they have been literally flying up.[38]

In an editorial in the *AJN* in 1931, Mary Roberts further commented on the idea of a national board of nurse examiners. She referred to the National Board of Medical Examiners and one of its requirements that applicants "shall be graduates of medical schools rated as approved by the AMA," and she raised the interesting question of whether schools of nursing should be accredited by a nursing organization such as the NLNE. Roberts said that if a national organization assumed responsibility for standards in the schools, the state boards of nurse examiners could devote more time to the enforcement of the legal requirements for the practice of nursing. She closed with the following statement: "A national board is a costly device even when forty-one states and three territories register the diplomats of the National Medical Board. A national board is undoubtedly a desirable although distant goal for nurses."[39]

Among the May 1932 editorials in the *AJN*, there is a report that the ANA Committee to Outline a Definition of Nursing had presented its definition of professional nursing as follows:

Professional Nursing is a blend of intellectual attainments, attitudes and manual skills based on the principles of scientific medicine, acquired by means of a prescribed course in a school of nursing affiliated with a hospital, recognized for such purposes by the state, and practiced in conjunction with curative or preventive medicine by an individual licensed to do so by the state. Therefore, a professional nurse is one who has met all the legal requirements for registration in a state and who practices or holds a position by virtue of her professional knowledge and legal status.[40]

At its convention in 1932, the ANA accepted the offer from the NLNE to become the Educational Department of the ANA, without loss of its own autonomy. This action "gave the NLNE the professional and financial support of 100,000 nurses, and led to a closer alliance between the NLNE and the State Board[s] of Nurse Examiners."[41] As a result of this action, the executive secretary of the NLNE had the "privilege" of serving as educational secretary to the ANA.

At the meeting of the Legislative Section at the time of the 1932 biennial, Adda Eldredge reported on a study of the desirability of having all licensing boards in a state under one central control. Her report recommended that when such centralization was inevitable, the formerly freestanding nursing board should safeguard its responsibilities regarding the examining of candidates and grading of papers, ensure provision for a full-time educational director, and maintain its role of stating minimum requirements. All of this implied the provision of a sufficient budget and adequate personnel.[42]

Nursing and boards of nursing faced a number of challenges as the result of the Great Depression of the 1930s. There are frequent references to the lack of jobs for nurses and an abundance of nurses in many locales. In the July 1932 issue of the *AJN*, an article included a quote from the Birmingham Herald dated May 21, 1932. The newspaper said that the Alabama Board of Examination and Registration advised the hospitals of the state to discontinue their schools of nursing and employ their graduates. Further, the article reported that the board placed partial blame for this advice on the Grading Committee, which reported that too many nurses were being graduated from the schools at that time. A further recommendation was directed to the nurses in Alabama, urging them to return to their own communities to work in the hospitals and with the doctors there rather than trying to find employment in the cities.[43] Closure of schools or limitation of admissions were topics of discussion at the conference for boards of nursing representatives in 1933.[44]

Leaders and Changes: 1934–1943

The challenges facing nurses, schools of nursing, and nursing regulators required strong leadership by those involved in all of these areas. Each month in 1934, an administrative officer or educational director of a state board of nurse examiners was highlighted in the *AJN* and recognized with a picture and a biographical sketch. Those included were Adda Eldredge, Wisconsin; Ethel M. Smith, Virginia; Mabel E. Smith, Michigan; Clara F. Brouse, Ohio; Elizabeth C. Burgess, New York; Florence Dakin, New Jersey; Leila Halverson, Minnesota; Carol L. Martin, Nebraska; Elizabeth F. Miller, Pennsylvania; Clara Quereau, New York; Maude Sutton, Iowa; and Julie C. Tebo, Louisiana. Other individuals who provided important leadership in the regulation of nursing included: Anna Jamme, California; Roberta West, Pennsylvania; Josephine Thurlow, Massachusetts; Netta Ford, Pennsylvania; Daisy Urch, Minnesota; Bernice Anderson, New Jersey; Virginia Harrison, Missouri; Carrie Spurgeon, Louisiana; Adele Stahl, Wisconsin; Louise Alfsen, Washington; Lettie Christianson, Minnesota; Eleanor Moore, Oklahoma; Hazel Peeples, Florida; and Agnes Ohlson, Connecticut.

Adda Eldredge, one of those honored by the *AJN*, wrote an article for its June 1934 issue titled "Legislation and the Future of Nursing." It was a paper she had presented at a joint session during the Biennial Convention of the ANA in April. Eldredge was an active figure in the meetings of representatives of boards of nurse examiners and a leader in nursing. In her listing of the important points for a nursing law, she mentioned several that had been seen before and a number that anticipated problems faced by subsequent groups concerned with nursing regulation. Some of the latter included the careful selection of those persons who would set standards; a separation of those who were the examiners from the "administrative body"; and the placement of the law "under a commission capable of understanding the functions of the administration and not under one which classifies nursing with hotels, restaurants, beauty parlors, et cetera." She went on to say that there should be "as few absolute mandatory statements in the law as will make it workable." She felt that all laws should provide for registration by reciprocity based only on examination and said that the curriculum should not be included in the law, "nor any of the details of requirements." Eldredge said that the law should provide for the use of funds received and prevent "the legislature from taking them over for other purposes." She expressed her thoughts about national examinations as follows:

I have said nothing about national examinations, with intention. I believe those who most favor national examinations are under a misunderstanding. First, they believe the examination would not differ from their own state board. Second, they believe it would save financially, be in one fee, probably no higher than that in their own state. Third, that it would be unquestionably accepted in every state. I am sure that none of these beliefs are true."

Eldredge closed by saying,

We can do much with what we now have if we will use it.… It is often the interpretation of the law which may actually decide the question. I have been advised several times that the courts will accept interpretations of long standing as showing the intent of the law.[45]

At the convention in 1934, the ANA changed its bylaws and abolished the Legislative Section. A new ANA Legislative Committee was established and the activities related to education and boards of nursing were referred to the NLNE, now functioning as the ANA's Department of Education. In the report of the last Legislative Section meeting, the following statement appeared: "With this session, the ANA Legislative Section went out of existence because of the action of the delegates whereby state board problems are to be transferred to the League [NLNE]." The group that had been meeting as the ANA Legislative Section became the NLNE'S Committee on State Board Problems and continued to meet under that name from 1934 to 1949. However, the group still functioned under the aegis of the ANA, since the NLNE was the Education Department of the ANA. At the last meeting of the Legislative Section, the chair, Netta Ford of Pennsylvania, reported that the section had 271 members representing 29 states.[46]

Adda Eldredge discussed the relationship of a board of nursing to a professional organization and spoke of the importance of careful consideration in selecting nominees for appointment, but she did not mention a potential conflict of interest, when she said:

that each one of the people in being appointed to the board or committee should pledge themselves to stand for the principles for which the association stands, and that they will vote on no matter of vital importance to the association until its representatives on the board of examiners have had a chance to consult with the state association board of directors as to its reactions to such vital measures.[47]

Members and staff of boards of nursing in later years would raise questions of a possible conflict of interest in the close relationship between the boards and the nursing organizations. Government officials and the public raised questions about the role of professional associations in the regulation of members of the professions as the century progressed. Laws were changed to add public members to regulatory boards, legislators enacted laws requiring the regulatory boards to justify their continued existence (sunset legislation), and other pressures increased to separate the regulators from the professional associations.

An excerpt from the minutes of a meeting of the ANA Board of Directors held in New York in January 1936 was included in the *AJN* in the Legislation section:

With regard to legislation affecting nurses and nursing, the belief was expressed that *all matters concerned with legislation* affecting nurses or nursing are the *primary concern* of the ANA; that *all phases* of legislation dealing with problems concerning nursing education are to be referred to the NLNE which in its capacity as the Educational Department of the ANA will advise regarding them. In like manner it was believed that the NOPHN would act in an advisory capacity in regard to legislation dealing with public health nursing.[48]

The ANA Biennial Convention in 1936 was held in Los Angeles in June. At a business meeting of the NLNE, the delegates voted that the NLNE would accredit schools of nursing on a national basis and formed a standing committee to consult with state leagues and state boards of nurse examiners about the program and to put it into action. Clara Quereau, former secretary of the New York State Board of Nurse Examiners, was appointed to the position of professional secretary of the NLNE Committee on Accreditation.[49]

The following year a three-day conference for state boards of nurse examiners was held in conjunction with the NLNE Convention. Some of the topics discussed were the movement to reopen closed schools, the study of supply and demand of nurses, and efforts to either increase or decrease enrollments. There was a notation that subcommittees of the Committee on State Board Problems were working on examinations, methods of surveying schools, and upgrades of faculty. The statement was made that "problems referring to the legal aspects of licensure, model laws, et cetera, are the responsibility of the

ANA."[50] The ANA and the NLNE cosponsored the State Board Conference in 1938 with the major discussion centered on the *Curriculum Guide for Schools of Nursing* published by the NLNE in 1937. Topics included the use of the book in revising minimum requirements for schools of nursing and in studying the preparation of faculty members.[51]

An editorial by Mary Roberts, appearing in the April 1941 issue of the *AJN*, addressed the pros and cons of the National Board of Medical Examiners, noting funding problems and the fact that only about 14 percent of the graduates of medical schools take the examination. Roberts went on to say that this was no surprise to the ANA since the question of a national board for nurse examiners had been given careful consideration. She concluded, "It provides food for thought for those who think that a national board…would easily clear away some of the perplexities of our peripatetic profession."[52]

World War II began in Europe in 1939 and the United States became directly involved in 1941. Once again a societal event impacted the education, licensing, and practice of nursing. Boards of nursing that had previously been dealing with more nurses than were needed, now had to begin to look at their laws and regulations to facilitate an increase in the enrollments in schools, ways to issue licenses faster, and ways to facilitate interstate mobility of those licensed. A variety of sources and references speak to the activities in states and on the national level that were related to World War II. In 1941, the Committee on State Board Problems heard an appeal from Mary Beard, director of the American Red Cross Nursing Services, for the boards of nurse examiners to do all within their legal powers to speed up the registration of young nurses as soon as they graduated from their schools of nursing. She said, "Anything that impedes the enrollment in the Red Cross Nursing Service at this time is a great misfortune, since the need for nurses in the federal services is almost overpowering."[53] National and state nursing councils for war services were established and educational programs were encouraged to enroll more students and graduate them sooner. Boards of nursing were more liberal in the interpretation of the laws, and regulations were changed where necessary to be more flexible in relation to the time spent in the nursing education programs and the more frequent administration of the licensing examination. Congress appropriated funds for nursing schools to assist with increasing enrollments.

The war also served as an impetus to develop tests that could be administered more easily and scored in a more timely way. Interstate mobility for nurses presented increased problems for boards of nursing and states were urged to look at ways to facilitate licensure for those moving from one place to another. These topics were the subject of the 1942 State Board Conference held in Chicago, where Adda Eldredge was quoted by Irene Murchison as saying, "We can get a great deal more elasticity out of our present laws if we just try." Leila Given, of Wisconsin, said:

When more uniform standards are adopted, and when competency to nurse has the same implication in all states, and when our state board examinations are so constructed that they actually measure competency and…when state laws are enacted which allow for greater flexibility then a great many of the problems of interstate registration will be solved.[54]

In September, the boards of directors of the ANA and the NLNE both adopted a lengthy list of recommendations that were distributed to all boards. These recommendations dealt with examining ways to interpret laws and regulations more liberally, speeding up reciprocity, and finding other ways to accommodate the increased demand for nurses.[55]

Nurses representing the state boards of nurse examiners in 37 states attended a conference sponsored by the ANA in New York in December 1942. Topics discussed included the following: utilizing all nurse manpower and making it available as soon as possible, determining how the nurse practice acts and board regulations in the various states affected the acceleration of the basic professional curriculum, increasing the student enrollment, and investigating legislative problems concerning auxiliary workers. The members developed two general recommendations at the meeting. The first was that it was not a good time to seek new state legislation and the second advised that boards of examiners should cooperate with the state nursing organizations to study the existing laws and regulations to facilitate nursing practice in relation to the war effort. Secondly, the group recommended that a clearinghouse for boards be established at ANA and NLNE headquarters to make relevant information available to all boards. There were a large number of additional recommendations related to licensing by examination, by reciprocity, and by new legislation.[56]

In 1943, the United States Congress voted to establish the United States Cadet Nurse Corps. This action had an impact on boards of nursing because of the requirements to move those enrolled into the military nursing services sooner. For example, in states where the law permitted, the Cadets graduated after either 24 or 30 months and entered active military service. Where the law would not allow for early graduation, the Cadets remained in the school under supervision, but replaced staff nurses. In addition, the increase in numbers of students was phenomenal as a result of this program. Many individuals who otherwise may not have entered nursing schools did so during the several years the Cadet Corps existed. Students took advantage of the Cadet Corps both out of a desire to demonstrate patriotism and to do something for the war effort. The financial assistance also helped those who wanted to be nurses but could not otherwise afford to do so. By its first anniversary on July 1, 1944, the Cadet Corps had exceeded its recruitment goal by 500 when more than 65,000 students had been admitted to nursing schools. With the end of the war in August 1945, no students were admitted to the Cadet Corps after October 15, 1945, and the last to enter were graduated in 1948.

At the State Board Conference in the spring of 1943, the group adopted a recommendation that the NLNE Committee on State Board Problems be reorganized and become a joint committee of the ANA and the NLNE. Further, it was decided that one of its first responsibilities would be to determine the functions of a clearinghouse for state boards of nurse examiners and formulate policies necessary to implement these functions. The ANA Board of Directors adopted the recommendation.[57] In September, the Advisory Committee of the ANA Clearing Bureau on Problems of State Boards of Nurse Examiners (Clearing Bureau) met in New York. The Advisory Committee was composed of the following members: Chair Bernice Anderson from New Jersey, Stella Hawkins from New York, Mary Rothrock from Pennsylvania, and M. Cordelia Cowan from the District of Columbia. There were representatives from the ANA, NLNE, and the National Nursing Council for War Service (NNCWS). Cowan had been "loaned" to the ANA for three months as executive secretary to the Clearing Bureau and stayed on in a part-time role until August 1944. Initial tasks assigned to the Advisory Committee were the development of a suggested skeleton curriculum to facilitate the registration of nurses moving from state to state and the collection of information to give assistance to state boards and schools in relation to problems raised by curriculum acceleration.[58]

Refining Organizational Structure: 1944–1953

At its meeting in June of 1944, the ANA Board of Directors adopted recommendations from the conference of representatives of state boards of nurse examiners held in Buffalo that month. As a result of this action, the name of the ANA Clearing Bureau on Problems of State Boards of Nurse Examiners was changed to the ANA Bureau of State Boards of Nurse Examiners (Bureau); the former Clearing Bureau's Advisory Committee became the ANA Committee for the Bureau; and the functions of the Bureau were redefined and enlarged to include a program of constructive activities with a provision for field work.[59] By November 1944, Agnes K. Ohlson, educational director and secretary for the Connecticut State Board of Nurse Examiners was serving part time at ANA as an assistant executive secretary assigned to the Bureau.[60] She served as permanent secretary and chief examiner for the Connecticut Board of Nursing from 1936 until she retired in 1963. During that time, she was president of the ANA and also president of the International Council of Nurses. In her role with the Connecticut Board, Ohlson asked the ANA to support the organization of representatives of boards of nursing for the purpose of facilitating interstate mobility for nurses and to develop a national licensing examination.

An article in the June 1945 issue of the *AJN* described the work of the Bureau as an effort "quietly and unspectacularly carried on at national nursing headquarters for nearly two years which is already affecting a great many nurses and will ultimately affect a great many more." Accomplishments cited included changes to allow new graduates to take the licensing examination as soon as possible, the development of a minimum curriculum for use in evaluating the applications for registration by reciprocity, the continued development of the State Board Test Pool Examination (SBTPE), and the establishment of a clearinghouse for information about state boards of nurse examiners. Bernice Anderson of New Jersey chaired the ANA Committee for the Bureau.[61]

Another conference for representatives of state boards of nurse examiners sponsored by the ANA and the NLNE was held in December 1945 with 79 people from 41 boards in attendance. The following are two of the recommendations adopted by the group and forwarded to the appropriate organizations:

1. That the ANA Bureau of State Boards of Nurse Examiners explore the use of state board test pool results as a new approach to registration by reciprocity (endorsement).

2. That the ANA Bureau…prepare policies and procedures for the use of state boards when they are giving consideration to World War II veterans who have some training and experience in caring for the sick who apply for licensure as either a registered or a licensed practical nurse.

In the first recommendation above, the word "endorsement" is used in connection with reciprocity. This is the first use of this word found in the sources reviewed,[62] while "reciprocity" was the term used from the beginning of the regulation of nursing relative to the interstate movement of licensees. Usually one state would agree to recognize the credentials of a nurse from another state after determining for itself that the nurse met the requirements of the receiving state. Because the requirements for licensure in the individual states were so different, this process was difficult and time consuming. Endorsement was the term that became used to define the process by which a nurse licensed in one state could be licensed in another state. The receiving state would accept the verification of credentials such as education prior to entering nursing school, nursing education, performance on the licensing examination, and information related to any complaints or disciplinary action taken by another board of nursing. With a licensing examination that could be used by all boards and other movements toward consistency in requirements for licensure, endorsement replaced reciprocity as the method of interstate licensure.

In September 1946, representatives of 38 state boards of nurse examiners participated in a three-day conference sponsored by the ANA and the NLNE in Atlantic City. This meeting is significant because those in attendance reached a number of important decisions with long-term impact. Representatives present at the meeting the previous year, 1945, had discussed the need for a freestanding organization independent of the ANA or the NLNE, and Ella Van Horn from Illinois had been appointed as chair of a committee to study the issue. This committee posed the following four options for change in the organizational structure for consideration by the group in 1946:

1. That the ANA would establish a special committee with a nurse representative from each state board of nurse examiners and a small working committee with the full-time secretary and budget for field service, or

2. That an ANA section for nurse members and professional personnel of state boards be created, or

3. That a joint ANA-NLNE committee with representation from each state board be established, or

4. That a national association of state boards of nurse examiners be formed outside the professional organizations.

After discussion of these alternatives at several sessions of the conference, those in attendance decided to accept the first recommendation above with the proviso that "each state board would select a nurse best qualified to represent the work of her board" as its nominee for appointment to a proposed special committee of the ANA Board of Directors and that the chair of the NLNE Committee on State Board Problems would become a member of the working committee. This special committee replaced the existing Bureau and the NLNE Committee on State Board Problems. There were two other important recommendations from this meeting. The first called for the ANA Bureau (the name retained by the special committee) to compile data on foreign schools of nursing whose graduates had been licensed by a state board in the United States. In the second, the group asked that all students have instruction and a minimum of three months clinical experience in psychiatric nursing as a fifth basic course and that this occur as rapidly as sound educational programs could be provided.[63]

On January 1, 1947, Leila I. Given, RN, joined the staff of the ANA as assistant executive secretary to work with the ANA Bureau of State Boards of Nurse Examiners and the ANA Committee on Legislation. Given had been director of the Bureau of Nursing Education for the Wisconsin State Board of Health.[64]

The newly appointed ANA Bureau of State Boards of Nurse Examiners, as established by the action taken in 1946, met twice during the conference held in September 1947 in Seattle. Representatives from 40 boards attended the conference. One representative from each state recommended by the state board of nursing and approved by the ANA Board of Directors served on this Bureau. The Working Committee of the Bureau developed a number of recommendations that were subsequently approved by the ANA Board of Directors including the following:

- That a Working Committee for the ANA Bureau of State Boards of Nurse Examiners to consist of 5 members be appointed from a list of 10 names, nominated by the committee, with consideration for geographic representation.

- That a full-time executive secretary be appointed for the ANA Bureau of State Boards of Nurse Examiners and that adequate clerical and stenographic service, office space, and equipment be provided.

- That a minimum budget of $15,000 be provided for carrying on the work of the ANA Bureau.[65]

Another significant conference sponsored by the ANA Bureau of State Boards of Nurse Examiners was held in Chicago in May 1948. Representatives from boards of nurse examiners in 46 states and the District of Columbia were in attendance. The program consisted of presentations on topics of common interest to all in attendance and a large number of recommendations were adopted. The following were selected from that list to illustrate continuing issues for boards of nursing:

- That the state nurse practice acts be amended as soon as possible to implement the "principle of mandatory licensure for all who nurse for hire."

- That boards of nurse examiners be composed solely of professional nurses "to the end that the profession shall maintain its autonomy," and if it is necessary to include practical nurse members in states that provide for the licensure of practical nurses, "that such representation shall be made by a professional nurse who is employed as a faculty member of a school of practical nursing" and who is otherwise qualified for appointment.

- That the conference supports participation by all states in the SBTP within five years and that the Working Committee of the ANA Bureau confer with the NLNE Department of Measurement and Guidance so that a committee from the Bureau may be appointed to assist in formulating policies pertaining to the SBTPE.

- That each state consider "the adoption of the philosophy or principle of interstate registration as an endorsement of the evaluations made by the original state." Such action would negate the necessity of obtaining items such as high school of nursing school records from original sources. In addition, the conference group stated that applicants should not be required to rewrite examinations if grades are not identical and renewal of registration in the original state should not be required in order to be endorsed if the original license remains unrevoked.

One of the most significant actions was the vote to recommend that consideration be given to the development of integrated examinations in the six areas tested (medical, surgical, communicable disease, obstetric, pediatric, and psychiatric nursing) and that such examinations be considered for the 1949 SBTPE Series.[66]

For the first time, the official directory published in the *AJN* in January 1949 listed the members of the ANA Bureau of State Boards of Nurse Examiners by name, with Virginia H. Harrison of Missouri recorded as chair. Editorials in the *AJN* that same year supported mandatory licensing laws and an editorial by Mary Roberts in June was titled "State Boards Consider the Future." After commenting on the fact that state board members had been meeting in national conferences since 1942, Roberts noted that the ANA Committee of State Boards of Nurse Examiners, which later became the Bureau, and the NLNE Committee on State Board Problems had provided important official channels for communication.[67]

At the State Board Conference in San Francisco in May 1950, representatives from 42 states were present. Elizabeth Kemble, director of the NLNE Department of Measurement and Guidance presented a progress report on the integrated licensing examination now used by 47 states, the District of Columbia, Hawaii, and British Columbia in Canada. Kemble said that the reporting of the results in standard scores would "provide a sound basis for comparing one test result with another…and open the way to further progress in solving problems related to interstate registration." The group asked for guidance in determining the appropriate time limit and sequence for administration. Leila Given reported that PNs were being licensed in 29 states, Hawaii, and Puerto Rico.[68] In other action at this meeting, the group voted unanimously that "the State Board Committee and Conference continue to function under ANA." This action was taken in relation to the ongoing study of the structures of the nursing organizations.[69]

At the NLNE Convention in 1951, Carrie Spurgeon, chair of the Bureau reported that the examiners of the various states were working together toward adopting a standard score of 350 as the passing score on the state board examinations.[70]

The major nursing organizations began a comprehensive study in 1945 to determine how these organizations in the United States should be structured. Organizations that were studied included the ANA, the NLNE, the NOPHN, the National Association of Colored Graduate Nurses, the American Association of Industrial Nurses, and the Association of Collegiate Schools of Nursing. Other organized groups were also part of the study to determine how the national nursing organizations could best serve nurses and the nation.[71] This study continued over more than six years and produced a series of recommendations and revisions. At the conclusion of the Biennial Convention of the ANA and the Annual Convention of the NLNE in 1952, what had been six organizations were now three—the ANA, the National League for Nursing (NLN), and the American Association of Industrial Nurses. The National Association of Colored Graduate Nurses had disbanded in 1951 with its functions transferred to the ANA. The NLNE, the NOPHN, and the Association of Collegiate Schools of Nursing became the NLN. Several other groups became a part of the NLN, including the Joint Committee on Practical Nursing and Auxiliary Workers in Nursing Services, the Joint Committee on Careers in Nursing, the National Committee for the Improvement of Nursing Services, and the National Nursing Accrediting Services.[72] With this reorganization, the name of the Bureau was changed to the ANA Special Committee of State Boards of Nursing Education and Nurse Registration (ANA Special Committee) and was housed solely within the structure of the ANA.

In June 1953, the ANA Special Committee met in Cleveland, with representatives from 45 states in attendance. M. Annie Leitch had replaced Leila Given as assistant executive secretary of the ANA, and thus staff to the Special Committee. Leitch served as president of both the Michigan State Nurses Association and the Michigan League for Nursing Education and she served as a member of the Michigan Board of Registration of Nurses.

At the meeting in Cleveland, in 1953, Bernice Anderson reported on the work of the Subcommittee on Preparation of More Flexible Standards to be Used as a Guide by State Boards, which she chaired. The subcommittee's recommendations included the following three:

1. That, with the permission of all states, the Evaluation and Guidance Service of the NLN make available to the national state board committee, complete reports in unidentified form, of the actual performance on the SBTPE of all new candidates in all schools for the past two years.

2. That the committee, after study of these reports of the first two years of full participation recommend the adoption of a national score for purposes of interstate licensure only. Individual states could continue to use their own standards for original licensure.

3. The candidates for interstate licensure who receive scores above the determined national score for interstate licensure be granted licenses upon state verification of the original licenses without further investigation of the nursing programs or secondary education.

The following were selected as the members of the Working Committee of the ANA Special Committee, later known as the Executive Committee: Chair Adele Stahl, Wisconsin; Louise Alfsen, Washington; Carrie Spurgeon, Louisiana; Edna Antrobus, New Jersey; Miriam Daughtry, North Carolina; and Louise Streuter, Kentucky.[73] During the decade ending in 1953, the representatives of the boards of nursing formed a more cohesive organizational structure for their national meetings and became actively involved in the development of the SBTPE.

ANA Special Committee of Boards of Nursing Strengthens: 1954–1963

The organization for representatives of boards of nursing, now known as the ANA Special Committee of State Boards of Nursing Education and Nurse Regulation, met in Chicago in April 1954. The meeting attendees included 120 representatives from 42 states and Alaska. For the first time, the Working Committee of the ANA Special Committee conducted an orientation for recently appointed members. A series of recommendations from an advisory committee to the NLN appointed by the ANA Special Committee to work with the NLN Evaluation and Guidance Service were presented and adopted. Included was the decision that a new series of the SBTPE for professional nurses every three years was feasible, and a plan for the board in each state to nominate individuals to participate in the preparation of each series, with expenses to be borne by the NLN, was approved. Jurisdictions wishing to participate more frequently would pay the expenses for their representatives. In addition, boards would assume the responsibility of "developing a detailed statement outlining the principal abilities and skills that should be included in a licensing examination" and recommending individuals to develop the core outline for each examination and others to participate in the preparation of the initial draft of questions for each series. Finally, board members and professional staff would review the initial draft and return their comments to the NLN.[74]

Two references to regional meetings were found in the review of available resources for information about the early organization of boards of nursing. In later years, these meetings became known as "area meetings." The first reference to such a meeting appeared in the January 1955 issue of the *AJN*, with the mention of a meeting of the Midwest Regional Conference of State Boards of Nursing held in Minneapolis in October 1954. There were 39 board and staff members in attendance. The group heard reports of national subcommittee work and discussed local concerns and issues.[75] The second was a lengthy report of the Southern Regional Conference of State Boards of Nursing that was attached to the minutes of a meeting of the Virginia State Board of Nurse Examiners in 1958. Carrie Spurgeon of Louisiana chaired the Southern Regional Conference, where 13 states were represented. The group agreed that one of its purposes was to act as a group of states to facilitate the exchange of information between the ANA Special Committee and these states. Annie Leitch was present and presented a brief history of the ANA Special Committee and the State Board Conference.[76] *(see fig. 2-B)*

At the annual meeting for representatives of state boards in 1955, the name of the group was reported as the ANA Special Committee of State Boards of Nursing. For the first time, a representative from the Virgin Islands was present, along with 113 others, when the group convened in St. Louis in April. Ruth Feider of California presented a report of the Subcommittee on Evaluation of Programs Currently Being Offered by the Military. Another report stated that individuals had been selected to help in the preparation of each series of the SBTPE, and the Subcommittee to Prepare a Blueprint for the SBTPE had been appointed. The program for the conference included a session during which a representative from the Treasury Department's Bureau of Narcotics presented a talk on assistance to boards from his agency.[77]

In 1956, the ANA Board of Directors reiterated its previous decision that membership on boards of nursing would be limited to RNs. The editorial in the March issue of the *AJN* concluded with the following:

Considerations have led the ANA's Committee on Legislation and its Board of Directors to conclude once more that only professional registered nurses "who are best qualified by general and professional educational preparation and educational experience should be appointed to the state licensing board for nurses." This does not exclude the possibility that a well qualified professional nurse who teaches in an educational program for practical nurses or directs it, might make a valuable contribution as a board member. Nor does it mean that the ANA frowns on the appointment of an advisory committee which includes practical nurses. It does believe, however, that practical nurses are not qualified by experience or education to undertake the complex task of administering licensing laws.[78] *(see fig. 2-C)*

At the State Board Conference in Chicago in May 1957, all except five states and territories were represented, with 134 members attending. The work of the Subcommittee on Educational Standards had been in progress for several years and was completed in 1956. Robert H. Morrison, PhD, former assistant commissioner of Education for New Jersey, served as leader of the working conference on the work of the subcommittee. Participants in the program included Bernice Anderson, New Jersey; Marguerite Nicholson, Virginia; Paula Weims, Illinois; and Nancy Lawson, Minnesota. The focus of the program was on standards for nursing education and other aspects of nursing education related to the work of boards of nursing.[79]

The ANA Special Committee met in Atlantic City in June 1958. Two reports discussed at this meeting were of particular interest to the representatives from the various boards of nursing. The first stated that 20 states had achieved mandatory licensure. The second declared that all jurisdictions except the District of Columbia had laws for the licensure of licensed practical nurses (LPNs). Those present discussed the importance of security measures for the administration of the licensing examinations and the inconsistencies between states that continued to interfere with interstate licensure. A subcommittee was studying the licensure of nurses from other countries with the hope to standardize the process where possible. The group also discussed the movement to establish a council of practical nursing programs within the NLN.[80]

In 1959, the ANA Board of Directors authorized publication of the *Guide for the Use of State Boards of Nursing in Developing Standards for Pre-service Programs Preparing for Professional Nurses.* This booklet had been in preparation since 1953 and was designed for use by the boards in developing their own standards.[81] At the meeting of the ANA Special Committee in Philadelphia in May 1959, the theme was "responsibilities of boards of nursing in understanding and interpreting the role of the nurse in comprehensive patient care and the maintenance and interpretation of legal standards for nursing practice." At the business session, the group heard reports from the subcommittees on the Blueprint for Licensing Examinations, on the Preparation of State Board Records, and on Preparation of the Manual for Members of State Boards of Nursing. After hearing the report from the Subcommittee to Make a Detailed Study of Licensure of Nurses from Other Countries, the group adopted a recommendation to take steps to improve the interchange of information between the ANA Special Committee, boards of nursing, and the ANA International Unit.[82] *(see fig. 2-D)*

Evolution of a Council: 1964–1973

An article in the News section in the June 1964 issue of the *AJN* was headlined "ANA Decries NLN Action on State Board Relationships." The article included a letter to the ANA from Lois Austin, president of the NLN, which read, in part,

> the NLN Board of Directors viewed the matter of licensing examinations as a contractual relationship between the NLN and its consumers—the state boards of nursing—and that this required that the NLN Test Service have additional direct communications and negotiations with the boards.

The article went on to say that to that end, in January, the NLN Board authorized the establishment of the NLN Advisory Committee of Boards of Nursing. The ANA asked the NLN to reconsider the decision since the ANA believed it would "endanger the system used today through which state boards of nursing cooperatively develop and use licensing examinations." In support of this request, the ANA stated the following concerns:

> It would appear that the appointment of an NLN Advisory Committee would make it possible to bypass the ANA [Special] Committee of State Boards of Nursing and permit development of policies and procedures regarding licensure examinations by persons outside the nursing profession.
>
> This action of the NLN board ignores the existence of the SBTP as an entity and the role of the ANA Committee of State Boards of Nursing as the instrument through which the pool expresses its wishes on all matters relating to the SBTPE, the licensing examination used today in all states.
>
> In 1952 this committee was asked to review its functions and recommend its place in the new structure of nursing organizations created at that time. The committee voted unanimously that it belonged within the ANA because of [*sic*] the work of state boards is closely related to legislation and the setting of standards. The boards of directors of the ANA and the newly formed NLN approved the arrangement [at that time].[83]

In the same issue of the *AJN*, Barbara G. Schutt, in her editorial, "Cause for Concern," stated,

> In 1961, following a request from the ANA committee, the executives of ANA and NLN signed a document which embodied the current relationships and responsibilities of each. That document was scheduled for review last year. In the ensuing discussions, it appeared to the ANA that the NLN was developing a shift in philosophy about these relationships. This seemed to be confirmed when, on April 16 the ANA president received official word of action the NLN board had taken in its January meeting. That board was authorizing the appointment of an NLN state board advisory committee with which NLN staff members would work directly. Meanwhile, the League had proceeded to appoint an interim advisory committee to meet immediately prior to ANA's committee this month. In transmitting this information on April 29 to all state boards and state nurses associations, ANA's president observed:

> *The NLN now views the matter of the licensure examination as merely a contractual relationship between NLN and each individual board of nursing rather than the fulfillment by the NLN of the wishes of the SBTP, as expressed through the ANA committee....Such an arrangement providing for over fifty independent contracts between NLN and individual boards of nursing operating without the common regulations now established by the Pool, and respected by its members, would create risks of such a nature that the benefits now derived from the Pool would be endangered...and the facilitation of interstate licensure by endorsement would be seriously hampered.*

Schutt concluded,

> The decision makers over these many years have recognized that *the pooling of thinking and the planning which controls the standards governing the entrance of the new practitioner into the profession must take place under the aegis of the profession.* This demands a functioning unit—the Pool—under the organization which speaks for the profession, because its membership is limited to professional nurses—The ANA. However complex the system, whatever the two national organizations involved, this is a principle which every nurse should be able to understand and stand for.[84]

The concerns of the ANA and the NLN were apparently resolved during the June 1964 meeting of the ANA Special Committee of State Boards of Nursing. The president, executive director, and legal counsel of the ANA, as well as the general director of the NLN and the staff of the NLN Test Services, presented basic information and their organizations' views of philosophies, practices, and suggestions for future action. NLN staff agreed that the ANA Special Committee was the policymaking group for the SBTPE, but expressed concern about not being more involved in discussions preceding the formulation of policy. Inez Haynes, general director of the NLN, announced that the NLN Advisory Committee would not meet again. She stated that further action by the NLN would be dependent upon action taken by the ANA Special Committee. The ANA Special Committee approved several changes concerning security measures in the basic contract provisions that formed the basis for contracts between the NLN and individual boards of nursing for use of the SBTPE and agreed to provide consultation through its Executive Committee.[85]

The following year (1965), the ANA and the NLN signed a new agreement, the "Statement of the Respective Responsibilities of the ANA and the NLN with Respect to the State Board Test Pool Examination." No changes were made in the new statement other than to add recommendations on enforcement of security regulations previously adopted by the ANA Special Committee of State Boards of Nursing. The ANA Special Committee set the policies for the development and administration of the SBTPE and the NLN Test Services; provided expert consultation; and arranged for printing, scoring, and reporting.[86]

At the ANA Convention in 1966, the delegates adopted an extensive revision of the bylaws that changed the structure of the organization. As a result, an article was added to the bylaws to create the ANA Council of State Boards of Nursing (ANA Council.) For the first time, the structure for representatives of boards of nursing to meet together and take action was identified as an official council within the ANA bylaws. This action meant that the ANA Council was the new name for the ANA Special Committee and a statement in the bylaws assured that this council would have the composition, relationship, and responsibilities of the ANA Special Committee of State Boards of Nursing and recognized that the importance of the work of this group to the ANA warranted inclusion in the formal structure of the association. Members of the ANA Council continued to be appointed by the ANA Board of Directors upon recommendation by their respective state boards of nursing. The ANA Council was given autonomy in establishing its rules; in devising ways to bring about uniformity in standards, records, and practices; in establishing policies for the SBTPE; and in conducting conferences for those concerned with the work of the state boards. The Executive Committee, elected by the members of the

ANA Council, had as one of its duties the preparation of an annual budget for submission to the ANA Board of Directors. Another duty was to appoint committees, including a Committee on Blueprint for Licensing Examinations. The specific tasks of this committee were spelled out in the bylaws.[87]

In January 1967, Eleanor J. Smith joined the ANA staff as adviser for the Council of State Boards of Nursing. She replaced M. Annie Leitch, who retired in 1966 after 14 years as director of the ANA Council and the ANA Special Committee. Smith was executive secretary of the Maryland Board of Examiners of Nurses and then held the same position with the Vermont Board of Nursing prior to joining the ANA staff. Smith had also been president of the Maryland State Nurses Association.

The July 1970 meeting of the ANA Council of State Boards of Nursing laid the foundation for action later in the decade. In the News section of the July issue of the *AJN*, the following statement appeared:

Miami Beach, Fla.—The Council of State Boards of Nursing, since its inception twenty five years ago, a part of the ANA, will during the next year be considering the pro's and con's of separate incorporation. This plan was voted by the Council during its meetings here April 28–May 1 in response to a proposal from the New York Council member.

The proposal called for the boards that take part in the SBTPE to form a federation separate from, but closely tied to the ANA. Each member board would pay dues based on the number of nurses currently licensed in the member board's state. The new federation would also seek independent financing for its programs and research. The proposal was to be discussed at the regional meetings during the year and the boards would "take the results of their cogitations to the 1971 Council meeting."[88]

In other action, the ANA Council members voted to endorse a resolution on student employment adopted by the National Student Nurses Association in 1969. The essence of the resolution was that only RNs could give professional nursing care; that students were not licensed to practice; that students should not attempt to substitute for licensed nursing personnel; and that such an attempt would be detrimental to their education, patients, and efforts to improve nursing care standards.[89]

The ANA Council of State Boards of Nursing met in Dallas, Texas in 1971 and voted to remain a structural unit within the ANA. Hazel Peeples of Florida was elected chair of the ANA Council. A special committee was appointed to develop plans for a study of the SBTPE. State boards, since 1969, had been contributing money to begin this study and the funds would be used to finance initial meetings of the new committee. Additional money was to be sought from other sources and the NLN Division of Research was asked to conduct the study. In other action, the ANA Council voted to ask the NLN to set aside 10 percent of the fees received from all test pool examinations for research and development.[90]

On January 1, 1971, Eleanor Smith left her position with the ANA Council of State Boards of Nursing to become executive secretary of the Virginia State Board of Nursing.[91] For the next two years, the staff person assigned to the ANA Council, as listed in the official directory published twice a year in the *AJN*, was Lillian Davidson, who was also assigned to the ANA Committee on Legislation. In 1973, Anna Kuba joined the ANA staff as coordinator for the ANA Council.

At the 1972 meeting of the ANA Council of State Boards of Nursing in Detroit, a special luncheon was held to celebrate the 25th anniversary of the annual meetings of the ANA Council and its predecessor organizations from 1947 forward. Eula Benton from Kansas presented a brief history of the organization. She reminded the group that the ANA Bureau of State Boards of Nurse Examiners, once known as the Bureau on State Board Problems, had been established so that boards in the states would have "an opportunity to discuss and, hopefully, solve some of the problems" common to all boards of nursing. She stated that "someone rightfully made the comment that the Bureau was correctly named, because there were so many problems." Benton described the first meeting of the group that formed the basis for the ANA Council when the ANA Committee for the Bureau of State Boards of Nurse Examiners met in Seattle, on September 3, 1947. One of the major actions was to vote to "submit ten names to the ANA

Board of Directors from which five would be selected by that Board to serve on the Working Committee of the Bureau." The five selected were Chair Agnes Ohlson, Connecticut; Anna Beckwith, Montana; Blanche Graves, Nebraska; Virginia Harrison, Missouri; and Nina Wooton, Tennessee. Benton listed the permanent committees of the ANA Council as follows: the Executive Committee, the Committee on Nominations, the Committee on Blueprint for Licensing Examinations, the Committee on Educational Standards, the Committee to Review all the Various Aspects Relating to the SBTPE, and the Committee to Select Item Writers. She also described numerous subcommittees involved in projects common to the boards of nursing who were members of the ANA Council.[92]

In 1973, the ANA Council of State Boards of Nursing met in Minneapolis. The members considered a report from Lorraine Sachs, director of the NLN Test Services, regarding preliminary data from a study of examination scores. She included data that showed that nurses from other countries had a high failure rate and that they tested lowest in psychiatric nursing. In addition, only 24 percent of those tested were from English-speaking countries. At the same meeting, the ANA Council adopted a resolution that "by 1980 all nurse faculty members in all programs preparing persons for licensure as nurses have as a minimum qualification an earned master's degree with graduate preparation in nursing and teaching."[93]

Development of National Licensing Examinations: 1903–1978

One of the most significant activities accomplished by the nursing organizations and the representatives of state boards of nursing during the first 40 years of nursing regulation in the United States was the development of a national examination that was eventually used by all states and the District of Columbia. To emphasize the importance of this activity, the information on the development of these examinations is consolidated here, at the end of this chapter on the organizations for representatives from the boards of nursing, rather than being dispersed throughout the discussions of activities for the decades from 1903 through 1973.

From the beginning, the licensing examinations were constructed and administered by members of the boards. For the most part the questions were essay-type and most states used some form of practical testing or skill demonstration by the candidates as a part of the examination. Before the transition to the national examination, some states had begun to use objective-type questions. The section that follows presents some of the activities involved in the development of the national examinations.

At the NLNE Convention in St. Louis in April 1914, Marietta Squire of New Jersey presided at a meeting of the representatives of boards of nurse examiners. At that meeting, Jane Hitchcock of New York presented a paper on the problems of writing and reading and scoring examinations. There was discussion about the numbers of states that required "practical demonstrations" with three responding positively. These states allowed from 15 to 55 minutes for the demonstrations. There was also a discussion of fees for repeating the examinations. As with many other aspects of activities of the boards, there were a variety of ways of handling the issue. In Minnesota, the candidate paid $2 for each subject repeated, while in Connecticut, the nurse who failed more than three subjects was not allowed to take another examination, but if unsuccessful on only one subject, the nurse could take the examination on that subject twice without additional charge. Still on the subject of fees, some states reported surplus funds while others had deficits. One board reported that members were paid $5 a day for expenses at meetings and 30 cents a paper for grading examinations. The group also discussed reciprocity and instances of attempted evasion of the law.[94]

R. Louise McManus was one of the most influential persons and the primary leader in the development of the national examinations. A faculty member and administrator in nursing at Teachers College, Columbia University, she chaired the committee that responded to the call for a national examination. In a paper written for the National Council of State Boards of Nursing, Inc. (NCSBN®) in 1980, entitled "State Board Test Pool Inception," McManus discussed the 1933 agreement between the ANA and the NLNE that resulted in the NLNE accepting "responsibility for advisory services to the state boards of nurse examiners in all matters including examinations." She went on to describe how the Committee on Education of the NLNE appointed a Subcommittee on State Board Examinations that continued to work on licensing examination problems for "at least the next ten years." In 1937, the *Curriculum Guide* was published. A standardized guide for curricula in schools of nursing seemed to lead naturally to the idea "that there should be developed, by and for the nursing profession, a comprehensive nursing test service." The Joint Committee on Nursing Tests, with members representing the NLNE; the Association of Colleges of Schools of Nursing; and the Division of Nursing Education at Teachers College, Columbia University, was organized in 1938 and chaired by McManus. Its purpose was to establish a cooperative nursing test bureau to provide standardized tests and other needed measurement tools. The prospectus prepared for the Carnegie Foundation, in a request for funding, included plans for tests that could be scored by machines, test scoring and related statistical test reporting, and test advisory services. The services proposed included preadmission examinations, achievement testing, and licensing examinations for state boards of nursing.[95]

The Joint Committee was disbanded when it was not successful in achieving funding. However, the NLNE continued the project with the appointment of a Committee on Nursing Tests in 1939, again with McManus serving as chair. The NLNE was unable to provide the $1,000 needed to proceed, but authorized the committee to borrow the money from private sources. Eula Benton, in her 1972 history of the ANA Council of State Boards of Nursing, said that the money was borrowed from R. Louise McManus and Isabel Stewart.[96] The results were that the first preadmission examinations were administered in 1941 and flourished. The profits enabled the committee to finance the beginnings of the Achievement Test Service and later the SBTPE.[97]

Prior to the development of the Committee on Nursing Tests, at meetings and conferences of the representatives of the state boards of nurse examiners there were many incidents of discussions and action related to the licensing examination. The ANA Board of Directors, in January 1928, asked the Legislative Section to direct a study of the state registration examinations with the goal of promoting uniformity in registration and to make recommendations for the future.[98] Two papers on examinations were presented at a special conference for state boards of nurse examiners sponsored by the NLNE in Chicago in 1933. In "The Value and Use of the New Type Examination," Sister Berenice Beck of Wisconsin compared the new-type and the essay-type examinations, listing the advantages and disadvantages of both. A meeting of the Committee on State Board Problems was held at the close of the NLNE Convention on June 8, 1935. Several papers were presented in the morning session on topics including application forms for the examination, analysis of state board examinations, and the practical examinations. During the afternoon session there was "lively discussion, in closed session, of some of the administrative problems common to many boards." A subcommittee presented a report including recommendations that were accepted and forwarded to the NLNE for adoption. These included the following:

1. That objectives for the examinations be "more clearly defined" and examinations developed to better attain these objectives.

2. That examinations become tools to promote uniformity of standards in nursing education.

3. That the current examinations covering from eight to twelve subjects be abolished and replaced with broader examinations "such as the areas suggested for the new curriculum."

4. That a central council or committee be established to

    a. construct an examination to be used in all states;

    b. develop standards for scoring and grading examinations; and

    c. provide advice for boards in other matters.

5. That research be conducted relative to the advisability of giving the "nursing practice

6. examinations through practical demonstrations."[99]

At the 1942 State Board Conference, R. Louise McManus presented a report of the Committee on Nursing Tests and discussed the progress in constructing tests measuring competency in medical and surgical nursing that could be used as part of the licensing examination. Several boards indicated their willingness to use these examinations.[100] In 1943, under the direction of Ida Somers, the Committee on Nursing Tests' first full time staff member, the work on the SBTPE proceeded and the "tremendous task of preparing the thirteen tests comprising the initial examination series" was accomplished in less than six months.[101] The literature shows the use of the term "State Board Test Pool" to describe the structure that nursing boards joined in order to use the examinations.

An important announcement in the history of the regulation of nurses in the United States appeared in the *AJN* in January 1944.

The State Board Test Pool, established by the NLNE, begins to function this month with seven full members and two partially-participating members. Cooperatively prepared, objective, machine-scored licencing [*sic*] examinations in each subject-matter and clinical area are made available to state boards that have membership in the pool. Answer sheets are scored, raw and percentile scores of each candidate in each test are reported to the board. Decision as to the candidate's passing or failing, as well as the grade to be assigned to each test, will rest always with the board of nurse examiners in the state.

Prompt reporting of test results is made possible by the use of machine-scored answer sheets and punch-card reports of the candidate's relative standing in each test. Consequently, licences [*sic*] can be issued more promptly and enrollment of young graduates in the military services can be hastened.

The initiation of the State Board Test Pool marks a real mile-stone in cooperative professional activity and will lay the foundation for improvement in nursing education by providing a means of self-evaluation for individual nurses, for schools of nursing, and for states.[102]

In her report to the NLNE Board of Directors, Adelaide Mayo, executive director, made the following statement regarding the achievements of the testing service over the past decade:

Nobody could envision at that time the testing service which the NLNE would be conducting ten years later—a State Board Test Pool encompassing all 48 states in 1950, the D.C., Hawaii, and the Canadian province of British Columbia; a pre-nursing test service used by 377 schools; an achievement test service, a graduate nurse test service; and tests for practical nurses as well.... Nursing is, I believe the only profession that has provided itself with the means for evaluating its practitioners at every stage of their preparation—a "cradle to the grave" coverage, I have heard it called. And we did it all in the forties![103]

An article, "The State Board Test Pool" by R. Louise McManus, published in April 1944, reported that several thousand candidates had taken the SBTPE since January and that 17 states had membership in the test pool. She included the following test areas available in the pool: medical nursing, surgical nursing, nursing of children, obstetric nursing, communicable disease nursing, psychiatric nursing, nursing arts, anatomy and physiology, chemistry, microbiology, pharmacology, social foundations of nursing, nutrition, foods, cookery, and diet therapy. McManus said, "No attempt was made comprehensively to measure the subject-matter content, but rather to secure evidence of the *abilities of* the nurse which were the expected outcomes of the total program of instruction—namely, her ability to nurse."[104]

At a conference for representatives of state boards of nurse examiners in December 1944, those in attendance adopted a number of recommendations that were forwarded to the ANA and NLNE boards of directors. Both groups accepted the recommendations from this meeting. Recommendations relevant to the examinations follow:

- • That an individual school, on request and at a fee set by the NLNE Board of Directors, be permitted to secure information as to its standing as compared with that of other schools within its own state and within all states participating in the SBTP.

- • That the possibilities of using the results of the SBTPE in a plan for nationwide reciprocity be explored.

- • That an SBTP be developed for the examination of PNs or attendants.[105]

A major consideration that consumed a large portion of the State Board Conference held in September 1946 was related to concerns about the SBTPE and its financial support. At that time there were 27 state boards with membership in the test pool and these boards were using an average of 10 tests. After extensive discussion, the following recommendations were adopted and forwarded to the NLNE Board of Directors and subsequently accepted:

---

1. That the SBTP service be continued.

2. That the NLNE Board be asked to subsidize the deficit in the test pool budget until the following suggestions could be put into effect to make the service self-sustaining:

    a. That state boards that have indicated the ability to pay more for testing services be contacted so that the increased income may be forthcoming.

    b. That a battery of integrated comprehensive tests be available by August 1947.

    c. That the cost of the comprehensive examination be not less than $3 per candidate.

    d. That any state board using the individual tests for state board examinations after August 1, 1947, be required to pay 35 cents per examination per candidate.

3. That the Committee on Reciprocity and Registration of the ANA Bureau of State Boards be asked to study the implications of the above as it relates to interstate practice.[106]

In October 1949 the following historic announcement was made:

The State Board Test Pool Examination Series 949 which is now making its "debut" throughout the United States consists of six examinations: Medical Nursing, Surgical Nursing, Obstetric Nursing, Nursing of Children, Communicable Disease Nursing and Psychiatric Nursing. It has been possible to reduce the total number of tests in the licensure series to six clinical tests by integrating pertinent content from contributing theory courses into major clinical areas.[107]

An article, "The State Board Test Pool Examination," was published in the *AJN* in 1953. The article, prepared by the staff of the Department of Measurement and Guidance of the NLNE, described the activities during the previous 10 years in the development of a national licensing examination. The article closes with the following:

Regardless of the way in which the nursing profession finally decides to handle the problem of safeguarding the standard of nursing care in this country, the accomplishments that have been realized through the State Board Test Pool establish the nursing profession as a pioneer in this area. In no other profession is it possible to compare the performance of a candidate in any jurisdiction with that of all candidates in all other such jurisdictions throughout the country. There seems to be every reason to believe that the profession will retain its leadership status in the licensing field.[108]

Another important milestone occurred at the 1975 meeting of the ANA Council of State Board of Nursing in New Orleans. At that meeting the members took action to set uniform testing dates beginning in 1976 with a new examination for each administration. Thelma M. Schorr, editor of the *AJN*, commended the ANA Council for this action in her July editorial.[109]

In 1980, the NLN published *An Historical Survey of the Test Services of the National League for Nursing* by Eleanor A. Lynch, RN, a member of the staff of the NLN Department of Test Development. Lynch dedicated the publication to McManus "who provided much of the leadership necessary to the development of standardized tests in nursing." Lynch included some statistics to show the growth of the SBTPE. By 1978, the number of individuals taking the SBTPE for RN licensure was 118,277 and for PN licensure, 54,521.[110]

Conclusion

In the middle of the decade of the 1970s, the ANA Council of State Boards of Nursing was approaching the 75th anniversary of the original registration laws for nurses enacted in the United States in 1903. All states; the District of Columbia; and the territories of American Samoa, Guam, Puerto Rico, and the Virgin Islands now had licensing laws, and representatives were eligible to participate in the meetings of the ANA Council. A national licensing examination had been in use for 30 years as the result of cooperative efforts of the professional organizations and the boards of nursing. The ANA Council provided a forum for representatives of the boards of nursing to meet together. There were changes in society and in the state governments, including demands for accountability for regulation and more public involvement in regulation. Some members of the ANA Council had recognized that there may need to be a change in the structure of its organization. Once again the leaders in the work of boards of nursing would be called upon to take action and there were exciting years ahead.

CHAPTER THREE
COUNCIL TO COUNCIL

We were an audacious nucleus of members of the ANA's Council of State Boards of Nursing who dared to propose that there be a self-governing, incorporated body responsible for all aspects of state board work.

Mildred Schmidt, 1983[1]

Activities: 1950–1977

THE FIRST MEETINGS of representatives of boards of nursing began in the early 20th century, soon after the first few of these boards were established in state law. Through the years the meetings were supported by the American Nurses Association (ANA) and the National League of Nursing Education (NLNE), later the National League for Nursing (NLN). The group functioned under a variety of titles. During those years some of the board of nursing representatives expressed concern about employees of state governments operating under a professional association rubric. In 1950 the representatives considered the issue and voted to remain within the ANA structure. However, questions continued to be raised about the appropriateness of the decision. In 1966 the ANA added bylaws that established the ANA Council of State Boards of Nursing as an official unit of the professional association. Even though the ANA Council had autonomy in establishing its rules and policies for the development and use of the State Board Test Pool Examinations (SBTPEs), membership on the ANA Council was limited to ANA members (registered nurses [RNs]) approved by the ANA Board of Directors. Seven states and the District of Columbia had separate boards for RNs and practical/vocational nurses (PN/VNs). The boards of practical/vocational nursing in those jurisdictions were required by ANA bylaws to select an RN to represent their respective board. Also, the ANA Council was funded and staffed by the ANA and reported regularly to the ANA Board of Directors.

The change in the bylaws that provided for the ANA Council did not ease the minds of individuals aware of the increasing criticism that professional boards were self-serving instruments of the professions they regulated. Members of the ANA Council envisioned the potential for problems related to conflicts of interest, particularly in the area of examination development. By 1970 the general public and many state legislators were concerned with consumers' rights. Licensing boards received criticism for what appeared to be a close tie to the professionals they regulated and the professions that were represented by the regulated persons. No specific charges were brought against a nursing board, but the staffs became attuned to these concerns.

Consumers, also known as public members, and licensed practical/vocational nurses (LPN/VNs) were added to licensing boards by legislatures throughout the country. However, these full-fledged members of boards could not represent their respective states as members of the ANA Council. Some legislatures around the country were scrutinizing the work of licensing boards more closely than in the past by requiring numerous written reports and testimony of board members and staff. Other legislatures passed sunset legislation requiring a state licensing board to present an extensive evaluation report to the legislature periodically, usually every four years, for the purpose of justifying the continuation of the board with the same or modified structure and function. Yet other states created departments of regulation, merged boards, or required shared staff.

During this same time the ANA experienced a period of financial crisis, and because the ANA Council was required to restrict some committee activities, the vulnerability of the ANA Council became apparent. As a result, in 1970 Mildred Schmidt of New York, a member of the ANA Council, proposed that a free-standing association be established. After a year of study by boards of nursing, the proposal was overwhelmingly defeated. The ANA Council during its 1971 annual meeting adopted a resolution to remain within the ANA. But the pressure on individual boards and dissatisfaction with the structure of the ANA Council caused the ANA Council to appoint an ad hoc committee "to examine the possibility of the Council establishing itself as a self-governing, incorporated body."[2]

In 1974 the ANA Council appointed an ad hoc committee to study the relationship of the council to the ANA. The current structure was thought by some to give the appearance of a conflict of interest. Sidney Willig, a professor of law at Temple University and a critic of licensing boards and their relationship to the professions they regulated, studied the ANA Council minutes and the ANA bylaws. He served as a consultant to the Ad Hoc Committee on Organization of the Council (Ad Hoc Committee) and Schmidt reported Willig's conclusion as follows:

There is a need for an independent federation or national association of State Boards of Nursing to serve as an organization through which the constituent and participating state boards of nursing of the United States and/or North America, may Counsel together and obtain such services as they may desire, to discharge their responsibilities for the administration of nursing practice laws and for the protection of the public interest as it is affected by the practice of nursing.[3]

During the 1976 meeting of the ANA Council, the Ad Hoc Committee presented its report and recommended that a national association of state boards of nursing be formed. Rather than take action at that time, the group decided to study the recommendation. The ANA Council committees and members of each of the four areas into which the ANA Council was divided studied the proposal during the next year. Assignment of the member boards to geographic areas is shown in the chart on the following page.

Area I	Area II	Area III	Area IV
Alaska	Illinois	Alabama	Connecticut
Arizona	Indiana	Arkansas	Delaware
California*	Iowa	Florida	District of Columbia*
Colorado*	Kansas	Georgia*	Maine
Guam	Michigan	Kentucky	Maryland
Hawaii	Minnesota	Louisiana*	Massachusetts
Idaho	Missouri	Mississippi	New Hampshire
Montana	Nebraska	North Carolina	New Jersey
Nevada	North Dakota	Oklahoma	New York
New Mexico	Ohio	South Carolina	Pennsylvania
Oregon	South Dakota	Tennessee	Rhode Island
Utah	West Virginia*	Texas*	Vermont
Washington*	Wisconsin	Virginia	Virgin Islands
Wyoming			

*Two member boards—one regulating RNs and one regulating LPN/VNs.

The March 1977 minutes of the ANA Council Executive Committee reported on a general discussion "of the problems in carrying out the functions of the Council as it is presently structured." As a result of the discussion, the Executive Committee decided to propose a revision of the ANA Council's rules to delete most standing committees and permit the Executive Committee to appoint ad hoc committees or task forces to accomplish defined goals.[4]

During the April 5, 1977, meeting of Area II in Kansas City, members discussed issues of reorganization and realized that much information was needed before they could support or reject a specific proposal. Elaine Ellibee of Wisconsin, chair of the meeting, offered to contact a non-government attorney for advice on how to organize in order to gather needed information. It was agreed that Ellibee should make the contact. Area II members were encouraged to send financial contributions to Ellibee, which would be placed in a non-governmental bank account to support these explorations. According to Ellibee, the $50 check from Joyce Schowalter of Minnesota arrived first. By July 27, 1977, after the Task Force on Reorganization of the Council of State Boards of Nursing was established, 27 individuals and organizations had sent a total of $14,980.[5]

Thus, when the ANA Council annual meeting began June 7, 1977, at the Regency Hotel in Denver, members were prepared for the discussion on possible reorganization. They had some idea of the complexity of the issues surrounding the formation of an independent organization and the type of information that was needed to make an informed decision. During the Area II meeting, and between sessions of the annual meeting, the Area II members developed a motion for consideration at the ANA Council business session.

As anticipated, during the business meeting, Mildred Schmidt moved to adopt the recommendation from the 1976 Ad Hoc Committee that a national association of state boards of nursing be formed.[6] Joyce Schowalter, on behalf of Area II, moved to refer the motion to a task force charged with proposing "a specific plan to accomplish transition of the ANA Council of State Boards of Nursing to an independent organization." The amended motion on which the delegates voted by ballot read,

that the motion (made by Mildred Schmidt) be referred to a four-member task force composed of one council member elected today by each area and that the ANA Board of Directors be requested to appoint an ex-officio member who shall have voice but no vote. The task force shall propose a specific plan for consideration by the council in 1978 and that such plan include but not be limited to a transition of the ANA Council of State Boards of Nursing to an independent organization. A plan for an independent organization shall include but not be limited to: articles of incorporation, including the appropriate jurisdiction in which to incorporate; tax status; bylaws, including membership, officers and committees; finances; transition from ANA including the date of starting a new organization; and transfer of ownership of SBTPEs. The task force shall be supported by contributions from council members and other interested individuals and groups, provided that no corporate funds be accepted from any groups and will function to the extent of the monies received. There shall be no staff to this task force. The task force shall send a report including but not limited to a financial statement and a specific plan with rationale to all boards of nursing at least 60 days prior to the 1978 council meeting for presentation at that meeting.[7]

Schowalter explained that the motion to commit was "proposed to reinforce or approve the idea of moving to an independent organization while authorizing a specific group of people to present a specific proposal with the hope that at the time a vote is taken, each will be in a better position to cast a vote not only for the concept but also for the specifics of implementing the concept."[8] Margaret Pavelka of Nebraska and Elaine Ellibee both stated that the proposal "did not reflect any opposition to the American Nurses Association."[9] Representatives from at least eight other nursing boards spoke in favor of the motion (Arizona, California, Indiana, Maine, New York, Oklahoma, South Dakota, and West Virginia.) Only one opposition opinion was recorded. Mary McRee of North Carolina spoke against the motion "because it would delay a vote and there is urgent need to proceed with priorities, issues and commitments of the council."[10]

Of the 89 votes cast, 78 were affirmative and 11 were negative, and the chair, Lynne Illes of Iowa declared the motion to commit was carried. Following a period of reflection, each area elected its task force member as follows:

Area I	**Beverly Andre**, Oregon; later replaced by **S. Gertrude "Trudy" Malone**, Montana
Area II	**Elaine Ellibee**, Wisconsin
Area III	**Helen "Pat" Keefe**, Florida
Area IV	**Mildred Schmidt**, New York

The task force elected Elaine Ellibee as chair and the ANA later appointed a member of its board of directors, Barbara Nichols, an ex-officio member with voice but no vote. The following year Nichols became president of ANA.[11]

The Special Task Force—State Boards of Nursing

The new task force first became known as the Task Force on the Reorganization of the Council of State Boards of Nursing. But during its first meeting in August 1977 David Grams, an attorney and consultant from a private law firm, Boardman, Suhr, Curry and Field in Madison, Wisconsin, advised that "the current Task Force become a voluntary association whose title would be Special Task Force— State Boards of Nursing to provide formalization of the group and to establish procedures for handling contributions made."[12] The members of the Special Task Force—State Boards of Nursing (Special Task Force) agreed and elected the following officers:

President	**Elaine Ellibee**
Vice President	**Trudy Malone**
Vice President	**Pat Keefe**
Secretary-Treasurer	**Mildred Schmidt**

Later Pat Keefe became the secretary.

According to minutes from that first meeting, the Special Task Force selected a parliamentarian, Henrietta Marjan of Palos Heights, Illinois, and authorized Mildred Schmidt to talk with representatives of the W. K. Kellogg Foundation regarding funding the Special Task Force. A timetable of activities; a plan for communication with ANA staff, the ANA Board of Directors, and ANA Council membership; and a variety of other organizational activities were also established.[13]

During the next nine months the Special Task Force held 30 days of meetings and two telephone conferences; met with representatives of the ANA Council Executive Committee, the ANA, the National League for Nursing (NLN), the Kellogg Foundation and the American Nurses Foundation (ANF); and had four consultations. Volunteer staff support was provided by staff of the Wisconsin Board of Nursing, especially Sharon Weisenbeck and Albert Kelm, both associate directors. In addition to David Grams, Wade Boardman and Rebecca Erhardt of the same law firm provided legal services.[14] Trudy Malone remarked, "The frequent meetings of the Task Force were more in number than I could have imagined. With the voluminous amount of reading material we sent each other, our work was more time consuming than I had anticipated."[15] *(see fig. 3-A)*

Recognizing the need to control the development and use of the licensing examinations, the Special Task Force expended much effort to clarify current and future relations with the ANA, the NLN, and each state. In proposing contract language, the Special Task Force was guided by the desire to establish the fact that the new organization would have a position of absolute control over the licensing examinations. The new organization would also have the authority to contract with any test service, but the Special Task Force believed that the current arrangement with the NLN should be maintained at that time. As a result three proposed contracts or agreements were drafted for consideration by a new organization once the decision was made to establish it based on the report of the Special Task Force. The proposed contracts or agreements were between the following parties:

- the new organization and each state (document described the rights and responsibilities of each party and listed the contract fee);

- the new organization and the NLN (the NLN would agree that the new organization owned the contents of the licensing examinations and would pay a royalty fee to the organization); and

- the new organization and the ANA (the ANA would agree to transfer its "right, title and interest… in or to the State Board Test Pool Examinations" to the new organization).[16]

Funding

In February 1978 the Kellogg Foundation awarded $28,000 to the Special Task Force, to be administered by the ANF, acting as the fiscal agent of the Special Task Force, to support activities necessary to meet the directives of the ANA Council's 1977 motion. On February 17, in her daily log, Ellibee recorded that the Kellogg Foundation provided the funds "to put forth the necessary efforts and actions to result in the establishment of an independent, quasi-governmental organization composed of Boards of Nursing of the United States, Guam and the Virgin Islands. Much jubilation."[17] The final financial report from the ANF to the Kellogg Foundation indicated that all except $4.40 of the grant was spent. Expenses included administrative costs, travel consultants, and the June 1978 organizational meeting in Los Angeles.[18]

The Kellogg Foundation also expressed an interest in providing funding for an independent organization as it traversed its developmental years. Therefore, the Special Task Force initiated preliminary negotiations and began investigating other potential sources of support.

Incorporation

The Special Task Force minutes document the intense and extended consideration of whether or not to form a legal corporation prior to creation of a new organization by the ANA Council. Timing of such incorporation was a contested point among task force members, the attorney and the parliamentarian. Eventually the Special Task Force decided to file the articles of incorporation in Wisconsin prior to the 1978 ANA Council meeting, with the corporation officers to be the members of Special Task Force. The initial meeting of the corporation took place on April 2, 1978, and these articles stood until replaced June 7, 1978, by the National Council of State Boards of Nursing, Inc. (NCSBN®)

Communication

The Special Task Force kept the ANA Council membership (all boards of nursing) fully informed of the progress of the Special Task Force through major mailings in February and March 1978, each including numerous attached written materials. Likewise, Barbara Nichols sent a written report to the ANA president after each meeting. Having been provided many documents covering the history and development of the ANA Council and working papers prepared in 1975 and 1976 by the Ad Hoc Committee on the Organization of the Council, Nichols told Ann Zimmerman, ANA president, in her September 14, 1977, report that "Task Force members contend that the deliberations regarding the Council of State Boards of Nursing becoming a self-governing incorporated body have not been precipitous but rather a series of systematic discussions regarding the advantages, disadvantages, and alternatives to the present structural arrangements within ANA since 1970."[19] Communications continued to be open and direct, which resulted in full understanding of all perspectives by all parties.

Each Special Task Force member kept their respective area members informed and sought suggestions and advice. Records show that positive feedback and thoughtful ideas were received regularly. One month before the 1978 annual ANA Council meeting, Pat Keefe expressed her personal thoughts to Area III as follows:

Working through this assignment has caused me, personally, to change my mind. I can share with you now that two of the negative votes on that historic motion which was referred to the Task Force were mine. However, study of the documents and information that we had to review during the past year as well as events that have occurred both in our own state and nationally have caused me to move from a "Doubting Thomas" attitude to a sincere conviction that not only is it possible for the Council to become an independent association, but that it is strongly desirable that we do so. There is no question in my mind that such an association can be established and financed. I feel that not only can we continue to produce the licensing examinations, but that there is great potential for us to carry out other activities we have been unable to consider in the past because of necessary limitations of finances. I expect that we may all be called upon to devote more time and effort to make the association a viable one if we move to establish it, however, I feel strongly that it will lead to a strengthening of the nursing profession by continuing to emphasize through licensure the individual accountability of each nurse for her practice and the services she delivers to her patients.[20]

Final Meeting of the ANA Council of State Boards of Nursing

Included in the packet of information for the 1978 annual business meeting of the ANA Council was the report of the Special Task Force. In addition, all persons attending the meeting were invited to an information gathering to meet with the Special Task Force. The information session was well attended and provided an opportunity for task force members to explain the proposal for the formation of an independent organization and respond to inquiries.

On June 5, 1978, members of the ANA Council acted on the pending motion made the previous year by Mildred Schmidt on behalf of the Ad Hoc Committee on Reorganization of the Council. The motion stated:

> that a National Association of State Boards of Nursing be formed by state and territorial boards of nursing of the United States through which its members may counsel together, act collectively, and obtain such services as they may desire in discharging their respective responsibilities for the protection of the public through the administration of their nursing practice acts.[21]

Following amendment, the delegates "voted (83 yes and 8 no) to separate from ANA and establish and [*sic*] independent organization known as the National Council of State Boards of Nursing, Inc." Before adjourning for the last time, the ANA Council acted to refer all motions it had adopted that implied a continuation of effort to the newly established NCSBN.[22] Pat Keefe, quoted by G. Malone, S. Fondiller, and D. Heidorn in their book, *From an Idea to an Organization*, described her experience that momentous day as follows:

> A death occurred in my family causing me to postpone my flight to Los Angeles until June 5. All the way there I wondered how it had gone between my Task Force and Council colleagues. Late in the evening, tired and anxious, I entered the hotel lobby and was greeted exuberantly by members of the Council. The atmosphere was one of complete euphoria, making me feel as if I was returning in triumph from some campaign or war.[23]

The Organizational Meeting—National Council of State Boards of Nursing, Inc.

The next day, June 6, 1978, under the guidance of parliamentarian Henrietta Marjan and attorney David Grams, the first organizational meeting of the new NCSBN was held. The first order of business was the enrollment of member boards. The number of boards of nursing eligible for membership was 61. That number included the boards from 50 states, the District of Columbia, and 2 territories (Guam and the Virgin Islands). Of these boards, 45 licensed both for registered nursing and practical/vocational nursing, 8 licensed only for registered nursing, and 8 licensed only for practical/vocational nursing. The secretary called the roll of boards of nursing that had filed the necessary application of membership. With representatives from 52 of the eligible boards of nursing in attendance, the chair declared a quorum present.

Next, the articles of incorporation and bylaws were adopted. The purposes for the creation of NCSBN were stated in Article II of the NCSBN Articles of Incorporation as follows:

> The purposes for which the Corporation is organized are educational and charitable purposes, including the lessening of the burdens of government by providing an organization through which Boards of Nursing act on matters of common interest and concern affecting the public health, safety, and welfare including the development of licensing examinations in nursing.[24]

The following persons were elected to serve on the first NCSBN Board of Directors:

President	**Elaine Ellibee**, Wisconsin
Vice President	**S. Gertrude "Trudy" Malone**, Montana
Vice President	**Pat Keefe**
Secretary	**Helen "Pat" Keefe**, Florida
Treasurer	**Mildred Schmidt**, New York
Director—Area I	**Elaine Laeger**, Arizona
Director—Area II	**Joyce Schowalter**, Minnesota
Director—Area III	**Margaret Rowland**, Texas-RN
Director—Area IV	**Marianna Bacigalupo**, New Jersey
Director-at-large	**Ruth Siegler**, South Carolina

The contract fee for the 1979 fiscal year was set at $1,000 per member board. A projected budget was accepted with the provision that the board of directors had the option of adjusting it according to income. The new organization accepted the assignment of the ANA Council's rights and responsibilities in connection with the SBTPEs. Three contract forms were approved: (a) NCSBN'S test service contract, (b) the agreement between NCSBN and each member board of nursing, and (c) the agreement between NCSBN and the NLN.

Representatives of the member boards present also acted to authorize the board of directors to appoint a search and screen committee for an executive director and to select a site for the permanent offices of NCSBN. In the interim, the headquarters were located in Madison, Wisconsin.[25]

Comparison of Organizations

The similarities and differences of the two councils are shown below:

	ANA Council	**NCSBN**
Full Name	ANA Council of State Boards of Nursing	National Council of State Boards of Nursing, Inc.
Funding	ANA	Contract fees from member boards, royalties from NLN for exams
Members	One RN representative from each board of nursing, appointed by ANA	Boards of nursing using the licensure examination(s)
Voting Body	ANA Council members	Delegate assembly consisting of officially designated representatives or alternates from each member board
Officers	Executive Committee elected by membership, chair and vice chair elected by Executive Committee	President, vice president, secretary, treasurer, representative from each of four geographic areas, delegate-at-large—all to be elected by delegates at annual meeting
Committees	Executive, Nominating, Blueprint, Administration of Examination, Standards	Executive, Nominating, Examination, Administration of Examination, Bylaws, Finance, Nursing Practice and Standards

	ANA Council	**NCSBN**
Fees	None	Annual contract fee from each member board, amount determined by delegate assembly
Budget	Developed by ANA, all meeting expenses paid by ANA	Proposed by Finance Committee, approved by delegate assembly
Staff	ANA coordinator and assistant	Executive director hired by board of directors, headquarters staff hired by executive director
Headquarters	Kansas City, Missouri	Temporary—Madison, Wisconsin Permanent—Chicago, Illinois

The Aftermath

Following the organizational meeting, both President Ellibee and Mariana Bacigalupo of New Jersey, chair of the ANA Council in 1978, officially notified Anne Zimmerman, ANA president, of the action taken by the ANA Council on June 6, 1978. Each acknowledged the support from ANA over the years and expressed not only appreciation but also the anticipation of a close working relationship between NCSBN and the ANA.[26] The ANA Board of Directors received Bacigalupo's letter during the 1978 ANA Convention and accepted the action and notice of separation "with great regret." Executive Director Myrtle K. Aydelotte, in her June 28, 1978, letter of response continued:

> The ANA firmly believes, as does, drawing upon discussion, the 1978 House of Delegates, that the Association has the responsibility for setting the standards of   education and practice and for enunciating these. The new National Council of State Boards of Nursing carries with it the heritage of the Association and its posture on matters relating to standards and credentialing. It is urged that, as the Association continues to carry out this responsibility as a professional association, the National Council will serve to implement the positions and standards of the Association through its activities.
>
> The American Nurses' Association will be seeking ways to establish a cordial and continuing cooperative relationship with the National Council. The Board extends its best wishes to the National Council for success in its effort to develop a viable and responsible organization.[27]

A week later, in a telephone call from Barbara Nichols, the new president of the ANA, President Ellibee learned of the 1978 resolution that "reaffirmed the 1976 ANA House of Delegates mandate that the ANA Council of State Boards of Nursing be maintained" and directed the ANA Board of Directors to "take all necessary steps to assure that this new independent organization or any other similar organizations, do not usurp the authority and responsibility of ANA to establish and implement standards relating to state laws pertaining to licensure, nursing education and nursing practice which safeguards the health and welfare of the public."[28]

The July 15, 1978, issue of *The American Nurse*, the official publication of ANA, reported that the ANA House of Delegates had adopted a related motion. The body acted "to develop a liaison between ANA and the new organization for the purpose of communicating the standards and positions relating to nursing appropriately developed by this professional association."[29]

Within two months President Ellibee received a call from President Nichols indicating that the ANA did not wish to proceed with business related to NCSBN until all persons had resigned from the ANA Council. Each member of the ANA Council originally had been approved by the ANA Board of Directors consistent with ANA bylaws. But since all boards of nursing, not their members or employees, were now members of NCSBN, it was appropriate that individuals resign from the ANA Council. Whether or not they remained members of ANA was their personal decision.[30]

The new organization started with great enthusiasm and trust. In July 1978, the first NCSBN Board of Directors was presented with "an accurate accounting of the present financial status of the former Special Task Force—State Boards of Nursing, W. K. Kellogg Foundation Grant and the new National Council of State Boards of Nursing, Inc." The statement showed that nine boards had paid the contract fee ($9,000); four persons had made contributions ($90); coffee money had been collected at the June organizational meeting ($92.75); and the former Special Task Force had transferred its remaining funds ($1,484.88) to NCSBN. Therefore the balance in the new bank account as the board began its challenging work was $10,667.63.[31]

Several Firsts

On October 2, 1978, the first office of NCSBN officially opened in Madison, Wisconsin, with office space at Boardman, Suhr, Curry & Field, NCSBN's legal firm. The first employee was administrative assistant Sharon "Shari" Lawler, a person who "developed the office procedures and necessary systems of the Council in exemplary fashion."[32]

Other than the ANA, the National Federation of Licensed Practical Nurses was the first national nursing organization to recognize NCSBN by extending an invitation to its 1978 annual meeting.[33] Over the next months many more groups, as well as individuals, indicated their awareness and support.

A contract fee was now required for participation in NCSBN and for use of the licensing examinations, the first of which was received by NCSBN from the Georgia Board of Nursing (RN).[34]

Conclusion

For more than a quarter of a century representatives of boards of nursing worked to establish an organization that operated independent of any interested group. A variety of attempts eventually resulted in a proposal for a structurally sound organization—NCSBN—that almost all members of the ANA Council of State Boards of Nursing were able to support.

CHAPTER FOUR
GOVERNANCE

Where there is no law, but every man does what is right in his own eyes, there is the least of real liberty.

Henry M. Roberts, **Robert's Rules of Order Newly Revised**[1]

THE COMPONENTS THAT ARE NEEDED for a successful organization are many and varied with some more important than others. When these components come together, they make up the governance of the organization. "Governance" goes beyond "government" and is a term that describes the interrelatedness of the past and present entities of an organization. Governance is the exercise of power, the making of decisions, and the articulation of the interests of those individuals and groups that comprise the organization. This chapter begins with what are generally considered to be the two most important components, but the remainder will not necessarily be presented with any sort of ranking intended. The entities that make up the governance of the National Council of State Boards of Nursing, Inc. (NCSBN®) are presented in the sections that follow.

Articles of Incorporation

Articles of incorporation generally state the purpose for which the organization exists and describes its overall financial status, including reference to the fact that no benefit will be received by directors, officers, or others.[2] The NCSBN Articles of Incorporation included, among its statements, that there would be no attempts to influence legislation or political campaigns, and that NCSBN would adhere to requirements to maintain its tax-exempt status. There is a provision for dissolution of the corporation, including disposal of assets, and for amendment to the articles.[3]

NCSBN was originally incorporated in Wisconsin, the state where most of the meetings of the Special Task Force—State Boards of Nursing had been held. The original offices of the organization were located in Madison. Elaine Ellibee, who was the corporation's first president and initial registered agent, lived in Wisconsin, thereby fulfilling Wisconsin law, which required that NCSBN must have an agent who resided in the state. In 1984, it became necessary to change the designated agent because Ellibee no longer resided in the state. Gifford Zimmerman, a legal counsel for NCSBN, recommended that NCSBN use the United States Corporation Company as its registered agent. That company is a for-profit organization that serves thousands of corporations by satisfying the statutory requirements for registered agents to reside in the state of incorporation by maintaining offices in all states. At the annual meeting in 1984, the NCSBN Delegate Assembly, composed of representatives of the member boards, adopted a resolution to change the name and address of the principle office from Ellibee's to that of the United States Corporation Company.

At that same meeting, the delegates learned that the NCSBN attorneys had advised that there were substantial questions regarding the allocation of responsibilities between the delegate assembly and the NCSBN Board of Directors in relation to Wisconsin law. The attorneys suggested that NCSBN should reorganize in another state where the division of responsibilities between the two bodies would be specifically authorized to avoid future questions. As a result, the delegate assembly adopted the following additional motions related to reincorporation:

- NCSBN would reincorporate as a Pennsylvania not-for-profit corporation.

- The reincorporation would occur in FY85 with necessary actions presented to the 1985 delegate assembly.

- The contracts with member boards would include a contract provision to permit the assignment of their agreements and a reincorporated NCSBN without the consent of the member boards.[4]

During the following year the board of directors worked closely with legal counsel to identify a plan of reincorporation that would be the least disruptive to ongoing activities. To that end, the method chosen was a merger in which a Pennsylvania not-for-profit corporation (NCSBN-PA) would be formed in advance. The current Wisconsin not-for-profit corporation (NCSBN-WI) would then be merged into the new corporation. The merger format was chosen because the existing operation and contracts of NCSBN-WI would automatically be carried over to NCSBN-PA. The articles of the new incorporation document, while conforming to Pennsylvania law, made few changes to those in the Wisconsin document. One noticeable change was the addition of the following statement: "except to the extent such powers are reserved to the Delegate Assembly as set forth in the Bylaws of the Corporation." This specifically acknowledged that the delegate assembly could reserve for itself certain powers to manage the corporate affairs of NCSBN that might otherwise be vested in the board of directors. The bylaws, attached to the form for Pennsylvania, remained the same, and the current board of directors was listed as the board for the merged organization.[5]

The merger required two actions by the 1985 delegate assembly. First, on August 21, the NCSBN-WI Delegate Assembly convened at 9 a.m. in Chicago. After some preliminary business, the delegate assembly adopted the motion to approve the plan of merger as required by Wisconsin law in order for NCSBN to become a Pennsylvania not-for-profit corporation. This meeting was adjourned at 9:38 a.m.[6] The meeting of NCSBN-PA was called to order in the same location at 9:40 a.m. and the delegate assembly adopted a motion to approve the plan of merger as required by Pennsylvania law to confirm the incorporation of NCSBN in the Commonwealth of Pennsylvania.[7] The appropriate articles of incorporation and attached documents were filed and, at the time of writing, NCSBN remains incorporated in the Commonwealth of Pennsylvania.

Bylaws

Robert's Rules of Order Newly Revised describes bylaws in general as the document of a society that contains "its own basic rules relating to itself as an organization, rather than the parliamentary procedure that it follows." Further, bylaws define the basic characteristics of the organization, prescribe how it functions, and include all rules the society considers important enough that they cannot be easily changed and cannot (with limited exception) be suspended. Bylaws generally include articles that state the name of the organization, its objective, members, officers, meetings, board of directors, committees, parliamentary authority, and provision for amendment.[8]

The bylaws of NCSBN adopted by the first delegate assembly met the criteria stated above. Although the purpose of NCSBN has been relocated in the document through the years, the substance has not changed. From 1978 through 2003 the statement of purpose in the bylaws read as follows:

> The purpose of the National Council is to provide an organization through which state boards of nursing act and counsel together on matters of common interest and concern affecting the public health, safety and welfare, including the development of licensing examinations in nursing.

The only article in the NCSBN Bylaws that has never been amended or revised is the one that states the name of the organization. The original bylaws established the delegate assembly as the legislative, policymaking body of NCSBN and described the board of directors as the administrative body. The duties of both were established and the board of directors comprised the president, vice president, recording secretary, treasurer, area directors, and a director-at-large. The term of office was one year for officers and two years for directors. All boards of nursing that paid the contract fee and used at least one examination were eligible for membership. In those states where there was one board for the regulation of registered nurses (RNs) and another for licensed practical/vocational nurses (LPN/VNs), each member board had one vote in the delegate assembly and each paid the full fee. Where the two groups were regulated by one board, the member board had two votes and paid the same fee paid by the member boards with one vote. This arrangement was contentious until it was corrected, first by an amendment to change the fee payment, and later by an amendment that gave every member board two votes in the delegate assembly. The Nominating Committee was elected annually by the delegate assembly and the bylaws established the following standing committees: Budget/Finance, Bylaws, Examination, and Security/Administration of Examination. The board of directors and the delegate assembly both had authority to appoint other committees. The process for amendment or revision was clearly stated. An article on indemnification has continued to be a part of the NSCBN Bylaws and *Robert's* has always been identified in the bylaws as the parliamentary authority for NCSBN and, as such, has been used in reference to questions not answered by the bylaws.[9]

The original bylaws were reviewed by the first Bylaws Committee, whose chair, Joyce Schowalter of Minnesota, presented a large number of amendments at the 1979 NCSBN Annual Meeting. The majority of these amendments were designed to clarify the language and make it consistent throughout. Some of the more substantive changes included the following:

- A state board of nursing was defined as any legally constituted body or agency of any state, territory, or political subdivision of the United States of America that bears the designation "Board of Nursing" or a similar title.

- The qualifications for the office of president were amended to require that the candidate must have served on the board of directors.

- The term of office for the president, vice president, secretary, and treasurer was lengthened to two years and the word "recording" was deleted from the title of the secretary.

- A definition of "open meetings" was added and provision made for executive sessions.

- Consistent use of the words "session" and "meeting" was applied throughout. The parliamentarian explained that the delegates assembled during several meetings within the annual session.

- A second member from a member board licensing only practical nurses was added to the Examination Committee and the statement that these representatives could only attend the meetings related to the LPN/VN examinations was deleted.

- The Nursing Practice and Standards (NP&S) was added as a standing committee.[10]

In the years from 1980 through 1986, the bylaws were amended annually. Marjorie Doyle of New York served as chair of the committee from 1980 through 1983 and was followed by Corinne Dorsey of Virginia who served from 1984 through 1988. In 1980 a clause was added to prohibit an officer from holding elected or appointed office in a state, regional, or national association if that office could be a perceived or actual conflict of interest. In 1983 the delegate assembly adopted an amendment to authorize the board of directors to adopt the budget rather than requiring the delegate assembly to do so. The delegate assembly agreed to authorize the Examination Committee, rather than the board of directors, to select item writers and designated the task of reviewing and proposing changes to model laws and administrative rules to the NP&S Committee. It is interesting to note that in several instances amendments made one year were either deleted or amended the next year. For example, the amendment in 1979 that added a representative from a practical/vocational nursing board to the Examination Committee was deleted soon thereafter.

At the meeting of the delegate assembly in 1986, the Bylaws Committee recommended that it be designated as a special committee with the addition of members deemed appropriate by the board of directors to undertake a total bylaws revision. The delegate assembly adopted the recommendation and Dorsey was named to chair the Bylaws Special Committee.[11] During the subsequent year, the Bylaws Special Committee completed the revision, with the exception of Article X which dealt with committees, and presented it to the delegate assembly at the annual meeting in 1987, where the revisions were adopted and amended. In addition, the Bylaws Special Committee asked to be continued for another year to complete the revision of Article X and to make recommendations about the NCSBN Standing Rules. The delegate assembly agreed to this continuance.[12] The following year the delegate assembly amended and adopted the changes to Article X, and agreed to repeal the standing rules. This action was taken with the proviso that the rules would remain in effect until they were incorporated into the appropriate documents. The proviso also authorized the board of directors to transfer all remaining standing rules not presented as part of the proposed bylaws revision to the current NCSBN Standing Rules, a manual on convention rules, or other designated documents. The Bylaws Special Committee believed that the information contained in the standing rules, for the most part, described procedures for accomplishing the work of NCSBN and decided to place certain important language in the bylaws and to recommend the action described above for the remainder of the material. The Bylaws Special Committee recognized that some of the items added to the bylaws increased the specificity of the language but also believed that these items should be less easily changed than by a simple majority vote. According to the rationale for the changes in the bylaws, the NCSBN Standing Rules were largely procedural statements to guide the operation of the association. Most of them were more appropriate as part of a policy document that would be changed without action by the delegate assembly. There were some provisions that were less subject to change or appropriate for change by the delegate assembly that were incorporated into the bylaws.

Highlights of the major revisions adopted by the delegate assembly in 1987 and 1988 follow:

- The preamble that stated the purpose of NCSBN was deleted and the title of Article II was changed from "Objectives" to "Purpose and Functions." The revised Article II incorporated language from the preamble and amendments to the original objectives, now called "functions."

- The duty to establish the geographic divisions within NCSBN known as areas was transferred from the board of directors to the delegate assembly.

- In the article related to officers that provided for employees of member boards other than nurses to hold office, a requirement that candidates must have had a year of experience with a member board was deleted and a section on removal from office was added.

- In the article on meetings, a section was added on proxy voting, and the wording related to the cancellation of the annual meeting in the event of a national emergency was changed. The revision to this article also described how voting would take place by mail, telephone, and proxy.

- In the article on the delegate assembly, the revision stated that no officer could serve as a delegate, authorized proxy voting at special sessions of the delegate assembly, and added to the duties of the delegate assembly the approval of policy and position statements and strategies that give direction to NCSBN.

- The board of directors was authorized to conduct the performance evaluation of the executive director, determine the categories and number of staff, and adopt personnel policies. The board was also authorized to adopt rules and structure for itself to carry out its functions.

- Two standing committees were added—the Communications Committee and the Long Range Planning Committee (LRPC). The name of the NP&S Committee was changed to the Nursing Practice and Education (NP&E) Committee. Standing committees were authorized to recommend to the Board of Directors that the board appoint subcommittees that would report to the standing committees. The revision allowed individuals other than members and staff of member boards to serve on subcommittees. Standing committees were required to establish operating procedures subject to review and modification by the board of directors.

- The duties of the Communications Committee were stated to include oversight of publications and computer based information systems, the administration of the awards program, the planning of the program for the annual meeting, and the coordination of educational conferences. The LRPC was charged with reviewing NCSBN's mission statement, structure, and evaluating the effectiveness of both in meeting the purpose and functions of NCSBN. This committee was also given the responsibility for reviewing goals, objectives, and strategies and proposing revisions.

- The entire section on indemnification was rewritten to be consistent with the corporation laws of Pennsylvania.[13]

There were relatively few amendments to the bylaws from 1988 through 1993. The chairs during that time were Ann Bissonette of New York (1989–1990) and Libby Lund of Tennessee (1991–1994). Bissonette had served on the Bylaws Special Committee and was the first public member of a member board to chair a standing committee of NCSBN. In 1990 the delegate assembly agreed to changes in the bylaws to remove the reference to campaign guidelines. They also changed the duty of the Committee on Nominations from the requirement to present a slate of two candidates for each office to submit a slate of candidates for the offices to be filled. This change permitted presenting one or more candidates for each office rather than requiring that two be presented. The fiscal year was changed from July 1 through June 30 to October 1 through September 30. This change was made to make the period more congruent with the cycle of NCSBN activities.[14] In 1991 an amendment to the bylaws expanded one of the qualifications for candidates for the office of president by adding the alternatives of serving on a committee, or as a delegate to the requirement of serving on the board of directors prior to election.[15]

In 1992 the delegate assembly authorized a revision of the NCSBN Bylaws to be acted on by the 1993 delegate assembly.[16] Work on the revision was not completed until 1994 when Libby Lund, chair of the Bylaws Committee, presented the proposed revision to the delegate assembly. The delegate assembly adopted the revised bylaws as amended.[17] A careful review shows a more polished document, a greater consistency in the use of terminology, and the addition of an article on the executive director. The following are some of the changes made:

- The office of secretary was deleted and the executive director was named as corporate secretary.

- There was a provision for a second delegate-at-large to preserve the number of members on the board of directors as nine.

- There was a change to state that an officer *shall* be removed for conviction of a felony, rather than *may* be removed.

- There was clarification that the board of directors, committees, and member boards may make motions in meetings of the delegate assembly.

- Authorization was added for consultants and others selected for their expertise to serve on special committees.

Other changes made with the 1994 revision included a reduction in the specificity of the duties for the delegate assembly and the board of directors. In the rationale included in the Report of the Bylaws Committee, the statement was made that "when bylaws are too specific, it implies something not listed is restricted." Others argued that without specificity, bylaws might be interpreted too broadly. Over the years, from time to time, there have been concerns within the organization regarding role clarification for the two bodies. This revision did not resolve these concerns.[18]

The bylaws revision also deleted the following standing committees: Administration of Examination, Communications, and Bylaws. The deletion of the Administration of Examination Committee was understandable considering the movement to computerized adaptive testing (CAT). However, the Communications Committee and LRPC provided service to NCSBN, the board of directors, the member boards, and the delegate assembly. These committees also allowed more individuals to participate in the work of NCSBN. The deletion of the Bylaws Committee is unusual in organizational structure. As a standing committee, it reports to the delegate assembly and is subject to direction by the delegate assembly. Without the standing committee status, a bylaws committee would be a special committee, appointed as needed and directed by the board of directors and thus would initially report to the board of directors. This change increased the role of the board of directors in the amendment of bylaws. For example, the board of directors could determine which amendments were presented to the delegate assembly for action. In other changes, references to "nursing licensing examinations" or "licensing examinations" were changed to "NCLEX®" (National Council Licensing Examinations) throughout the revised bylaws. In addition, the revision included the following:

- A person filling a vacancy on the board of directors would be "serving until the next annual meeting" rather than "serving the remainder of the term." This reversed a change made earlier to prevent the frequent turnover in the membership of the board of directors.

- A member of the Committee on Nominations was prohibited from being a candidate for office rather than being allowed to resign from the committee in order to run for office.[19]

In the *NCSBN Book of Reports* for the annual meeting in 1997, the Report of the Bylaws Task Force states that Sharon Weisenbeck of Kentucky was the chair.[20] In the minutes of the meeting of the delegate assembly in 1997, Joey Ridenour of Arizona, chair of the Bylaws Committee, presented the proposed amendments to the bylaws. One amendment added the copyright symbol to the acronym NCLEX wherever it appeared in the bylaws. The section on election of officers in the absence of a majority vote was amended to clarify the procedure for this revoting, and to define the number of candidates to be included in the second ballot for officers other than for the directors-at-large. For directors-at-large a third ballot could occur, and if there was no majority at that time, the election would be determined by lot. Other amendments changed the procedure for determining the chair of the Committee on Nominations from one where the member receiving the highest number of votes in the election became chair to one that permitted the committee to select its own chair following the election. Another change stipulated that the Committee on Nominations' first meeting must occur at the time of the first meeting of the board of directors in the new fiscal year.[21]

The board of directors presented a proposed amendment to the bylaws in 1998 that was adopted by the delegate assembly. The recommendation changed the wording in the article pertaining to the delegate assembly by altering the sentence: "The Delegate Assembly, the legislative body of the National Council, shall provide direction for the National Council through adoption of the mission, goals and objectives, adoption of position statements, and actions at any Annual Meeting or special session." The proposed amendment removed the authority of the delegate assembly to adopt goals and objectives. The rationale for the change stated that for two years the board of directors had studied and developed six strategic initiatives and 23 outcomes that were adopted by the delegate assembly in 1997. The amendment would allow the board of directors to develop the strategic initiatives and outcomes, and report them to the delegate assembly annually rather than requiring the delegate assembly to act on them.[22] However, the delegate assembly adopted an amended motion that restored the intent of the original bylaw using the new language "strategic initiatives and outcomes" in place of "goals and objectives" but retaining the authority for the delegate assembly to adopt them.[23]

In 2000, Cynthia Van Wingerden of the Virgin Islands chaired the Bylaws Audit Group that reviewed the NCSBN Bylaws and analyzed the data from the governance survey conducted in January 2000 and the responses given on a survey of attendees at the 2000 area meetings. The audit group identified the following areas for further study:

- The need to clarify and define the boundaries of authority of the delegate assembly and the board of directors.

- The need to ensure a governance structure and process to adequately prepare the delegate assembly to make effective and timely decisions that are fiscally sound and take into account the long range impact.

- The need to reexamine the election process to ensure appropriate continuity and ongoing development of effective leadership.

- The need to review the process for committee appointments, determination of charges, and lines of communication to optimally support the strategic plan.[24]

At the delegate assembly meeting, Van Wingerden presented a recommendation for the delegates to authorize the creation of a committee for a comprehensive review and potential revision of the bylaws. The recommendation was adopted.[25]

The Bylaws Committee, with Laura Rhodes of West Virginia-RN as its chair, began its review of the current and earlier bylaws of NCSBN and the bylaws of other organizations. The committee consulted with staff and legal counsel, and was briefed on the articles of incorporation and applicable provisions of Pennsylvania corporation law. Further, the committee received suggestions from the standing committees, the member boards, and from the attendees at the mid-year meeting. Following its meeting in March, 2001, the board of directors, in an unprecedented move, forwarded a list of 23 suggestions for consideration by the Bylaws Committee. The entire list was included in the minutes of the meeting. The following are examples of the suggestions included on the list:

- Allow democratic process to direct board election and representation for internal groups (i.e., public members, licensed practical/vocational nurses (LPN/VNs), etc.).

- Explore president-elect instead of vice president. The president-elect would hold office for one term, likewise the president.

- Explore immediate past president as possible nominating committee chair.

- Better define "Open Meetings." If meetings are open to the public, is confidential information protected and what are the safeguards?

- Determine who has the authority to address test vendor issues, delegate assembly or board.

- Determine the executive director's explicit authority including: power to sign checks and undisputed administrative authority.
- Have board of directors approve the audit report.
- Address "dissolution" of the organization in the bylaws.[26]

At the 2001 annual meeting in Pittsburgh, Chair Rhodes presented the proposed revisions of the bylaws to the delegate assembly. As with the "revisions" of 1987 and 1993, the changes were more consistent with "amendment" than "revision." The majority of sections had no change, or the change was merely technical. With a few exceptions, the delegate assembly adopted the proposal as presented. Some strengths of the changes include the rearrangement of the content and revision of the format; new language that referred to officers as the president, vice president, and secretary; named the area directors and directors-at-large as directors rather than officers; the elimination of the requirement to hold a pre- and post-annual meeting session of the board of directors; and the reestablishment of the Bylaws Committee as a standing committee. However, the latter change also specified that the direction of the Bylaws Committee would be limited to the board of directors and the delegate assembly. Apparently member boards, other committees, and the Bylaws Committee itself could no longer propose changes in the bylaws. Other changes resulting from the action on the bylaws in 2001 include the following:

- Changed the description of the delegate assembly to the "membership" body of NCSBN from the "legislative" body, as it had been described in the original bylaws.
- Removed the language giving authority to the delegate assembly to select the test service. Instead, the board of directors was to select the test service and present the decision to the delegate assembly for approval.
- Removed the authority of the delegate assembly to act on the audit report and deleted the requirement for provision of quarterly financial reports to the member boards.
- Expanded the reasons for removal from office, but a felony conviction was returned to the status of *may be* rather than *shall be* as a cause for removal.
- Changed the provision that all meetings within NCSBN were open meetings, except when in executive session, to apply only to the delegate assembly.[27]

Laura Rhodes continued as chair of the Bylaws Committee in 2002, and the committee completed a revision of the standing rules of the delegate assembly.[28] In 2003 the Bylaws Committee was charged by the board of directors to review the governance structure of the organization and to address comments received previously, particularly regarding the continuity of the board.[29] At its April 30–May 1, 2003, meeting, the board of directors heard a report on the work of the committee from Chair Rhodes and legal counsel. In an unprecedented action, the board of directors deleted the proposed items pertaining to the board of directors and terms of office, then agreed to forward only the remaining proposals to the delegate assembly for consideration and action at the annual meeting.[30]

At the meeting of the board of directors in December 2003, the board gave the Bylaws Committee the following directives:

- Research the pros and cons of making the Bylaws Committee a standing committee, study other standing and ad hoc committee structures, and address the requests from the Disciplinary Resources Panel and Advanced Practice Panel.
- Delete the requirement that the Committee on Nominations observe a board of directors meeting.
- Allow the Committee on Nominations to select its chair and vice chair.[31]

The bylaws have been amended or revised almost every year in the 25-year history of NCSBN. The theme that has persisted over the years is the search for clarification of roles in the governance of the organization. This remains a challenge for the years ahead.

Standing Rules

In addition to the articles of incorporation and the bylaws, *Robert's* lists standing rules as a third element for an organization. Standing rules are those that "are related to the details of the administration of a society rather than to parliamentary procedure." These rules can be adopted or changed in the same way "as any ordinary act of the society." *Robert's* further states, "An example of such a rule might be one setting the hour at which meetings are to begin, or one relating to the maintenance of a guest register."[32]

At its organizational meeting, NCSBN adopted standing rules. Examples of items included follow:

- The listing of the states assigned to each area.
- Procedures for conference calls and mail votes.
- Convention committees and their duties.
- Procedures for conducting elections.
- The duties of the board of directors related to the staff of NCSBN.[33]

In 1979 the delegate assembly amended the standing rules in three areas by adding specificity to the duties of the officers and committees, stating fees for membership, and establishing a procedure for expense reimbursement. Another amendment added a section on the process of amendment of the standing rules.[34] The ongoing review of the standing rules was done by the Bylaws Committee. The delegate assembly amended the standing rules every year except one prior to 1988. Details of the amendments to the standing rules between 1979 and 1988 are not included here. These standing rules are found in the books of reports and the minutes of the delegate assembly meetings for those years.

As shown in the section above on bylaws, at the annual meeting in 1988 one of the proposals from the Special Bylaws Committee was to repeal the standing rules. The committee proposed to place some of the content in amendments to the bylaws and asked the delegate assembly to authorize the board of directors to transfer the remainder to one of the following: the current board of director's standing rules, a manual on convention rules, or a similar document. Further, the proposal included a recommendation for each committee to establish procedures to expedite its work, subject to review and modification by the board of directors. These proposed changes were adopted by the delegate assembly and all of the provisions mentioned above were accomplished within a few years. Most of the standing rules eventually became a part of the *NCSBN Policy and Procedure*. At the end of the first 25 years of the organization there are policies and procedures in the following 10 categories: organization, member relations, board of directors, committees, annual meetings, external relations, publications, finance, personnel, and research. The largest numbers of policies are located within the categories of the board of directors and the annual meetings, respectively.[35]

Another document used for governance by the delegate assembly of NCSBN is what *Robert's* describes as "the Standing Rules of the Convention." *Robert's* says that a committee on standing rules drafts the proposal and submits it for consideration. These rules often contain both parliamentary and non-parliamentary elements and apply to the one session only. It is not unusual, though, for these rules to continue to be used at another annual meeting unless a change is necessitated by items on the agenda or an amendment in the bylaws. Standing rules of a convention may be suspended under certain conditions.[36] From 1978 through 1991, the delegate assembly of NCSBN operated under the provisions of such standing rules. Titled Rules of Conduct for the Delegate Assembly, these rules were reviewed annually and amended as necessary to fit specific circumstances. In accordance with usual organizational procedure, the delegate assembly considered and adopted these rules immediately following the report of the Registration Committee at the opening session. Beginning in 1992 the name of these rules was changed to the Standing Rules for the Delegate Assembly. This title continued through the annual meeting in 2003.

Organizational Planning

The board of directors, under the leadership of President Joyce Schowalter, recognized that after almost five years of growth it was time for NCSBN to initiate organizational planning. At its meeting in January 1983 the executive director presented a report on long range planning, and the board of directors adopted a motion to appoint the LRPC.[37] Subsequently, Ruth Elliott of Tennessee was appointed to chair this committee and continued to serve in that capacity through the annual meeting in 1986. The board directed the LRPC to report to the board every six months, and made provision for the chair to be present to discuss specific items on the agenda for the board of directors meeting.[38]

At the 1984 annual meeting Chair Elliott presented the Report of the Long Range Planning Committee, including a recommendation for the delegate assembly to adopt, for the first time, an NCSBN mission statement, as follows:

The mission of the National Council of State Boards of Nursing, Inc., is to promote public policy related to the safe and effective practice of nursing and in the interest of public welfare.

It strives to accomplish this mission by acting in accordance with the decisions of its members on matters of common interest and concern affecting public health, safety and welfare.

To accomplish its aims, the National Council provides guidance and services to its members in performing their functions which regulate entry to nursing practice, continuing safe nursing practice, and nursing education programs.

The delegates adopted the mission statement, and also adopted a motion that the identification of goals and objectives be completed for presentation to the delegate assembly in 1985.[39]

At the 1985 meeting the delegate assembly adopted these goals and objectives, as well as a motion that the strategies and accompanying financial plan to implement the long range plan be presented to the delegate assembly in 1986.[40] The 1986 NCSBN Delegate Assembly amended one objective as follows: "Implement a planning [instead of financial] model to be used as a guide for the development of NCSBN."[41] They then accepted the Report of the Long Range Planning Committee. In another motion, the delegate assembly directed the board of directors to report on its prioritization of the goals and objectives at the 1987 annual meeting.[42] The LRPC had fulfilled its charge and there was no further mention of activities related to long range planning until 1988. The goals and objectives adopted appear in Appendix A.

In February 1988 the board of directors had completed the prioritization of the goals and objectives, and agreed that the organizational plan (consisting of the goals, objectives, and implementing strategies) would be published annually in the *NCSBN Book of Reports* with the budget for the coming fiscal year.[43] At a 1988 session of the NCSBN Delegate Assembly, the board of directors presented the updated two-year organizational plan and the delegates approved a recommendation that the board of directors and the committees identify strategies already in use that give direction to NCSBN. The board of directors defined "strategies that give direction" as those that involve the long-term commitment of significant NCSBN resources.[44]

As stated in the section above on bylaws, the delegate assembly amended the bylaws in 1988 to add the LRPC to the list of standing committees of NCSBN. In August 1989 the board of directors appointed Marcia Rachel of Mississippi to chair this committee.[45] She served in this capacity through the annual meeting in 1994. At its April 30–May 1, 1990, meeting, the board of directors accepted the recommendation of the LRPC for a six-year evaluation and planning cycle.[46] The LRPC recommended and the delegate assembly reaffirmed the mission statement adopted in 1984.[47]

The delegate assembly adopted revisions to the NCSBN goals and objectives in 1992.[48] In 1994 the bylaws were again revised and the LRPC was deleted from the list of standing committees. However, a Long Range Planning Task Force (LRP Task Force) was appointed in 1995 with Leola Daniels of Idaho as its chair through 1996. At the delegate assembly in 1996, the delegates replaced the original mission statement with the following: "The mission of the National Council of State Boards of Nursing is to advance the safe and effective practice of nursing in the interest of protecting the public's health and welfare."[49]

Sharon Weisenbeck of Kentucky chaired the LRP Task Force in 1997 and presented its report at the annual meeting that same year. The report included a recommendation made to the board of directors to "consider input from the LRP Task Force in discussions relating to long range and short range planning for the National Council."[50] A review of the minutes of the meetings of the board of directors in 1997 showed that Chair Weisenbeck presented a report of the LRP Task Force at the February meeting. At that time the board of directors voted to move forward with the LRP Task Force recommendation to focus the board on spending approximately 80 percent of its time on planning, and to dissolve the LRP Task Force within three years. The LRP Task Force was not included on the list of committees, task forces, and other groups for the following year. At the same meeting the board considered a revision to the mission statement developed by two of its members and agreed to forward the statement for discussion at the area meetings. Following that action the board of directors adopted a "role statement" as follows: "The role of the NCSBN is to serve as a consultant, liaison, advocate and researcher to member boards and as an education information resource to the public and policy makers."[51]

In May the board of directors held a session on long range or strategic planning. Dr. Jamie Orlikoff facilitated the session.[52] At its next meeting in June the board of directors heard a report from NCSBN staff member, Ruth Elliott, director for Nursing Education and Practice, on future direction for development of the organization. The board agreed that the fall retreat should focus on developing the long range planning approach toward the identification of an agenda for safe and effective consumer health outcomes. Further the board said that, "It is anticipated that environmental scans, a preferred futures approach, membership needs assessment and trend analysis, and, perhaps, information from external organizations, will become part of the long range planning process."[53] At the annual meeting in 1997 the delegate assembly, for the second consecutive year, adopted a revised mission statement as follows:

The mission of the National Council of State Boards of Nursing is to lead in nursing regulation by assisting Member Boards, collectively and individually, to promote safe and effective nursing practice in the interest of protecting public health and welfare.[54]

In 1998 the delegate assembly adopted an amendment to the bylaws that renamed the terms "goals and objectives" for the organizational plan to "strategic initiatives and outcomes." Following this action the delegate assembly amended the strategic initiatives and outcomes that had been proposed by the board of directors.[55] The strategic initiatives and outcomes as adopted appear in Appendix A.

The delegate assembly revised the mission statement once again in 2003. The mission statement at the end of the first 25 years of the NCSBN reads, "The National Council of State Boards of Nursing (NCSBN), composed of Member Boards, provides leadership to advance regulatory excellence for public protection."[56]

Over the years, the board of directors has continued to manage the ongoing activities of NCSBN by reviewing and revising the tactics to accomplish the strategic initiatives and outcomes. In its role as manager of the affairs of NCSBN, the board of directors has carefully and consistently assured that the needed resources are available for the accomplishment of these tactics and the successful operation of the organization.

Vision Statement

As NCSBN continued to develop and approach its 15th anniversary, President Carolyn Hutcherson of Georgia-RN challenged the board of directors to think beyond the present when she asked, "Do we, as an organization, dare to develop an alive, exciting vision for the future and consciously make decisions to move toward that vision?"[57] The Report of the Board of Directors for 1992 stated that the board had begun considering a vision for the organization and planned to present a document to the members for comment.[58] At three meetings of the board of directors that year, work sessions related to organizational vision were held. A draft vision statement was shared with the LRPC and discussed at the area meetings in spring 1993.

At the August annual meeting President Rosa Lee Weinert of Ohio reported to the delegate assembly that the board of directors had designed the following vision statement: "The National Council will be the international authority and leader on the regulation of nursing."[59] Subsequently, the board of directors revisited the vision statement from time to time when working with consultants in relation to governance and the organizational structure. The minutes of the February 1995 meeting state that the board of directors adopted alternate language for the vision statement, as presented by the LRP Task Force.[60] In August 1995, the board of directors reported to the delegate assembly that based on information supplied by members participating in the "Future Directions" session at the 1994 annual meeting, trend analysis results, and the recommendation of the LRP Task Force, it had "designed a five-year long range planning process and decided to use as an internal working statement of the National Council's vision: 'The National Council will be a worldwide leader in the regulation of nursing.'"[61]

At a 1997 board of directors work session facilitated by Dr. Jamie Orlikoff, the board learned that the mission of an organization is "who you are," while the vision of the organization is "what you want to be."[62] The next change in the vision of NCSBN appeared in the *NCSBN Business Book* for the annual meeting in 2002 and read as follows: "the NCSBN will advance optimal health outcomes by leading in health care worldwide."[63] The following year the board of directors adopted a new vision statement at its September 2003 meeting. Thus the vision statement for NCSBN at the end of its first 25 years is "building regulatory expertise worldwide."[64]

Members

Robert's describes a member of an assembly as "a person having the right to full participation in its proceedings—that is, the right to make motions, to speak in debate on them, and to vote."[65] Membership in NCSBN is consistent with this definition. However, it is different where individuals are the members. Since the beginning, a governmental agency that was empowered to license and regulate the practice of nursing in any state, territory, or political subdivision of the United States of America has been eligible for membership in NCSBN. Each of these entities has agreed to use one or more of the NCLEX exams under certain terms and conditions, and has paid the required fee in order to be accepted by the delegate assembly of NCSBN as a member board. The membership process was completed upon payment of the fee and execution of a contract for use of the examination. Membership privileges included the right to vote, as described in the bylaws, and to participate in the development of the NCSBN examinations. The member boards were assigned by the board of directors to one of the four geographical areas established by the delegate assembly. This description of membership in NCSBN remains the case after 25 years. A table showing 60 member boards in the four areas in 2003 appears on the following page:

Area I	Area II	Area III	Area IV
Alaska	Illinois	Alabama	Connecticut
American Samoa	Indiana	Arkansas	Delaware
Arizona	Iowa	Florida	District of Columbia
California *	Kansas	Georgia *	Maine
Colorado	Michigan	Kentucky	Maryland
Guam	Minnesota	Louisiana *	Massachusetts
Hawaii	Missouri	Mississippi	New Hampshire
Idaho	Nebraska	North Carolina	New Jersey
Montana	North Dakota	Oklahoma	New York
Nevada	Ohio	South Carolina	Pennsylvania
New Mexico	South Dakota	Tennessee	Rhode Island
Northern Mariana Islands	West Virginia *	Texas	Puerto Rico
Oregon	Wisconsin	Virginia	Vermont
Utah			Virgin Islands
Washington			
Wyoming			

*Two member boards—One regulating RNs and one regulating LPN/VNs. When NCSBN was organized, there were also two boards in Colorado, the District of Columbia, Texas, and Washington.

When the member boards participated in the activities of NCSBN, and when individual board members and employees (of boards) served as officers or on various committees of NCSBN, they brought with them a variety of laws and regulations that affected their actions in these roles. Perhaps the most important were those related to a real or perceived conflict of interest. Others included administrative procedures acts, freedom of information acts, and contract laws. An example of how a state position could impact the service of its representatives can be found in a decision made in Virginia in the early 1990s. In that decision, members of NCSBN committees and one member of the board of directors from that state were prohibited from receiving reimbursement from NCSBN for travel, lodging, meals, and other expenses. The reason for this was that the Virginia Board of Nursing had what it called a sole-source contract with NCSBN and it was determined that payment of funds by NCSBN to the board of nursing representatives would constitute a conflict of interest. This decision stands to this day.

In the very first edition of the NCSBN quarterly, *Issues*, published in spring 1980, the lead article, by NCSBN president Mildred S. Schmidt of New York, was entitled "To Whom is the NCSBN Accountable?" Schmidt reported that this was a frequently asked question about the new organization. She pointed out that the accountability of the former American Nurses Association (ANA) Council of State Boards of Nursing was spelled out in the ANA Bylaws—it was accountable to the ANA Board of Directors and required to report to that board and to the ANA House of Delegates. In answering the question her title posed, Schmidt reminded the reader that the member boards of NCSBN are administrative agencies of state governments responsible for implementing the nurse practice acts in their respective states. Each member board is accountable to the people of their state. When member boards come together to the annual meeting, they "act collectively through the voting body, the Delegate Assembly. Delegates are cognizant of the provisions of the statutes and regulations in their respective states." She closed the article with the following: "As the NCSBN matures and reaches toward its full potential, in terms of its purposes, the question as to whom is the Council responsible should underlie the deliberations and actions of the Member Boards."[66]

Delegate Assembly

Since the beginning of the organization, each member board has designated its delegates, who serve as members of the delegate assembly at the annual meeting or any special meeting of that body. Each member board has had two votes that may be cast by either one or two delegates. A delegate had to be a member or an employee of a member board. The delegate assembly elects the members of the board of directors and amends or revises the bylaws and the articles of incorporation. *Robert's* stated the following: "A convention is an assembly of delegates chosen…as representatives of constituent units or subdivisions of a much larger body of people in whose name the convention sits and acts."[67] In the early meetings of the delegate assembly, the majority of the member board representatives were employees rather than members of the boards. In more recent years, there have been an increasing number of board members serving in the delegate assembly.

Originally described in the bylaws as the *legislative* body of NCSBN, the delegate assembly was redefined in the 2001 bylaws revision as follows:

The Delegate Assembly, the *membership* [emphasis added] body of the National Council, shall provide direction for the National Council through resolutions and enactments, including adoption of the mission and strategic initiatives, at any Annual Meeting or special session. The Delegate Assembly shall approve all new National Council memberships; approve the substance of all NCLEX® examination contracts between the National Council and Member Boards; adopt test plans to be used for the development of the NCLEX® examination; approve the NCLEX® examination test service; and establish the fee for the NCLEX® examination.[68]

In the original bylaws and continuing with the 1987 revision, there was more specificity included in those bylaws related to the authority of the delegate assembly. Much of this definition of authority is included in the statement above, but in less specific terms. In addition to the change listed above, the following duties of the delegate assembly, included previously, were removed in the bylaws revisions between 1994 and 2003:

- That it should approve fees to be charged by the council as recommended by the board of directors.

- That it should approve the annual budget for the Council as developed by the board of directors.

- That it should establish the criteria for and select the testing service to be utilized by the Council.[69]

There has been only one special meeting of the delegate assembly, held from December 14 to 15, 1997. The purpose of that meeting was to act on recommendations related to the nurse licensure compact to support a standard approach to a mutual recognition model of nursing regulation.[70]

Historically, the delegate assembly has acted swiftly on the business before it, something commented on by many first-time attendees. This continues to be the case, and is no doubt facilitated by the hard work of the delegates and the NCSBN committees, board of directors, and staff members.

The *NCSBN Book of Reports* (later the *NCSBN Business Book*) for each annual meeting, minutes of all delegate assembly meetings, and reports of all meetings of the delegate assembly document the major accomplishments of NCSBN during its first quarter century. The locations, dates, and a few actions for each meeting have been selected for inclusion in this chapter in the list that follows. Many of these actions will be discussed in detail in later chapters.

June 6–7, 1978, The New Otani Hotel and Garden, Los Angeles, California
- Organizational Meeting.
- Enrolled members.
- Adopted articles of incorporation and bylaws and took other actions essential for proceeding with the new organization.

June 6–8, 1979, St. Anthony's Hotel, San Antonio, Texas
- Authorized modifications of the examination procedure for handicapped candidates with special needs.
- Adopted a new test plan for the licensing examination for RNs.
- Recognized Martha Chesser, LPN and member of the Georgia State Board of Licensed Practical Nurses for "her historic presence as the first LPN to serve as a voting member of the Delegate Assembly."[71]

June 4–6, 1980, The Radisson Downtown Hotel, Minneapolis, Minnesota
- Adopted the logo for NCSBN from a design submitted by Ray Showalter, executive director of the Kansas Board of Nursing and later assistant executive director for NCSBN. *(see fig. 4-A)*
- Adopted a recommended passing score of 1600 for the new comprehensive RN licensing examination.
- Authorized the implementation of a disciplinary data bank.

June 9–12, 1981, The Sheraton Plaza Hotel, Chicago, Illinois
- Elected, by ballot, a new testing service—CTB/McGraw-Hill.
- Authorized the development of a direct application process between applicants and the test service.
- Changed name of licensing examination to National Council Licensing Examinations for Registered Nurses and Licensed Practical/Vocational Nurses. (NCLEX-RN® and NCLEX-PN®).

June 22–25, 1982, The Copley Plaza, Boston, Massachusetts
- Adopted the NCSBN Model Nursing Practice Act.
- Authorized the appointment of a committee to study issues related to the regulation of advanced nursing practice.

August 23–26, 1983, The Westin Hotel, Chicago, Illinois
- Agreed to the total number of items for the RN and LPN exams.
- Authorized the development of a new LPN test plan based on findings of a validity study.
- Adopted the NCSBN Model Administrative Rules and Regulations.
- Elected H. Jean Bruhn of Pennsylvania as director-at-large, the first LPN elected to the \board of directors.

August 26–29, 1984, The Portland Marriott, Portland, Oregon
- Paid tribute to Ray Showalter, associate executive director of NCSBN, following his recent, untimely death.
- Adopted the mission statement for NCSBN.
- Approved the test plan for the NCLEX-PN.

August 20–23, 1985, The Chicago Marriott Downtown, Chicago, Illinois
- Approved the reincorporation of NCSBN from a Wisconsin not-for-profit corporation to a Pennsylvania not-for-profit corporation through a plan of merger.
- Adopted the goals and objectives contained in the long range plan for NCSBN.
- Authorized investigation regarding assistance with medications by unlicensed personnel.

August 5–9, 1986, The Williamsburg Lodge, Williamsburg, Virginia
- Adopted the final report of the Study of Nursing Practice Role Delineation and Job Analysis of Entry-Level Performance of Registered Nurses.

- Adopted a position paper titled "Advanced Clinical Nursing Practice."
- Adopted a resolution stating a position of neutrality on the part of NCSBN on the issue of education for entry into the practice of nursing.

August 25–29, 1987, The Chicago Marriott Downtown, Chicago, Illinois
- Authorized NCSBN and the Commonwealth of Puerto Rico Board of Nurse Examiners to enter into an agreement to provide the NCLEX as the sole test in English for RNs and LPNs and to allow the continued use of the board's test in Spanish.
- Authorized the board of directors to act on the membership of Puerto Rico in NCSBN.
- Agreed to report the results of the NCLEX as pass or fail.
- Approved a monograph titled The Regulatory Management of the Chemically Dependent Nurse.
- Permitted the Delaware Board of Nursing to administer the NCLEX-PN six times in Germany to U. S. Army graduates of its 91C Program.

August 16–20, 1988, The Marriott Hotel, Des Moines, Iowa
- Agreed to proceed with the development of CAT, with the development of examination items and field testing for RN candidates only at this time.
- Agreed that NCSBN investigate the feasibility of computerized clinical simulation testing (CST®) for initial and continued licensure.
- Approved the development of a competency evaluation program for nurse aides and authorized the board of directors to select a test service and approve a test plan.
- Adopted a resolution strongly opposing the proposal of the American Medical Society to prepare registered care technicians.
- Adopted the first complete revision of the bylaws.

August 1–5, 1989, The Hyatt Regency Hotel, Chicago, Illinois
- Elected Helen Kelley of Massachusetts as secretary of NCSBN—the first LPN to serve as an officer.
- Adopted a resolution that NCSBN and its member boards would work cooperatively with federal and state agencies in implementing PL 100-203 relating to the regulation of nurse aides.
- Approved uniform standards for licensure by endorsement and requirements for foreign nurse graduates.

August 6–11, 1990, The Holiday Inn By-the-Bay, Portland, Maine
- Adopted guidelines for responding to requests for endorsement of position statements and endorsed the "Statement on Assistive Personnel to the RN" developed by the Tri-Council for Nurses.
- Approved a document titled "Concept Paper on Delegation and a Statement on Endorsement Issues Related to Peer Assistance/Alternative Programs."

July 29–August 2, 1991, The Hyatt Regency Hotel, Chicago, Illinois
- Agreed that CAT would be the examination method for all NCSBN licensure exams and that its implementation would occur in all jurisdictions at the same time.
- Adopted the documents, "Conceptual Framework for Continued Competence" and "Nursing Care in the School Setting: Regulatory Issues."

August 18–22 1992, The Antlers Doubletree Hotel, Colorado Springs, Colorado
- Selected Educational Test Service (ETS) as the testing service for the NCLEX.
- Authorized the implementation of the Nurse Information System.
- Approved a policy statement for modifications to the examination for candidates with disabilities.
- Rejected a resolution to develop means to finance annual participation of a representative of each member board to attend meetings of the delegate assembly.
- Adopted a document titled "Joint Statement on Maintaining Professional and Legal Standards During a Shortage of Nursing Personnel" prepared in collaboration with the ANA and the National Federation of Licensed Practical Nurses (NFLPN).

August 4–7, 1993, The Hilton at Walt Disney World® Village, Orlando, Florida
- Rejected the establishment of a disciplinary database for nurse aides.
- Agreed that the board of directors would determine the methodology to implement educational programs for nursing education program surveyors and for disciplinary investigators.
- Adopted a position paper titled "Regulation of Advanced Nursing Practice" as well as language on advanced nursing practice to be incorporated into the NCSBN Model Nurse Practice Act and the NCSBN Model Nursing Administrative Rules.

August 3–6, 1994, The Fairmont Hotel, Chicago, Illinois
- Adopted "Model Guidelines: A Nondisciplinary Approach for Chemically Impaired Nurses."
- Established a Special Services Division (SSD) of NCSBN.
- Authorized several actions related to assuring regulatory sufficiency of nurse practitioner credentialing examinations and addressing the need for additional mechanisms to facilitate interstate mobility.

August 1–5, 1995, The Regal Riverfront Hotel, St. Louis, Missouri
- Adopted a recommendation that NCSBN collaborate with the nurse practitioner specialty certification bodies to make progress toward legally defensible, psychometrically sound nurse practitioner examinations sufficient for member boards to rely on for licensure.
- Authorized the board of directors to appoint a committee to study issues related to telecommunication practice across jurisdictional lines and to develop guidelines to assist member boards in such regulatory issues.

August 6–10, 1996, The Baltimore Inner Harbor Marriott, Baltimore, Maryland
- Authorized the board of directors to continue developing the concept of a regulatory model that incorporates the characteristics of a multistate license.
- Agreed to continue efforts toward development of an electronic verification information system.

August 19–23, 1997, The Chicago Marriott Downtown, Chicago, Illinois
- Accepted the following motion: "That the National Council endorse a mutual recognition model of nursing regulation and authorize the Board of Directors to develop strategies for implementation."
- Empowered NCSBN to act as the reporting and querying agent for member boards to the National Practitioners' Data Bank (NPDB) and the Healthcare Integrity and Protection Data Bank (HIPDB) created by the United States Congress.

December 14–15, 1997, The Holiday Inn O'Hare, Chicago, Illinois (Special Meeting)
- Approved the proposed language for an interstate compact in support of a standard approach to a mutual recognition model of nursing regulation.
- Approved strategies for implementation of such an interstate compact and recommended that states adopting such models include an implementation date no earlier than January 1, 2000, with all coordinated licensure information systems and supporting services fully operational before implementation.

August 4–8, 1998, The Hyatt Regency, Albuquerque, New Mexico
- Approved a position paper on the approval of nursing education programs.
- Continued research and development of CST as a component of the NCLEX-RN.
- Rejected a resolution to replace the four annual area meetings with a single national mid-year meeting.

July 27–31, 1999, The Atlanta Marriott Marquis, Atlanta, Georgia
- Selected National Computer Systems, Inc., as the testing service for the NCLEX.
- Adopted uniform core licensure requirements for initial licensing of RNs and LPN/VNs.
- Agreed to discontinue development of CST as a potential component of the NCLEX-RN.

August 8–12, 2000, The Hyatt Regency, Minneapolis, Minnesota
- Adopted uniform advanced practice registered nurse (APRN) licensure and authorization to practice requirements.
- Agreed to phase out the SSD.
- Agreed to combine area meetings into a single mid-year conference.
- Agreed to lead in the development of an action plan to delineate and establish congruence among education, practice, and regulation for the respective roles of nurses.

August 6–11, 2001, The Hilton Pittsburgh, Pittsburgh, Pennsylvania
- Agreed to recognize the professional responsibility of nurses to accept or decline overtime assignments based on their self-assessment of their ability to provide safe care.
- Adopted a revision of the bylaws.

August 13–17, 2002, The Westin Hotel, Long Beach, California
- Authorized negotiations with the test service for international administration of the NCLEX for licensure in the U.S. jurisdictions.
- Approved the Nurse Licensure Compact for APRNs.
- Adopted the action plan of the Practice, Regulation, and Education Congruence Task Force.
- Elected Greg Harris of Arizona as the first public member of a member board to serve on the board of directors.

August 5–8, 2003, The Hilton Alexandria Mark Center, Alexandria, Virginia
- Agreed to develop a position paper on the regulation of nursing assistive personnel.
- Adopted a revised mission statement.

Board of Directors

In *Robert's*, the following statement is made: "A board within an organized society is an instrumentality of the society's full assembly, to which it is subordinate."[72] The board of directors of NCSBN was described in the original bylaws as the *administrative* body of the organization and was charged to conduct the business of NCSBN between the annual meetings of the delegate assembly.[73] In the 2002 revision of the bylaws, the authority of the board of directors is delineated as follows:

> To transact the business and affairs and act on behalf of the National Council except to the extent such powers are reserved to the delegate assembly as set forth in these bylaws and provided that none of the Board's acts shall conflict with resolutions or enactments of the Delegate Assembly.[74]

As with the amendments and revisions to the authority of the delegate assembly, amendments and revisions of the bylaws have broadened the stated duties of the board of directors.

The minutes of the board of directors from 1978 through 2003 reveal a continuing search for clarification of the roles of the board of directors and the delegate assembly. Working with several outside organizational experts, surveys of member board satisfaction, and other tools, the board of directors worked to resolve this question. Two documents from Vedder, Price, Kaufman and Kammholz, the legal firm that serves NCSBN, speak to these efforts. The first, dated November 4, 1985, is addressed to the board of directors. The subject is "guidelines for exercising the management authority of the Board of Directors." It begins with a review of applicable sections of the Pennsylvania nonprofit corporation law and follows with a summary stating that the board of directors has broad authority, the responsibility for management of activities, and also has authority to delegate certain authority to corporate officers such as the executive committee, the executive director, or other staff members. The document goes on to list operating guidelines as follows:

- The board of directors should monitor and supervise the continuous operation of NCSBN. This is accomplished largely through receipt and review of written reports and may not require much discussion or action.

- The board of directors has the power to direct activities and make legal commitments on behalf of NCSBN. All major policy and program decisions require more discussion and should be acted upon by the board of directors.

- The board of directors need not become involved in details of program implementation or routine management of continuing activities. These activities should be delegated.

- Efficient, responsible management by a board of directors is accomplished by the proper use of committees. This includes standing, special, or ad hoc committees. The board, in turn, must have sufficient confidence in the committees so that it does not find it necessary to redo the work of the committees it has appointed.

The remainder of the document provides an example of how these guidelines might be applied to a specific activity.[75]

The second document is dated February 19, 1988, and is addressed to the executive director of NCSBN, Eileen McQuaid Dvorak, in response to a request from the board of directors for a written presentation of an examination and opinion as to the authority and duties of the delegate assembly, the board of directors, and the NCSBN committees in the management and direction of the organization. This request was made by the board of directors following its review of the proposed bylaw revisions regarding committee structure done in preparation for their presentation to the 1988 delegate assembly. The author is William F. Walsh of Vedder, Price, Kaufman and Kammholz. As in the previous document, Mr. Walsh reviewed applicable sections of the Pennsylvania nonprofit corporation law and the NCSBN Articles of Incorporation. Consistent with the bylaws at that time, the following statement was made: "In other words, we think that the most appropriate interpretation is that the delegate assembly had the prerogative to legislate as to any aspect of council operations which it chooses to address." Walsh went on to say that the description of the duties of the board of directors in the bylaws "largely complements the reservation of ultimate corporate authority to the delegate assembly. The board of directors is authorized to conduct business of the Council between sessions of the delegate assembly." Walsh argued that this statement in the bylaws was a strong indication "that the Board of Directors is to have and exercise general management authority and responsibility, subject only to the ultimate power of the Delegate Assembly to make controlling decisions." In relation to authority of NCSBN committees, Walsh stated that "the overall activities of all Council Committees remain subject to the general management authority of the Board of Directors between sessions of the Delegate Assembly."[76]

The board of directors of NCSBN appointed all standing and special committees, and periodically received and commented on the reports from these committees. Many of the interim and final reports were presented to the delegate assembly either as information or for action if they contained recommendations that were within the authority of the delegate assembly. As the parliamentary authority of NCSBN, the information in *Robert's* related to committees applies to the NCSBN Committees. *Robert's* states that standing committees perform continuing functions and remain in existence for the life of the group that establishes them. Standing committees are specified in the bylaws and report "to the assembly of the society, and not to the executive board (or Board of Directors) unless the bylaws provide otherwise."[77]

The purpose of NCSBN is accomplished through a coordinated effort among the committees, the board of directors, and the delegate assembly. NCSBN has had an organizational chart from its early days that shows the relationship of these entities. The organizational charts from 1989, 1998, and 2003 represent three decades and illustrate the changes in authority within the organization. *(see fig. 4-B)* The differences in these charts are mainly in the role of standing committees as summarized below:

- In the 1989 chart the authority flows in a solid line from the member boards to the delegate assembly to the board of directors. There is a solid line to the standing committees from the delegate assembly and a broken line from the board of directors to the standing committees.[78]

- In the 1998 chart there is a solid line of authority from the delegate assembly and the board of directors to the standing committees.[79]

- In the 2003 chart there is a solid line of authority from the board of directors to all standing committees, a broken line from the delegate assembly to the Examination Committee and no line of any kind from the delegate assembly to the other standing committees.[80]

The lists of the individuals who have served on the board of directors of NCSBN from 1978 to 2003 can be found in Appendix B. The majority of these members have been on the staff of the member boards, with a large number of RN members, an increasing number of LPN/VN members, and one public member of these various boards. Because of the exceptional leadership provided by those individuals who have served as president of the organization, a few words about each, their years served, notable quotations, and greatest accomplishments are highlighted in this chapter. For a full picture of the tenure of each president, this section should be read along with the accomplishments of the delegate assembly shown above since the president served as the presiding officer at each session of the delegate assembly. There have been 14 presidents and all have been executive officers of their respective member boards. The office has been held by representatives from each area, with 2 presidents from Area I, 4 from Area II, 6 from Area III, and 2 from Area IV. The first 4 presidents were the members of the Special Task Force—State Boards of Nursing (Special Task Force) that developed the plan for NCSBN. Mildred Schmidt said in 1983 that none of the 4 was interested in being an officer, but that Parliamentarian Henrietta Marjan asked "if we were afraid to assume responsibility for what we were creating?" As a result, the four Special Task Force officers were the nominees for the offices of president, vice president, secretary, and treasurer presented to the members for election at the organizational meeting in 1978.

Presidents

Elaine Ellibee, 1978–1979 *(see fig. 4-C)*
From Wisconsin, Ellibee served as the executive officer for the board of nursing in that state and represented Area II on the original Special Task Force, which she also chaired. Because of a change in the organization of the board of nursing in Wisconsin in 1979, Ellibee had to resign from the presidency in the spring prior to the first annual meeting. She spoke of significant dates during that first year including October 2, 1978, when the NCSBN office officially opened in Madison and February 16, 1979, when the W. K. Kellogg Foundation awarded its grant of $446,000 to NCSBN. She summarized what all of the effort of the Special Task Force meant to her as follows:

> It was an education and enlightenment never to be achieved in any other way; an honor and privilege yet almost illusive, a strong emotion of contributing to a piece of the public good. I have a continuing pulsating belief in the protection of the public—as it relates to nursing—that is the sole purpose for the existence of a board of nursing. May we have created the council, truly, for just that, and not, through time, allow it to be eroded into but another, self-serving organization involving nurses and our divergent purposes.[81]

Gertrude (Trudy) Malone, 1979 *(see fig. 4-D)*
Malone was the executive officer for the Montana Board of Nursing and represented Area I on the original Special Task Force. She was the first person to serve as vice president of NCSBN and succeeded Ellibee to the office of president less than three months before the first annual meeting. She lists as important accomplishments, while on the board of directors, the decision to locate the headquarters office in Chicago and the appointment of Eileen McQuaid (later Dvorak) as the first executive director.

She made the following statement about her tenure:

The year I served on the Board of Directors proved to be the ultimate task of my career with the National Council. I am grateful for the opportunity to have served as President and am immensely proud of being part of it all.[82]

Mildred S. Schmidt, 1979–1981 *(see fig. 4-E)*

Schmidt, executive secretary of the New York Board of Nursing, represented Area IV and served as treasurer on the original Special Task Force. She was also the first treasurer of NCSBN. During her two one-year terms as president, Schmidt saw the adoption of a new test plan that would become the NCLEX-RN. The testing service was changed from the National League for Nursing (NLN) to CTB/ McGraw Hill. A problem for the new organization arose with reports of a major examination security break in New York that threatened the resources of NCSBN. To avoid conflict of interest, Elaine Laeger, the vice president presided through all discussions of the investigations. The R. Louise McManus Award was established to be given to a person or organization making great contributions to furthering the purposes of NCSBN. Schmidt summed up her beliefs about nursing regulation and NCSBN in the following statement:

During its first five years, the National Council has emerged as an organization of stature, strengthening the image of boards of nursing as state government agencies concerned with protecting the public health, safety and welfare and fostering within our profession an increased respect and recognition of this crucial role.[83]

Helen (Pat) Keefe, 1981–1982 *(see fig. 4-F)*

Representing Area III from Florida where she served as the executive officer for the board of nursing, Keefe was the first secretary of NCSBN. She had also served in that capacity with the Special Task Force. She said she attended the first meeting of the Special Task Force unconvinced that it was the right thing to do. She was concerned that they might "create another 'splinter group' to divide nursing." The strong convictions of the others led her to change her mind. She was also swayed by the fact that the Florida Board of Nursing was preparing for sunset review and that raised issues of conflict of interest, professional bias, and the rights of the consumer. Arriving late for the 1978 meetings because of a death in her family, Keefe said, "I entered the hotel lobby and was greeted exuberantly by members of the Council. The atmosphere was of complete euphoria, making me feel as if I was returning in triumph from some campaign or war."[84] While Keefe was president, NCSBN adopted the NCSBN Model Nursing Practice Act and began a study of advanced nursing practice and its regulation.

Joyce Schowalter, 1982–1984 *(see fig. 4-G)*

Schowalter, executive director of the Minnesota Board of Nursing, was the first president after the Special Task Force members. Elaine Ellibee recalled Schowalter's role in the beginning of NCSBN when she said that Schowalter presented the motion in 1977 that called for the creation of a task force to study the reorganization of the ANA Council of State Boards of Nursing. During her tenure as Area II director on the first NCSBN Board of Directors, she chaired the Bylaws Committee and worked with the committee that developed the specifications for the new testing service. She participated in the negotiations for three potential test services. While president, Schowalter led the organization to establish a contract with American College Testing (ACT) to conduct a nationwide project to examine the validity of the NCLEX-RN® Test Plan—"A Study of Nursing Practice and Role Delineation and Job Analysis of Entry-level Performance of RNs." The study has been called a "landmark effort." The first LRPC was appointed and presented the mission statement for NCSBN that was adopted by the delegate assembly. The first LPN was appointed to the board of directors when H. Jean Bruhn, LPN and member of the Pennsylvania State Board of Nursing, was named director-at-large after the incumbent became vice president. She was subsequently elected to this office by the delegate assembly in 1983. The first R. Louise McManus Award, created two years before, was presented to Mildred Schmidt. Representatives of regulatory agencies in Canada were invited to the annual meeting. This marked the beginning of an international interface. In 1982 NCSBN completed the final year of the three-year grant from the W. K. Kellogg Foundation and began to function on fees for services. Schowalter said "In retrospect, the $1.8 million budget for FY83…would have been only a dream in the minds of the Council's organizers in 1978, the year we functioned on donations."[85]

Sharon Weisenbeck, 1984–1986 *(see fig. 4-H)*

While she was an associate director for the Wisconsin Board of Nursing, Weisenbeck volunteered her time with the original Special Task Force, recording and preparing minutes and handling correspondence. At the time of the 25th Anniversary of NCSBN, she was the only person from the original organizers still actively involved with the organization. Weisenbeck was executive director of the Kentucky Board of Nursing when she was president of the NCSBN Board of Directors. Among the accomplishments during her tenure was an independent survey of the member boards to gauge their needs that was conducted by Touche Ross and Company. The results showed a need for positions or guidelines on continued competency, impaired nurses, and advanced practice. All were accomplished and continue to be reviewed and revised. Weisenbeck was the first president to attend all four area meetings while in office and she welcomed the following new members to NCSBN: the California Board of Vocational Nurses and Psychiatric Technicians, the Northern Marianas Islands Commonwealth Board of Nurse Examiners, and the District of Columbia Board of Nursing. The special project that led to CAT was initiated and a new corporate logo was adopted. *(see fig. 4-Q)* Weisenbeck has said, "Through NCSBN, I was privileged to be mentored by women who were absolutely profound in their knowledge and their understanding of regulation for the public good." In her president's report in 1985, she said,

> Living as we do in the age of space traveling, it is my privilege to report that the National Council is securely in orbit…As we continue our "orbit," we look to the stars, but our feet are squarely on the ground of the good Earth.[86]

Ruth Elliott, 1986–1988 *(see fig. 4-I)*

Elliott, executive director of the Tennessee Board of Nursing when elected president, brought to the office the experience of having chaired the LRPC for the past several years. The focus of her effort during her term of office was on service to the member boards. The first Member Board Award was presented to the Kentucky Board of Nursing, and Executive Director Eileen McQuaid Dvorak received the first Meritorious Service Award. NCSBN and the Irish Nursing Board hosted a workshop in Dublin, Ireland designed to enhance understanding among state boards and councils throughout the world. NCSBN received a substantial grant from the W. K. Kellogg Foundation for exploration of the CST Project. Office automation was completed and NCSBN assumed publication of the *State Nursing Legislation Quarterly*. Elliott was later associated with the Oklahoma Board of Nursing and in 1996 joined the staff of NCSBN as director of Education and Practice, leaving that position in 1999. In the 10th anniversary booklet, *The Promise Continues: A Decade of Progress*, Shirley Fondiller quotes Elliott who described NCSBN as a "pathfinder organization" with its primary objectives being service and usefulness to the members, "based on vision, values and organizational determination." She spoke with cautious optimism as she looked to the future:

> The road ahead is full of challenges and opportunities. Communications is essential between the National Council and its Member Boards. Sensitivity and responsiveness to Member Board needs will remain high. The road ahead will take commitment, involvement and the vision of each member of our organization. The challenges are great today in this environment of changes. We must work together to master these changes and shape the future of the National Council.[87]

Renatta Loquist, 1988–1990 *(see fig. 4-J)*

Loquist had served on the board of directors and on NCSBN committees prior to her election as president in 1988. She was executive director for the South Carolina Board of Nursing at that time. A review of the NCSBN accomplishments in the earlier section on the delegate assembly shows that there were significant events during her tenure. When Eileen McQuaid Dvorak, the first executive director for NCSBN resigned, Loquist provided the leadership in the process for the selection of Jennifer Bosma and the transition to a new administrator for the NCSBN staff. However, the major focus of NCSBN during Loquist's two years as president was on testing. The Nurse Aide Competency Evaluation Program (NACEP) was developed through a contract with The Psychological Corporation. This test was used in a significant number of states. The field tests on CAT were done and evaluated. With the amendment to the bylaws in 1988 that provided for a standing committee on long range planning, a six-year long range plan was begun. In her 1988 President's Message in *Issues*, reflecting on the 10th Anniversary of NCSBN, Loquist said,

> As the organization strives to meet its membership needs, we must look beyond ourselves and diligently expand collaborative relationships with relevant organizations to facilitate the development and promotion of health related public policy. Providing specific opportunity for direct dialogue, interaction and mutual decision making enhances our ability to promote the inclusion of the regulatory perspective in national and regional health care issues. The pioneer spirit which gave birth to the organization a decade ago, must remain alive in each of us as we face the challenges of regulation and licensure tomorrow.[88]

Carolyn Hutcherson, 1990–1992 *(see fig. 4-K)*

Hutcherson was executive director for the Georgia Board of Nursing and Area III director on NCSBN Board of Directors at the time of her election as president. As displayed in her statement challenging NCSBN to develop its vision of the future, quoted at the beginning of the Vision Statement section in this chapter, Hutcherson had the future of the organization in strong focus during her presidency. During her tenure the major activities of NCSBN were directed toward future testing. Hutcherson presided at the delegate assembly meeting when the historic decision was made to implement CAT for the NCLEX. NCSBN thus became the first health care regulatory organization to use CAT for national high-stakes testing for licensure. Hutcherson participated in the first Leadership Roundtable for Advanced Nursing Practice. The Commonwealth of Puerto Rico Board of Nurse Examiners was accepted as a member board of NCSBN and the federal Americans' with Disabilities Act (ADA) resulted in discussions and action by the Administration of Examinations Committee and the delegate assembly. Hutcherson joined the staff of NCSBN in 1994 as the senior policy analyst. In her 1992 president's report to the delegate assembly, Hutcherson said,

> On my wish list for the upcoming years is the hope that a system can be developed to ensure that each year at the Delegate Assembly, Member Board representatives examine the organizational "big picture," establish priorities and collaboratively set organizational direction. From this annual review of strategic direction the Board of Directors would then enact its duty to conduct the business of the National Council between Delegate Assemblies;" and each operational unit (committee, team, staff) could operationalize its responsibilities. This unity of direction and strategy would seem to strengthen the National Council's move into the future.[89]

Rosa Lee Weinert, 1992–1994 *(see fig. 4-L)*

While executive director for the Ohio Board of Nursing, Weinert had served as a member of the NCSBN Committee on Nominations and on the NCSBN Examinations Committee. Under her leadership as president, the board of directors adopted the first vision statement for NCSBN in 1993—"The National

Council will be the international authority and leader on the regulation of nursing." Her term was a time of transition with the change to a new test service and a new way of administering the licensing examination. NCSBN received a grant from the Robert Wood Johnson Foundation to support the development of the Nurse Information System. NCSBN purchased computers for use by the member boards in the transmission of data to the NCLEX® Data Center, the testing centers, and the member boards. In her president's report to the delegate assembly in 1994 Weinert said,

> To me, by far the greatest accomplishment this past year stemmed from the action taken by the Board of Directors on Monday, October 25, 1993, at 2:05 PM, EST. The action was to proceed with the implementation of computerized adaptive testing (CAT) for NCLEX® on April 1, 1994. It's incredible to remember that just a few years ago the concept of this futuristic methodology of testing was merely presented to the Delegate Assembly for study and that just a short year ago we were busy recruiting candidates for the beta test. Now in May 1994 (when this report was written), CAT is fully implemented and is successfully proceeding according to the comprehensive plan projected and developed by the various committees of the National Council and skillfully coordinated by the staff.[90]

Marcia Rachel, 1994–1996 *(see fig. 4-M)*

Rachel chaired the NCSBN LRPC from 1988 to 1994 and was a member of the Bylaws Committee. She was executive director of the Mississippi Board of Nursing when elected president of NCSBN. During her term, NCSBN received an additional grant from the Robert Wood Johnson Foundation for the continued development of the Nurse Information System and registered trademark status for CST (and later for NCLEX) from the United States Patent and Trademark Office. Continuing to improve communications with the member boards and the public, the public Web site of NCSBN was launched and the use of e-mail and the electronic transfer of data were enhanced. In ongoing negotiations with the national certification bodies, Rachel led in the effort toward determining that their certification examinations for nurse practitioners were legally defensible, psychometrically sound, and sufficient for member boards to accept as a basis for regulation. In a partnership between the National Association for Practical Nurse Education and Service (NAPNES) and the SSD of NCSBN (see below), a certification examination for LPN/VNs in long-term care settings was developed and implemented. In her 1995 president's report Rachel said,

> I firmly believe that we must maintain open lines of communication with the various nursing and health care groups. The National Council's special knowledge and expertise places us in the position of being their primary source of information about nursing regulation.[91]

Thomas Neumann, 1996–1998 *(see fig. 4-N)*

Neumann was administrative officer for the Wisconsin Board of Nursing and served as vice president and Area II director on the board of directors. He served as chair of the Nursing Practice and Education Committee. During his presidency NCSBN endorsed mutual recognition as the model of nursing regulation, and Neumann presided at the only special session of the delegate assembly in the first 25 of the organization. At that meeting the language to implement an interstate compact for mutual recognition was adopted by the delegates. The Nurse Information System was renamed Nurse System (Nur*sys*®) and the Commitment to Public Protection through Excellence in Nursing Regulation Project began. On the occasion of the 20th Anniversary of NCSBN Neumann said,

> We are positioned to optimistically view the new curves ahead of us, ready to leap beyond the danger zones, and evade the death which awaits those who ignore strategic planning and decision

making. Just like the visionaries of 1978, we must be willing to take the risks in changing the face of regulation to reflect the current needs of Member Boards and the public we purport to protect.[92]

Jo Elizabeth (Joey) Ridenour, 1998–2002 *(see fig. 4-O)*

Ridenour came to the office of the president having served as a member of the Arizona State Board of Nursing before accepting the position of executive director of that board. She served as Area I director on the NCSBN Board of Directors just prior to her election to the presidency. Ridenour focused on leadership development for all of the components of the organization during her tenure. With a vacancy in the executive director position for NCSBN, Ridenour provided leadership beyond that normally expected from the president in the interim before the position was filled. Other activities accomplished during the four years of Ridenour's tenure included the selection of a new test service, discontinuance of activities related to CST, and the approval of an NCSBN affiliation with the Nurse Licensure Compact Administrators (NLCA). The organization began to explore the international administration of the NCLEX. The board of directors approved a revised position paper on advanced nursing practice. NCSBN initiated a leadership development program for member board executive officers and presidents to enhance regulatory and governance competencies. In 2003 Ridenour, reflecting on her presidency and NCSBN said,

> NCSBN's core mission is assisting Member Boards to further develop competencies of the individuals who carry out the mission of the state boards…. To me, the real success of NCSBN occurs when the Member Boards apply the tools and knowledge to meet their public protection mission at the state level.[93]

Donna Dorsey, 2002– *(see fig. 4-P)*

Dorsey, executive director of the Maryland Board of Nursing, was treasurer of NCSBN from 1987 to 1991, served on nine committees, and was vice chair of the NLCA at the time of her election as president of NCSBN. With only one year of her term complete at the time of the celebration of the 25th anniversary of NCSBN, Dorsey had already made her imprint on the organization. Under her leadership, the board of directors reviewed the governance philosophy and structure of NCSBN and revised the mission, vision, and values statements. The board adopted a new logo for NCSBN *(see fig. 4-R)* and reviewed and revised the *NCSBN Policy Manual*. In 2003 Dorsey presided at the events commemorating the 25th anniversary of NCSBN and the 100th anniversary of the first laws to regulate nursing in the United States, which were adopted in 1903 in New Jersey, New York, North Carolina, and Virginia. The commemorative book for the 25th anniversary closed with this quote from President Dorsey: "Every question we answer leads to another question as we collectively learn to better protect the public." In commenting on NCSBN in 2003 Dorsey said,

> It has been said that in today's environment, an organization needs to be knowledge based and nimble to cope with the changing world. To that end, the Board of Directors and the regulatory leaders within the NCSBN Member Boards will take us to a place we have never gone before. We will never stop investigating and will never be satisfied we know enough about safe and effective nursing practice.[94]

The Supporting Cast

The growth, accomplishments, and success of NCSBN are due, in no small part, to the individuals who have been members of the NCSBN staff. Beginning in 1978 with a staff of one in the small office in Madison, Wisconsin and concluding in 2003 with a budgeted staff of 66 members in a spacious office overlooking Lake Michigan in Chicago, the committees, boards of directors, member boards, and the delegate assemblies have received the support of people who are knowledgeable about the organization and the role of the staff in it. All of those who have served on NCSBN committees know how important staff support has been in the accomplishment of the work assigned to the committees. A list of employees of NCSBN is found in Appendix C. It is as complete as possible, having been assembled 25 years after the first staff member was hired. The staff has been led by four outstanding leaders in the position of executive director since its inception. Each executive director was appointed by the NCSBN Board of Directors following a search for qualified candidates by a committee appointed for that purpose.

Executive Directors

Eileen McQuaid Dvorak, 1979–1988 *(see fig. 4-S)*
The first executive director, McQuaid Dvorak, was appointed in 1979. She had been a staff member for the New York State Board of Nurse Examiners. During that time she was active in the ANA Council of State Boards of Nursing and served as the first chair of the NCSBN Examination Committee. McQuaid Dvorak set the standard for her successors and was recognized as a leader among her peers in other organizations. She resigned from her position with NCSBN in 1988.

Jennifer Bosma, 1988–1998 *(see fig. 4-T)*
Bosma was director of Testing for NCSBN from 1985 to 1988 when the board of directors appointed her acting executive director. After an extensive search, the board selected her as the second executive director. Bosma had exceptional knowledge about testing and an unusual ability to explain the complexities of testing in readily understandable language. This expertise was essential as the organization moved to a new testing modality in the years she served. Bosma resigned at the end of 1998.

Eloise Cathcart, 1999–2000 *(see fig. 4-U)*
The board of directors selected Cathcart to succeed Bosma early in 1999. Cathcart's tenure with NCSBN was shortened when her health necessitated her resignation late in 2000. Cathcart brought her experience as a leader in nursing to the position and a number of changes in the operation of NCSBN occurred in her time with the organization.

Kathy Apple, 2001– *(see fig. 4-V)*
In 2001, while a member of the board of directors and executive director for the Nevada Board of Nursing, Apple was appointed as executive director of NCSBN. She quickly adapted to the new role, supervising the relocation of the office and organizing the staff to provide effective and efficient services to the member boards as the organization moved into a new century. She has traveled widely to meet with individuals within and outside NCSBN and has become a recognized leader.

Legal Service

Another group of individuals essential to the success and achievement of NCSBN are those who have provided legal advice to the delegate assembly, the board of directors, the committees, and the staff. They have also been helpful to the member boards, particularly in the negotiations of contracts between NCSBN and the boards. There have been three men who have served as counsel to the organization. The first was David F. Grams of Boardman, Suhr, Curry and Field in Madison, Wisconsin. Grams served from 1978–1980, and he was also counsel to the original Special Task Force prior to 1978. He had the assistance of other attorneys, especially Rebecca Erhardt.

When the NCSBN office moved to Chicago, the board of directors decided to select a Chicago firm, Vedder, Price, Kaufman and Kammholz to provide legal services. Thomas O'Brien served as chief counsel to NCSBN from 1980 until 1996. O'Brien was recognized by NCSBN with its Meritorious Service Award in 1996. His untimely death in September of that year was mourned by many associated with the organization who had the good fortune to have worked with him. Over the years other attorneys were called upon to address issues within their specialties. In 1996, Thomas G. Abram, of the same firm as O'Brien, was named chief counsel and continues in that capacity.

Parliamentarians

The parliamentarian serves as a consultant and advises the president, other officers, committees, and delegates on the application of parliamentary procedure. This parliamentary procedure assures the authority of the presiding officer to rule on questions of order and to respond to inquiries. Every president of the organization has had the opportunity to appoint and work closely with well-qualified parliamentarians. A parliamentarian often assists with the development of the order of the agenda, and for NCSBN helps to prepare the "script" used by the president and others during the business sessions. Other areas of assistance are found when the parliamentarian assists the resolutions committee, the tellers committee, and individual delegates who may seek assistance in the preparation of motions. These women have provided essential advice to the bylaws committees and often cooperate with legal counsel in this regard. Seated close to the president during the meetings of the delegate assembly for consultation, the president may ask the parliamentarian to provide information needed by the members. NCSBN employs a registered parliamentarian who has met prescribed standards in order to use that credential. The following is a list of those who have provided this valuable service:

Henrietta Marjan	1978–1983 (also served the original Special Task Force)
Ardeth Inman	1984, 1986–1991
Doreen Kinney	1985
Nancy Sylvester	1992–1998
Julia Von Haam	1999–

Headquarters

A national organization must have a headquarters office located centrally and with reasonable access. Dallas, Texas and Chicago, Illinois were the finalists in the headquarters selection process used by the board of directors in 1979, and Chicago was ultimately chosen. NCSBN has occupied five different offices during its first 25 years at the following locations:

1 Pinckney Street, Madison, Wisconsin	1978–1979
303 East Ohio Street, Suite 2010, Chicago, Illinois	1979–1984
625 North Michigan Avenue, Suite 1544, Chicago, Illinois	1984–1989
676 St. Clair, Suite 550, Chicago, Illinois	1989–2003
111 East Wacker Drive, Suite 2900, Chicago Illinois	2003–

Finances

In April 1977 at the Area II meeting, Joyce Schowalter of Minnesota gave $50 to begin the funding needed to determine how a freestanding organization could evolve. Over the next several months boards of nursing, individual board members and staff added $17,700.[95] As mentioned in the previous chapter, the money remaining from the Kellogg Foundation and the donations were the basis of the budget when NCSBN was first organized in 1978. The total projected budget for the year ending December 31, 1979, was $334,155. The sources of support and revenue were listed as follows:

Public Support
  W. K. Kellogg Foundation Grant $285,525

Revenue
  Royalties $ 24,630
  Contract Fees $ 25,000

In its first year NCSBN received $53,500 in contract fees from 55 member boards. The first board to pay the fee was the Georgia Board of Nursing. In March 1979 NCSBN was awarded a three-year grant from the W. K. Kellogg Foundation in the amount of $444,035 to support program development until the organization could become completely self-supporting. After completion of negotiations with the ANA and NLN for the transfer of ownership of the State Board Test Pool Examination (SBTPE) to NCSBN, royalties from the examination began to arrive. At the meeting of the board of directors on November 28, 1978, the treasurer reported that the first royalty check from the testing service had been received in the amount of $14,996.28. At that same meeting the board of directors learned that NCSBN had received final approval from the Internal Revenue Service of its tax exempt status as a 501(c)(3) organization.[96] At the completion of the Kellogg Foundation grant in 1982, when NCSBN began to conduct its activities on a fee-for-service basis, the annual budget stood at $1.8 million. Over the years NCSBN received grants to support specific projects and research but has continued to rely on similar types of revenues as were in place from the beginning—royalties from tests and publications, membership fees, fees for service, and investment income.

The annual budget for FY03 was for a revenue of $35,368,000 and expenses of $31,173,000.[97] Under the leadership of strong treasurers, well-qualified support staff, and able consultants and the effective oversight of the board of directors, NCSBN at age 25 is a financially sound organization. The individuals who have served as treasurer are as follows:

Mildred Schmidt, New York	1978–1979
Merlyn Maillian, Louisiana-RN	1979–1981
Nancy Dean, Georgia-RN	1981–1983
Gertrude Hodges, Maryland	1983
Nancy Wilson, West Virginia-PN	1983–1986
Donna Dorsey, Maryland	1986–1991
Carol Osman, North Carolina	1991–1993
Charlene Kelly, Nebraska	1993–1998
Barbara Morvant, Louisiana-RN	1998–2002
Sandra Evans, Idaho	2002

Special Services Division

NCSBN initiated another activity to generate revenue when, in June 1993, the board of directors discussed the "general advisability of diversification of revenue sources." The board reached the agreement that more investigation and consultation must occur prior to further discussion and that the member boards should be advised of these preliminary reports at the annual meeting.[98] At the August meetings, the board heard a report from Executive Director Bosma on activities related to the exploration of revenue-generating services and decided to appoint the Revenue Generation Focus Group to work on such services. This group comprised the newly elected treasurer, Charlene Kelly of Nebraska; the former treasurer, Carol Osman of North Carolina; Judie Crume of Alabama; and Marcella McKay of Mississippi.[99] The Revenue Generation Focus Group presented a report to the board of directors in October and the board adopted a motion that NCSBN should develop the concept of creating a structure for the introduction of products and services that would generate revenue beyond that necessary to meet expenses in order to provide financial resources to support the mission of NCSBN.[100] In December the board received reports from the Revenue Generation Focus Group and the Finance Committee, adopting the following guidelines under which the revenue-generating structure would function if adopted by the delegate assembly:

- Before each project is approved for implementation, it must have a business plan that includes at least the following components: anticipated benefits and consequences of the project, resources needed, market analysis, risk analysis, return on investment projections, potential exit strategies, and milestones to be met for project continuation.

- Before approving each project for implementation, the governing entity shall direct that the data in the business plan be validated from sources independent of the persons proposing the project. The larger the investment involved, the greater the expectation that these sources will be external to NCSBN.

- Every approved project should have an anticipated rate of return greater than the return that could be obtained by investing the funds in investment vehicles specified in the organization investment policies.

- If a project involves a market or a technology that is new to NCSBN, a joint venture should be considered.

- No project shall detract in any manner from the promotion of nurse competence; the protection of the public health, safety, and welfare; and the reputation of NCSBN.

- Consideration shall be given, when projects are developed with other organizations, to the consequences of the benefits to NCSBN.

Action on one guideline was deferred until the March 1994 meeting of the board, pending staff's obtaining consultation in rewording. This guideline called for $600,000 to be allocated from NCSBN's undesignated, unrestricted fund balance for financing potential revenue-generating projects. In addition, the board reviewed advice from legal counsel regarding structural, corporate, and tax issues that would be associated with the formation of a structure to support revenue-generation activities. Following discussion, the board asked legal counsel to draft an article for the bylaws proposing an organizational structure for a new division. Later in the same meeting, the board acted to clarify the marketing of program services with the following statement:

The purposes of the proposed new division shall include the assumption that the development of a new division does not preclude the marketing of products and services in the program area, e.g., Nurse Information System, Clinical Simulation Testing and Computerized Adaptive Testing.[101]

A letter addressed to Bosma from William F. Walsh, an attorney with Vedder, Price, Kaufman and Kammholz, was attached to the minutes of this December meeting. The letter was a review of "corporate and income tax issues relating to the possibility of creating a new division, within the corporate structure of NCSBN, to develop and conduct new programs aimed at generating net revenue." Walsh reviewed the need for a bylaws amendment and discussed tax advantages of a separate subsidiary corporation and the possible need to amend the statement of purpose in the articles of incorporation. In the conclusion of his letter, Walsh stated that a new division for revenue generation presented "no substantial immediate risk to the basic tax-exempt status of the National Council."[102]

In January 1994 Director of Communications Susan Woodward and Executive Director Bosma discussed the modifications to an informational packet on revenue generation based on comments from former members of the board of directors. The board approved the changes and Woodward advised that the packets would be mailed to the member boards.[103] At its March meeting the board of directors reviewed comments from the member boards on the revenue generation packet and adopted another guideline as follows: "Any net revenue over expense generated shall be reviewed annually by the Board of Directors who shall determine the extent to which such funds shall be transferred to the unrestricted/undesignated fund balance." There was a footnote appended to any guideline related to money transferred that read as follows: "The Finance Committee's recommendation shall be sought prior to any Board of Directors' decision relative to these guidelines."[104] The member boards discussed the revenue generation concept at the area meetings in the spring of 1994. In May the board heard a report on the result of these discussions, agreed to changes in the wording of the proposed bylaws amendment, and to provide a diagram of the governing entity and its relationship to the NCSBN units. The board asked that these items be sent to the member boards as soon as possible and that the LRPC and the Bylaws Committee discuss the relationship to the current mission statement and purpose of NCSBN, respectively.[105]

There were several items in the *NCSBN Book of Reports* for the annual meeting in 1994 related to the revenue generation proposal. These included the recommendation from the board of directors that "the Delegate Assembly authorize the establishment of a Special Services Division (SSD) of the NCSBN through adoption of an Article of the NCSBN Bylaws," a paper entitled "Concept of Revenue Generation for the National Council," and supporting documents. The paper defined the concept of revenue generation and defined the terms and framework for the SSD. A section of this paper discussed the question, "Why now?" In response, the paper elucidated several factors that had converged to heighten interest in revenue generation at that time:

- A number of new services, identified as needed by the member boards, exceeded available funds in the operating budget, leading to use of the accumulated fund balance, which would be depleted in future years without additional revenue sources.

- Due to the use of the accumulated fund balance for the testing projects, CAT and CST, the projected surplus of $7 million at the end of FY96 was reduced to approximately $3 million in 1999.

- A number of "potentially high-revenue possibilities" consistent with the areas of expertise and the reputation of NCSBN had arisen; the decision was made to not take advantage of them because the appropriate structure did not exist within NCSBN.

The paper continued with a summary of the activities of the board of directors and focus groups, legal advice, and the involvement of the Finance Committee and the member boards. Bosma had discussed the structures used for revenue generation with the executive staff of nine other organizations. The administrative guidelines mentioned above were stated. The board of directors had discussed several possibilities in the determination of the governing entity for the SSD and selected a chief executive officer with appropriate staff to be the governing entity. The paper also discussed evaluation measures and future activities. Some of the potential revenue sources listed included the Nurse Information System, the Disciplinary Data Base, educational programming, reading tests for nurses, examination application services, baccalaureate examinations, and others. The paper concluded with a flow chart and a form for revenue generation. The proposed bylaws article established the purpose and scope of the SSD and stated that the executive director of NCSBN may serve as the chief executive officer for the SSD.[106]

The delegate assembly adopted, by a two-thirds vote, the recommendation from the board of directors to amend the revised bylaws by adding the new article to establish the SSD.[107] At the board of directors meeting on August 7, 1994, the board of directors established a SSD designated fund in the amount of $600,000 and authorized the expenditure of up to $100,000 in FY95. The board also appointed Jennifer

Bosma as the executive officer of the SSD and adopted the administrative guidelines as printed in the 1994 *NCSBN Book of Reports.*[108]

Philip LaForge joined the NCSBN staff as marketing manager prior to the June 1995 meeting of the board of directors. At that meeting, Bosma reported to the board about SSD projects including a pilot study of certification for LPN/VNs in long term care, test development materials and workshops, and a computerized nursing care plan tool.[109] Bosma also reported on the SSD to the delegate assembly at the 1995 annual meeting. The major activities of the first year of the program were devoted to idea generation and careful examination of these ideas using the administrative guidelines. She stated that LaForge would have day-to-day responsibility for market research and business plan development. Bosma concluded the report with the following: "The quality of the initial ideas, the willingness of members and staff to work voluntarily to develop them, and the shaping of several promising services and products have provided evidence that the 1994 delegates' vision for the SSD may well be realized in the near future."[110] LaForge presented a report to the board of directors in October regarding the projects in research and development, which included: (a) the Certification Examination for Practical Nurses in Long Term Care (CEPN-LTC), (b) the Care Plan Creator (a program based on the CST databases), (c) test construction workshops, and (d) the NCLEX results telecenter.[111]

The board of directors again heard from LaForge in January 1996 when he reported on the SSD with emphasis on negotiations with a potential partner for development of products based on the Nursing Information Retrieval System (NIRS).[112] In May the board of directors received more information on a "plastic license project." In addition, the board agreed to move the tactic to "explore the development of additional tests of unlicensed assistive personnel other than OBRA defined nurse aides" from the organizational plan to the SSD as a more appropriate location for the action to occur. OBRA refers to the federal Omnibus Budget Reconciliation Act included the Nursing Home Reform Act.[113] In a report in June, the board learned that the SSD revenue realized by May 31 exceeded the projected revenue for FY96. LaForge reported on the CEPN-LTC program, test construction workshops in partnership with The Mosby Company, Plastic Licenses, and on the potential for a predictor instrument for nurse managers.[114] At the annual meeting, the Report of the Special Services Division included information on the initial marketing of the CEPN-LTC, the workshops for nursing educators, and the Care Plan Creator. Year-round testing with CEPN-LTC began in August 1996 in partnership with Assessment Systems, Inc. (ASI). Mosby authored a preparation book for CEPN-LTC that was published in March. The SSD was in the process of linking with a nursing education publisher to develop software products derived from the NIRS.[115] At the meeting of the delegate assembly in August, the delegates adopted a resolution "that the NCSBN investigate the use of plastic card technology (Smart Card)."[116]

In May 1997, after reviewing a report from the Unlicensed Assistive Personnel Task Force, the board of directors supported one of its recommendations. The recommendation called for a potential venture between the SSD and the American Association of Critical Care Nurses.[117] At the same meeting the board discussed potential participation in examination study and review development by the SSD. The board determined that this exploration did not conflict with the SSD Administrative Guidelines.[118] In August the board of directors voted to increase the SSD designated fund by $450,000 to support further development of projects as the SSD was expected to break even in 1999. The board also agreed to add a tactic to the FY98 organizational plan to develop a five-year evaluation plan for the SSD to be reported on to the delegate assembly in 2000. The board directed a smaller scale review of the SSD in FY98.[119] The Report of the Special Services Division in 1997 highlighted its activities for the year. The SSD's role in the CEPN-LTC was described as follows: "SSD provides project management services to NAPNES for its long-term care credentialing program." A total of 682 LPN/VNs had been tested as of the end of April and approximately 5,000 copies of the study guide were sold since the inception of the program. In the Plastic Nursing License project, the SSD developed a program to help member boards change their paper license issuance programs to ones that could produce more durable and secure plastic cards. The SSD contracted with three member boards for the production and distribution of plastic licenses.[120]

At a meeting in August 1998, the board of directors accepted the report of Stuart Meyer, a consultant, on the evaluation of the SSD. The board agreed, based on the consultant's recommendations, to have the Finance Committee periodically review the fiscal status of all SSD projects.[121] In November, the board approved the internal allocation of the revenue from the programs to test nurse aide competency to the SSD.[122]

A report regarding the SSD project, NCLEX® Results-by-Phone was received by the board of directors in February 1999. The board approved its availability to all member boards at a cost per candidate of $7.95. The board asked the SSD staff to survey the member boards regarding their interest in revenue sharing and to make a report of the findings for the review of the board.[123] At the May meeting the board reviewed the SSD project assessments by the Finance Committee. The board approved "continuing SSD (much as it is currently structured) with no additional infusion of capital and increased attention to governance and operational structures" pending the 2000 evaluation. The board asked Executive Director Cathcart and the staff to develop possible evaluation methodologies. The board reaffirmed that the NCLEX® Study Review Project of the SSD reported directly to Cathcart.[124] In December the board learned that a consulting firm had been engaged to conduct a thorough evaluation of the SSD and to report to the Finance Committee, the board of directors, and the delegate assembly in 2000.[125]

The Finance Committee made recommendations to the board of directors regarding the SSD in February 2000. The recommendations that were accepted by the board were as follows:

1. Phase out SSD as a separate entity and explore the feasibility of integrating selected products within the National Council's programs;

2. Implement strategies for marketing National Council products and services; and

3. Ensure that all ventures shall not conflict with the National Council's mission, goals, core expertise and tax status.[126]

At the annual meeting, the delegates considered the recommendations stated above. A review of the development and expansion of the SSD was considered in the rationale for the recommendations. At the time of the recommendations 12 products were marketed under SSD. These were the National Nurse Aide Assessment Program, Results-by-Phone, Plastic Card for Licensed Nurses, Assessment Strategies for Nurse Educators, NCLEX® Study and Review, video on interpersonal boundaries, Nurse Practice Acts Review on the Web, Interactive Care Plan Creator, CEPN-LTC, Online Bookstore, Clinical Simulation Testing Seminars, and Unlicensed Assistive Personnel Training. The report considered by the delegates included information from the required five-year evaluation that was done by an external consulting firm, Value Enhancement Strategies, Inc. The following three alternatives for the future of SSD were presented as the result of the evaluation:

1. Grow the SSD and build one or two businesses, rather than a series of products, which was the current approach, and invest approximately $4-6 million in product development to generate a net operating income of approximately $1 million over four years;

2. Maintain the current structure of the SSD; or

3. Close the SSD and shift the successful products to the program side of NCSBN. This process would retain most of the benefit of SSD programs for NCSBN and its member boards by maintaining those programs that are most closely related to the organization's core business. Unsuccessful projects would be canceled to prevent further drain on the NCSBN's resources.

The board of directors, upon the recommendation of the Finance Committee, put forth the third option for consideration by the delegate assembly.[127] The delegate assembly adopted this recommendation and the phase-out of the SSD followed.[128] The Report of the Board of Directors in the *NCSBN Business Book* in 2001 stated that the phase-out was accomplished. Several of the projects listed above continue as a part of the overall program of NCSBN.[129]

Relationships With Other Organizations

Marcia Rachel, in her president's report in 1995 said, "I firmly believe that we must maintain open lines of communication with the various nursing and health care groups."[130] The books of reports, the business books, the minutes of meetings of the board of directors and the delegate assembly, *Issues*, *Council Connector*, and the biweekly *Newsletter to the Member Boards* are replete with information about the relationships of NCSBN with other organizations. Several policy statements in the *NCSBN Policy and Procedure* relate to this important aspect of the history of NCSBN. One of these policies established the basis for such liaisons and stated that the relationship was "maintained to exchange relevant information, promote understanding of the NCSBN mission and expand opportunities for contributions to policy and regulatory discussions." The liaison relationships occurred at several levels:

- Meetings between top elected and staff officers of each organization.

- Representation by members of the board of directors, the executive director, or other staff members to annual or other scheduled meetings as speaker or attendee.

- Staff-to-staff contacts to maintain continuity and consistency of organizational interaction.[131]

Another policy speaks to the endorsement of position statements of external organizations. In 1990, the Tri-Council on Nursing, comprising the American Association of Colleges of Nursing (AACN), the ANA, the American Organization of Nurse Executives (AONE), and the NLN, asked NCSBN to support its position paper on assistive personnel. The delegate assembly adopted criteria for decisions on such requests for support and then agreed to support the position paper.[132] This policy on requests for endorsement, revised by the board of directors in 2002, remains basically the same and authorizes the board to endorse position papers if any or all of the following criteria are met:

1. the statement addresses an issue that is consistent with the Member Boards and the NCSBN organization mission, strategic initiatives and outcomes;

2. the statement addressed an issue that is consistent with a prior Delegate Assembly or Board of Directors action that supports the content of the statement; and

3. the statement complements a position statement of the NCSBN.[133]

As early as 1978, representatives from NCSBN participated in the activities of other organizations. The president attended the annual meeting of the NFLPN and Marilyn Boyd, president of the Virginia Board of Nursing, attended the annual meeting of the Federation of Associations of Health Regulatory Boards, now the Federation of Regulatory Boards (FARB). Subsequently, the board of directors agreed to join that organization and this membership continues in 2003. In 1979, the executive liaison with the ANA was initiated and Ruth Seigler of South Carolina, a member of the board of directors, was named to the Commission on Graduates of Foreign Nursing Schools (CGFNS) Board of Trustees. Subsequently, several other representatives from NCSBN served on that board.[134] In 1990, representatives from the Citizen's Advocacy Center (CAC) attended an NCSBN Board of Directors meeting and sought support to encourage attendance of public members of member boards at its meetings. The CAC was started to provide technical support and networking opportunities for public members of professional licensing boards and peer review organizations. Eventually, NCSBN became a member of CAC and members of staff and representatives from the member boards have participated in its activities.[135] NCSBN has been a member of the Council on Licensure, Enforcement and Regulation (CLEAR) for a number of years.

In 1987 the board of directors began to set aside time for an open forum during its meetings to provide an opportunity for individuals and groups that wished to present information or discuss activities of NCSBN to meet with the board. Representatives of other organizations took advantage of the open forum at many meetings over the ensuing years. Vivien DeBack of the National Commission on Nursing Implementation Project (NCNIP) attended the first open forum on February 10, 1987. She briefed the board of directors and the staff on project functions and goals and reported that the NCSBN proposal to be included in the project was being considered.[136]

A list of organizations with which NCSBN had liaison association was attached to the minutes of a November 1996 meeting of the board of directors. The list described the types of liaisons as categories. These categories were executive liaison, participation liaison, annual meeting liaison, and staff liaison. The organizations listed as executive liaisons were the AACN; the ANA; the AONE; the CGFNS; the Division of Nursing, United States Department of Health and Human Services; the NAPNES; the NFLPN; the NLN; and the National Organization for Associate Degree Nursing. To further define these, "executive liaison" meant that the executive officer of NCSBN met periodically with the executive officer of the organization. There were 12 listings for participation liaison. This category listed members of the NCSBN Board of Directors or staff who were participants in these organizations, including the following:

- Marcia Rachel, former president, and Carolyn Yocom, director of Research Services, were members of the Coalition of Nursing Futures of the American Academy of Nursing.

- Eileen McQuaid Dvorak, executive director, and Doris Nay, associate executive director, were presidents of the board of directors of FARB.

- Jennifer Bosma, executive director, was a member of the Certification Commission of the American Society of Association Executives.

- Bosma and Kristin Helquist, associate director for Policy and External Relations, served as board members of CLEAR and other staff members served on committees of that organization.

- Vickie Sheets, director for Nursing Practice and Regulation, was on the Executive Committee for the National Practitioner Data Bank.

The advanced practice leadership roundtables, initiated in 1991, were held annually thereafter with representatives from all certifying bodies and associations of advanced practice RNs invited to participate. Representatives of NCSBN attended at least 13 annual meetings of other organizations, and there were staff liaisons with 17 additional organizations.[137]

The Report of the Board of Directors in the *NCSBN Business Book* for the annual meeting of 2003 lists 46 meetings attended by board members and staff during the year. Examples that show the diversity of these meetings include the following:

- National Coordination Council for Medication Error and Reporting

- Institute of Medicine Annual Meeting

- Joint Commission on Accreditation of Healthcare Organizations Symposium on "Homeland Defense: Blueprints for Emergency Management Responses"

- National Conference of State Legislatures Health Policy Conference Meeting

- Council of State Governments

- American Medical Association House of Delegates Interim Meeting

- National Governors Association Winter 2003 Meeting

- Alliance for Nursing Accreditation
- National Nursing Research Roundtable
- National Student Nurses' Association
- Telehealth Leadership Council
- American Association of Nurse Anesthetists[138]

Representatives of NCSBN also attended the International Council of Nurses Congress in 2003.

The relationships with other organizations have not been without controversy from time to time. Three issues that produced considerable discussion were the development of the original NCBN Model Nursing Practice Act and the NCSBN Model Administrative Rules, the regulation of advanced nursing practice, and the effort that led to the mutual recognition of licenses. There are numerous entries in the minutes of various NCSBN meetings that describe discussions of areas of mutual interest and concern with representatives of other organizations. Even with controversy and discussion, there continues to be an effective interchange of information between the organizations whose members are agencies of state government—the member boards—and those organizations whose members are those regulated by the member boards. All share the common goal of safe and effective health care for people.

Reviewing the minutes of the sessions of the delegate assembly from 1978 to 2003 shows that lists of organizations represented at the meetings began to be recorded in 1983. The following lengthy list demonstrates the interest in NCSBN by these organizations:

- Alberta Association of Registered Nurses
- American Academy of Nurse Practitioners
- American Association of Colleges of Nursing
- American Association of Critical Care Nurses
- American Association of Medical Assistants
- American Association of Nurse Anesthetists
- American Association of Nurse Practitioner Certification Programs
- American Board of Nurse Specialists
- American College of Nurse-Midwives
- American Hospital Association
- American Medical Association
- American Nurses Association
- American Nurses Credentialing Center
- American Organization of Nurse Executives
- American Psychiatric Nurses Association
- American Red Cross
- Assembly of Hospital Schools of Nursing
- Association of Diploma Schools of New Jersey
- Association of Operating Room Nurses
- Association of Women's Health, Obstetrics and Neonatal Nurses
- British Columbia Council of Practical Nurses

- California Nurses Association
- Canadian Nurses Association
- Citizens Advocacy Center
- City of Hope National Medical Center
- College of Nurses of Ontario
- College of Licensed Practical Nurses of Manitoba
- Commission on Collegiate Nursing Education
- Commission on Graduates of Foreign Nursing Schools
- Division of Nursing, United States Department of Health and Human Services
- Federation for Accessible Nursing Education and Licensure
- Institute for Hospital Clinical Nursing Education
- International Consultants of Delaware
- Irish Nursing Board
- Manitoba Association of Registered Nurses
- Midwest Alliance on Nursing
- National Association for Practical Nurse Education and Service
- National Association of Boards of Pharmacy
- National Association of Clinical Nurse Specialists
- National Association of Massage Therapists
- National Association of Orthopedic Nurses
- National Certification Board for Pediatric Nurse Practitioners and Nurses
- National Certification Corporation
- National Commission on Nursing Implementation Project
- National Federation of Licensed Practical Nurses
- National League for Nursing
- National League for Nursing Accrediting Commission
- National Organization for Associate Degree Nursing
- National Student Nurses Association
- New York State Nurses Association
- Northeast Coalition of Hospital and Diploma Schools of Nursing
- Ohio Council of Diploma Programs
- Oregon Nurses Association
- Planning Committees for International Conference of Nurse Regulatory Bodies
- Registered Nurse Association of New Brunswick
- Registered Nurse Association of Nova Scotia
- Saskatchewan Registered Nurse Association
- United Kingdom Central Council for Nursing, Midwifery and Health Visiting
- United States Army Medical Command[139]

Conclusion

This chapter on governance has reflected on the documents, people, location, finances, and organizational relationships of NCSBN. The information presented demonstrates the interrelatedness of the components of the organization and their evolution from the past to the present. The exercise of power, decision making, and the way the people and groups articulated their interests over time are shown above. The groundwork has been laid to build for the future of NCSBN. The result of the coordination of activities described here begins to explain the extraordinary success of NCSBN in its first 25 years and presents the structure for the chapters that follow.

CHAPTER FIVE
COMMUNICATION

A major goal of the Board [of Directors]...has been to strengthen the communications between the National Council and its Member Boards as well as between the National Council and major nursing organizations. With the hiring of a Director of Communications and a full time Copy Editor and the establishment of the Communications Committee, we have been able to improve the National Council's image through its publications.

> **Renatta Loquist,**
> President, NCSBN, 1990[1]

THE MEMBERS AND LEADERS of the National Council of State Boards of Nursing, Inc. (NCSBN®) knew, from the beginning, that both internal and external communications were essential to the success of the organization. Evidence of the emphasis placed by the early leaders on communicating outside of NCSBN can be seen in the articles appearing in the *American Journal of Nursing* (*AJN*), *Nursing Outlook*, and other publications; the presence of the officers at a number of national meetings; and the establishment of liaison relationships with nursing and regulatory associations within the first 12 to 18 months following the organization of NCSBN.

Early Communication and Publications

Three of the priorities set by the board of directors for 1980–1981 related to communications: the establishment of a disciplinary database, the preparation of an information booklet for examination candidates, and the conducting of conferences on the revised test plan for registered nurse (RN) licensure.[2] In September, to further facilitate inter-organization communication, the board agreed that the executive director would mail a monthly update on the general activities of NCSBN to each member of the board of directors.[3] In April 1980 the board of directors determined that it was time for NCSBN to initiate a publication to be distributed to the member boards and other interested organizations and individuals. The board authorized Executive Director Eileen McQuaid (later Dvorak) to prepare a quarterly publication to achieve this purpose.[4] In her report to the delegate assembly, McQuaid listed the publication of *Issues* as a major communication objective for the year to fulfill this action of the board of directors. She also reported that she had written an article on the new test plan for RNs in *Nursing Outlook*, and that she had spoken on this same subject at three sessions.[5]

The first edition of *Issues* was published in the spring of 1980. A column, written by the executive director, introduced *Issues* to the readers. In addition, three articles appeared: "To Whom is the NCSBN Accountable?" by Mildred S. Schmidt of New York, president of NCSBN; "The Single Score: A Controversial Issue" by Phyllis Sheridan of Idaho, chair of the Examination Committee; and "Professional/Legal Definitions: Are There Differences?" by Thelma L. Cleveland of Washington-RN, chair of the Nursing Practice and Standards Committee.[6] *(see fig. 5-A)*

In 1980 NCSBN had a book for candidates for RN licensure in publication through the Chicago Review Press. One of the board of directors' priorities for 1981–1982 was to publish a similar book for practical/vocational nurse (P/VN) candidates for licensure. In her report to the delegate assembly, Executive Director McQuaid listed two additional publications related to examinations that were issued during 1980. These were the test plan for the RN licensure examination and the report, by Angelina M. Jacobs, of research on the comparison of critical incidents as reported by graduates from different types of nursing programs.[7]

Executive Director Eileen McQuaid Dvorak reported in 1982 that she had completed the book on licensure examinations for P/VN candidates and that it had been published through the Chicago Review Press. Royalties from the two study guides went to NCSBN.[8] That same year the board of directors approved the production of a video with the Chicago Review Press as an extension of the material found in the study guides.[9]

The next year saw an increased emphasis on communications. In January 1983 the board of directors decided that staff would prepare "an economical, simply produced" newsletter to be sent to the member boards every two weeks, which would become known as the *Newsletter to the Member Boards. (see fig. 5-B)* The first *Newsletter to the Member Boards* was distributed in February 1983 and continued until 2000. Throughout this time a wealth of information arrived in the offices of the member boards every other week. While some of the recipients felt somewhat overwhelmed by the many questionnaires and surveys attached, the information provided was invaluable. The *Newsletter* was an effective, informative communication tool, often accompanied by attachments that proved even more substantive than the content of the *Newsletter* itself. An attachment to a 1983 *Newsletter* provided a list of publications addressing issues relevant to the member boards. This list included all the publications available from the NCSBN office at that time: *Issues; The Model Nursing Practice Act; Comparison of Critical Incidents about Baccalaureate, Associate Degree, and Diploma Nurses Test Plan for the National Council Licensure Examination for Registered Nurses,* by A. Jacobs; *Test Plan for the National Council Licensure Examination for Practical Nurses; RN Test Plan* Audio Cassette Tape, issued by CTB/McGraw-Hill; and *Practical Nurse Role Delineation and Validation Study for the National Council Licensure Examination for Practical Nurses.* Publications available from the Chicago Review Press included the following National Council Licensure Examination (NCLEX®) study guides: *The National Council Licensure Examination for Registered Nurses,* by E. Dvorak, M. Kane, L. Laskevich, and R. Showalter and *The National Council Licensure Examination for Practical Nurses, NCLEX—RN Video Tape,* by E.Dvorak and R. Showalter. Also listed was the *Diagnostic Assessment Program for the NCLEX-RN,* which was available to RN candidates for the NCLEX through Assessment Systems, Inc.[10] The following three new publications were added to the list in 1984: *NCSBN Model Administrative Rules and Regulations for Nursing; Ensuring Job-Related Validity of Nursing Licensure Examinations,* by A. D'Costa; and *Video for Candidates for P/VN Licensure.*[11]

The Report of the Executive Director in 1983 showed that the circulation for *Issues* was 7,200. The publication was sent to member boards, schools of nursing, health care agencies, people in other organizations, and interested individuals. In cooperation with the Chicago Review Press, staff prepared scripts and acted in the production of the video projects for use by candidates preparing to take the RN and P/VN examinations.[12] In December the board of directors authorized revisions of the study guides for the NCLEX.[13]

Committees Related to Communications

In 1983 the board agreed to establish a Publications Advisory Committee. The area directors and the director-at-large comprised this committee that was charged to advise the staff on a continuing basis on how best to serve the needs of the member boards with publications.[14]

The board of directors established a Public Relations Committee in May 1985 with Renatta Loquist of South Carolina as its chair, and charged the committee to cover broad functional areas such as inter-organizational relations, public information, and convention program planning. In addition, this committee was asked to review criteria and selection of awards candidates and prepare an annual action plan for public information and press releases.[15]

In 1987 the Public Relations Committee explored the feasibility of publishing, on a recurring basis, a summary of new governmental legislation in order to provide assistance to the member boards. The committee also recommended, and the board accepted, the guidelines for member board participation at the board meeting open forums. The board of directors also changed the name of the Public Relations Committee to the Communications Committee.[16]

At its February 1988 meeting, the board of directors received a report from the Communications Committee that presented a number of activities of the committee. In response, the board took the following actions:

- To reaffirm its existing policy of quality publications: the biweekly *Newsletter to the Member Boards*, the bimonthly *Issues*, and the quarterly *SNLQ*.

- To direct staff to review methods of increasing publication revenues to offset existing costs as well as methods of reducing costs without sacrificing quality.

- To reject a request from the American Nurses Association (ANA) for it to include the *SNLQ* in its publication brochure and manage the subscription sales to a select ANA internal mailing list.[17]

A change in the bylaws made the Communications Committee a standing committee in 1988. In January 1989 the board accepted a report from Jean Caron of Maine, chair of the Communications Committee, regarding the information to be included in the area meeting manuals, the recipients of awards for 1989, and the publication of NCSBN data.

The 1990 Communications Committee Report listed other changes that would result in the inclusion of the following sections in *Issues*:

- Guest editorials by member board executive directors.

- Reports from area directors regarding regional issues that may have national impact.

- NCSBN department updates.

- A regular column highlighting NCSBN publications.

- Professional news such as job openings, honors, etc.[18]

In 1992 the board of directors adopted a Communication Crisis Plan, as proposed by the Communications Committee, which defined a crisis as "an unexpected incident or event that warrants public notification via media." It continued with a listing of principles NCSBN would employ when faced with a communication crisis situation as follows:

- Act in an ethical, humane fashion.

- Act quickly and immediately; identify a chief spokesperson.

- Employ an efficient decision-making process.

- Be open with as much information as possible that does not compromise confidentiality or impact legal ramifications.

- Ensure accuracy and validity of information.

- Be available to the media.

- Express concern.

- Reassure that measures have been taken to prevent future occurrences.

- Consider needs and best interests of member boards first.

- Respect member boards' communications processes and needs.[19]

The term "task force" was used in place of "committee," when Iva Boardman of Delaware, chair of the Communications Evaluation Task Force reported on recommendations from the task force to the board of directors, including the following:

- To expand the distribution of all NCSBN communications targeting employers other than those in acute care settings as first priority.

- To revise and expand the communication processes and content to reflect current emerging trends and issues.

- To establish a formal evaluation process for all NCSBN communications and establish a task force to facilitate such a process.[20]

The Report of the Communications Evaluation Task Force was presented in the 1997 *NCSBN Book of Reports*. Chair Roselyn Holloway of Texas-RN listed the recommendations presented to the board of directors during the year, resulting in the following board actions:

- The approval of the Communication Evaluation Process Matrix. The Communications Evaluation Process Matrix was designed to examine all types of communication in relation to purpose, effectiveness, relevance, accessibility, fiscal impact, and format. It also established criteria for each.

- The direction that each NCSBN committee use the matrix to evaluate publications related to the function of the committee.

- The agreement to convene the Communications Evaluation Task Force on a triennial basis, beginning in FY99, to review NCSBN communications for the purpose of providing direction and suggestions for change.[21]

Other Publications

The board of directors, in 1981, directed that a "reference bank" of the states' practice acts and rules and regulations be developed and maintained.[22] In order to facilitate information sharing with the member boards, the board of directors decided that a summary of major actions from each board meeting would be distributed immediately after each meeting.[23]

The first NCSBN informational brochure providing a written "explanation of the organization" was published in 1984. The brochure emphasized NCSBN'S role of service to the members boards at the direction of the member boards.[24] Executive Director Dvorak continued to report on communications efforts in her report to the delegate assembly in 1985. Dvorak included a description of the new edition of the *Study Guide for NCLEX-RN* that introduced the rationale for each answer. In cooperation with CTB/McGraw-Hill, NCSBN was now providing NCLEX Summary Profiles to help nursing education programs analyze the performance of their graduates. The Summary Profiles provided aggregate information about the performance of graduates of the school of nursing in comparison with the performance of graduates from other schools. In addition, the publication of the *Diagnostic Assessment Test* was transferred from Assessment Systems, Inc., to CTB/McGraw-Hill.[25]

In May 1987 the board of directors decided to make a formal proposal to the ANA to assume the publication of the *State Nursing Legislative Quarterly (SNLQ)* because the ANA was no longer publishing it.[26] The *SNLQ* was a journal that "addressed legislative and regulatory trends in nursing." With the ANA's approval, the first issue of the *SNLQ* from NCSBN was anticipated by the end of the year. In 1987, NCSBN also issued its first annual report and the board of directors approved the initiation of an electronic mailing system to improve communications between the NCSBN office and the member boards.[27] That same year the delegate assembly adopted a resolution requiring that, beginning with the 1988 annual meeting, the *NCSBN Book of Reports* would contain a listing of the actions taken by the previous delegate assembly and a description of the progress made in the implementation of actions.[28] When the first NCSBN-published *SNLQ* was issued in January 1988, complimentary copies were distributed to the member boards. The subscription rate for others was $30 a year.[29]

The 1987 summer edition of *Issues* presented a new column entitled Washington News. The accompanying editor's note stated that the new feature was intended to provide the reader with information on current federal programs of interest to regulators and health care professions.[30] At its October 1987 meeting, the board of directors created a new committee of the board—the Convention Planning Committee. Since the responsibility for convention planning was no longer assigned to the Communications Committee, its size was reduced from four members to three.[31]

The April 1988 *Newsletter to the Member Boards* reported that the fourth edition of the NCLEX study guide had been published and was available from the Chicago Review Press.[32] The delegate assembly adopted a motion that NCSBN evaluate current and future publications related to the licensing process, legal responsibilities, and NCSBN services.[33]

In 1989 the board agreed to continue to use onsite meetings as its primary meeting method with telephone conference as the secondary method. After considering the report of the Convention Planning Committee, the board of directors acted to agree to the development of a delegate assembly orientation manual; to consider having a keynote speaker at future annual meetings; and to include a list of the current staff and a glossary in the *NCSBN Book of Reports*.[34] In April the board directed that obsolete videos on NCLEX be withdrawn from distribution.[35]

At the 1989 annual meeting the delegate assembly asked that an appropriate committee explore the feasibility of developing audio-visual materials for use by the member boards. The delegates indicated that the material should focus on the role of regulation.[36]

In January 1990 the board of directors accepted recommendations from the Communications Committee on criteria for staff bylines. The byline was permitted for articles authored by staff that required original thought or research, but it was not permitted when an article reported NCSBN activities and was written as part of normal job responsibilities. The board of directors also directed staff to explore a toll-free number for calls to the NCSBN office.[37]

President Loquist reported in April to the board of directors on correspondence from Vanderbilt University asking NCSBN to review the licensure requirements in all 50 states as they affect non-traditional programs and to develop a position paper. The board discussed ways to respond to this and similar requests and asked the Communications Committee to consider creating a vehicle for responding to issues raised by the member boards, the board of directors, the committees, and others.[38] In July the Communications Committee reported on and the board of directors approved the creation of an "as needed" publication entitled *Emerging Issues* to disseminate information about developing areas of concern related to nursing and regulation. At the same meeting the board discussed the feasibility of a general purpose audio-visual presentation on regulation for use by the member boards.[39]

Also in 1990, the delegate assembly adopted a recommendation from the Communication Committee, chaired by Judi Crume of Alabama, that the committee develop a defined plan for creation and use of audio-visual materials and report back to the delegate assembly in 1991.[40] Two reports to the 1990 delegate assembly addressed changes to *Issues*. The Report of the Board of Directors listed its actions to increase the frequency of publication and to change the format to include information around four major themes each year: research, practice and education, testing, and communications.[41] *Issues* listed several new publications in its Publications List: *NACEP Expanded Evaluation Blueprint* (NACEP—Nurse Aide Competency Evaluation Program), *NACEP Job Analysis*, and *Licensure Examination Statistics for 1986–1988*.[42]

In 1991 the delegate assembly decided not to pursue the development of audio-visual materials at that time.[43] The Report of the Board of Directors explained the publication of *Emerging Issues* and stated that the topic for the first issue was "Implications of the Americans with Disabilities Act on Test Administration." This new publication allowed for rapid distribution of information that was needed by the member boards.[44]

Crume, chair of the Communications Committee, reported that the committee participated in the development of a communication service—the Resource Network. The network was designed to provide information services tailored for member boards by member boards. It would make available the multiple resources within NCSBN and its membership through a coordinated communication program that could be individualized depending upon the needs of each member board.[45] An announcement of another new publication appeared in the *Newsletter to the Member Boards* in December 1991. The title of this new publication was *The NCLEX® Process*, and it focused on the development, application, scoring, and reporting processes for the NCLEX.[46]

In January 1992 the board of directors reviewed its rating of objectives for the communications plan, listing the three top communications objectives for the year as follows:

1. To establish communications that facilitate a responsive exchange between external and internal audiences.

2. To enhance the NCSBN image and credibility through utilization of a variety of professional communications vehicles.

3. To create and seek communications opportunities that promote, inform, and educate on issues regarding the regulation of nursing practice and education.[47]

In February, on the recommendation of the Communications Committee, the board adopted a policy for authorship of articles by NCSBN committees, board of directors' members, contractors, and staff. The policy required the inclusion of a statement related to the responsibility for stated opinions, a confirmation of the accuracy of facts, and an acknowledgement that conclusions and positions stated were consistent with those of NCSBN.[48] *(see fig. 5-C)*

NCSBN initiated another new publication titled *Insight—NACEP News and Issues* in the summer of 1992. The publication was designed to provide information for the registration, testing, and regulation of nurse aides and for discussion of federal laws and regulations that required this regulation of nurse aides.[49]

In 1993, the board voted to discontinue publication of the study guides for the licensing examinations that were available through the Chicago Review Press. The board instructed staff and legal counsel to negotiate the discontinuation to coincide with the implementation of computerized adaptive testing (CAT) in 1994 since the guides would be obsolete at that time.[50]

The board of directors continued to address issues related to communications in 1994. In January the board approved a new format for the *SNLQ*. The publication was to be converted to a bimonthly online product available solely to the member boards via the NCSBN Network (NCNET) beginning in April.[51] NCNET was an electronic network for the member boards which was used to deliver a variety of software. In May the board learned that two organizations were interested in acquiring the rights to publish the *SNLQ*.[52] But the following month the board adopted a motion reserving the publication rights to the *SNLQ* for NCSBN in order to allow for future exploration of options for maximizing the publication's market potential.[53]

The NCSBN staff began to mail material directly to the individual members of all but six of the member boards in 1995. Prior to this the mailings had been sent to the member boards for re-mailing to the individual members.[54]

An article in *Insight* in the summer of 1995 reported on the publication of the *Nurse Aide Job Analysis* by NCSBN. The study included nurse aides in home health, nursing homes, and hospitals and found that the typical nurse aide was female, white, and between the ages of 26 and 35 years. In all three settings, the majority cited previous job experience as preparation for their current positions.[55]

Early in 1996, NCSBN introduced another publication entitled *Policy Currents*. The purpose of the publication was to provide more timely and enhanced information on legislative activities. The sections within *Policy Currents* were Legislative Activity (which covered federal and state activity), Member Board Exchange, Have You Heard?, and Final Thoughts. The first issue was attached to the *Newsletter to the Member Boards* in early March with subsequent distribution each month.[56] In May the board of directors reviewed a survey, "Are We Doing the Right Things?" that was taken at the area meetings. The board asked staff to explore appropriate ways that information included on the survey could be obtained from those attending the annual meeting.[57] In June the board of directors decided to repeat the survey at the annual meeting with an offer to waive the fee for the 1997 annual meeting as an incentive for completing the survey.[58]

The Report of Staff Activities in the 1996 *NCSBN Book of Reports* included descriptions of the following work related to communications: the development of an organizational structure for networking with essential regulatory policymakers and the production of a video describing NCSBN for use by member boards and for orienting new committee volunteers.[59]

Executive Director Jennifer Bosma, in her Report of Staff Activities in the 1997 *NCSBN Book of Reports*, called attention to a new monthly publication, *The Education Connection*, for distribution to the member boards. The staff also conducted a readership survey related to the effectiveness of the *NCSBN Book of Reports*. Based on this survey, a decision was made to publish what would be called the *NCSBN Business Book* in place of the traditional *Book of Reports* for the attendees at the annual meeting. The intent of this action was to provide information relating to the reports necessary for decision making on matters to be considered for action by the delegate assembly. A separate publication was planned to include the reports that did not require action from all committees, task forces, and other entities.[60]

NCSBN announced the release of the video *Breaking the Habit: When Your Colleague is Chemically Dependent* in 2001. The focus of the video was the challenge faced by nurses working with chemically dependent colleagues. Vickie Sheets, NCSBN director of Practice and Regulation, prepared the material with Linda Smith from the Intervention Project for Nurses and Jean Stevens, former president of the Washington Nursing Commission. Sheets and Emmaline Woodson, from the Maryland Board of Nursing, appeared in the video.[61]

Communicating Online

An article in the *Newsletter to the Member Boards* dated January 9, 1998, stated that reports of NCSBN committees were available online. The board of directors decided to take this step since the *NCSBN Business Book* would contain only those reports necessary for delegate assembly business. Thus, the member boards would have online access to all reports and the *NCSBN Book of Reports* would no longer be available.[62]

An announcement in a 1999 *Issues* reported that the *Curriculum Guide to Regulatory Criteria for Family Nurse Practitioners Seeking Prescriptive Authority to Manage Pharmacotherapeutics in Primary Care* was available. The announcement advised that while copies of the publication were available from the United States Department of Health and Human Services' Division of Nursing, the model curriculum guidelines and the recommended regulatory criteria were available on the NCSBN Web site.[63]

In March 2000 Susan Woodward, director of Communications, advised the board of restructuring within the Communications Department of NCSBN. News briefs would now be posted on the Web site in lieu of the biweekly *Newsletter to the Member Boards*. In addition, the public and VIP Web sites would be the new focus for dispersing communications, allowing for a greater distribution of information. The goal of these changes was to provide concise reports with significant and timely content.[64] NCSBN began publishing the *Council Connector* online in November 2000. This bimonthly newsletter continues to be available online for all who wish to read it, including the public. The final edition of *Issues* was published in 1999.

An article in a 2002 *Council Connector* reported that the board of directors had selected a new logo. The article described the rationale behind the new logo's imagery as follows:

The dancing squares give a feeling of movement as the organization advanced to stay on the cutting edge of nursing regulation and collaborative efforts with other organizations. The dancing squares symbolize a melting pot where individual elements combine to form a unified whole. The individual elements represented are the members, the programs, the services, the NCSBN staff and departments and the environment in which we work. Each of the squares is a different color, also representing individuality. The individual elements "line up" on their way to becoming the NCSBN where they join together to achieve the organization's mission.[65]

Conclusion

In 2003 NCSBN continues to recognize the importance of both internal and external communications in the accomplishment of its mission and goals. Many talented and creative people have served on committees dealing with communications. The structure for this effort has evolved from committees of the board of directors, to a standing committee, back to a special committee or task force over the years. Throughout, each of the NCSBN executive directors has made a difference in communicating with member boards, individuals, and organizations. More specifically, staff members who provided support for the committees, the board of directors, and the executive directors deserve recognition. David L. Heidorn joined the staff 1982 as a researcher/writer, and later served as director of Information Services until he left the staff in 1986. Wayne J. Chamberlain was director of Communications from 1986 to 1990. Susan Woodward was director of communications from 1990 to 2000. Leslie Uriss was managing editor on the staff of NCSBN from October 2000 to September 2001. Amanda Bird followed in that position through 2003. Those who have worked in various capacities with Information Technology at the NCSBN offices deserve much credit for effective, timely, and technically current communications.

CHAPTER SIX
PUBLIC POLICY

We must all remember that state movement toward registration is not a question that merely affects nurses. It is a part of a movement toward the betterment in general education. It is a part of the movement to elevate women by fitting them for the better performance of their duties. It is a part of the effort to develop the human race and bring it to a nobler type. It is not only a nurse's affair, it is a question of the age, an educational question, a question for woman, for the public, and a part of human advancement.

Lizzie M. Cox
Indiana, 1906[1]

THE EARLY RECOGNITION that regulation extends far beyond its benefit to the nurse was inherent in the importance of public protection to the regulation process. The quotation above sets the stage for a review of areas of public policy that were benefited by the involvement of those who regulate nurses. The founders of the National Council of State Boards of Nursing, Inc. (NCSBN®) were aware of the necessity to be selective when considering positions on issues facing nursing and society in general. This awareness was part of the basis for establishing a free-standing organization to provide services for the members, the boards of nursing, and to represent those members in public forums on issues related to the protection of the public health, safety, and welfare. Helen "Pat" Keefe of Florida, a member of the Special Task Force—State Boards of Nursing, the group selected to develop the plan for the organization of the NCSBN, was quoted by Gertrude Malone, Shirley Fondiller, and David Heidorn in their book, *From an Idea to an Organization*, as saying in 1983,

---

I went to that first meeting [of the Special Task Force in 1977] totally unconvinced that we were doing the right thing, because I was concerned about creating another "splinter group" to divide nursing. As a long-time loyal member of the ANA [American Nurses Association], I strongly opposed further fragmentation. In the months that followed, I gradually changed my mind. Part of that conversion was due to the strong convictions of my colleagues about the need for a new organization. The other part was due to my experiences in preparing to undergo sunset review in

Florida where issues of conflict of interest, professional bias and the rights of the consumer were undergoing heated debate. Slowly my outlook changed.[2]

With this statement Keefe, president of NCSBN from 1981 to 1982, revealed that she, one of the four members of the Special Task Force that conducted the planning to organize NCSBN, had some misgivings but soon came to recognize that the organization could meet its objectives and also have an appropriate voice in public policy issues.

First Steps in Public Policy

During the first 10 years of the NCSBN there was very little mention or any question of the NCSBN taking a position on or responding to public policy issues or questions. The first mention was found in Keefe's report as secretary in 1980 in which she described how she and Executive Director Eileen McQuaid (later Dvorak) had attended a meeting called by the National Center for Health Statistics. The purpose of this meeting was to develop a plan for obtaining the cooperation of all states to gather statistics on health care professionals.[3] Around that time federal funding for collecting this data was cut, and it was hoped that the states would provide continued funding for this purpose. Workforce data collection was, and still is, a concern for some member boards and for national and state planners. The subject was not specifically addressed in the NCSBN documents from that time. At the 2002 board of directors meeting President Donna Dorsey of Maryland and Director-at-Large Polly Johnson of North Carolina discussed a meeting of Colleagues in Caring that was held in November. At that meeting those present discussed strategies on how to give the nine participating boards of nursing the ability to collect and submit workforce data.[4]

In 1983 the board of directors decided to send a letter to the ANA advising that the Nursing Practice and Standards (NP&S) Committee had reviewed the Social Policy Statement of the ANA. The letter stated that the committee concluded that the statement was a "useful resource document," and that the board agreed to recommend the statement to the member boards for their consideration, as appropriate.[5]

Nurse Shortage

Executive Director Eileen McQuaid Dvorak reported in 1988 that the NCSBN had been invited by the Commission on the Study of the Nursing Shortage of the United States Department of Health and Human Services to participate, "in terms of its analysis of the current situation in nursing in the United States." In another entry in her report, McQuaid Dvorak stated that the NCSBN staff had participated in the International Congress of Nurse Regulation on the Nursing Implementation Project. The purpose of the project was to implement the principle of nursing regulation as adopted by the International Congress of Nurses.[6] The following year McQuaid Dvorak included the following statement in her report to the delegate assembly:

Partly as a result of the nurse shortage, and partly as a result of our growing sense of "global village," the international regulation of nursing is a policy issue receiving increased attention. The International Council of Nurses, through funding provided by the W.K. Kellogg Foundation, is sponsoring a Regulation of Nursing Implementation Project to which the Executive Director of the National Council was named as one of two representatives of the United States. (The other representative is the Deputy Director of the American Nurses' Association.) A project group consisting of English-speaking nations from North America, the Caribbean, and southern Africa have held two of three meetings. The cooperative project selected by the U.S. representatives is a statement to be issued jointly by the National Council and ANA on the nurse shortage. An outline of the joint statement was presented to the Board of Directors and routed to the Subcommittee on the Nurse Shortage of the Nursing Practice and Education Committee for further refinement and expansion.[7]

The Subcommittee on the Nurse Shortage, chaired by Ann Petersen of Utah, reported to the delegate assembly at the annual meeting in 1989. The subcommittee developed short- and long-term strategies that member boards and the NCSBN could use to minimize the negative consequences of the nurse shortage. The specific strategies developed included reviewing existing rules, questioning any pressure to relax standards, ensuring the appropriate delegation of nursing, questioning unduly restrictive language in law or regulation, reviewing the *NCSBN Model Nursing Practice Act* (*MNPA*) and *Model Nursing Administrative Rules* (*MNAR*), evaluating examination scheduling and reporting, and comparing the National Council Licensure Examination (NCLEX®) with the Canadian Nurses Association Test Service Examination (CNATS).[8]

As the NCSBN addressed some public policy issues and received requests for support on nursing issues, legislation, litigation, and other related items, the leadership recognized the need for policies and positions to provide a basis for response to these requests. Prior to making its first endorsement of a statement from another group, the delegate assembly adopted the Guidelines for Responding to Requests for Endorsement of Position Statements in 1990, as discussed in Chapter 4.[9]

The board of directors developed a policy in 1992 regarding requests for letters of support that stated, "the NCSBN will consider requests for letters of support from Member Boards and national organizations only."[10]

Jennifer Bosma, NCSBN executive director, reported on staff activities in the 1995 *NCSBN Book of Reports*. Under the heading Public Policy Programs she noted that the staff had conducted a survey of other associations to collect information on governmental affairs programs in similar organizations.[11] The board discussed the public policy focus of the NCSBN in 1995 and developed "priorities and parameters." The board indicated that their public policy work would focus on monitoring issues on a national level, analyzing these issues, and disseminating information to the member boards. Further, the board determined that, over time, a program of monitoring and assuring that the regulatory perspective was heard in "government affairs" would be developed. Carolyn Hutcherson, a former president, had recently joined the staff as senior policy analyst and the board discussed her role in that position.[12]

In October 2000 the board of directors once again discussed the framework and process for the development of the NCSBN public policy positions. The board agreed that it was to be involved and have the opportunity to make final edits and content decisions on significant NCSBN policy issues before statements were made to the media. The board also stated that the NCSBN does not make statements for individual member boards and should not make decisions without member board consideration. The board was to continue to review this framework and determined that the president would provide final review of all policy statements.[13] At the next meeting the board of directors reviewed a proposed policy entitled "Framework for Influencing Public Policy." The policy was referred back to the staff for redrafting.[14] The board of directors heard a report from the Nursing Practice and Education (NP&E) Committee that recommended approval of the *Framework for Influencing Public Policy* at the January 2001 meeting.[15] The board amended and adopted the policy.[16]

Toward the end of the 1990s it was becoming apparent that a shortage of nurses of a magnitude not seen before was looming in the new century. Factors contributing to this shortage have been described extensively in nursing literature in recent years. These factors have their bases in many and varied aspects of society. Although shortages had occurred in the past, all predictors indicated that this one would be the most profound. The first reference to this shortage was a brief statement in the minutes of a board of directors meeting on November 14, 2000. At that meeting the board of directors reviewed a draft of a statement on the nursing shortage and referred this draft to the NP&E Committee for its consideration.[17] At the January 2001 board of directors meeting the board adopted the paper as revised by the NP&E Committee and published it on January 29 as the *NCSBN Response to the Nursing Shortage*. The response appears below in its entirety.

The National Council of State Boards of Nursing understands that the need for public protection through regulation has never been greater, due in large part to the nursing shortage. Failure to maintain standards of practice could lead to an increase in errors, increased risk for patient harm, and a lack of public confidence.

During shortages of health care professionals, one potential and predictable policy direction is to deregulate, thereby reducing practice standards. As the primary mission of the NCSBN member boards of nursing is protection of the public's health and safety, any such trend of deregulation is assumed to increase the risk of harm to patients.

Therefore, the nursing regulatory community is actively working to assure an adequate supply of competent licensed nurses through a number of initiatives. Boards of nursing will:

- Participate strategically at state and national initiatives created to address nursing supply and demand issues.

- Influence national, state and local efforts to improve patient safety in health care.

- Continue timely, humane and effective intervention when state nurse practice acts are violated.

- Support regulatory authority over nursing scope of practice.

- Maximally utilize current categories of nursing and unlicensed assistive personnel without lowering standards and in accordance with regulations.

- Track workplace-related complaints and issues brought to the attention of boards of nursing.

- Collect, analyze, and disseminate comprehensive data describing present and future nursing education and practice environments as related to public protection.

- Uphold standards for entry into the profession, including requirements for U.S. licensure for graduates of foreign nursing schools.

An increasingly growing shortage of nurses, anticipated to reach critical proportions by 2010, is a matter of public protection. Inadequate numbers of appropriately prepared professional nurses threatens the nation's health and safety. Factors contributing to this shortage include:

- Aging of both the nurse workforce and the faculty members preparing the workforce.

- An inadequate supply of young professionals choosing a nursing career (due largely to competing and more attractive career opportunities in other fields).

- Growing concerns over stressful and/or unsafe working conditions for nurses.

- Increasing demand for nursing care, due to aging of the general population and greater need for chronic and community-based care.

NCSBN continues to support the education and licensure of practical/vocational nurses, registered professional nurses, and advanced practice nurses. NCSBN also supports regulatory oversight of nursing assistants and other unlicensed assistive personnel. Coordinated efforts to promote nursing and to ensure an adequate supply of nurses in the future will serve both the public and the nursing profession's best interests.

NCSBN strongly opposes the implementation of any expedient solutions to the shortage that lead to the inefficient and unsafe delivery of nursing care because of the likely adverse impact on public health, safety and welfare.

Collaboration among those who practice nursing, educate nurses, supervise nurses, and regulate nursing is essential to maintain the public's trust, health, safety, and welfare during the predicted nursing shortage ahead. The NCSBN pledges its support to assist in seeking solutions for the nursing shortage from the perspective of regulatory public protection.[18]

In May 2001 President Joey Ridenour of Arizona reported that the ANA had established a nursing leadership consortium known as The Call to the Profession to develop new strategies to address the nursing shortage. After expressing an interest in participating in this consortium, the NCSBN Board of Directors approved NCSBN membership in it and decided that the new executive director would represent the NCSBN Board of Directors.[19] In August Executive Director Kathy Apple reported to the board of directors about a meeting of the Steering Committee for The Call to the Profession. Seven organizations, including the NCSBN, were represented on the Steering Committee, whose task it was to provide a structure to create solutions for ensuring safe, quality care for all health care consumers and a sufficient supply of nurses for the future.[20] In October the board discussed a consensus document, "Americans for Nursing Shortage Relief," and identified the need to include the role of the licensed practical/vocational nurses (LPN/VNs) in relation to the shortage. Since this inclusion was documented in the NCSBN nursing shortage statement, the board decided that citing its paper in the consensus statement would be adequate. The board approved the Emergency Nurses Association request to endorse the consensus document and to ask that the NCSBN statement be considered for inclusion by reference and that the NCSBN endorsement highlight the need for public protection.[21]

The delegate assembly adopted a somewhat related resolution at the annual meeting in August. The resolution read,

NCSBN promotes safe and effective nursing practice in the interest of protecting public health and welfare. Therefore, the Council recognizes the professional responsibility of nurses to accept or decline overtime assignment based on their self-assessment of ability to provide safe care.[22]

An article in the *Council Connector* reported on a study done by the American Health Care Association (ACHA) that showed that the baby boomer retirement levels coupled with fewer nurses entering the health care field in the next decade "will present serious problems for the elderly." In another finding the report said the estimated need for LPN/VNs in long-term care would grow by 71 percent from 1991 to 2020. The AHCA recommended that the President and Congress work together to add 60,000 new LPN/VNs and registered nurses (RNs) to the profession by January 1, 2002.[23] In a second article the AHCA reported on its research survey. The percentage of hospital executives citing labor and staffing as one of their key issues had nearly doubled in 2000 from 1999.[24] Articles in the *Council Connector* in 2002 continued to provide information about the nursing shortage. Representatives from the NCSBN participated in the four-day summit, The Call to the Profession. The purpose of the meeting was to develop a strategy to address nurse staffing and nurse shortage issues to ensure that consumers continued to receive safe nursing care. Emphasis was placed on retention and recruitment of people into the profession. The group drafted a strategy and identified 10 areas in which to concentrate their efforts.[25] Another article, also published in the *Council Connector*, reported on a study, *Health Care's Human Crisis: The American Nursing Shortage*, funded by the Robert Wood Johnson Foundation. The principle findings of this study were stated as follows:

The current nursing drought is not like previous shortages; it is about to get worse, and the tried and true solutions of the past are unlikely to solve it. This nursing shortage reflects dissatisfaction with the profession by nurses and competition from other career opportunities for women.

The study also found that "sustainable solutions" would need collective efforts by those concerned, including nurses, nursing leaders, educators, leaders in the health care industry, labor organizations, policymakers, philanthropists, and consumers.[26]

At the board of directors meeting in March 2003, President Donna Dorsey of Maryland announced that, consistent with the NCSBN policy on financial contributions to other organizations, the NCSBN was committing a donation of $5,000 to Nursing's Agenda for the Future. The money was to be applied to the funding of a proposal for an analysis of the cost of an inadequate nursing supply.[27]

Regulatory Impact of Acquired Immune Deficiency Syndrome

The public health issues and questions for the health care regulatory community as the result of Acquired Immune Deficiency Syndrome (AIDS) appeared in an article in *Issues* in 1988. The article examined the statistics for AIDS since it was first identified in 1981 and looked at the impact on employers and the relationship of AIDS to handicap discrimination laws. Further, the article discussed AIDS as it related to the health care worker and the Occupational Safety and Health Act (OSHA), Workers Compensation, and testing for AIDS in the workplace. The article concluded with the following: "Some states have begun considering the effect of the disease on health care workers. Nurses are playing a primary role in the development of this policy, because of their role in the treatment of AIDS patients."[28] In her column in *Issues*, Executive Director McQuaid Dvorak discussed the relevance of the article for the member boards. She said, in part,

> Information contained in this article on AIDS can be used by the regulatory bodies in any deliberation about the needs of patients with AIDS for competent accessible nursing care. Questions about safety for the patient, for the public, and for the practitioner will require access to all available data by members of boards of nursing who will be deliberating on commissions or omissions of actions by nurses who care for persons with AIDS. In concert with other regulatory bodies in the professions, boards of nursing will be considering at least conceptually their roles and responsibilities concerning guidelines and directives for nurses who are diagnosed as having AIDS.[29]

In April 1992 Vickie Sheets, director for Public Policy, Nursing Practice and Education for the NCSBN, reported on her initial work toward preparing information for dissemination to the member boards regarding HIV/AIDS. She reported that the Centers for Disease Control (CDC) Guidelines published in the fall of 1991 were still current, but were being revised. Her plan was to remind the member boards about the CDC Guidelines and alert them to the Dole Amendment, which required statewide plans. The board took action to include information in the May 8 issue of the *Newsletter to the Member Boards* and directed the NP&E Committee to collect information to assist the member boards to network on the subject.[30]

North American Free Trade Agreement

At a meeting in April 1990 Executive Director Bosma reported to the board of directors that she had consulted with Legal Counsel Thomas O'Brien regarding a federal free trade agreement and implications for the member boards. The board directed that the information be made available to the membership.[31] The next mention of a free trade agreement appeared in an attachment to the *Newsletter to the Member Boards* in 1992. The attachment was an *Emerging Issues* entitled "The Proposed North American Free Trade Agreement." The agreement (NAFTA) was initiated in October and was awaiting expected implementing legislation. A "professional service annex" to NAFTA provided a generic blueprint aimed at encouraging all professions to reach mutual recognition agreements. The NCSBN continued to monitor the implementation and provided information to the member boards as it became available.[32] In November 1993, an article in the *Newsletter to the Member Boards* presented information on NAFTA in a question and answer format that included the following:

> Q. *I thought NAFTA was a trade agreement. What does it have to do with nursing regulation?*
> A. Although NAFTA is basically a trade agreement, the portions that have to do with trade in

services touch upon regulation of professionals. Chapters on cross-border trade and temporary entry are the most relevant.

Q. *Does NAFTA mean we would have to extend "reciprocity" to any licensed nurse coming to our jurisdiction from Canada or Mexico?*
A. No. The temporary entry chapter allows for business persons to come into the United States to engage in business activity. However, they may not engage in hands-on professional practice without applying for and meeting all your requirements for licensure, and being granted a license by your board.

Q. *We know something about Canadian nurse licensure, the CNATS examination, etc., but what is the system in Mexico?*
A. The National Council has sent correspondence to Mexican regulatory authorities requesting an exchange of information regarding the basics of each country's nursing regulatory and educational systems. To date, no response has been received.[33]

Executive Director Bosma reported to the board of directors in June 1994 about a trilateral linkage conference and a meeting at the office of the United States Trade Representative at which participants from Canada and Mexico were present.[34] An article in the *Newsletter to the Member Boards* discussed the Trilateral Initiative for Nursing, a meeting of representatives from the Canadian, Mexican and United States nursing communities. The meeting was held under the auspices of the Center for Quality Assurance in International Education and the Mexican Ministry of Education. The objective of this initiative was to share information among representatives from professional organizations involved in educational standard development in the three countries, and ultimately to develop common educational standards within the professions. Representatives were present from the following United States organizations: the American Association of Colleges of Nursing (AACN), the ANA, the American Nurses Credentialing Center (ANCC), the Commission on Graduates of Foreign Nursing Schools (CGFNS), the NCSBN, the National League for Nursing (NLN), and the Pan American Health Organization/World Health Organization. The group decided to hold future meetings.[35]

Another article in the *Newsletter to the Member Boards* in January 1995 provided information about NAFTA and regulatory boards. The NCSBN urged boards of nursing to phase out citizenship and permanent residency as requirements for licensure. The article emphasized that all licensure requirements must have objective criteria and that these requirements were necessary to protect the consumer.[36] In June 1996 Bosma presented information to the board of directors on future activities of the Trilateral Initiative for Nursing.[37] The January issue of the *Newsletter to the Member Boards* reported that materials related to NAFTA were "being finalized at the national level" and that no further information was needed from the member boards.[38] The Trilateral Initiative for Nursing issued a comprehensive publication describing aspects of nursing education standards and professional nursing practice throughout the three countries. Bosma and Senior Policy Analyst Carolyn Hutcherson participated in the assessment and description of professional nursing standards as they existed at the time.[39]

Roy Swift, the director of Personnel Certification for the American National Standards Institute, met with the board of directors in 2003 to provide information about trade agreements. Swift reported that the existing and future trade agreements included the globalization of professions, bilateral reciprocity and mutual recognition to increase productivity, and the creation of standards and certification mechanisms to support globalization. The board planned to continue discussion of how to best position the NCSBN in the global community.[40]

Health Care Reform

The reform of health care delivery was another public policy and nursing issue that the NCSBN addressed in the decade of the 1990s. In October 1990 the board of directors reviewed a letter from

Lucille Joel, the president of the ANA, regarding a plan for the reform of the delivery of health care. The board of directors received reports and took actions related to health care reform at most meetings during 1991 and 1992. Some of these reports and actions included:

- Member boards' responses to Nursing's Agenda for Health Care Reform were reported.[41]
- A final report on these responses in October was requested.[42]
- The NP&E Committee's comments regarding Nursing's Agenda for Health Care Reform was presented by NP&E Committee Chair Neumann.
- The recommendation from the NP&E Committee that the delegate assembly endorse (in concept) Nursing's Agenda for Health Care Reform was declined.
- The NP&E Committee was not discouraged by the board from taking the recommendation to the delegate assembly.[43]

In August 1992 the delegate assembly adopted a resolution that the NCSBN support, philosophically, the basic concepts inherent within Nursing's Agenda for Health Care Reform, but stopped short of endorsing it.[44] Eventually it was endorsed by most of the nursing related professional organizations in the United States.

Director-at-Large Judi Crume of Alabama, Executive Director Bosma, Associate Executive Director Doris Nay, and Director for Public Policy, Practice and Education Vickie Sheets attended a 1993 national nursing summit, "The Nurse of the Future," sponsored by the ANA. The board of directors agreed to send a letter to the member boards summarizing the meeting. The NCSBN planned to do a news release regarding the health care reform plan being developed within the federal government by the Clinton administration at the time it became available.[45] Later in September, the board again heard a report on the health care reform plan. The board took the following actions: (a) They decided that the health care reform plan proposed by the administration of President William Clinton was not specific enough for the NCSBN to make a unique comment, and (b) They decided to respond to questions about the plan directed to the NCSBN by focusing on the protection of the public and the appropriate role of advanced practice registered nurses (APRNs).[46]

Relative to Nursing's Agenda for Health Care Reform, the board of directors identified the need to reconvene the nursing summit and to assure that LPN/VNs were included in discussions on the role of nursing in reformed health care. The board planned to include discussions of health care reform and regulation at the board retreat with attention to the impact on nursing, regulation, boards of nursing, and the NCSBN.[47]

In October 1993 the board of directors again conducted a thorough review of the issue of health care reform and studied another report from the NP&E Committee related to implications on the work of the NCSBN. Sheets presented another report on the implications of health care reform for nursing and nursing regulation.[48] At the December meeting the board directed staff regarding approaches to collecting information, and communicating with the member boards and with policymakers on the federal level. The board also reviewed a legal opinion on the federal preemption provision included in the proposed Clinton health security act. The information was to be included in an *Emerging Issues* to be sent to the member boards and shared with NCSBN liaison organizations at meetings.[49]

At the March 1994 board of directors meeting Nay reported on activities and correspondence regarding health care reform, including letters from Linda Aiken of the Physician Payment Review Commission, and Secretary of Health and Human Services Donna Shalala.[50] Most issues of the *Newsletter to the Member Boards* in 1994 had articles about health care reform, including state activities and the proposal pending in Congress. However, the Clinton health security act was defeated in Congress.

Patient Safety

The board of directors received a report from Teresa Mullin of Virginia, the NCSBN representative to the National Coordinating Council for Medication Error Reporting and Prevention (NCCMERP) in 1995.[51] There were continuing reports of the work of this group in subsequent minutes of board meetings. An article in the *Newsletter to the Member Boards* in 1997 provided more detail about the NCCMERP. It was "established to address the growing concerns related to medication errors and to help bring the health care community together in a unified problem solving effort." It was described as a "collaboration of some of the nation's leading health care and consumer organizations to address challenges regarding the safe use of medications." A brochure listed goals and objectives for three categories: medication error reporting, medication error understanding, and medication error prevention. The NCSBN was a voting member of NCCMERP and continued to be represented by Mullin until 1998.[52] In subsequent years the board of directors appointed the following to succeed Mullin: Barbara Newman of Maryland, 1998; Harriett Johnson of New Jersey, 1999; Barbara Newman, 2000; Debra Brady of New Mexico, 2002; and Polly Johnson of North Carolina, 2003. At its meeting in August 2000, the board of directors continued its interest in medication errors when it voted to support participation in the initiative of the Citizen's Advocacy Center (CAC) to study medication error reporting.[53] The following year, the board of directors agreed to send a letter to the NCCMERP to clarify the role of the member boards and the position of the NCSBN during its participation in the conference, "When Medical Mistakes Happen: Alternates to Disciplinary Action."[54] Later in the year, the board noted the NCCMERP workshop scheduled for October. Deborah Burton of Oregon attended for the NCSBN and was listed as a speaker.[55] The board of directors, in August 2002, discussed bills that had been introduced in the United States Congress related to patient safety. The board decided to comment on the proposed legislation in support of patient safety, but also to address the concerns of the board.[56] In March 2003 the board of directors discussed the federal Patient Safety and Quality Improvement Act of 2003. The board noted its concern for the lack of designation of boards of nursing as exempt agencies and for the impact of the act on discipline reporting requirements. The board decided to send a "letter of education" to the sponsors of the bill.[57]

Reform of Health Care Workforce Regulation

One of the major public policy issues addressed by the NCSBN during its first 25 years resulted from a study conducted by the Pew Health Commissions Taskforce on Health Care Workforce Regulation. This study was published in December 1995 and was entitled *Reforming Health Care Workforce Regulation: Policy Considerations for the 21st Century*, hereafter, the Pew Report. Preliminary information from the report was available prior to December. In June 1995 the board of directors decided to pursue the development of a conference to be jointly sponsored with the CAC on the topic of reforming professional and occupational licensing and regulation.[58] Gary Fillerman, from the Pew Health Professions Commission, presented an overview of the Pew Report at the annual meeting in August. Following this presentation, the board of directors decided to devote time at the October retreat to consider the recommendations emerging from the Pew Report.[59] At its October 1995 meeting the board of directors heard a report of its Nursing Regulation Task Force. The board agreed with the items developed by the task force and requested the development of an outline with visual aids about the Pew Report and its recommendations that could be used by the member boards.[60]

In January 1996 the board devoted time to discuss the "current environment with respect to regulatory reform." The board took the following action at that meeting:

- Gave direction regarding the NCSBN involvement in related activities, including organizational response to the Pew Report recommendations.

- Determined that the NCSBN should take a leadership role in proposing regulatory models for the future and in championing discussions of model evaluations with other nursing groups and other health professional regulatory groups.

• Assigned coordination of activities to the Nursing Regulation Task Force.

• Asked that discussion of the issue be included on the area and the annual meeting agendas.[61]

In May the board of directors reviewed and commented on a draft of a response to the Pew Report recommendations from the Nursing Regulation Task Force.[62] Libby Lund of Tennessee, chair of the Nursing Regulation Task Force, reported to the delegate assembly in the 1996 *NCSBN Book of Reports*. The task force recommended that the delegates adopt the NCSBN's response to the Pew Report. In her report Lund presented, as background to support the recommendation, an overview of the Pew Report that was released in 1995. She said it focused on 10 issues surrounding the regulation of health professionals, as follows:

1. States should use standardized and understandable language for health professions regulation and its functions to clearly describe them for consumers, provider organizations, businesses, and the professions.

2. States should standardize entry-to-practice requirements and limit them to competence assessments for health professions to facilitate the physical and professional mobility of the health professions.

3. States should base practice acts on demonstrated initial and continuing competence. This process must allow and expect different professions to share overlapping scopes of practice. States should explore pathways to allow all professionals to provide services to the full extent of their current knowledge, training, experience, and skills.

4. States should redesign health professional boards and their functions to reflect the interdisciplinary and public accountability demands of the changing health care delivery system.

5. Boards should educate consumers to assist them in obtaining the information necessary to make decisions about practitioners and to improve the board's public accountability.

6. Boards should cooperate with other public and private organizations in collecting data on regulated health professions to support effective workforce planning.

7. States should require each board to develop, implement, and evaluate continuing competency requirements to assure the continuing competence of regulated health care professionals.

8. States should maintain a fair, cost-effective, and uniform disciplinary process to exclude incompetent practitioners to protect and promote the public's health.

9. States should develop evaluation tools that assess the objectives, successes, and shortcomings of their regulatory systems and bodies to best protect and promote the public's health.

10. States should understand the links, overlaps, and conflicts between their health care workforce regulatory systems and other systems which affect the education, regulations, and practice of health care practitioners and work to develop partnerships to streamline regulatory structures and processes.[63]

The proposed NCSBN response presented comments and recommendations including policy options on each of these. The detailed response can be found in the 1996 *NCSBN Book of Reports* or in a special pull out section in a 1996 edition of *Issues*. The concluding statement in the NCSBN response was the following:

Boards of nursing are willing and committed to pursue needed regulatory reform. We have the talent, the skills and the dedication to come to the table to pursue true reform that reaches for the Pew vision while maintaining the focus on quality and safety of care. The support of reform at the level needed will include financing, operational change efforts and effective coordination of efforts. We trust that the importance of this effort will not go unrecognized and unsupported by the Pew Health Professions Commission and the Pew Charitable Trusts.[64]

In order to complete the response, the task force coordinated a number of activities including the joint conference with CAC in December 1995, a fact sheet that reported NCSBN and member board activities, dialogue with Pew representatives, preparation of a regulatory response packet, and member board dialogue on the recommendations.[65] The delegate assembly adopted the response as presented by the task force.[66]

At a meeting in September 1996, the board of directors affirmed the acceptability of the Interprofessional Work Group response to the Pew Report based on the response adopted by the delegate assembly. After reviewing changes suggested by other organizations, the board gave direction for resolution and authorized the president to be the final reviewer.[67] A 1997 article in *Issues* reported that a document titled *Interprofessional Work Group Recommendations Regarding Regulation of Health Professions* had been added to the NCSBN Web site. The Interprofessional Work Group was composed of 16 health professions organizations, including the NCSBN, and represented more that 4 million health care practitioners.[68] A May 1997 issue of the *Newsletter to the Member Boards* included excerpts from a press release from the Pew Health Professions Commission. After reporting background information about the commission, the reader was reminded that continued work would include the examination of education and continued competence and accountability of physicians, nurses, and other health professionals. The commission would also focus on how to encourage reductions in the health care workforce. An earlier report indicated that by the year 2000 one-half of the nation's hospitals would be closed, and there would be a surplus of providers, including 200,000 to 300,000 nurses.[69]

At a meeting of the board of directors in February 1998, Hutcherson reported that the Pew Commission had compiled all comments received on the 1995 Pew report. More comments were received from nursing than from any other profession. A new eight-member task force had been appointed and a report was due in 1998.[70] In November, an article in the *Newsletter to the Member Boards* reported on the recent release of another report from the Pew Taskforce on Health Care Workforce Regulation. The article stated that NCSBN groups would review this report for implications for the member boards.[71] The board received a report regarding The Policy Futures Panel response to this pew report in February 1999. The fourth and final report from the Pew Health Professions Commission was released in December 1998. The Nevada Board of Nursing asked the board of directors to prepare a response and the staff was directed to do so.[72] At the same meeting the board established a panel consisting of Mary Wakefield, Vickie Sheets, Carolyn Hutcherson, NCSBN staff, along with Anna Yoder of Massachusetts and Kathy Apple of Nevada, to develop analysis documents related to the final Pew Report.[73] The panel's report offered major recommendations for all health professional groups as follows:

- Change professional training to meet the demands of the new health care system.

- Ensure that the health professions workforce reflects the diversity of the nation's population.

- Require interdisciplinary competence in all health professionals.

- Continue to move education into ambulatory practice.

- Encourage public service of all health professional students and graduates.

The specific recommendations for nursing were listed in the report as follows:

- Adjust educational programs to produce the numbers and types of nurses appropriate to local or regional demand, rather than institutional and political needs.

- Delineate the knowledge and outcome competence appropriate for each level of nursing education in order to maximize efficiency, improve coordination and articulation of programs, and reduce professional conflict and public confusion.

- Radically revamp the content and learning experiences in the nursing curriculum to produce graduates with the competencies needed for differentiated practice.

- Integrate the research, teaching, and practice enterprises of nursing education programs in order to further nursing's professional and practical goals.

In addition to the above, the report included the following specific recommendations for advanced practice nursing:

- Reorient advanced practice nursing education programs to prepare advanced practice nurses for the changing situations and settings in which they are likely to practice.

- Regardless of the payer source (Health Care Financing Administration (HCFA) or an all-payer pool), federal funding for graduate medical education should be made available to support the training of advanced practice nurses and other non-physician providers in clinical settings.

- Develop standard guidelines for advanced nursing practice and reinforce them with curriculum guidelines, examination requirements, and accreditation regulation.

- Emphasize the practice styles that are a critical part of advanced practice nursing including the emphasis on preventive and health-promoting interventions and attention to psychosocial, environmental, and resource factors.

The report listed 21 competencies for the 21st century, recommendations for accreditation, and recommendations for refining the Federal Graduate Medical Education Policy.[74] In May the board of directors reviewed and commented on the analysis of the final Pew Report, and requested revision to include a description of the future state of nursing regulation. The analysis was to be sent to the Member Boards for review and comment.[75] No further evidence of activity related to the pew reports was available.

The United States Supreme Court issued a decision in a case in 1995 that came to the attention of the NCSBN board of directors. The five to four decision upheld an appeals court ruling that found that four LPN/VNs were supervisors and not protected under the National Labor Relations Act that affords employees the rights to organize and engage in collective bargaining without employer interference. That law had been amended in 1947 so that the term "employee" would not include supervisors. Writing a lengthy dissent, Justice Ginsberg pointed out that the act expressly excludes supervisors and expressly includes professional employees, defining a professional employee as one whose work is "predominantly intellectual, varied in character…[involving]…the constant exercise of discretion and judgment in its performance…and requires knowledge 'in a field of science or learning customarily acquired by a prolonged course of specialized intellectual instruction and study…'"[76] The NCSBN board of directors requested an analysis of the decision to determine whether it held any implications for the member boards, and subsequently this analysis was published as an *Emerging Issues* and distributed to the member boards.[77]

Institute of Medicine Studies

The Institute of Medicine (IOM) produced several studies that drew the attention of the NCSBN. In 1996 a press release announced a study to explore the relationships among staff labels, the mix of different types of nursing personnel, and the quality of patient care. The title of this study was "Nursing Staff in Hospitals and Nursing Homes. Is It Adequate?" The NCSBN staff and the board of directors studied the information and planned to share it with the member boards.[78] The board of directors heard a report of a second IOM study on errors in health care in February 2000. The president stated that the NCSBN should respond to the IOM study report. She said further that careful consideration must be given to the findings and recommendations in relation to the accountability of individual member boards before making the response.[79] In June the NP&E Committee presented a position statement on this IOM report and asked the board to adopt it.[80] Later in the meeting Katherine Thomas of Texas-RN, chair of the NP&E Committee and David Swankin, president of the CAC, spoke to the board about the IOM report:

The CAC was soliciting interest in a pilot program with the Administrators of Medicine (AIM) to implement a unified health care collaborative project which would establish a communication network to refute implications of the IOM Report whereby regulatory boards were misrepresented as a solely punitive force. AIM had expressed interest in including NCSBN on their advisory committee. The participating pilot groups would provide oversight for this effort. The Board discussed the following actions specific to the IOM Report: 1) establish a research agenda to explore issues of breakdown in nursing practice, 2) determine future appropriate responses of NCSBN to the IOM study, and 3) determine the best way to provide states with language to facilitate discussion of this report at the local level. The NP&E committee drafted a response to the IOM Report. The Board requested that a panel discussion on this topic occur at the Delegate Assembly. The Board also asked staff to pursue a fall summit meeting with possible collaborative partners (Federation of State Medical Boards, AIM, Council on Licensure Enforcement and Regulation (CLEAR), Pharmacy, Federation of Associations of Regulatory Boards (FARB), Joint Commission on the Accreditation of Healthcare Organizations (JCAHO), etc.) to establish dialog about a unified stance promoting regulation as a fundamental aid in the protection of the public.[81]

At another meeting in June 2000, Associate Executive Director Donna Nowakowski presented the revised response to the IOM report that was drafted by the NP&E Committee. The board of directors approved its use for response to the public and use by the member boards. The response was posted on the NCSBN Web site.[82] At the annual meeting Katherine Thomas, chair of the NP&E Committee, presented the committee report, including the response to the IOM report on patient safety and medication errors that was issued in November 1999. The following is an excerpt from the response:

The National Council of State Boards of Nursing finds the IOM report's emphasis on setting national goals to ensure health outcomes and patient safety laudable. These patient safety goals should be based on broad evidence and expert opinion. The research agenda should include evaluation of the drivers of errors, identification of underlying factors or "root causes," and approaches for error prevention. A national focus calls forth leadership and research that will provide analysis and application of findings needed to establish standards and safety expectations. Such a multifaceted approach needs to be based on a collaborative effort between public and private sectors of health care.

Regulation influences expected quality in health care organizations and individuals by defining minimum levels of competence, expected performance and assurance of an acceptable level of safety for everyone accessing the health system. The IOM Report cites the importance of regulatory and legislative efforts in defining minimums and assuring a basic level of safety. The National Council asserts that it is critical that regulatory boards are engaged to be a part of the solution to medical errors. The National Council shares many of the concerns raised by the committee regarding medical errors and their impact on patient outcomes since a major responsibility of regulatory boards is to identify and remedy behaviors and practices that have the potential to place patients at risk.[83]

Also in August 2000, the board of directors approved a letter from the NCSBN in support of Senator Edward Kennedy's bill related to the IOM report.[84]

The NP&E Committee asked the board of directors in 2001 to review and make recommendations or consensus points related to another IOM report: *Crossing the Quality Chasm: A New Health System for the 21st Century*. The board decided to discuss this report and other IOM reports at the fall summit.[85] In April 2003 the IOM released another report entitled *Health Professions Education, A Bridge to Quality*. This report explored ways to improve the quality and safety of health care. Polly Johnson of North Carolina, a member of the NCSBN board of directors, was a member of the task force that was instrumental in writing this report. The report was identified as important to the member boards because the recommendations targeted oversight organizations to integrate common core competencies into their processes with the aim of creating an outcome-based education system.[86]

Conclusion

This chapter has presented an overview of several public policy issues addressed by the NCSBN. Public policy consideration by the NCSN began to increase in the early 1990s. Explanations for the increase include the vision of the staff and the board of directors, outcomes of evaluations of the organization, and the recognition of the role of the member boards in public protection. The presence of the NCSBN continues to be essential when public policy issues that are consistent with the purpose of the organization are discussed. This review of public policy actions by the NCSBN reveals one of the many ways in which the organization continues to fulfill its purpose and mission after 25 years.

An appropriate closing statement for this chapter was found in "The Parable of the UPs and DOWNs" in an address presented by Katherine Thomas at the NCSBN Annual Meeting in 2002. This parable addressed the need for cooperation and the willingness to understand the role and position of others. It is consistent with the role of the NCSBN as it participates in the public policy arena for nursing in the new century.

The Parable of the UPs and DOWNs

I want to share with you a story. I don't know where it originally came from. I heard it told by Katie Sherrod, a journalist with the *Fort Worth Star Telegram*. It's called "The Parable of the UPs and DOWNs." I challenge you to think of yourself in both roles. The parable goes like this…

What makes an UP an UP and DOWN a DOWN, is that an UP can do more to a DOWN than a DOWN can do to an UP. That's what keeps UPs up and DOWNs down. The UPs tend to talk to each other and study the DOWNs, asking the DOWNs about what's up, or what's coming down for that matter. The DOWNs spend a lot of time taking the UPs out to lunch, to dinner, to explain their DOWNness. The UPs listen attentively, often in amazement about the experiences of being a DOWN. They contrast one DOWN's experience with another DOWN's experience and at times don't worry to much about what the DOWN's are up to because the DOWNs really never get together. If they did, the UPs would have to shape up.

After a while, the DOWNs weary of talking to the UPs. They tire of explaining and justifying their DOWNness. They think, "If I have to explain my DOWNness one more time, I'll throw up." And so they form a process which they call "networking and support groups." This makes the UPs nervous. You know, three UPs is a board meeting; three Downs is a pre-revolutionary activity.

Some UPs hire DOWNs, dress them up, and then send them down to see what the DOWNs are up to. We sometimes call this "affirmative action" or in our business, "advisory groups or task forces." This creates a serious problem for the DOWN. That DOWN doesn't know whether he or she is an UP or a DOWN. That's why DOWNs in the middle often burn out.

The UPs think they are really trying to understand DOWNness. Of course, the UPs never have to explain their UPness—that's why they are UPs rather than DOWNs.

There is good news and bad news in this parable. The good news is we are all both UPs and DOWNs. The bad news is that when we're UP we are often stupid. That is not because UPs are not smart. It's that UPs don't have to pay attention to DOWNs the way DOWNs have to pay attention to UPs. DOWNs always have to figure out what UPs are up to. But, the only time UPs worry about DOWNs is when DOWNs get uppity.

I used to think that when a DOWN became an UP he or she would carry over the insights gained from being a DOWN. Not so.

Who often has more insights about how society functions, how organizations function, about what's really going on? Frequently, it is the DOWNs not the UPs. UPs are too busy trying to maintain the system, to generate insight into what's really going on or how to change it. So our source of insightful information comes from DOWNs, not from UPs. Yet it is the UPs we often call leaders.

Leadership is not magic. The best leadership is the empowering of people to engage with their world. It is crossing the UP/DOWN lines to understand and act together. Leadership is less command over others than it is service with others.

Few in the world have had to deal with more rapid changes as regulation has in the past decade. These days we are challenged with getting rid of the arbitrary UP/DOWN relationships based on traditional lines of authority. We need to find ways of standing side by side—with consumers, with advocacy groups, with the profession, with each other—so that we can eliminate the barriers to creating a new vision for the future.[87]

CHAPTER SEVEN
MODEL NURSING LAWS
AND REGULATIONS

One of the very real difficulties which we encounter in attempting to set up adequate laws is the fact that the practice of nursing is hard to define.

Elizabeth C. Burgess, 1936[1]

Early Models

THE IMPORTANCE OF model nursing laws and regulations had been recognized soon after the first such laws were enacted in the United States. For example, in 1912 Sophia Palmer, speaking in support of a committee of state board representatives, stated that the group could draft proposed laws and amendments that could then be used for guidance by the state associations.[2] In the report of the Committee on Legislation at the American Nurses Association (ANA) Convention in 1917, Chair Anna Jamme of California presented "Essential Points of Registration Laws." This may have been the first attempt at a model nurse practice act.[3] At a meeting of the ANA Board of Directors in 1936 a decision was made to develop "principles governing the provisions" to be written into the "ideal nurse practice act." This board decided that a review of all existing legislation "currently in effect" should be a part of the study. A report of the same meeting included the following statement: "All matters concerned with legislation affecting nurses or nursing are the primary concern of the ANA. All phases of legislation concerning nursing education are to be referred to the National League of Nursing Education (NLNE), as the Education Department of the ANA, for advice."[4] Following the action that established the NLNE as the ANA Education Department, the meetings and programs for representatives of boards of nursing became a part of this new structure. The board of nursing representatives had limited involvement regarding ANA activities related to legislation, efforts to define nursing, and the development of model nurse practice acts by other groups within the ANA. Also in 1936, in an article in the *American Journal of Nursing (AJN)*, George V. Fleckstein, former attorney general for New York, recommended that a model practice act be developed for use in establishing and amending the nursing practice acts in the states.[5]

The ANA Board of Directors had appointed a Committee to Outline a Definition of Nursing in 1932.[6] The work of this committee resulted in what are apparently the first definitions of professional nursing and the professional nurse developed by the ANA. The May 1937 issue of the *AJN* reported those definitions as follows:

Professional nursing is a blend of intellectual attainment, attitudes and manual skills based on principles of scientific medicine, acquired by means of a prescribed course in a school of nursing affiliated with a hospital, recognized for such purposes by the state and practiced in conjunction with curative or preventive medicine by an individual licensed to do so by the state.

A professional nurse, therefore, is one who had met all the legal requirements for registration in a state and who practices or holds a position by virtue of her professional knowledge and legal status.[7]

Sophia Palmer of New York, editor of the *American Journal*, wrote in 1913, "It is to be remembered that every law outlives its usefulness after a time and has to be amended in order that there may be progress."[8] At a meeting of the ANA Board of Directors in 1937 there was a report of a joint project between the ANA and the NLNE that describes the legislative program for the formulation of "principles of legislation affecting nurses and nursing which might be helpful to states in amending their nurse practice acts." This article also mentioned the development of a "Digest of the laws requiring the registration of nurses and attendants to include board rules."[9] In this quotation, "board rules" refers to the rules of state boards of nursing.

At a conference for the representatives from the boards of nursing in 1947, the group recommended "that the paper presented by Mrs. Freda Erhardt entitled 'Characteristics of a Good Nurse Practice Act' be made available to the ANA standing Committee on Legislation and that it be recommended for publication in the *AJN*."[10] The following year the ANA issued a revision of its *Nurse Practice Act Suggestions*. The publication included "Suggestions for Major Provisions to be Included in a Permissive Nurse Practice Act" and "Suggestions for Major Provisions to be Included in a Mandatory Nurse Practice Act." There was no mention as to which group within the ANA prepared this publication, although it is likely that it was done by the ANA Committee on Legislation not by the ANA Bureau of State Boards of Nurse Examiners, the organization for representatives of the boards. Whether or not these representatives either participated or commented is not known.[11]

The representatives of boards of nursing at their meetings each year heard papers on a variety of subjects related to their work. Committees within the group worked on projects to facilitate interstate mobility of nurses by developing greater uniformity within the state laws and the regulations of the boards. In 1973 Elaine F. Ellibee of Wisconsin, later the first president of the National Council of State Boards of Nursing, Inc. (NCSBN®), presented a paper entitled "The Philosophy and Purpose of Licensure." She began the paper by saying,

---

In our society today, where the focus appears to be so acutely centered on the rights of the individual, I believe that we, as members and employees of state boards of nursing, must look at the purpose of licensure, understand it, and wholeheartedly support its tenets.

She continued with definitions of law, reminding the reader of the role "custom" plays in creating and enforcing the law and the "police power" of the state in activities "where the life, morals, general welfare and the health of the people are involved." She also noted that recent developments had resulted in "limits on the police power as it comes into conflict with personal freedom and the right of privacy." She pointed out that the discretion of a licensing body to judge "moral fitness" of an applicant was becoming more narrow and that "it may become even narrower." Ellibee quoted Frank P. Grad of the Columbia Law School in relation to the purpose of a licensing law:

It protects the public against unfit and inept practitioners of professions or occupations affecting the public health and safety, and it permits various professions and trades to advance from a common set of minimum standards, so as to improve their rendition of services, thereby advancing both the public interest and the legitimate interest of the field.

Additionally, Ellibee discussed the philosophy of professional licensure that makes it different from the licensure of business or other occupations. To do so she examined the following considerations:

- The nature of the authority which licenses or authorizes action.
- The purpose sought to be accomplished by the licensing authority.
- The nature of the act to be performed.
- The character, training, and skill necessary for the proper performance of the act.

Ellibee continued with the following,

With that structure of philosophy, it would seem then that our purpose is, on the one hand, to secure for society the benefits which come from the services of a highly skilled group and, on the other hand, to protect society from those who are not highly skilled, yet profess to be, or from those who, being highly skilled, are nevertheless so unprincipled and void of integrity as to misuse their superior knowledge to the disadvantage of the people.

She concluded with,

The properly credentialed registered nurse should be the advocate of the consumer; the members of state boards of nursing, and we as employees of those boards, well recognizing the minimal levels of licensure, must be the advocates of protection for the public; there must be protection from the unskilled or the incompetent practitioner of nursing; our major concern cannot be the advancement of the uncredentialed individual.[12]

Another paper presented by Virginia C. Hall at the ANA Council of State Boards of Nursing Conference in 1975 was titled "The Legal Scope of Nursing Practice." She noted that, of the 51 jurisdictions included in a survey, 22 had amended the definition of nursing practice in the law within the past five years. Hall pointed out that the results of this activity were mixed. She recommended that each state that had not changed its law should examine and be clear as to the questions, "what does the present law say and not say" and "what would a proposed amendment do or not do for them," before going forward with any change because this amendment "is new and superficially sounds more modern." The paper includes the following ANA "model definition adopted some years ago":

The term "practice of professional nursing" means the performance, for compensation, of any acts in the observation, care and counsel of the ill, injured or infirm or in the maintenance of health or prevention of illness of others, or in the supervision and teaching of other personnel, or the administration of medications and treatments as prescribed by a licensed physician or a licensed dentist; requiring substantial specialized judgment and skill and based on knowledge and application of the principles of biological, physical and social science. The foregoing shall not be deemed to include acts of diagnosis or prescription of therapeutic or corrective measures.[13]

Hall pointed out that 39 states currently used all or parts of this definition in their nursing practice acts. (There are threads from this definition in existing laws in 2003.) She said that the first sentence could stand alone as the definition and the second as a prohibition. In the discussion of the definition, she said that its vagueness "permits an interpretation in accordance with the traditional concepts of nursing care which it no doubt was intended to encompass and nothing more." In discussing new definitions, Hall described both a total redefinition and a definition that retained all or parts of the old with the added permission to perform certain "additional acts." In relation to amendments regarding additional acts, Hall preferred those pertaining to acts that had achieved "recognition as proper by professional nursing and medical opinion." She said "It is self-executing and automatically puts the stamp of legality on acts which are considered by the relevant professions as proper, thus permitting the content of the legal scope of nursing practice to change as the profession itself changes." When she discussed a total redefinition, Hall cited the definitions of New York and others that followed its lead. Terms defined in New York included "diagnosing" and "treating" in relation to the "nursing regimen." "Medical and nursing regimen" and "medical diagnosis" and "diagnosis" were distinguished by definition in the New York law. The practice of professional nursing was then defined, in relevant part, as "diagnosing and treating human responses to actual or potential health problems…and executing medical regimens prescribed by a licensed or other wise legally authorized physician or dentist."[14]

Hall cited the new definition enacted in California as the most successful at the time. However, it too had problems because the "best part of the amendment is not the definition but the preamble," which described the intent of the legislation but did not have the force of law. Hall reported that this preamble recognized "the existence of overlapping functions between physicians and registered nurses" and stated that the legislative intent was to provide clear legal authority for these overlapping functions as well as "to permit additional sharing of functions within the organized health care systems which provide for collaboration between physicians and registered nurses." Hall ended the paper with a review of the beginning effort to regulate advanced nursing practice. She briefly discussed a review of medical practice acts and noted that a few states exempt nurses from the practice of medicine.[15]

ANA Model Nurse Practice Acts

The ANA published many model practice acts over the years, including 1976, 1978, 1980, 1981, 1990, and 1996. Sharon M. Weisenbeck and Patricia A. Calico, both of Kentucky, wrote in a 1991 publication about a model definition of nursing adopted by the ANA in 1955.[16] It has been difficult to determine what role, if any, the members of the ANA Council of State Boards of Nursing played in the development of these publications prior to 1980. However, in the minutes of the Executive Committee of the ANA Council in March 1976, there is a report of a request from the ANA Congress on Nursing Practice to review and comment on the definitions of the practice of nursing and the definition of the practice of practical/vocational nursing to be included in the revision of the model nurse practice act.[17] Corinne Dorsey of Virginia, director of a school of practical nursing while serving as a member of the Virginia Board of Nursing, recalled that she was asked to review and comment on the practical nursing definition by the executive secretary of the Virginia Board during the middle of the 1970s. At a subsequent Executive Committee meeting in 1976, Anna Kuba, coordinator of the ANA Council, reported that the 1976 revision of the model nurse practice act was mailed to the state boards of nursing on August 12, 1976.[18]

In 1978 the ANA Congress of Nursing Practice appointed the Ad Hoc Committee on Legal Aspects of Nursing Practice to examine the position statements and the 1976 model nurse practice act of the ANA relative to the current statutes and regulations of the states. Ruth Q. Seigler of South Carolina was listed as a representative to this committee from NCSBN. The result of the work of this group was *The Nursing Practice Act: Suggested State Legislation*, published in 1980.[19]

The ANA published a revised *Model Nurse Practice Act* in May 1996. It was developed under the direction of the ANA Congress of Nursing Practice. The publication acknowledges the information received from the ANA Ad Hoc Committee on Credentialing of Advanced Practice. The extent of the involvement of NCSBN in the development of the model was limited to its representation on the ad hoc committee. Most of the model is consistent with many state statutes and there is some consistency with the *NCSBN Model Nursing Practice Act* (*MNPA*). The introduction focused on the changes in nursing practices, particularly advanced nursing practice, and the inconsistencies in state regulation of advanced practice. Several statements about boards of nursing and the various laws that govern these agencies were general and did not apply to every board. Examples of such statements include the following:

- "The disciplinary sections of existing practice acts are not comprehensive and do not cover all activities/known deficiencies in nursing practice."

- "Statutes dedicate seats [on boards of nursing] to specific specialties or classes of nurses....Instead of periodic review and adjustment or board compositions, seats are added as groups request representation."

- "By focusing solely on discipline and licensure, boards of nursing tend to avoid the larger issue of institutional infringement on nursing practice...and, by ignoring existing practice setting structures, boards all too often inappropriately use their existing power only to sanction nurses who cannot control the work setting or the staff utilized."[20]

In the section of the model that discussed the major provisions, there was mention that previous ANA models "only regulated registered nurse practice," when in fact the regulation of licensed practical/vocational nurses (LPN/VNs) was included in previous models. Advanced nursing practice was included under the definition of nursing practice, not as a level of practice requiring separate licensure, as set forth in the *MNPA*. The discussion on what was referred to as "certification of schools of nursing" stated that the "ANA believes the profession should regulate education." The model removed authority from the board of nursing to certify schools of nursing. The ANA model had a section on Reciprocity and Endorsement, despite the fact that the term reciprocity has rarely been used in statutes and regulations in the past 25 or more years. The last section of the model, Legislative Issues of Concern When Drafting Practice Acts, calls attention to other state statutes as well as federal law that may impact the practice of nursing.[21]

At a meeting in June 1997 the NCSBN Board of Directors discussed the possibility of a joint approach to a model nursing practice act by NCSBN and the ANA.[22] In August NCSBN staff reported to the board that the ANA Board of Directors had endorsed collaboration with NCSBN on a model. An initial meeting was scheduled to be held on October 9 of that year.[23] At the November meeting of the board of directors, there was a discussion of an agenda item titled "Model Nursing Practice Act Collaboration." Doris Nay, assistant executive director, reported on the initial meeting with representatives from the ANA to discuss possible collaboration on the development of a model nursing practice act. Areas for future discussion were identified.[24] However, a search of subsequent NCSBN Minutes and other papers failed to locate further reference to the topic or any subsequent meetings. In a telephone conversation between Corinne Dorsey and Doris Nay in December 2006, Nay confirmed that no further effort at this collaboration occurred. Her recollection was that the ANA decided not to pursue the collaborative effort. At the November 1998 meeting the board of directors reviewed the NCSBN Operational Plan for FY99, and adopted a motion that read,

Pending the outcome of discussion between NCSBN and the ANA staff regarding the need to delay the joint work on a model nursing practice act, this tactic [related to the collaborative project] and associated funding will be deleted from the organization's work plan.[25]

ANA Study of Credentialing in Nursing

At the meeting of the ANA Council of State Boards of Nursing in 1977, the group heard a report on the ongoing "Study of Credentialing in Nursing," presented by Dr. Inez Hinsvark, project director for the study. Hinsvark described the background work that led to the contract between the ANA and the University of Wisconsin-Milwaukee, School of Nursing to conduct the study. She discussed the most generally recognized credentialing mechanisms: accreditation, certification, and licensure, as well as "more subtle types of credentialing." The latter included registration, degree designation, and approval. She commented that approval could "have very strong to very weak meaning depending on who is doing the approving and what standards the approval is based upon." In the study approval meant "the recognition status of an agency or institution for a particular function."[26]

Hinsvark said that "in spite of the understood need for planning, in 1975 the ANA implemented a mechanism for accrediting programs for the preparation of nurses functioning in expanded roles and for maintenance of competency." At the same time, she reported, the National League for Nursing (NLN) Board of Directors agreed to set a goal to continue to develop accreditation criteria to evaluate continuing education offerings sponsored by nursing schools and nursing service agencies. Hinsvark concluded this section by saying "These actions show the overt divisiveness of the twin organizations which in 1952 were created to solve nursing problems, and to involve the community, while maintaining professional autonomy in matters where it was appropriate." She stated that further problems resulted when specialty organizations set up their own credentialing programs. Hinsvark suggested that the ANA Council should participate in the study. Marianna Bacigalupo of New Jersey, Margaret Rowland of Texas-RN, and Elaine Laeger of Arizona, members of the ANA Council of State Boards of Nursing, attended the meeting of the cooperating groups in September 1977. The ANA Committee to Study Credentialing in Nursing (Study Committee) agreed upon and the ANA approved of the following goals:

- To assess current credentialing mechanisms in nursing including accreditation, certification, and licensure.
- To suggest ways for increasing the effectiveness of credentialing.
- To recommend future directions for credentialing in nursing.

The definition of credentialing for this study was stated as:

---

the range of mechanisms assessing the performance of individuals or agencies. Agencies can be further divided into nursing service and nursing education; credentialing mechanisms under these three subcategories—individual, nursing service, nursing education—can be either governmental or non governmental.

Following Hinsvark's presentation, the ANA Council of State Boards of Nursing voted to authorize the Executive Committee to act on behalf of the council as a cooperating agency in the "Study of Credentialing in Nursing."[27] A report of the work of the Study Committee is discussed later in this chapter.

Standards and Definitions

The foregoing discussion of the activities related to the laws, regulations, and studies that occurred among several groups other than NCSBN is presented to provide a limited overview of the status of efforts to establish model language for laws and regulations related to nursing licensure, education, and practice. When the NCSBN Delegate Assembly adopted its original bylaws in 1978, it accepted the following objectives pertinent to laws and regulations:

- Identify and promote desirable and reasonable uniformity in standards and expected outcomes in nursing education and nursing practice.

- Identify, explore, and take positions on trends and issues affecting nursing education and nursing practice.

- Identify and assist in efforts to promote the continued competence of practitioners of nursing.[28]

The Standards Committee was originally established by the NCSBN Board of Directors as a special committee in 1978. It became a standing committee with an amendment to the bylaws in 1979 and the name was changed to the Nursing Practice and Standards (NP&S) Committee. The duties of this committee included the following:

- To propose and periodically review model statutory definitions of professional and practical nursing practice.

- To propose and periodically review model laws pertaining to nursing practice and standards, licensure, license renewal, disciplinary actions, approval of nursing education programs, and any other matter which comes under the legal purview of member boards.

- To prepare written information about standards of nursing practice and nursing education to the extent that these matters relate to the legal definitions of nursing practice for dissemination to member boards and other interested parties.[29]

The week following the decision by the ANA Council of State Boards of Nursing to establish NCSBN as a free-standing organization, the ANA convened in Hawaii from June 9 to 14, 1978. The action of the ANA Council of State Boards of Nursing had raised questions and a special forum was held to discuss, with the NCSBN officials present, the reasons for the formation of the new organization and its plans. The ANA House of Delegates adopted the following resolution:

WHEREAS, the existing ANA Council of State Boards of Nursing has voted to separate from ANA and to form an independent association of State Boards of Nursing, and

WHEREAS, the ANA House of Delegates recognizes the right of any group to organize for any purpose it so desires, and

WHEREAS, the ANA House of Delegates believes that the national professional nursing organization <u>must</u> maintain an organizational structure concerned with the administration and implementation of state laws pertaining to licensure, nursing education and nursing practice which safeguards the health and welfare of the public.

THEREFORE, BE IT RESOLVED, that this 1978 ANA House of Delegates reaffirm the 1976 ANA House of Delegates mandate that the ANA Council of State Boards be maintained as set forth in Article 10 of the Bylaws, and

BE IT FURTHER RESOLVED, that in view of the establishment of an independent association of Council of State Boards of Nursing, the ANA Board of Directors take all necessary steps to assure that this new independent organization or any other similar organizations, *do not usurp the authority and responsibility of ANA to establish and implement standards relating to state laws pertaining to licensure, nursing education and nursing practice which safeguards the health and welfare of the public.* [Emphasis added].[30]

The ANA House of Delegates agreed to a related motion to develop a liaison between the ANA and the new organization "for the purpose of communicating the standards and positions relating to nursing appropriately developed by this professional association."[31]

The delegates at the final meeting of the ANA Council of State Boards of Nursing who agreed to establish an organization with a membership comprising agencies of state government accepted the responsibility of developing model laws and regulations when they adopted their bylaws. The NCSBN Board of Directors, in July 1978, appointed Marian Klappmeier of Maine as chair of the Committee on Standards.[32] However, she was unable to serve and Eleanor Smith of Virginia was appointed in September.[33] Smith had to resign due to other responsibilities, and in January 1979 Thelma Cleveland of Washington-RN was named chair.[34] The report of the Area III meeting held in the fall of 1978 included an expression of concern that focused on the urgent need for the Committee on Standards to attempt to coordinate the efforts of the various groups working on standards. Ruth Seigler of South Carolina, director-at-large, suggested "that the Committee design a blueprint utilizing the expertise of appropriate groups to develop a commonly accepted definition of nursing."[35] At the June 1979 meeting of the board of directors Chair Cleveland presented the first draft of a paper titled "The Differences Between Legal and Professional Definitions of Nursing," which provided the statutory definition of the licensed professional nurse and the statutory definition of the "associate level of nursing practice."[36] This draft was included in the report to the delegate assembly in 1979, except the model definitions presented were of "professional and practical nursing" and did not use the term "associate level," included in the earlier report.[37]

At this same meeting, Margretta Styles from the ANA Committee to Study Credentialing in Nursing presented a summary of the committee's report entitled "The Study of Credentialing in Nursing." The delegate assembly adopted a motion that asked the newly renamed NP&S Committee "to review the Credentialing Report with regard to the recommendation that the 'professional society develop a definition of practice.'"[38]

The following statement was included in the 1980 Report of the Nursing Practice and Standards Committee:

It is commonly recognized that the chief responsibility of Boards of Nursing is to regulate the practice of nursing within the respective states so that the public health, safety and welfare of the people are safeguarded. In order to accomplish this, the practice of nursing must be defined. All other parts of a practice act, such as the requirements for licensure, standards of preparation and practice, and grounds for disciplinary action evolve from this definition.[39]

A fifth working draft of "The Difference Between Statutory and Professional Definitions of Nursing Practice," dated March 4, 1980, stated that the NP&S Committee had concluded that definitions of professional and statutory nursing both exist and "that they do, indeed, differ." The name of this paper had changed as the drafts were revised to use the word "statutory" in place of "legal." "The Study of Credentialing in Nursing" of the ANA recommended that "a generally accepted definition of nursing," developed by the professional society, be used by credentialing agencies including those that license nurses. The study made no reference to different definitions and recommended that a single definition be used by all. Other references argued that statutory and professional definitions should differ because of their nature. In the United States Department of Health, Education and Welfare report about health manpower credentialing, licensure was defined as:

---

the process by which an agency of government grants permission to an individual to engage in a given occupation upon finding that the applicant has attained the minimal degree of competency to insure that the public health, safety and welfare will be reasonably well protected.

The NP&S Committee concluded that the phrase beginning "minimal degree of competency" pertained to a statutory definition of nursing but not a professional definition. The committee stated that the distinction between the two types of definitions was apparent when comparing the origins of the definitions, purposes of the definitions, content of the definitions, and implications of the definitions. The report concluded with the following table:

	Statutory Definitions	**Professional Definitions**
Origin	State government based on input from the public, professional organizations, and case law.	Individual professional nurses and professional organizations with or without consultation from inside or outside the profession.
Content	Establishes the essential and current functions of nursing practice.	Describes the nature of nursing in terms of optimum functions that meet perceived and anticipated societal needs.
Purpose	To delineate and establish the independent and accountable practice of nursing, to assure the public of safe and effective nursing care, to prohibit the practice of unqualified and incompetent persons, and to serve as a basis for establishing essential standards of nursing education.	To gain consensus within the profession as to the nature of nursing and its various components and levels, to communicate nursing's purpose and social significance, and to serve as a basis for promoting ethical and optimal standards of practice and education.
Implications	Failure to act in accordance with the essential scope of nursing practice or functioning beyond the defined scope of practice may result in disciplinary actions.	Failure to practice within the description and standards of nursing practice may affect employment opportunities, professional recognition and professional status.[40]

In her report to the delegate assembly of NCSBN in June 1980, Chair Cleveland discussed the major areas of the NP&S Committee's work during the past year. The listing included the following:

- Delineation of the difference between statutory and professional definitions of nursing practice.

- Development of a statutory definition of nursing practice.

- Development of guidelines for assisting jurisdictions undertaking statutory changes in their nursing practice acts.

- Development of an outline of essential content for a model nursing practice act.

- A recommendation to the 1980 delegate assembly concerning the report of the Credentialing Study that called for the development of a definition of nursing practice by the professional society (ANA).

The NP&S Committee conducted a forum at the annual meeting to discuss positions on the differences between professional and statutory definitions of nursing practice and the recommendations from the committee as to who should develop definitions of nursing practice.[41]

Seigler, who had been appointed to the ANA Ad Hoc Committee on Legal Aspects of Nursing, reported to the delegate assembly on the activities of that committee, including the publication of *The Nursing Practice Act: Suggested State Legislation* in 1980.[42]

Writing about the original *MNPA*, Weisenbeck and Calico stated that the United States Department of Health, Education and Welfare's 1977 definition of licensure was the basis for the work of the NP&S Committee. They discussed professional and legal definitions of nursing as follows:

As an organized profession, nursing has a responsibility to define nursing to adequately describe the nature and components of the occupation. To define the occupational practice, the nursing profession must interact with the public to meet the needs of the public. Although a professional definition of nursing should originate from professionals and evolve with the practice as needed, a legal definition is influenced by (1) case law, (2) interpretation within the context of the existing nursing practice act, and (3) a determination of whether certain actions fall within the bounds of the legal definition. A legal definition is static and is limited to what is necessary or indispensable. The professional definition, however, should assure advancement, flexibility, and growth, and should outline the scope of nursing practice and communicate nursing's purpose and social significance. The legal definition determines the basis for licensure, sets essential standards of nursing education practice, and prohibits or removes unqualified and incompetent persons from the nursing practice.

In its statement on "The scope of nursing practice" published in 1987, the ANA addresses professional and legal regulation of practice. The ANA states that there are "parallel relationships of the component parts of professional and legal regulations of nursing practice." Although the definitions differ in origin, purpose, content, and implications, they are related and interdependent in response to societal needs.[43]

Another reference that discussed the differing nature of statutory and professional regulation was a paper presented by Hildegard E. Peplau titled "Internal vs. External Regulation" to the Society of Clinical Specialists in Psychiatric Nursing at the New Jersey State Nurses Association Convention in October 1983. Peplau was a professor in the College of Nursing at Rutgers University. She said, "External regulation refers to control of a profession that arises from duly constituted authority that lies outside the profession." She enumerated sources of external regulation including federal agencies such as the Food and Drug Administration and the Department of Health, Education and Welfare and described the state boards of nursing as having "even larger and often more compelling regulatory power over nursing." Peplau stated that internal regulation "refers to self-governance of nurses by nurses within the profession." This self-regulation, she argued, takes place on several levels, including personal, work site, sites where health care and education take place, and state and national nursing organizations. She continued with a discussion of the roles of these entities and concluded with a discussion of a balance between internal and external regulation. She said,

Balance of powers of government and of the professions rests on clearly understood jurisdictions of each party. Certainly the public must be protected, but not only the law and the boards of nursing have that aim – the nursing profession shares it.

Finally she expressed concern about the trend for nurses to turn more toward external regulation for titles and certification "instead of to ANA to credential them beyond the basic license." The paper also included the following table, which was titled "Characteristics of Regulation of the Profession":

Internal Regulation (within profession)	External Regulation (outside profession)
Purpose: To ensure advancement of nursing while serving the public interest.	Purpose: To protect the public.
Dependent upon self-discipline and peer evaluation	Dependent on surveillance, complaints and reports of others, investigation, and court action
Compliance is voluntary	Compliance is mandatory
Penalties of non-compliance are - professional censure - withdrawal of credentials such as certification and accreditation - disciplinary actions including recommendations for investigation to the board of nursing	Penalties of non-compliance are - dismissal from employment - loss of license - court judgments such as, imprisonment etc.
Standards and criterion measures are developed and revised by changing groups of selected and elected nurses from within the profession.	The profession's standards and recommended nominees for appointment to Boards of Nursing and other agencies may or may not be used in establishing rules and regulations and Board appointments. - Board appointments tend to be political - Board selects and adopts standards
The expertise and critique of a larger number of nurses provides broader input to development and review of self-regulatory measures and procedures.	Statutes define qualifications at a minimum level—higher and broader expertise in selecting Board members being at the pleasure of the governor, critique and final approval by the attorney general.[44]*

*Note: the reference to final approval by the attorney general was not the case in all jurisdictions. Peplau was speaking to nurses in New Jersey.

In October 1981 Barbara Nichols, president of the ANA, directed a memorandum to the presidents and executive directors of the state nurses associations, executive directors of the state boards of nursing, and various units of the ANA. A report titled "Legal Regulation of Nursing" was attached to the memorandum. The report was prepared by Frances I. Waddle, coordinator for Ethical and Legal Aspects of Nursing Practice of the ANA. Nichols noted that the report should be considered with two ANA publications as references: *The Nursing Practice Act: Suggested State Legislation and Nursing: A Social Policy Statement*. Waddle had been executive officer of the Oklahoma Board of Nursing and an active member of the ANA Council of State Boards of Nursing prior to her employment with the ANA. She had served on the Ad Hoc Committee on the Organization of the Council in 1976 that made the initial recommendation that began the process to establish a free-standing organization for the boards of nursing. In her report, Waddle cited several areas that had implications for legal regulation, including changes to the state nursing practice acts, changes in the organization of state government, and sunset laws requiring evaluation of state boards of nursing. In her introduction Waddle said, "One of the functions of a profession is the credentialing of individuals, educational programs and organized services the profession judges qualified to provide such services." She also said that the support for legal regulation through the state practice act is a component of credentialing and that legal regulation allows the applicant to show that minimum competence needed for the protection of public health, safety, and welfare has been attained. She added, "It is the function of the profession to establish the scope of practice and desirable qualifications for each area of practice and to upgrade practice beyond the minimum qualifications established for licensure."[45]

Waddle continued by addressing the purpose of the paper: "To identify for the ANA Board of Directors, trends and issues in the legal regulation of nursing practice and the profession's responsibility to protect

the legal regulation of nursing practice in the various jurisdictions." Waddle discussed recent changes in the state nursing practice acts with emphasis on the inclusion of either "additional acts" clauses or new definitions. She also stated that the 1976 ANA model nurse practice act was widely circulated but never released as a publication. However, it did include an additional acts clause in the definition of practice by a registered nurse (RN). A considerable portion of the paper related to how states have addressed advanced practice. She highlighted the 1971 change in the Idaho nursing practice act that authorized nurses to "diagnose and treat patients under rules and regulations jointly promulgated" by the state boards of nursing and medicine and implemented by the board of nursing.[46]

Waddle examined the inclusion, in either law or regulation in the various states, of a requirement or acceptance of professional certification as a basis for recognition of advanced practice. Another topic discussed was that of sunset laws. Waddle said, "The idea behind such laws is that all government programs and agencies should undergo periodic review. And those that are no longer needed or are not living up to expectations should be abolished or modified. By 1981, 36 states had enacted such laws. All boards of nursing that had been reviewed were recreated. The board of nursing in New Hampshire was under review and was subsequently recreated by the legislature there in 1982. Another area of discussion in the report was that of board composition. Waddle addressed the increasing number of boards with public members and the addition of LPN/VNs, and reported that a few boards still had positions for physicians and hospital administrators. She also reported that 30 boards of nursing were housed in another department or agency rather than being independent. The report also cited several examples of the use of legislation and regulation to deal with recent issues such as the nursing shortage. For example, Arkansas adopted rules to allow nurses licensed in other countries to be licensed in the state without examination, Texas had a proposed rule to license nurses educated in other selected countries without examination, and California proposed rules to allow the work permit to be extended up to two years for persons failing the state board examination. Waddle concluded with the following:

> In view of the present climate and the significant factors identified in the report, it is imperative that ANA and constituent associations evaluate carefully any proposed amendments to the nursing practice act at this time and that efforts be directed to protecting and enhancing the practice of nursing.[47]

NCSBN Model Nursing Practice Act

A definition of a model act was found in a 1979 publication of the Council of State Government and was reprinted by NCSBN in 1982:

> [A model act is] a piece of legislation which seeks to address, in comprehensive fashion, a determined need. Model bills are often reform legislation intended to provide order in an area where existing legislation is out of date, internally inconsistent, too broad and too narrow, or for some reason inadequate to implement current state policy.[48]

In 1981 the NP&S Committee worked through a fourth draft of the proposed model nursing practice act (*MNPA*) and included a recommendation for its adoption by the delegate assembly in the report presented by Chair Cleveland at the annual meeting.[49] The following actions related to the proposed *MNPA* were taken by the delegates:

- To recognize and endorse the committee's continuing effort to produce an MNPA that reflects a relative consensus of the member boards by the end of the 1982 delegate assembly meeting in order to protect public health, safety, and welfare and to fulfill its obligation under the W. K. Kellogg Foundation grant.

- To accept the organizational structure of the proposed MNPA.

- To support the continued work of the committee within the organizational structure in the development of rules to complement the proposed MNPA.

- To ask member boards to submit written comments to the committee regarding those articles and sections that they support, as well as those about which they recommend change by October 1, 1981.

- To take action on the proposed MNPA at the 1982 meeting of the delegate assembly.[50]

The NCSBN Board of Directors decided in March 1982 to distribute the Working Draft #5 of the proposed MNPA to the member boards with a request for thorough study in preparation for the meeting of the delegate assembly.[51] A report of the NCSBN-ANA Liaison Committee in the 1982 *NCSBN Book of Reports* described the discussion by this committee of the draft MNPA. The NCSBN representatives Joyce Schowalter of Minnesota, Nancy Dean of Georgia-RN, and Merlyn Maillian of Louisiana-RN met with the ANA representatives in 1981 in Kansas City. The ANA representatives expressed concern about the proposal and indicated a desire to articulate standards from a single point of view. The ANA representatives also questioned the need for both a professional and legal definition.[52]

The views of the ANA representatives were not consistent with those of the NP&S Committee or the member boards when the NCSBN Delegate Assembly gathered in Boston in 1982 to consider and act on the proposed MNPA. In her report to the delegates Chair Cleveland recommended that the delegates adopt the proposed model as presented in the *NCSBN Book of Reports*. Highlights from the introduction to the model reported there are important to the action taken. The NP&S Committee was charged in the bylaws to propose and periodically review model statutory definitions of professional and practical nursing and to propose and periodically review model laws pertaining to matters under the legal purview of the member boards. The introduction includes the reminder that financial support for this activity was included in the grant obtained by NCSBN from the W. K. Kellogg Foundation. The committee referenced the issue of models developed by professional associations and models from organizations of regulatory boards such as the ANA and NCSBN respectively: "A model act developed by the NCSBN may be especially helpful since it reflects the combined experiences of persons closely associated with the regulation of nursing practice, i.e., members and executive staff of boards of nursing." There is also reference to the need for some uniformity in laws among the states "to insure a common understanding throughout the country of what constitutes the legally recognized profession of nursing and its practice." The uniformity was also important in facilitating the mobility of nurses. The introduction emphasized the importance of the definition of nursing practice as the basis for everything else in the model. The 1982 MNPA was comprehensive. There was emphasis on the fact that each state would amend its laws consistent with the individual state public protection statutes and the model was considered as a guide. Nurses, board of nursing members, and staff were reminded to look beyond the section of state law known as the nursing practice act for sections of law applicable to the regulation of nursing including, but not limited to, administrative procedures acts, freedom of information acts, privacy acts, and medical or pharmacy acts.[53]

The delegates discussed, amended, and adopted the *MNPA*. The amendments were not extensive, but important. Two of these responded to concerns raised by nursing organizations at earlier meetings and during discussion on the motion to adopt the *MNPA*. The first of these was to substitute the word "approval" for "accreditation," as it applied to educational programs throughout the document. The second was to delete the definition of "specialist" and any other reference to "specialists." The delegates also voted to delete from the Comments section the following statement: "The titles, Licensed Nurse and Licensed Affiliate Nurse are suggested as possible substitutions for the Registered Nurse and the Licensed Practical Nurse titles, respectively." The evolution of definitions of nursing can be found in Appendix D, but because the definition of practice clearly must be the basis for the other sections of a practice act, only the definitions of "Nursing," "RN" and "LPN/VN" are included there. The entire model practice act as adopted in 1982 was an early publication by NCSBN. The introduction to the *MNPA* concluded with a listing of the members who worked on the project for three and one-half years:

Thelma Cleveland, Washington-RN, chair	1979–1982
Rebecca Eden, Ohio	1979–1980
Ruth Elliott, Tennessee	1980–1982
Anne Kellett, New Jersey	1979–1981
Albert Kelm, Wisconsin	1978–1980
Ruth McMahan, Alaska	1978–1980
Margaret Pavelka, Nebraska	1978–1982
Arlene Sergeant, Oregon	1980–1981
Mary Shilling, South Carolina	1978–1982
Therese Sullivan, Montana	1981–1982

These representatives of the NCSBN member boards worked together to accomplish an early milestone for the organization. In 1982 the delegate assembly adopted the *MNPA* as amended. In other action, the delegates accepted a proposed NCSBN model nursing rules and regulations (MNRR) for study by the member boards with suggestions for revisions to be submitted to the NP&S Committee by October 1, 1982.[54] At the June 1982 meeting of the board of directors, the board authorized the NP&S Committee to conduct a workshop for representatives of the member boards during FY83 to assist them in using the *MNPA*.[55] Language from the *MNPA* was used by a number of states as their laws were revised or amended after 1982. In a 1983 article in *Issues*, Joan Bouchard, then executive director for the Wyoming Board of Nursing, described the process used to secure support for a major change in the Wyoming Nursing Practice Act based on the *MNPA*. She said, "Except for minor grammatical changes, the legislature signed into law a nursing practice act that was the same as the final proposal presented by the Board."[56]

NCSBN Model Nursing Rules and Regulations

In 1983, the board of directors heard a report from the Area IV director that representatives of member boards at the area meeting had raised questions regarding the appropriateness of NCSBN developing standards in the proposed MNRR. In response, the board of directors asked the staff to prepare information related to the difference between professional and legal standards in nursing practice and to circulate it to the member boards.[57]

Chair Therese Sullivan of Montana reported to the delegate assembly in 1984 and presented the statement on the NCSBN Model Legal Standards that had been developed by the NP&S Committee. The delegate assembly adopted the statement,[58] which was included in the *NCSBN Book of Reports*. It summarized the development of the *MNPA* and the MNRR, and stated questions that had been raised as to whether the development of model legal standards was an appropriate activity for NCSBN. The statement presented a distinction between legal and professional standards:

- Legal standards—reflect minimum criteria essential to safeguard the public health, safety, and welfare and must be written in specific language to be enforceable.

- Professional standards—encompass more than essential, minimum criteria, are designed to reflect standards of excellence, and are written in more general language. In addition, these standards, written by a professional association, are generally not legally enforceable.

The statement concluded by citing the case *Tuma v. Board of Nursing*, 100 Idaho 74, 593 P.2nd 711 (1979), where Idaho statute provided that unprofessional conduct was grounds for disciplinary action.

There were no legal standards to determine what constituted unprofessional conduct. Therefore, the disciplinary action taken by the Idaho Board of Nursing was reversed by the Idaho Supreme Court. NCSBN concluded that it was appropriate for boards of nursing to develop legal standards for practice and that it would continue to assist the member boards in this effort.[59]

In the report of the NP&S Committee presented to the delegate assembly in 1983, Chair Sullivan stated that the committee had completed work on the MNRR and was working on a position paper on the regulation of advanced nursing practice and another on continued competence, as requested by the board of directors, to include the documentation of current regulatory practices.[60] She presented the MNRR, based on the *MNPA*, and developed as a guide for member boards to use in revising their rules and regulations. The delegate assembly discussed and amended, largely for clarity, the proposed model. The delegates then adopted the *NCSBN Model Nursing Rules and Regulations* (*MNRR*),[61] which was published by NCSBN. Again, because of the importance of this document to the member boards and as an accomplishment of NCSBN at the end of its first five years of existence, the enumeration of the standards of nursing practice for the RN and for the LPN/VN have been included here:

Standards Related to the Registered Nurse's Responsibility to Apply the Nursing Process

The Registered Nurse shall:
1. Conduct and document nursing assessments of the health status of individuals and groups by:
    A. Collecting objective and subjective data from observations, examinations, interviews, written records in an accurate and timely manner. The data includes but is not limited to:
        1) Biophysical and emotional status;
        2) Growth and development;
        3) Cultural, religious and socio-economic background;
        4) Family health history
        5) Information collected by other health team members;
        6) Client knowledge and perception about health status and potential, or maintaining health status;
        7) Ability to perform activities of daily living;
        8) Patterns of coping and interacting;
        9) Consideration of client's health goals;
        10) Environmental factors; and
        11) Available and accessible human and material resources.
    B. Sorting, selecting, reporting and recording the data.
    C. Validating, refining and modifying the data by utilizing available resources including interactions with the client, family, significant others, and health team members.
2. Establish and document nursing diagnoses which serve as the basis for the strategy of care.
3. Develop the strategy of care based on assessment and nursing diagnosis. This includes:
    A. Identifying priorities in the strategy of care.
    B. Setting realistic and measurable goals to implement the strategy of care.
    C. Prescribing nursing intervention(s) based on the nursing diagnosis.
    D. Identifying measures to maintain comfort, to support human functions and responses, to maintain an environment conductive to well being, and to provide health, teaching and counseling.
4. Implement the strategy of care by:
    A. Initiating nursing interventions through:
        1) Giving direct care.
        2) Assisting with care.
        3) Delegating care.
    B. Providing an environment conducive to safety and health.

    C. Documenting nursing interventions and responses to care.

    D. Communicating nursing interventions and responses to care to other members of the health team.

5. Evaluate the responses of individuals or groups to nursing interventions. Evaluation shall involve the client, family, significant others and health team members.

    A. Evaluation data shall be documented and communicated to appropriate members of the health care team.

    B. Evaluation data shall be used as a basis for reassessing client health status, modifying nursing diagnoses, revising strategies of care, and prescribing changes in nursing interventions.

Standards Related to the Registered Nurse's Responsibilities as a Member of the Nursing Profession

The Registered Nurse shall:

1. Have knowledge of the statutes and regulations governing nursing and function within the legal boundaries of nursing practice.
2. Accept responsibility for individual nursing actions and competency.
3. Obtain instruction and supervision as necessary when implementing nursing techniques or practices.
4. Function as a member of the health team.
5. Collaborate with other members of the health team to provide optimum patient care.
6. Consult with nurses and other health team members and make referrals as necessary.
7. Contribute to the formulation, interpretation, implementation and evaluation of the objectives and policies related to nursing practice within the employment setting.
8. Participate in the evaluation of nursing through peer review.
9. Report unsafe nursing practice to the Board and unsafe practice conditions to recognized legal authorities.
10. Delegate to another only those nursing measures which that person is prepared or qualified to perform.
11. Supervise others to whom nursing interventions are delegated.
12. Retain professional accountability for nursing care when delegating nursing interventions.
13. Conduct practice without discrimination on the basis of age, race, religion, sex, sexual preference, national origin or handicap.
14. Respect the dignity and rights of clients regardless of social or economic status, personal attributes or nature of health problems.
15. Respect the client's right to privacy by protecting confidential information unless obligated by law to disclose the information.
16. Respect the property of clients, family, significant others and the employer.

Standards Related to the Licensed Practical Nurse's Contribution to the Nursing Process

The Licensed Practical Nurse shall:

1. Contribute to the nursing assessment by:

    A. Collecting, reporting and recording objective and subjective data in an accurate and timely manner. Data Collection includes:

        1) Observation about the condition or change in condition of the client.

        2) Signs and symptoms of deviation from normal health status.

2. Participate in the development of the strategy of care by:

    A. Providing data.

    B. Contributing to the identification of priorities.

    C. Contributing to setting realistic and measurable goals.

    D. Assisting in the identification of measures to maintain comfort, support human functions and responses, maintain an environment conducive to well being, and provide health teaching and counseling.

3. Participate in the implementation of strategy of care by:
    A. Providing care for clients whose conditions are stabilized or predictable.
    B. Providing care for clients whose conditions are critical and/or fluctuating under the direction and supervision of the Registered Nurse, licensed physician or dentist.
    C. Providing an environment conducive to safety and health.
    D. Documenting nursing interventions and responses to care.
    E. Communicating nursing interventions and responses to care to appropriate members of the health team.
4. Contribute to the evaluation of the responses of individuals or groups to nursing interventions.
    A. Evaluation data shall be documented and communicated to appropriate members of the health care team.
    B. The Licensed Practical Nurse shall contribute to the modification of the strategy of care on the basis of the evaluation.

Standards Relating to the Licensed Practical Nurse's Responsibilities as a Member of the Health Team

The Licensed Practical Nurse shall:
1. Have knowledge of the statutes and regulations governing nursing and function within the legal boundaries of practical nursing practice.
2. Accept responsibility for individual nursing actions and competency.
3. Function at the direction of a Registered Nurse, physician or dentist.
4. Consult with Registered Nurses and/or other health team members and seek guidance as necessary.
5. Obtain instruction and supervision as necessary when implementing nursing techniques or practices.
6. Function as a member of the health team.
7. Contribute to the formulation, interpretation, implementation, and evaluation of the objectives and policies related to practical nursing practice within the employment setting.
8. Participate in the evaluation of nursing through peer review.
9. Report unsafe nursing practice to the Board and unsafe practice conditions to recognized legal authorities.
10. Conduct practice without discrimination on the basis of age, race, religion, sex, sexual preference, national origin or handicap.
11. Respect the dignity and rights of clients regardless of social or economic status, personal attributes or nature of health problems.
12. Respect the client's right to privacy by protecting confidential information, unless obligated to disclose such information.
13. Respect the property of clients, family, significant others, and the employer.[62]

Regulation of Nursing Education

In 1986 the North Dakota Board of Nursing asked the NCSBN Board of Directors for an *amicus curiae* brief to be filed on its behalf in litigation in that state. The litigation resulted from changes in regulations by the North Dakota Board of Nursing that essentially required that the minimum educational preparation for practice as an RN was a baccalaureate degree and the minimum for practice as a LPN/VN was an associate degree.[63] At its next meeting, the board of directors was advised by Legal Counsel Thomas O'Brien that the North Dakota request constituted a broad policy issue, and the board of directors authorized him to prepare and file the brief on behalf of NCSBN in support of the North Dakota Board of Nursing with respect to the legal power of boards of nursing to establish standards for approval and accreditation of education programs in nursing.[64]

Chair Sullivan presented an extensive report to the delegate assembly in 1986. Two major accomplishments included were the work of the Entry Into Practice Report Committee (a special committee chaired by Elizabeth Willey of Utah) and the development of guidelines on entry into practice. The purpose of the guidelines was to provide assistance for member boards regarding regulatory changes for entry into nursing practice in jurisdictions where such changes were being considered. Lists of a number of definitions and premises were included and the guidelines addressed issuing licenses and titles, defining scope of practice, and approving and monitoring education programs and testing. The following recommendations were included:

- Boards of nursing should cooperate and collaborate in resolving related issues.

- It is inappropriate for boards of nursing at this time to support a change in titles.

- Boards of nursing should consider seriously supporting statutory change that provides for grandfather or waiver mechanisms.

- Boards of nursing should attempt to maintain consistency in regulatory matters affecting interstate mobility and national licensing examinations.

- Boards of nursing should seriously consider that any statutory change in the scope of nursing practice should be defined in general rather than specific terms in order to provide for a natural evolution of nursing practice.

- Boards of nursing should take steps to assure that within their purview are all nursing programs that prepare individuals to meet entry into nursing practice requirements.[65]

The delegate assembly adopted the guidelines as amended.[66] The Entry into Practice Report Committee presented a comprehensive report of its study. The report included two recommendations. One called for NCSBN to monitor activities of state RN and LPN/VN associations related to entry level. The second called for NCSBN to take a formal position, either of neutrality, support, or non-support on proposed changes in educational preparation for entry into practice.[67] The delegates considered and adopted a resolution submitted by the Utah Board of Nursing and cosponsored by the Arizona, California-VN, Colorado, and Washington-RN boards. The resolution called for NCSBN to adopt a formal position of neutrality on changes in nursing educational requirement for entry into practice. It also stated that the resolution should be disseminated with its rationale to the nursing profession and that the NP&S Committee should monitor changes in states to report annually to the member boards.[68] The delegates received the final report of the research published by NCSBN as *The Study of Nursing Practice, Role Delineation and Job Analysis of Entry Level Performance of Registered Nurses*, and agreed that the study should be reviewed by the NP&S Committee to identify implications of the findings on the regulation of nursing.[69]

Changing Models of Nursing Education

The Subcommittee to Study the Regulatory Implications of Changing Models of Nursing Education, chaired by Sheila Exstrom of Nebraska, reported in 1991 that its work had focused on changing education models and how these changes might affect regulation. The conclusions reached by the subcommittee were the following:

1. Changes in nursing education are ongoing and reflect change in nursing practice, health care and public policy.

2. These changes have regulatory implications.

3. Multiple educational models exist for preparing nurses for licensure.

4. Currently regulatory criteria for licensure vary widely and may impede interstate mobility for some nurses.

5. Interstate mobility of nurses would be enhanced by more uniform licensure criteria.

The subcommittee recommended the following to the board of directors:

1. That the National Council review the Model Nurse Practice Act and Model Nursing Administrative Rules [*MNAR*, formerly *MNRR*] for possible revision based upon this study.

2. That the National Council refine and expand its licensure, nursing practice and education databases to enhance the Council's role as a clearing house for information regarding nursing regulation.

3. That the National Council determine the need to develop and distribute educational literature/ media regarding the difference between educational preparation and licensure.[70]

The Nursing Practice and Education (NP&E) Committee, formerly the NP&S Committee, finalized a paper entitled "Joint Statement on Maintaining Professional Legal Standards During a Shortage of Nursing Personnel" in 1992. The paper was prepared in collaboration with the ANA and the National Federation of Licensed Practical Nurses (NFLPN), and was part of the committee's report presented by Chair Thomas Neumann of Wisconsin. The following summary was provided:

The focus of this statement is to clarify the role of the regulatory mechanisms provided internally by the profession, and those provided externally by the state to assure public access to high quality nursing services. Further, the statement addresses the regulatory implications for nursing in labor market situations involving increased demands for nursing services and a resulting shortage of licensed nurses.

The paper looked at market forces and nursing services, regulatory implications, and professional and legal accountability for nursing practice. The conclusion of the paper stated:

The professional and regulatory communities renew their respective pledges to uphold existing professional and legal standards. Because the purpose of these standards is to protect the consumer of nursing services from unsafe and ineffective care, it is imperative that these standards and regulations be upheld and enforced at all times regardless of supply and demand issues. When ancillary personnel are used to assist in the delivery of nursing care, it is imperative, from both professional and regulatory perspectives, that such personnel be educated by and directly responsible to licensed nurses.

For these reasons, professional nursing will continue to: (1) closely monitor and address quality of care concerns through organizational and educational channels, and (2) promptly report violations of nurse practice acts to the state boards of nursing. State boards of nursing will continue to: (1) promulgate and enforce rules and regulations that protect the public from unsafe and ineffective nursing practice and (2) take corrective action against those individuals whose activities violate the respective state nurse practice acts. The American Nurses Association, the National Federation of Licensed Practical Nurses, Inc., and the National Council of State Boards of Nursing believe that such activities, which require a cooperative spirit between those who practice nursing and those who regulate it, are needed to maintain the public's trust, health, safety, and welfare during the current nursing shortage.[71]

The delegate assembly adopted the statement. In other action, the delegates directed the NP&E Committee to continue to monitor the member boards' position regarding entry into practice, but to report to the delegate assembly every two years instead of every year.[72]

Jan Zubieni of Colorado served as chair of the NP&E Committee in 1997 when the delegate assembly adopted a position paper developed by the Nursing Program Accreditation/Approval Subcommittee related to the use of the terms "approval" and "accreditation." The paper included the definitions of the two terms as stated in the *MNAR*:

Approval: Official recognition of nursing education programs which meet standards established by the board of nursing.

Accreditation: The official authorization or status granted by an agency other than a state board of nursing.

Member boards were urged to review their nurse practice acts and regulations for consistency.[73] The delegate assembly approved the position paper at its meeting in August. In addition, the delegates adopted a policy recommending that member boards conduct criminal background checks on applicants for licensure and that this action be incorporated into the uniform license requirements, the *MNPA* and the *MNAR*.[74]

Position Paper on Continued Competence

Sister Lucie Leonard of Louisiana-RN, a member of the NP&S Committee, presented a report to the 1985 delegate assembly regarding a position paper on competence. The purpose of the paper was to provide guidance to member boards that were considering the requirement of continued competence for license renewal, reinstatement, or endorsement. The definition included in the paper stated that continued competence encompasses the ongoing ability to render safe, direct nursing care or the ongoing ability to make sound judgment upon which that nursing care is based: "Competent behavior rests in the use of the scientific method from which the nursing process emanates." The paper concluded with the following:

Boards of Nursing have the responsibility to assure the health, safety, and welfare of the public by verifying that nurses practice competently. Although current research does not support any single method of ensuring continued competence, the Council recommends that individual Boards continue efforts to establish mechanisms that validate continued competence.

In so doing, each board of nursing should provide regulations that are based on the following principles:

- That evidence of current knowledge, skills and abilities be required after a significant period of absence from nursing practice; and
- That the mechanism be tied to the board's disciplinary process.[75]

The delegate assembly accepted the position paper on continued competence. In other action, the delegates adopted the following resolutions related to education for nursing:

RESOLVED: That the National Council of State Boards of Nursing provide a clearinghouse of information relative to individual state board positions and activities upgrading [their] nursing education requirements; and be it

FURTHUR RESOLVED: That the National Council of State Boards of Nursing periodically survey all states for information necessary to keep the clearinghouse of information as up to date as possible; and be it

FURTHER RESOLVED: That the National Council of State Boards of Nursing direct a committee of state board representatives to develop a report on entry into practice to be presented to the Delegate Assembly in 1986.[76]

At its meeting in 1987, the delegate assembly adopted a motion requiring NCSBN to explore mechanisms for identifying minimum levels of continued competence of licensed nurses and methods for determining the maintenance of minimum competence. The motion also authorized NCSBN to work jointly with professional organizations in this endeavor.[77]

In April 1989 the board directed the NP&E Committee to create a conceptual framework for continued competence, develop key concepts related to continued competence and licensure, and identify a mechanism for the maintenance of continued competence.[78]

At the meeting of the delegate assembly in 1996, Dula Pacquiao of New Jersey, chair of the NP&E Committee, presented the report of the committee and its subcommittees, including the Continuing Competence Subcommittee chaired by Shirley Brekken of Minnesota. Responding to the report of the NP&E Committee, the delegate assembly adopted the definition of competence and the standards of competence as a position of NCSBN, as well as a position statement titled "Assuring Competence: A Regulatory Responsibility." The definition of competence read as follows: "Competence is the application of knowledge and the interpersonal, decision making and psychomotor skills expected for the nurse's practice role, within the context of the public health, welfare and safety." Standards included statements that the nurse would do the following:

- Apply knowledge and skills at the level required for a particular situation.
- Demonstrate responsibility and accountability for practice and decision.
- Restrict and/or accommodate practice, if unable to safely perform essential functions of the nursing role due to mental or physical disabilities.

The statement proposed a regulatory model for competency assurance. It looked at ways to demonstrate and assess competence and remove incompetent practitioners. The statement declared, "The promotion of professional competence requires collaboration involving boards of nursing, individual nurses, employers, and educators."[79]

The Report of the NP&E Committee in 1991 included the "NCSBN Conceptual Framework for Continued Competence" developed by the committee. The purpose of this paper was to develop operational definitions as a conceptual framework on continued competence in nursing. The intent was that it would be used as a basis for future research, context for evaluating specific mechanisms, and a guide for setting standards by different jurisdictions. In addition to definitions, the report enumerated premises, mechanisms for assessing continued competence, and strategies to achieve or maintain continued competence and formed the model for assurance of continued competence presented in the paper. The following conclusions were reached:

The assurance of continued competence is a complex process that must be based on identified and accepted standards of nursing practice that are relevant to the practice area of the individual nurse. Such standards must be valid and reliable, i.e., one must be able to state that the specified standards are indeed appropriate to the particular type of practice setting that the documentation of implementation of those standards in the individual nurse's practice assures competence in the full realm of practice in the particular type of setting.

Assurance of competence requires assessment of the nurse's practice in relation to those standards. Such assessment should be objective and non-arbitrary. If assessment demonstrates the presence of continued competence, nothing further is required until reassessment is conducted at some specified time in the future.

When competence is judged to be absent, based on standards-based assessment, the specification of deficits and interventions (strategies) may be employed to correct those deficits. The achievement of competence through completion of prescribed deficit correction strategies is determined through reassessment of practice in relation to specified standards.

It should be recognized that the application of this model would represent a shift from a reactive to a proactive stance. Within this context, the responsibilities of Boards of Nursing would include:

1. considering mechanisms to document continued competence as a requisite for licensure and relicensure;

2. providing guidance to individual nurses seeking ways of attaining and maintaining continued competence; and

3. protecting the public, through disciplinary action, from actions of nurses who have not achieved continued competence.

Clearly a critical factor in the assurance of continued competence of nurses is the identification of valid and reliable standards of practice. Such standards have been identified within the professional community; however, within the regulatory community, standards of practice need to be developed and validated. This is perhaps the first step in developing truly effective mechanisms for assuring the public of the continued competence of nurses.[80]

The delegate assembly adopted the "Conceptual Framework for Continued Competence."[81] The NP&E Committee reported on other activities including the results of a survey of member boards on authority to issue declaratory statements and/or advisory opinions and where the authority is located, e.g., the administrative code, the nursing practice act, rules and regulations, or others. The report also included those member boards not authorized to issue such statements and opinions.[82]

Revisions of the *MNPA* and the *MNAR*

The NP&S Committee completed revisions of the *MNPA* and the *MNAR*, which were adopted by the delegate assembly at its meeting in 1988.[83] In addition, the delegate assembly authorized the NP&S Committee to review data relative to RN and LPN/VN competencies, synthesize the competencies, and determine their relationship to the competencies synthesized by the Task Force on Examinations for the Future.[84] The task force had been appointed in 1986 to explore and plan the development of new licensure examinations based on minimum competencies of evolving levels of practice. One of the tasks accomplished by the task force was to synthesize competencies for practice for nurses educated at two levels. Yet it did not examine the competencies of the LPN/VN.[85]

At the meeting of the delegate assembly in August 1989, Chair Leonard presented two recommendations from the NP&E Committee, the uniform standards for endorsement and the uniform requirements for foreign graduates, which were adopted by the delegates.[86]

That same year, the delegate assembly recognized Sister Lucie Leonard for her many contributions to NCSBN during the six years she served as a member of the NP&E Committee.[87] Leonard wrote an article for *Issues* in 1989 titled "Nursing Practice and Education Committee Contributions to the Nursing Regulatory Community." She listed the following documents that the committee had created from 1982 through 1989:

- The *MNPA* and the *MNAR* in 1982 and 1983, with revisions of both in 1988.

- Statements on the number of times a candidate may rewrite examinations, model legal standards and whether it is appropriate for NCSBN to develop such standards, and nursing activities of unlicensed persons.

- Position papers on continued competency and advanced nursing practice.

- Guidelines for entry to nursing practice.

- Monograph—*The Regulatory Management of the Chemically Dependent Nurse.*

- Concept paper on the Nursing Home Reform Act.

- Uniform standards for licensure by endorsement and for licensure of foreign educated nurses.

- Reports of ongoing activities by member boards on continued competence and entry into practice.

These accomplishments were achieved by the committee as a whole and with the assistance of subcommittees. One of the latter worked on the identification of LPN/VN competencies and synthesized the relationship of these competencies to the competencies hypothesized by the Task Force on Future Examinations.[88] In 1990, Leonard was again honored by NCSBN when she was awarded the Meritorious Service Award. She commented that her work had been a "labor of love and commitment to the mission of the National Council and the purpose of regulations."[89]

The NP&E Committee had worked on changes for the *MNPA*, and presented the changes to the delegate assembly in 1993. These changes were largely for clarification and to meet the requirements of computerized adaptive testing (CAT).[90] The delegate assembly adopted the revised *MNPA* and the proposed language regarding advanced nursing practice to be added to the *MNPA* and the *MNAR*.[91] More detail regarding the language for advanced nursing practice is found in Chapter 11.

Karen McDonald of North Dakota, chair of the NP&E Committee in 1994, presented the report of the activities of the committee in the *NCSBN Book of Reports*. This included the revision of the *MNAR*, which was completed with the following major changes:

- Added language for a "special" license for individuals unable to practice the full scope of nursing.

- Added more options on continued competence.

- Incorporated the language of advance nursing practice adopted in 1993.

The NP&E Committee also made two changes to the *MNPA*. The first change was the addition of the language for advanced nursing practice adopted the previous year. The second was the addition of the language on providing a special license, which described a non-disciplinary process for licensing an individual who is unable to practice safely the full scope of nursing but is able to practice safely within a modified scope of practice, or with accommodation, or both.[92] The delegate assembly adopted the changes to the *MNAR* and the *MNPA*.[93]

The Nursing Regulation Subcommittee, chaired by Libby Lund of Tennessee, reported that its charge was to develop a methodology to identify the benefits and cost of nursing regulation. The subcommittee identified fundamental principles of nursing regulation and a comprehensive list of functions currently within the regulatory domain. A survey of member boards was conducted and the responses were used for comparison and analysis of various regulatory approaches. The work of the subcommittee was to lead to the "development of a regulatory description of nursing within a reformed heath care delivery system as well as a proposal of an ideal regulatory model for the future."[94]

The December 1, 1995, *Newsletter to the Member Boards* contains a report of a November meeting of the Nursing Regulation Task Force. The task force discussed the responses to a survey, methods to identify costs and benefits of nursing regulation, and continued planning for the December conference, "Crafting Public Protection for the 21st Century, the Role of Nursing Regulation," cosponsored with the Citizens Advocacy Center. Activities implemented by the task force included the following:

- A multidisciplinary coalition on health professions regulation.
- More formalized monitoring of state-level regulatory reform activities.
- Initiation of a "regulatory successes" fact sheet.
- Development of a lexicon of delivery system restructuring terminology
- Activities related to the analysis of the Pew Commission recommendations.[95]

At its January 2001 meeting, the board of directors agreed to sponsor an LPN/VN forum during the 2001 annual meeting and to support a revision of the *MNAR* related to LPN/VNs. In addition, the board approved a recommendation to convene a Summit of States on approval and accreditation of nursing education programs and a roundtable on nursing program regulation.[96] In June, the board of directors agreed to the appointment of a subcommittee to work on a revision of the *MNPA* and the *MNAR* with a report to the delegate assembly in 2002.[97] An article in the April 2001 issue of the *Council Connector* announced that NCSBN planned to explore the value of mandatory continuing education. NCSBN had developed a research project to explore a link between continuing education and the development of professional abilities, which had been presented at the December 2000 meeting of the Interprofessional Workgroup of Health Professional Regulators. Four organizations agreed to join NCSBN in the study. These were the American Society of Clinical Pathologists, the American Speech-Language-Hearing Association, the Association of Regulatory Boards in Optometry, and the Federation of State Boards of Physical Therapy.[98]

As the result of a change in the bylaws, the name of the NP&E Committee was changed to the Practice, Regulation and Education (PR&E) Committee in 2001. In 2002 Cookie Bible of Nevada, chair of the PR&E Committee, presented the report of the work completed during the previous year. The report included a recommendation that the delegate assembly adopt the revisions to the *MNPA* and the revision to the *MNAR*'s fifth chapter, which covered nursing education. The recommendation was adopted.[99] At its meeting in February 2003, the board of directors assigned a subcommittee of the PR&E Committee to examine and revise the *MNAR* as needed. In addition, the committee was asked to review all delegate assembly actions for the potential need to revise either the *MNPA* or the *MNAR*.[100] The delegate assembly adopted a resolution that asked NCSBN to develop a position paper on the regulation of nursing assistive personnel, which included a model act and model rules with a report to the delegate assembly in 2004.[101] In the process of revising the *MNAR*, the subcommittee decided that instead of using separate documents for the *MNPA* and the *MNAR*, they would arrange the material for each in two columns in order to show the relationship between the two—section by section. To show agreement between the two it was necessary to propose some revisions to the *MNPA*. The work was completed by 2004 when the delegate assembly adopted the revisions of the *MNPA* and the *MNAR* in one document.[102] Although this action goes beyond the 25 years covered in this history, its inclusion is essential to the completion of the chapter. In order to show how the definition of nursing has changed over the years, and to reinforce the earlier statement that "the definition of nursing practice that appears in the nursing practice act is the basis for everything else in the law," the 2004 version is included in Appendix D with the definition from 1982.

Regulation of Nurse Aides

In 1989 the board of directors discussed the role of NCSBN in relation to the regulation of nurse aides as required by federal law. Details of the involvement of NCSBN in relation to nurse aides are found in Chapter 12. The board decided in January not to ask the NP&E Committee to develop model language for legislation related to implementing the Nursing Home Reform Act requirements. Instead, the board decided that NCSBN would serve as a clearinghouse for those member boards needing information on model language related to their implementation of the requirements of the law.[103] The delegate assembly adopted a resolution in August directing the NP&E Committee to develop standards to be included in the *MNPA* and the *MNAR* for regulating nurse aides through the approval of programs preparing nurse aides, and by maintaining a list or registry of those who have successfully completed approved programs and a competency evaluation.[104] In November the board of directors authorized the appointment of a subcommittee of the NP&E Committee for the purpose of developing model language for the regulation of nurse aides, with the work to be funded from moneys generated by the Nurse Aide Competency Evaluation Program.[105]

Joyce Smyrski of North Carolina, chair of the NP&E Committee's Subcommittee on Model Language for Nurse Aides, presented the proposed Model Nurse Aide Regulation Act and the Model Nurse Aide Administrative Rules to the full committee early 1990. The documents were intended to serve as guides for those states developing or revising statutory authority for the regulation of nurse aides. The subcommittee stated that it believed that boards of nursing should seek this legislative authority for the regulation of nurse aides in all settings in order to protect the public health, safety, and welfare, but recognized that there would be state-by-state variations. The document was presented in relation to the requirements of federal law and the *MNPA*. The delegate assembly adopted the two documents at its August 1990 meeting.[106]

Issues of Mobility, Endorsement, and Licensure

The delegate assembly adopted a resolution in 1987 to study licensure by endorsement in the following ways:

- Documenting and distributing requirements of each member board for licensure by endorsement of RNs and LPN/VNs.

- Studying the differences between the requirements of the member boards.

- Recommending to the delegate assembly, by 1989, actions of reasonable and desirable standards, which, if implemented, would facilitate licensure by endorsement while assuring public protection.

- Monitoring problems relating to licensure by endorsement and improvements in the process through reports to the delegate assembly.[107]

In 1990 the board of directors reviewed a draft of a paper entitled "The Regulatory Implications of the Supply/Demand for Nursing Resources," directed the NP&E Committee to forward it to the ANA and to the NFLPN for review, and to then prepare it for presentation to the delegate assembly.[108] Later in 1990, the board agreed to a request from the NP&E Committee to study nontraditional nursing models and their implications for licensure and interstate endorsement.[109]

Thomas Neumann of Wisconsin, chair of the NP&E Committee, presented the report of committee activities for 1990 in the *NCSBN Book of Reports*. The position paper, "Statement on Endorsement Issues Related to Peer Assistance/Alternate Programs" was included in the report and contained the following conclusions:

---

1. Boards have the responsibility to assure the health, safety, and welfare of the public.

2. Criteria for participation in confidential peer assistance/alternative programs need to be delineated.

3. The receiving board should require sufficient information about the substance abusing/dependent nurse for licensure by endorsement.

4. Licensees in confidential peer assistance/alternative programs should be informed that endorsement into another jurisdiction, with or without a confidential peer assistance/alternative program, may impose self disclosure requirements.

The statement listed the following recommendations:

1. Each board must address whether or not its application for licensure by endorsement should include questions regarding an applicant's substance abuse/dependency and participation in treatment programs.

2. Contracts between peer assistance/alternative programs and the participating nurse should include provisions addressing the nurse's responsibility to disclose:

   a. anticipated moves to new jurisdictions to the peer assistance/alternative program, and

   b. information regarding the nurse's substance abuse/dependency and treatment to the receiving jurisdiction.[110]

Regulatory Models for Nursing

Following the report of the Nursing Regulatory Task Force, in April 1996 the board of directors authorized the expenditure of $43,800 for up to 67 representatives of member boards to attend a conference to work on a proposed model for nursing regulation.[111] The conference was held in June, and that same month the board approved funding for a focus group to meet in July to review and refine proposed models, followed by a two-day meeting of the Nursing Regulatory Task Force to enhance and finalize plans for the annual meeting.[112]

The delegate assembly adopted a recommendation from the board of directors that the board be charged to continue to develop the concept of a regulatory model that incorporates the characteristics of a multi-state license by directing activities that included the following:

- Evaluating the impact of state-level regulatory processes on the multi-state licensing concept.

- Identifying core licensure requirements.

- Evaluating potential implications for board of nursing role and function.

- Identifying mechanisms for effective cross-state disciplinary processes.

- Analyzing current laws and regulations for potential impact on multi-state practice.

- Exploring the feasibility of a demonstration or pilot project and possible external funding.[113]

Nursing Practice Across State Lines

The 1997 Report of the Board of Directors included a position paper titled "Telenursing: A Challenge to Regulation," on the practice of nursing over distance using telecommunication technology. The paper described telenursing as follows: "The nurse interacts with the client at a remote site, using this technology, to electronically send and receive client health status data, initiate and transmit therapeutic interventions and regimens, and monitor and record clients' response and nursing care outcomes." The paper detailed a variety of other ways that nursing may be practiced using telecommunication and concluded with the following:

Telecommunications and information technology have brought forward new situations and challenges to nursing regulators. The first step in resolving these regulatory concerns is to answer the question, "*Does the provision of nursing services by electronic transmission constitute the practice of nursing?*" affirmatively: Yes. The delivery of nursing services by telephone or any other electronic means constitutes the practice of nursing.[114]

The delegate assembly adopted the position paper.[115] The delegates also decided that NCSBN would endorse a mutual recognition model of nursing regulation and authorize the board of directors to develop strategies for implementation to be adopted by the delegate assembly.[116] In December 1997 the delegate assembly met in special session and approved the nurse licensure compact for the mutual recognition model of nursing regulation.[117] Further discussion of this subject can be found in Chapter 10.

In 1999 Chair Zubieni reported that the NP&E Committee had completed two years of work on the proposed uniform core licensure requirements. In a supporting paper, the committee stated that it believed that increased consistency in licensure requirements was an appropriate direction for regulation in a rapidly shrinking world.[118] An executive summary described the purpose of this effort as follows: "To assure mobility of licensed nurses while maintaining licensure standards critical to protect the public health, safety and welfare." The committee's premises included the following:

- It is critical to focus on what the public needs rather than what the states are currently doing.

- It is crucial to avoid choosing the lowest common denominator.

- It is important that the committee define core to mean minimum and essential.

- It is essential that member boards be responsible for verification that applicants meet requirements.

- It is important to remember that the underlying goal is to promote public safety in the least restrictive manner.

The paper described the framework for licensure requirements was as follows:

The National Council's definition of competence is *the application of knowledge and the interpersonal, decision-making, and psychomotor skills expected for the nurse's practice role, within the contest of public health, welfare and safety.* The proposed *Uniform Core Licensure Requirements* are organized using the competence framework developed by the 1996 Continued Competence Subcommittee, which include the following components:

Competence Development—the method by which a nurse gains nursing knowledge, skills and abilities.

Competence Assessment—the means by which a nurse's knowledge, skills and abilities are validated.

Competence Conduct—refers to health and conduct expectations, including assurance that licensees possess the functional abilities to perform the essential functions of the nursing role.[119]

The delegate assembly adopted the paper and recommended that states move toward incorporation of the uniform core licensure requirements at the state level.[120]

At its meeting in June 2000 the board of directors agreed that the NP&E Committee should continue its work on the education content for the *MNPA* and the *MNAR*. The board also asked staff to remain in communication with the ANA about its continued competence model.[121]

Katherine Thomas of Texas-RN, chair of the NP&E Committee, presented the report of the committee's activities in the 2000 *NCSBN Business Book*. The committee recommended and the delegate assembly adopted the "Uniform Advanced Practice Registered Nurse (APRN) Licensure/Authority to Practice Requirements."[122] The requirements were developed to complement the "Uniform Core

Licensure Requirements" adopted the previous year for RNs and LPN/VNs. The "APRN Requirements" included licensure as an RN, completion of graduate education in an accredited nursing program, and certification by an appropriate specialty certification body. The requirements were designed to enable boards of nursing to promote the quality, consistency, and accessibility of advanced nursing practice within the state and across state lines. The "APRN Requirements" also addressed the uniform requirements for endorsement, renewal, and reentry of nurses educated in other countries.[123]

Conclusion

The PR&E Committee has consistently fulfilled its responsibilities to help achieve one of the original objects of NCSBN, which was to "identify and promote desirable and reasonable uniformity in standards and expected outcomes in nursing education and practice." Other committees and subcommittees have contributed to this achievement, and the PR&E Committee has carried out many other activities over the first 25 years of NCSBN. Other chapters will include reference to the accomplishments of this committee, but the importance of its continuing work on the *MNPA* and the *MNAR* is emphasized here by listing those who have chaired the committee, and the primary NCSBN staff members who have provided high levels of support over the years.

Committee Chairs

Marion Klappmeier, Maine	1978
Eleanor Smith, Virginia	1978
Thelma Cleveland, Washington-RN	1979–1982
Therese Sullivan, Montana	1982–1986
Sister Lucie Leonard, Louisiana-RN	1986–1990
Thomas Neumann, Wisconsin	1986–1992
Julia Gould, Georgia-RN	1992–1993
Karen MacDonald, South Dakota	1993–1996
Dula Pacquiao, New Jersey	1996–1997
Jan Zubieni, Colorado	1997–1999
Katherine Thomas, Texas-RN	1999–2001
Debra Brady, New Mexico	2000–2001
Cookie Bible, Nevada	2001–2003

Primary Staff to Committee

Ray Showalter
Marsha Kelly
Vickie Sheets
Donna Nowakowski
Nancy Chornick
Nancy Spector

In 1900 Lavinia Dock said,

Restrictive legislation affecting the professions, then, is not to be gained once and forever; this is another point for us to remember. It does not mean just one effort, but continuous efforts for the rest of time.[124]

This chapter has demonstrated that NCSBN recognized the necessity for model laws and regulations, and that review and revision is "a continuous effort for the rest of time." As nursing practice has changed, NCSBN has responded by revising its models in order to provide assistance to the member boards as they continue to review the nursing law and regulations in the individual states.

CHAPTER EIGHT
EDUCATION

A few nurses, interested in forming a state association, met in the spring of 1900 in New York City. The focus of the meeting was on educational standards, "better trained women at the head of all schools," and concern about the caliber of "nurses" and their abilities from varied and different levels of training. The question asked at the meeting was "Do we desire to make it so that those who bear the name of nurse shall be so not in name only, but in deed and in truth?" "If so, a state association is necessary which can work for state registration and a uniform system of education."

> ### Sophia F. Palmer
> ### The American Journal of Nursing, 1900[1]

IT HAS BEEN ARGUED that the movement toward legislation for the regulation of nurses in the United States was directed at improving the education of nurses rather than at public protection. But the legitimate counterargument that is often made is that improving the education of those who provide nursing care to the public is basic to protecting the health of citizens. There is no question that there were an increasing number of training programs purportedly preparing individuals to nurse the sick prior to the enactment of the first nursing practice acts. Over the subsequent years, with the development of standards resulting from these laws, the weaker schools closed and the stronger grew. Boards of nursing have been involved in the regulation of nursing education programs for one hundred years. In 1978, when the National Council of State Boards of Nursing, Inc. (NCSBN®) was organized, after more than 75 years of development and refinement, boards of nursing had developed systems for program approval that included minimum standards for these programs. National programs were in place for the accreditation of the nursing education programs preparing individuals for licensure as either registered nurses (RNs) or licensed practical/vocational nurses (LPN/VNs).

With this background, the early leaders of NCSBN put greater effort into revising the test plans for the licensing examinations, adopting the *NCSBN Model Nursing Practice Act (MNPA)* and the *NCSBN Model Nursing Administrative Rules (MNAR)*, and completing the foundation for future actions of the organization. This chapter will cover the role of NCSBN in assisting the member boards to meet their responsibility in the approval of nursing education programs, maintaining the relationship with the Commission on Graduates of Foreign Nursing Schools (CGFNS) to assist in the evaluation of nurses educated in other countries, and providing educational opportunities for the members and staff of the boards of nursing. Discussion of activities related to continuing education and competence and the issue of the appropriate education for beginning the practice of nursing are found in Chapter 7, and are mentioned only briefly in this section.

Regulation of Nursing Education Programs

In 1980 the Report of the Nursing Practice and Standards (NP&S) Committee in the *NCSBN Book of Reports* stated that the committee was continuing its work on the proposed model nursing practice act (MNPA), including the provisions to "develop and enforce reasonable and uniform standards for nursing education programs, approve nursing education programs that meet the prescribed standards and deny or withdraw approval of nursing education programs that fail to meet the prescribed standards."[2] The delegate assembly adopted the *MNPA* at the 1982 annual meeting.[3]

At a meeting in 1982 the board of directors identified major activities for the coming year, one of which was the exploration of ways to serve the member boards in additional functional ways, including the approval of education programs and the orientation of new members of member boards.[4] In an *Issues* article published in the summer of 1982, Ruth Elliott of Tennessee presented a historical overview of the role of boards of nursing in the regulation of nursing education programs. Elliott reported that questions about the continued role of boards of nursing in the process of approving education programs were being raised during the sunset reviews of boards. Elliott continued with a differentiation between legal and professional accreditation. She said that "legal standards aim to assure the student of an essential education program in preparing for initial licensure." In addition, she argued, these standards provided for the enforcement required for safe and effective nursing care, and legal standards were designed to serve as grounds for denial, withdrawal, or granting of provisional accreditation to nursing programs. Elliott concluded the article with the following:

> Although the accreditation role of state boards will be challenged in the future, the charge to them will be to demonstrate that reasonable and uniform standards for nursing programs have been developed and enforced in a manner that benefits not only the general welfare of the public but also the student as a consumer![5]

Elliott used the term "accreditation" for both legal and professional recognition, while both the *MNPA* and the *MNAR* used the term "approval" for the legal recognition.

The delegate assembly adopted the *MNAR* as amended at the annual meeting in 1983. The following is a listing of headings for the section on nursing education programs:

Section III. Standards of Nursing Education

A. Purpose of Standards

    1. To ensure safe and effective practice by graduates of nursing education programs.

    2. To serve as a guide for the development of new nursing education programs.

    3. To foster the continued improvement of established nursing education programs.

    4. To provide criteria for the evaluation of new and established nursing education programs.

B. Approval of Nursing Education Programs (Including provisional approval, full approval, continuing approval, denial, withdrawal, reinstatement or closure of nursing education programs.)

C. Organization and Administration

D. Resources, Facilities and Services

E. Students

F. Faculty

G. Curriculum[6]

The member boards used this part of the model as they reviewed and revised the regulations within the individual states.

NCSBN actions related to the entry to practice issue are discussed in detail in Chapter 7. These actions included the adoption of a resolution to appoint a committee to develop a report on the issue,[7] the adoption of the position paper "Guidelines on Entry Into Nursing Practice," and the adoption of a motion that the NCSBN clearinghouse for information on jurisdictional activity related to the issue be extended to include information on activities of state nursing and practical nursing associations.[8] Further, the delegate assembly adopted the resolution that NCSBN maintain a position of neutrality on the issue.[9] Karen MacDonald, the executive director of the North Dakota Board of Nursing, reported the following in a 1986 *Issues*:

> By January 1, 1987, North Dakota nursing education programs are to offer specific degree curriculums. Practical nurse programs must offer the associate degree, registered nurse programs, the baccalaureate degree. This was among the new administrative rules enacted by the North Dakota Board of Nursing in January 1986. The new rules stem from the definitions of licensed practical nurse and registered nurse found in the Nurse Practice Act. They also are rooted in the fact that the North Dakota legislature has delegated nursing education program governance to the Board of Nursing.[10]

North Dakota remains the only state that has taken this type of action related to nursing education.

In the September 5, 1986, issue of the *Newsletter to the Member Boards*, there was a request for those boards that had been challenged on their authority to approve nursing education programs to send relevant papers to the NCSBN office. This request was the result of discussion at the annual meeting regarding the ability of NCSBN to help states deal with such challenges.[11] The Report of the Board of Directors in 1987 includes board approval of a recommendation that NCSBN take a more active role in the dissemination of information regarding legal issues facing member boards.[12]

A series of articles in *Issues* in 1985 and 1986 reported on trend analyses conducted by the Long Range Planning Committee with forecasts for 1984 to 1994. One of these, "An Analysis of Trends in the Legislation and Regulation of Nursing Practice," included the following observations related to education:

- The role of state boards of nursing in approval of nursing education programs will continue to be challenged.

- Identical standards for the three types of programs preparing graduates for the NCLEX® [National Council Licensure Examination] will continue to be an issue.

- The difference between legal standards for nursing education programs and standards for accreditation of programs will continue as an issue.

- The relationship of the state boards of nursing to other state agencies sharing responsibility for approval of nursing programs will continue to be investigated.[13]

A later article, "An Analysis of Trends in Nursing Education, Continuing Education for Nurses, Political and Societal Impact," continued the discussion. The following statements are from the forecasts on nursing education:

- Nurses are primary sources of health education, and effective education for any of the health professions must rest on a firm foundation in both theory and practice. These two components must be integrated and students be made aware of their interrelationship.

- Nursing curricula will show an increasing emphasis on ethical and humanistic aspects of professional practice.

- Nursing research, needed to develop a valid system for assessing the role and function of the nurse and for developing systems of delivering and evaluating client care, will increase.

- Diploma programs will continue to decline; associate degree programs will remain significant in number, but the rapid growth seen in the 1960s and 1970s will not continue; baccalaureate and RN completion programs will increase; and both masters and doctoral programs will increase. Licensed practical nurse programs are on the decline nationwide.

- The declining number of college-age students and enrollment by women in a greater variety of professions will have an impact in enrollment at all levels of nursing education.

- An increase in non-traditional education patterns, such as creative class scheduling, possible credit for life experiences, extension programming, and the greater use of computers will emerge.

- Clear definitions are needed to delineate roles, functions, and competencies of technical and professional nurses. Responsibilities appropriate to each of these roles need to be classified in the marketplace setting.[14]

With these forecasts as a guide, NCSBN continued to examine the issues related to the regulation of nursing education programs.

At a meeting of the board of directors in 1987, President Ruth Elliott of Oklahoma reported on the possibility of collaboration in a research program with the National League for Nursing (NLN) to explore the approval or accreditation process for nursing education programs. Several member boards had expressed interest in participating in a pilot study.[15] The following appeared in the *Newsletter to the Member Boards* on March 18, 1988:

The National Council has received several inquiries about a recent survey circulated to member boards from the National League for Nursing (NLN) on the approval/accreditation process for schools of nursing. The survey was initiated and circulated by the NLN and was not generated within the National Council.

The survey evolved as a result of a requested meeting by NLN with five member boards who had expressed interest in (and volunteered to meet with NLN) exploring efficient and effective methods of school of nursing approval/accreditation without duplication of efforts between NLN and boards of nursing. The National Council is supportive of such meetings and member board efforts at participation in meetings and dialogue with any organization/agency, which the member board believes will assist it in more efficiently and effectively carrying out its role in monitoring nursing practice and education on behalf of the public's health, safety, and welfare.[16]

In 1988 the delegates defeated a resolution that the NP&S Committee review the relationship between the criteria for state approval and the criteria for voluntary accreditation, and report to the delegate assembly in 1990 with the comparison and possible models of approval relationships for member board consideration.[17]

NCSBN resource materials show that there was limited activity related to the role of the member boards in the area of nursing education program approval between 1988 and 1995. In response to a report from the Nursing Practice and Education (NP&E) Committee in June 1995, the board of directors revised the tactic related to approving nursing education programs for the NCSBN Organizational Plan as follows:

> Conduct a comparison of Member Board rules regarding education program approval with National Council model education rules to draw out implications for board of nursing approval process; provide each Member Board with individual comparison data as well as the comparison of the NCSBN model rules with the NLN criteria and guidelines.[18]

The Supplemental Report of the NP&E Committee in the 1995 *NCSBN Book of Reports* lists the following activities:

- Compared National Council Standards for Education with NLN Criteria and Guidelines.

- Met with representatives of NLN and discussed their plans to work with selected boards of nursing to present workshops for educators and others comparing the roles and criteria for state education program approval and the NLN Criteria and Guidelines.

A subcommittee compared the educational standards from the *MNAR* with the criteria and guidelines of each NLN educational level council. The subcommittee planned to use this comparison data as the basis for additional work related to educational program criteria.[19]

Dula Pacquiao of New Jersey, chair of the NP&E Committee, described the activities of the committee, including the analysis of the nursing education rules and regulations, in its 1996 report. The committee compared the educational program approval rules of 55 member boards. They found that these were similar across jurisdictions with differences primarily in the standards for the curricula. The details of this analysis are found in the attachments for the NP&E Committee report in the 1996 *NCSBN Book of Reports.*[20] Appointed by the board of directors, the Subcommittee to Analyze Clinical Experience reported that it had developed proposed rules and guidelines for the selection and supervision of clinical experiences, and the selection and roles of preceptors. The subcommittee recommended to the NP&E Committee that its work be incorporated into the *MNPA* and the *MNAR.*[21]

In 1997 the Nursing Program Accreditation/Approval Subcommittee reported to the board of directors. The board approved a roundtable discussion for "involved players" to discuss the role of the boards of nursing in the approval of nursing education programs, and a potential partnership/collaboration among those involved. The subcommittee recommended that its position paper on the differentiation between the terms "approval" and "accreditation" be adopted.[22] The position paper was subsequently adopted by the delegate assembly at the annual meeting.[23] Eileen Deges Curl of Kansas, chair of the subcommittee, discussed the position paper in the *NCSBN Book of Reports*. The subcommittee accepted the *MNAR* definitions of approval and accreditation as follows:

> **Approval**—official recognition of nursing education programs which meet standards by the board of nursing.
>
> **Accreditation**—the official authorization or status granted by an agency other than a state board of nursing.

The subcommittee found that most member boards used the term "approval" to describe their oversight of nursing education programs. Some used "accreditation" and a few used both terms in the same way.

The paper concluded with the following:

Both approval and accreditation are important components in the successful operation of nursing education programs designed to protect the public and provide appropriate educational experiences for future nurses. Thus, it is important that boards of nursing review their state Nurse Practice Acts and Rules and Regulations to ensure that terminology is consistent with the inherent differences between the terms *approval* and *accreditation*.[24]

The subcommittee also issued the report, "Member Board Needs Assessment Regarding Approval/Accreditation of Nursing Education Programs." The findings of this report follow:

---

1. The terms *approval* and *accreditation* are used and interpreted differently among jurisdictions.

2. State boards of nursing indicated a need to continue in *initial* approval of nursing education programs.

3. Some state boards of nursing indicated interest in exploring alternative models for *continuing* approval of nursing education programs to decrease associated costs to the state and reduce redundancy. Member Boards identified increased interest in approving basic nursing education programs as compared to advanced practice nursing programs.

4. Data are needed from all types of nursing education programs and external organizations with respect to approval/accreditation issues.

5. Member Boards expressed interest in uniform standards to be used in approval/accreditation of nursing education programs to promote mobility and consistency. State rights were expressed as a significant value in the development of standards.

6. Member Boards expressed moderate support for analyzing the implications of the National Council seeking recognition by the Department of Education as an approved accrediting agency.

7. Member Boards perceived *unique* functions of state boards of nursing with respect to their responsibilities in approval/accreditation of nursing education programs.

8. Member Boards expressed interest in education programs for board staff and board members who have direct responsibilities in approval/accreditation or serve as survey visitors.

9. Member Boards expressed moderate support for National Council collaborating with other organizations in development of approval/accreditation models.

10. Member Boards expressed strong support for the role of National Council in sharing information regarding approval/accreditation issues and the analysis of trends and issues in nursing education.

The future activities of the subcommittee listed in the report related to meeting the needs identified by the assessment.[25]

In 1998 Jan Zubieni of Colorado, chair of the NP&E Committee, recommended that the delegate assembly approve the position paper developed by the Nursing Program Approval/Accreditation Subcommittee. Chair Curl, reporting for the subcommittee, said that the purpose of the paper was to make recommendations that boards of nursing may use in the approval process of nursing education programs based on an analysis of several studies conducted by NCSBN. The paper identified the unique role of the member boards in the approval process and described a mechanism to use the recognition of accreditation as an approach to be considered by boards of nursing in carrying out their responsibilities. The historical perspective, current processes, unique roles of boards of nursing, and comparison of continuing approval mechanisms were presented in the paper. Based on the findings of the research, the position paper included the following recommendations:

1. Boards of nursing continue to grant initial approval of nursing education programs based on the board's separate and distinct review.

2. Boards of nursing maintain a review process for continuing approval for nursing education programs which may include recognition of national nursing accreditation.

3. Boards of nursing continue to monitor and impose sanctions for programs that place public health, safety and welfare at risk.

4. Boards of nursing, through the NCSBN, collaborate with national nursing accreditation agencies to develop timely reciprocal feedback mechanisms between the boards of nursing and the national accrediting agencies for monitoring nursing education programs.[26]

The delegate assembly adopted the position paper.[27]

Two organizations granted accreditation to nursing education programs consistent with NCSBN definition of accreditation. The first to do so was the National League of Nursing Education (NLNE) when it developed an accreditation program in 1938. With the reorganization of nursing organizations in 1952, this accreditation function became an important part of the NLN. In 1996 an independent entity within NLN was organized—the National League for Nursing Accrediting Commission (NLNAC)—and began full operation in 1997. The NLNAC accredited baccalaureate and higher degree, associate degree, and diploma programs as well as practical nursing programs.[28] The American Association of Colleges of Nursing began the exploration of an accreditation service for baccalaureate and graduate education programs in the 1990s, and established the independent accrediting agency the Commission on Collegiate Nursing Education (CCNE), in 1996. Accreditation began the following year. In addition, from the mid-40s through the mid-90s, the National Association for Practical Nurse Education and Service (NAPNES) offered an accreditation service for practical nursing education programs.

At its October 1999 meeting, the board of directors discussed at length the involvement of NCSBN in the regulation of nursing education. As the result of this discussion the board made the following recommendations:

- That the NCSBN should conduct a NCLEX invitational meeting for nursing faculty.

- To add to the charge of the NP&E Committee that it focus on education issues, particularly an environment assessment.

- That the NCSBN explore collaborative relationships with other organizations and invite the president and chief executive officer of the NLN to a future Board meeting.

- That the NCSBN utilize multimedia approaches for Special Services Division (SSD) projects for outreach to nursing educators.

At the same meeting the board decided to remain involved in the Nursing Practice Education Consortium (N-PEC), sponsored by the Sigma Theta Tau International Honor Society of Nursing.[29] In October 2000 the board of directors decided to change the status of NCSBN in N-PEC from that of advisor to full member.[30]

Nancy Langston and Ruth Corcoran, the president and chief executive officer, respectively, of the NLN, met with the NCSBN Board of Directors in February 2000 and discussed possible collaborative opportunities. Two such opportunities were identified: linking visits of NLNAC with board of nursing visits and collecting and disseminating data.[31] At the annual meeting that year the delegate assembly adopted the following resolution:

That the National Council assume the leadership role and develop an action plan to clearly delineate and establish congruence among education, practice, and regulation for the respective roles of all nurses. The plan shall be developed in collaboration with a broad base of health care stakeholders for presentation no later than the 2002 Delegate Assembly for a decision regarding implementation of the plan with an interim report at the 2001 Delegate Assembly.[32]

An article in the December *Council Connector* provided more information on the resolution. A Practice, Education and Regulation Congruence Task Force (PERC Task Force) was appointed to explore the future of nursing from a regulatory perspective. The group was charged to "identify areas of mutual concern to regulators, educators, nurses and nurse executives in their efforts to assure safe, effective nursing care in a rapidly changing health care environment." The following statement appeared in the article: "The PERC Task Force serves as a neutral entity created solely for the purpose of studying these issues from the perspective of all nurses, regardless of academic preparation." The eleven members of the PERC Task Force represented a variety of practice areas, with Constance Kalanek of North Dakota and Margaret Kotek of Minnesota serving as co-chairs.[33]

In January 2001 President Libby Mehaffey and President-Elect Sharon Bernier, both from the National Organization for Associate Degree Nursing (NOADN), met with the board of directors to discuss the work of the PERC Task Force. They raised concerns that the purpose of the task force was to establish the baccalaureate degree as the "point of entry" to nursing practice. They requested a description of the role and a list of goals of the PERC Task Force.[34] In April, the board of directors received a letter from the Federation for Accessible Nursing Education and Licensure (FANEL) with a resolution "opposing the efforts of the NCSBN education, practice and regulation congruence task force that result in degradation of any existing levels of programs of nursing currently legislated in any state."[35] At the invitation of the NCSBN Board of Directors, Twyla Wallace and John Word, both from the FANEL Board of Directors, attended the May board meeting. They delivered a petition on behalf of their membership in opposition to the PERC Task Force. Wallace and Word described the mission of FANEL as follows: "to preserve the four current levels of nurse education." Area III Director Julia Gould of Georgia-RN explained that the PERC Task Force was looking at the congruence between practice, education, and regulation for public protection. Wallace and Word thanked the board for its consideration of the concerns of the FANEL membership and for its clarification of the work of the task force.[36]

In August NAPNES President Richard Kerr and Executive Director Helen Larsen met with the board of directors to discuss the NAPNES resolution drafted "in response to rumors that the NCSBN would no longer support the entry level of LP/VNs." Kerr and Larsen requested a letter to the NAPNES membership assuring that this was not the intent of NCSBN. The board of directors directed that a letter be written assuring that the National Council Licensure Examination for LPN/VNs (NCLEX®-PN) was not in jeopardy.[37] The Report of the PERC Task Force in the 2001 *NCSBN Business Book* included the following summary of activities by the task force:

- Developed a conceptual framework.

- Began the identification of congruence and incongruence.

- Involved external groups by asking for written comment and inviting the respondents to attend a fall meeting to obtain further information, provide clarity and facilitate dialogue.

- Developed a communication plan, including a site on the NCSBN Web home page for PERC Task Force activities.[38]

At its April 2001 meeting the board of directors agreed to convene the Summit of States on Approval/Accreditation of Nursing Programs, and a roundtable on nursing program regulation. The goal of these activities was "to begin dialogue among nursing regulators to explore the issues of quality nursing education and articulation of the role of the boards of nursing in nursing program approval." The summit was scheduled during the annual meeting with the roundtable to follow in the fall of 2001.[39]

The board of directors heard a report at its January 2002 meeting from Executive Director Kathy Apple about the final version of the "N-PEC Vision 2020 Statement," which examined the future of nursing. The board decided to respond with a formal comment rather than an endorsement, reflecting NCSBN's neutral position, consistent with the delegate assembly's 1986 *Resolution on Entry into Practice*, and the current NCSBN Strategic Plan.[40] In May the board approved the proposed Chapter 5: Nursing Education of the *MNAR* for consideration by the delegate assembly at the annual meeting, endorsed the Alliance for Accreditation's *Distance Education Statement*, and recommended that the delegate assembly adopt the action plan of the PERC Task Force.[41]

The PR&E committee, chaired by Cookie Bible of Nevada, included in its report for the year the work of the Subcommittee to Develop Model Act and Rules, chaired by Barbara Newman of Maryland. The subcommittee presented a revision of the *MNAR*'s fifth chapter, Nursing Education, in the 2002 *NCSBN Business Book*. The important regulatory elements addressed in the revision included:

- The differences in board processes related to education program approval vs. accreditation.
- Distance learning as an educational strategy.
- The importance of evidence-based outcomes for nursing practice evaluation.
- Language needed for the compact states.
- Qualifications for administrators and faculty, including certain alternate faculty.
- Provision of an appeal mechanism for programs denied approval, in accordance with due process rights.

The major headings in the new fifth chapter were the following:

- Purposes of standards
- Standards of nursing education
- Models for implementing standards
- Required components for nursing education
- Approval
- Withdrawal of approval
- Reinstatement of approval
- Appeal
- Closure of Nursing Education Programs and Storage of Records[42]

Co-chairs Kalanek and Kotek presented the Report of the PERC Task Force, published in the 2002 *NCSBN Business Book*. The task force developed the following four recommendations through the process of scenario planning:

1. Commit to an organizational environment of change and innovation in practice, education and regulation.

2. Promote regulatory excellence based on ongoing data collection and best practices.

3. Ensure that the United States and foreign educated graduates and new nurses are prepared for safe practice.

4. Establish scopes of practice for the roles of all nurses, measures of continued competence of all nurses and parameters of practice for nursing assistive personnel.

These recommendations addressed the most critical incongruencies identified by the task force and formed the basis of the action plan and potential tactics. The report continued with actions to accomplish the four recommendations cited above and are found in the 2002 *NCSBN Business Book*. There is a chart with substantial detail titled the PERC Action Plan. The Pathway to Congruence of Practice, Education, and Regulation diagram developed by the task force is clear and complete.[43] *(see fig. 8-A)*

NCSBN and the Commission on Graduates of Foreign Nursing Schools

The minutes of a 1913 meeting of the Graduate Nurses Examining Board of Virginia reported the following:

> A young woman of foreign birth and education applied in person, at the meeting, for a permit to nurse, until her European [Danish] credentials were obtained, etc. She was instructed to send in what papers she had for inspection and said she would do so. Nothing from or about her has been heard by the present secretary who was also unable to understand the name clearly enough to write it in the Minutes.[44]

This quote illustrates the challenges of regulating nurses educated in countries other than the United States. The boards continued to have difficulties in evaluating records and determining eligibility for licensure for these individuals. Late in the 1960s boards of nursing noted a substantial increase in numbers of nurses educated in other countries entering the United States and seeking licensure. The boards were challenged to determine whether or not these individuals were able to meet the educational requirements for licensure in the United States. On average only 15 to 20 percent of those educated in other countries and taking the State Board Test Pool Examination (SBTPE) were passing and becoming licensed.

Information on the Web site for the CGFNS says that the Division of Nursing of the United States Department of Health, Education and Welfare contracted for two studies to be conducted by the American Nurses Association (ANA) and Pace University. Findings of these studies were presented and reviewed at a conference sponsored by the Division of Nursing. The following organizations were represented at the conference: the ANA, the NLN, the ANA Council of State Boards of Nursing, the American Hospital Association (AHA), the American Medical Association (AMA), the US Department of Labor, the US Immigration and Naturalization Service, (INS) the New York State Education Department, the International Council of Nurses, and others. As a result, the CGFNS was established as a private, independent, non-profit organization charged to develop and administer a predictive test and to evaluate the credentials for internationally educated nurses. The following quotation is from the CGFNS Web site: "The mission of CGFNS International is to protect the public by assuring the integrity of health professional credentials in the context of global migration and to foster the equitable treatment of health care professionals as they expand their horizons."[45]

At the time that NCSBN was organized, Margaret Rowland of Texas-RN was the representative from the ANA Council of State Boards of Nursing to the CGFNS. She was asked to continue to represent the boards of nursing in this capacity until the CGFNS Bylaws were changed to officially recognize representation from NCSBN. In November 1978 the NCSBN Board of Directors heard a report about the recent administration of the CGFNS examination in October, and the receipt of grants by CGFNS from the American Journal of Nursing Company and the NLN. The INS was expected to change the federal regulations for H-1 visas to require the CGFNS certificate prior to the issuance of a visa. The H-1 visa allows foreigners to work in the United States. The CGFNS planned to administer its examination to foreign-educated nurses at five sites in the United States by October 1979.[46] At the same board meeting Lorraine Sachs from the NLN described her work with the CGFNS examination, and assured the board about the security of the SBTPE and the CGFNS examination and that there was no interchange of information between the two examinations. She went on to clarify that the CGFNS examination consisted of two nursing tests of three and one-half hours each and an English test.[47]

In June 1979 Adele Herwitz, the executive director of the CGFNS, met with the NCSBN Board of Directors and reported that two examinations had been given to 1,920 persons. She also presented to the board and discussed three recommendations for consideration by the NCSBN Delegate Assembly.[48] The delegate assembly amended and adopted the following recommendations:

1. That the State Boards of Nursing be urged to accept the Certificate issued by the Commission on Graduates of Foreign Nursing Schools as evidence of the required educational qualifications in lieu of individual transcripts and records from foreign nurse graduates.

2. That if the nursing education program was in a foreign country, Boards of Nursing be urged to require applicants for the SBTPE to provide the State Board the Certificate issued by the Commission on Graduates of Foreign Nursing Schools, prior to admission to the licensing examination.

3. That the State Boards of Nursing revise their application blanks and provide a place for the CGFNS Identification Number to be inserted.[49]

In March 1982 representatives from the CGFNS, including President Jessie Scott, Herwitz, and members of the board of trustees, met with the NCSBN Board of Directors to discuss the development of systems for data exchange and the maintenance of standards and the integrity of the examinations. The group requested that NCSBN make provision for the CGFNS identification number on the NCLEX application form. These items were important for study of the CGFNS examination as a predictor for success on the NCLEX.[50]

The minutes of the April 1991 meeting of the board of directors contains a report from the Foreign Nurse Issues Committee. The board agreed to appoint the Foreign Educated Nurse Credentialing Committee for FY92 to FY93, with Louise Waddill of Texas-RN as chair. The charge to the committee follows:

1. to conduct an assessment of Member Boards' needs for a central repository for information about foreign RN and LP/VN nursing education programs and/or a central service for collecting, maintaining and evaluating credentials of graduates of foreign nursing education programs (and, if a need is identified, to follow through with investigation of existing agencies' service capabilities); and

2. to develop criteria to guide evaluation of the comparability of foreign nursing education programs; and

3. to investigate regulatory implication of the participation of foreign-educated nurses in graduate nursing programs in the US, in which they may be expected to perform clinical activities without supervision; and

4. to assess Member Boards' needs for dialogue with Canadian regulatory authorities regarding requirements for licensure of nurses moving between the two countries.[51]

The board of directors heard a report from the Foreign Educated Nurse Credentialing Committee in March 1993. The board authorized negotiations with two agencies regarding provision of foreign educated nurse credentialing services to the member boards.[52] In July the CGFNS notified NCSBN that it would not seek NCSBN endorsement of foreign educated nurse credentialing services.[53] In August the CGFNS again declined to receive NCSBN endorsement for credentialing services. At the annual meeting the Foreign Educated Nurse Credentialing Committee reported to the delegate assembly that it had identified the following services needed by the member boards: evaluation services, a central repository for documents, and a center for information related to foreign education programs. Four agencies were found to be capable of providing all three and the committee had recommended the two agencies they felt would best serve the member boards.[54] The delegate assembly adopted the following resolution:

That the Board of Directors, on behalf of the NCSBN, endorse all agencies deemed acceptable according to the criteria to be established by the Foreign Educated Nurse Credentialing committee; such endorsement shall not include a monitoring component nor a fee. The Board of Directors will make recommendations to the 1994 Delegate Assembly regarding whether or not to add a method for ongoing quality assurance to the concept of endorsement.[55]

In December the board of directors endorsed all agencies deemed acceptable according to criteria established by the Foreign Educated Nurse Credentialing Committee and directed staff to disseminate the names of the four agencies found acceptable to the member boards.[56] The following year the delegate assembly adopted a recommendation from the board of directors to provide the member boards with a one-time list of foreign educated nurse credentialing agencies as evaluated by NCSBN based on the selection criteria established by NCSBN.[57]

President Joey Ridenour of Arizona and Casey Marks, director of Testing Services, reported in June 2001 to the board of directors on a joint CGFNS-NCSBN presentation given at the Fifth International Conference on the Regulation of Nursing and Midwifery.[58] In 2002 Marcia Rachel of Mississippi was the NCSBN representative to the CGFNS Board of Trustees, but resigned from that position concurrent with her resignation from the Mississippi Board of Nursing. Barbara Nichols, executive director of the CGFNS, advised NCSBN that the new CGFNS Bylaws would change the structure of the CGFNS Board of Trustees and a new appointment from NCSBN was not needed.[59] Subsequently, Rachel, a former president of NCSBN, was elected to the offices of treasurer and later vice president of the CGFNS.

The Subcommittee on Foreign Nurse Issues, with Patricia Polansky of New Jersey as its chair, continued its activities in 2002. The subcommittee was examining a process and guidelines for the member boards with regards to foreign nurse issues.[60] In 2003 the board of directors charged the subcommittee to review and update material for the member boards on foreign nurse issues centered on education, immigration, and endorsement. The group was also directed to make recommendations regarding the level of credential evaluations needed for regulatory purposes. In addition, the subcommittee was asked to review the services of available credentialing evaluation agencies and to make this information available to the member boards.[61] At its December 2003 meeting the board of directors asked staff to facilitate a telephonic special policy call for member boards to discuss current issues with representatives from the CGFGNS, and to plan for a focus group at the annual meeting.[62]

NCSBN and the CGFNS have continued a cooperative relationship for more than 25 years. As a result, the member boards have benefited from the services offered by CGFNS, both in the area of predictor examinations and in the evaluation of credentials of nurses entering the United States from other countries. These nurses have benefited in that licensure in the individual states has been facilitated by the work of the two organizations. The CGFNS has maintained a presence at the NCSBN annual meetings, most notably with the attendance of the Executive Directors Adele Herwitz, from 1977 to 1988, and Virginia Maroun, from 1988 to 1998, and Chief Executive Officer Barbara Nichols since

1998. Nichols represented the ANA at the meetings of the Special Task Force—State Boards of Nursing, whose work led to the organization of NCSBN, and subsequently served as president of the ANA. The following individuals served on the CGFNS Board of Trustees as representatives of NCSBN:

Margaret Rowland, Texas-RN	1978–1979
Ruth Seigler, South Carolina	1979–1983
Helen (Pat) O'Keefe, Florida	1983–1986
Bernadine O'Donnell, Pennsylvania	1986–1987
Lois Scibetta, Kansas	1987–1990
Carol Stuart, South Dakota	1990–1991
Louise Waddill, Texas-RN	1992–1995
Julia Gould, Georgia-RN	1995–2001
Marcia Rachel, Mississippi	2001–2002

Education for Members and Staff of the Member Boards

One of the first references to an educational offering for staff and members of boards of nursing was found in the *American Journal of Nursing (AJN)* in 1921 as follows:

An Institute for State Inspectors and Nurse Examiners, to be held at Teachers College, Columbia University, invited "all nurses who are engaged in such work to attend the Institute without fee, and to take part in the discussions and conferences." The Institute included a series of daily lectures by specialists in education and by nurses with wide experience in the inspection of nursing schools. Informal conferences would provide an opportunity for discussions of "all kinds of practical problems.[63]

In the report of the executive director at the 1980 NCSBN Annual Meeting, Eileen McQuaid listed objectives for the staff for the coming year. One of these was "to communicate with and provide educational and informational services for Member Boards." She also listed among the objectives for FY81 the following: "To plan and implement educational workshops for Board members and other persons who can aid the Member Boards in matters concerning the public health, safety and welfare."[64] The following year, McQuaid reported that educational conferences on the purposes of NCSBN and the revised test plan had been presented for 10 member boards and for 15 other groups.[65] In 1982 NCSBN began the practice of presenting educational sessions for the representatives of the member boards attending the annual meeting. Programs presented included an orientation for new members and staff, and a report of the Task Force on the Credentialing of Nursing.[66]

At the August 1983 meeting the board of directors agreed, among its activities for the coming year, to develop educational materials on NCSBN for use by the member boards in interpreting all services and activities to their publics and to conduct an educational seminar on disciplinary matters for the member boards.[67]

The delegates and other representatives of member boards attending the 1984 annual meeting attended several educational sessions to receive information for matters before them. These programs included: "Law & Ethics," presented by Kathleen Dirsche of New Jersey; "The Impaired Nurse," presented by Evelyn Polk of Georgia-RN, and Melva Jo Hendrix of Kentucky; "Entry Into Practice," presented by Phyllis McDonald of Montana, Sammy Griffin of North Carolina, and Donna Dorsey of Maryland; and "To be A Board Member," presented by Phyllis Salter, a consumer member from Idaho, Susan King, an RN member from Oregon, and Elizabeth Kinney, an LPN member from Iowa.[68]

In 1985 the annual meeting schedule again provided educational offerings for those in attendance. Some of the topics covered included the use of computer technology in regulations, the NCSBN Disciplinary

Data Base (DDB) Longitudinal Study, and computerized adaptive testing (CAT).[69] Presenters at the 1986 annual meeting included names that were, or would become, well known in the nursing and regulatory communities. John Atkinson, an attorney with the Federation of Associations of Regulatory Boards (FARB), and Lucille Joel, a professor at Rutgers University, offered a forum titled "Legal vs. Professional Regulation of Nursing." Pam Cipriano, past chair of the ANA Cabinet on Professional Practice, and Toni Masaro, a professor at the University of Florida Law School participated in a debate titled "Regulating Professional Approaches to Continued Competence." Madeline Naegle of New York and Ann Cantanzarite of Florida gave a presentation titled "Voluntary vs. Legislative Approach to the Impaired Nurse."[70]

At the May 1987 meeting of the board of directors, the board agreed to the concept of field consultation visits for FY88, contingent upon the approval of guidelines for selection of boards to be visited. The purpose of these visits was to promote an exchange of information to increase the knowledge of both the visitor and the member board.[71] At the annual meeting Leah Curtin gave a speech titled "Mastering the Changes: Future Societal Trends and Their Impact upon the Regulation of Nursing." At the same meeting Dr. Donald Lyman spoke on Autoimmune Deficiency Syndrome (AIDS).[72] In October the board of directors sponsored an orientation and training session for the board, committees, and staff members.[73] The board and 62 committee members attended. A second orientation and planning session was held in October 1988.[74]

The first NCSBN Regulatory Conference was held in Monterey, California, in February 1989, with over 100 people in attendance. Issues pertinent to the regulation of nursing were discussed at this conference.[75] The board of directors decided to conduct an NCSBN Regulatory Conference at least every two years.[76] At the annual meeting that same year, Lillian Gibbons, the executive director for the Commission on Nursing, reviewed the recommendations from the commission study. NCSBN representatives Ann Petersen of Utah, Tom Neumann of Wisconsin, Jeri Milstead of South Carolina, and Sister Teresa Harris of New Jersey served as a panel of respondents. Gibbons emphasized the following:

- The necessity to focus on client need as a method of determining both the education and utilization of nurses.

- The need to reexamine the educational system for new articulation patterns and creative models for educating the nurse of the future.

- The need for nursing, as an organized community, to focus its strengths and points of unity to assist with innovative thinking and policy influence in the health care delivery system.[77]

In 1990 the board of directors approved the redesign of the field service visits to member boards into a resource network and announced the program at the annual meeting.[78] The program was designed to provide consultative or advisory services tailored to specific needs of individual member boards at their request. The board of directors approved procedures and policies for the resource network in November.[79]

In 1991 the following were some of the topics included on the program for the NCSBN Regulatory Conference: "Protection of the Public: A Global Perspective"; "Issues in Examination and Licensure of the Handicapped Nurse"; "Endorsement Issues—Controlling Fraudulent Applications, Temporary Licensure of Travel Nurses, and Continuing Competence Certification." Other topics included "Advanced Practice—Pros and Cons of Licensure"; "The CGFNS Perspective"; "NCLEX® Test Development Process"; and "From Student to Practitioner: Making the Transition."[80] These topics presented information necessary for the continuing competence of members and staff of the member boards.

The board of directors reviewed the 1992 communication plan and rated the objectives. Based on that rating the board of directors listed, among the top three priorities, this one: to create and seek communications opportunities that promote, inform, and educate on issues regarding the regulation of nursing practice and education.[81] At the annual meeting, the delegate assembly adopted a resolution calling for the board of directors to explore the feasibility and desirability of establishing certification programs for member boards in the areas of nursing education programs and nursing disciplinary investigations.[82] The same year a list of 23 surveys and studies conducted by the member boards, and one conducted by the Citizens Advocacy Center (CAC), was published by NCSBN, thus providing a reference for member boards seeking information on the subjects of these surveys or studies. The information was entered into a database to be updated and distributed to the member boards periodically.[83]

In 1993 the delegate assembly took actions at the annual meeting related to enhancing the educational opportunities for the member boards. The delegates adopted a recommendation reported by Margaret Howard of New Jersey, chair of the Communications Committee, that the board of directors determine the methodology to implement educational programs for nursing education program surveyors that best meets the needs of the membership, consistent with the NCSBN Organizational Plan.[84] In a second action, the delegates adopted a resolution to authorize an Executive Directors Network Group to establish a committee comprising one executive director from each area to develop and recommend structure and procedures to facilitate the functioning of the executive directors of the member boards.[85] "Areas" refer to the geographic regions to which the member boards were assigned.

There were eight educational programs at the 1993 NCSBN Annual Meeting. The general topics of these presentations were the following: acquiring information for decisions, delegations issues, dual licenses, regulation and health care restructuring, relapse in chemical dependency, and limited license for disabled nurses.[86]

At its March 1994 meeting, the board of directors decided to discontinue the annual NCSBN Leadership Conference for the year. This meeting has been previously referred to as an orientation and planning conference for the board of directors and the committees. The board planned to evaluate alternative methods for orientation of committees, networking, and other issues. The board also decided to pursue holding a onetime conference to be jointly sponsored by national organizations on public policy and regulatory issues.[87] Again in October the board assessed the need for a leadership conference and identified a methodology by which such need could be determined. In addition, the board designated a Subcommittee (of the NP&E Committee) on Member Board Education Needs.[88]

Ruth Ann Terry of California-RN, chair of the Task Force to Develop Educational Programs for Nursing Education Program Surveyors, reported in the *NCSBN Book of Reports* in 1994 that the task force had developed six modules. The titles of these modules were: "Novice to Expert"; "Preparation and Planning for the Site Visit"; "Review and Critique of Documents"; "the Site Visit"; "Report Writing"; and "Follow Up." The subcommittee met with representatives from the NLN for a software demonstration and to learn about data collection methodology. The task force also suggested that NCSBN should consider sponsoring educational sessions for nursing education program surveyors as enrichment for the experienced surveyor.[89]

The topics of the educational/research programs at the 1994 NCSBN Annual Meeting included the following: education for nurses in advanced practice, stipulations for probation, enabling the challenged student, sexual misconduct in nursing, and delegation.[90] NCSBN cosponsored the "National Consumer Summit" in Washington, DC, in February 1994. The conference was initiated by the American Organization of Nurse Executives (AONE) and was planned for an audience representing more than 60 consumer organizations and more than 60 nursing organizations. The purpose of the meeting was to obtain information regarding consumers' perceived needs for a reformed health care system.[91]

After reviewing a survey of current committee members, the board of directors decided again not to conduct the NCSBN Leadership Conference in 1995. Instead, the board continued to look for alternative methods for orienting volunteers.[92] After reviewing a report of the Member Board Education Needs Subcommittee in May the board decided not to continue the subcommittee, but instead to contact appropriate representatives of the member boards as the need arose. In order to facilitate information flow from the most appropriate individuals, staff requested assistance from the member boards' executive officers and presidents to identify a cadre of persons willing to serve as "telephone consultants." The use of the title "executive officer" in place of "executive director" for the administrative officers of the member boards began to appear in NCSBN print and continued in ensuing references.[93] In August, the board of directors approved a budget amendment so that the Executive Officers Network could develop an orientation program for new executive officers. Another adjustment to the budget at the same meeting provided for planning for a CAC-NCSBN conference.[94]

The board of directors reported at the 1995 annual meeting that it had scheduled time for an informational forum to discuss trends impacting nursing regulation. In addition, the board decided to initiate an ongoing process for providing educational offerings for the members and staff of the member boards to expand knowledge of issues and activities that impact the regulation of nursing.[95] In October the Committee on Continuing Education (a committee of the board of directors) recommended, and the board adopted, a motion that all materials and programs developed by NCSBN for the primary purpose of professional development of the member boards be provided under the auspices of the National Council Institute for the Promotion of Regulatory Excellence, established by action of the board of directors. The board went on to say, "Continuing education credits for programs offered by the National Council in cooperation with other agencies will be sought for attendees." The board also said that programs would be offered without continuing education credits and that "The National Council Institute for the Promotion of Regulatory Excellence will develop and offer educational materials and programs in accordance with the needs of the Member Boards as identified in an annual survey."[96]

Chair Terry of the Task Force to Implement the Education Program for Nursing Education Program Surveyors reported in 1995 that the *Guidelines for Education Program Surveyors: A Series of Learning Modules*, was published in May and distributed to the member boards. Planned evaluations of the modules would be used for future revisions and change.[97]

In 1995 discussion occurred among the member boards regarding the external degree programs in nursing offered through the Regents' College Program in Nursing of the State University of New York. At least one state was reconsidering its position on accepting applicants for licensure from the college. An article in a 1994 *Issues* stated that the board of Regents' in New York served as the board of trustees for the State University of New York, which offered 26 degree programs, including the associate degree and baccalaureate degree in nursing. The article also reported that the university was accredited by the Middle States Association of Colleges and Schools and the nursing programs were accredited by the NLN and the New York State Education Department. The nursing programs were described as "an outcome based approach to nursing education."[98] On August 10, 1994, the Florida Board of Nursing determined that graduation from the Regents' College nursing program was not sufficient educational preparation for admission to the National Council Licensure Examination for RNs (NCLEX®–RN). Therefore, the Florida Board would not authorize graduates of the program to take the examination for licensure in that state. This action was taken after a review of the Regents' program.[99] In the June issue of the *Newsletter to the Member Boards*, another article appeared that indicated the timeliness of the issue. This article reported that Todette Holt, a nursing education advisor with the Pennsylvania State Board of Nursing had conducted a survey of the member boards. The survey asked the following two questions:

1. Has your Board of Nursing changed its position, or is it currently reexamining the approval for licensure by either examination or endorsement of the graduates of the [Regents'] Program?

2. If yes, what were the concerns brought to the board's attention that prompted it to reexamine licensure for Regents' graduates?

Holt received responses from 29 member boards, 25 of whom said there had been no change and no reexamination was in process. However, 4 said there were plans for review and data was being gathered.[100] Since most member boards accepted the Regent's program as the basic education required for nursing, these articles demonstrated the effort to keep the member boards informed on issues under review by others.

In June an announcement in the *Newsletter to the Member Boards* stated that Gary Fillerman, associate director of the Pew Health Professions Commission, would speak at the annual meeting on the thoughts of the commission regarding necessary regulatory reforms. The article noted that the Commission was supported by the Pew Charitable Trusts and had the mission of reducing professional education and practice barriers to health reform.[101] Subsequent discussions of the commission report and the response of NCSBN are found in Chapter 6. There were several other *Newsletter* articles and notices related to education in 1995. An announcement for the joint conference of NCSBN with the CAC appeared in August, putting forth the plan to hold the conference in December to provide an opportunity to discuss the recommendations from the Pew Health Professions Commission. The same issue featured a list of educational programs at the annual meeting, which included topics of continued interest from past years. Other topics listed were the following: "Moving Into Community-based Settings"; "Ethics of Regulation"; and "Empirical Studies of External Degree Graduates at Work."[102]

A symposium titled "The Future of Nursing Regulation" was conducted by NCSBN in Chicago in the fall of 1995. The participants were an invited group of nursing leaders in service, education, and regulation. A report of the symposium stated that the first day was spent "envisioning the competencies required of the entry-level nurse in 2005." This discussion was intended to give direction for test development. On the second day the group addressed the purposes, outcomes, and ideal characteristics of nursing regulation. The discussion was useful in the analysis of the current regulatory system and in developing a response to the recommendations from the Pew Health Professions Commission.[103]

The Report of Staff Activities in the 1996 *NCSBN Book of Reports* contained a summary of a survey of users for the purpose of evaluating the Modules for Education Program Surveys. Responses were received from 39 member boards, with 20 reporting use of the modules, primarily for staff development. Of these, 17 found the modules to be useful or very useful. Of the 19 that had not used the modules, 6 planned to do so.[104] Also in 1996, the board agreed to hold a public policy conference in FY97 for the member board executive officers and presidents, and the board of directors. The conference was recommended by the board committee, which had oversight responsibility for the Institute for the Promotion of Regulatory Excellence (the Institute).[105] The following description of the Institute was included in the report of Chair Tom Neumann in the 1996 *NCSBN Book of Reports*:

During its October [1995] meeting, the Board committee defined National Council's continuing education program, named the program the "Institute for the Promotion of Regulatory Excellence," reviewed its responsibilities in the development of the Program, and created a Member Boards Needs Survey that was distributed to all boards of nursing and returned with responses. The committee decided that the objective of the Institute would be to provide educational offerings for Member Boards (board members and staff) that expand and enhance the knowledge of issues and activities that impact the regulation of nursing. The Board of Directors required the committee to act as the coordinating group for the program, reporting to the Board with the following responsibilities:

- Survey member Board needs/distribute Call for Topics to National Council committees/ task forces;

- Identify/prioritize needs;

- Match needs with proposals;

- Identify delivery method;

- Choose educational offerings according to need;

- Refer topics to appropriate structural units for program development;

- Conduct evaluation activities;

- Assure quality of program;

- Deal with emerging issues; and
- Budget annually.

The report also listed, as the accomplishments of the Institute, the December 1995 conference with the CAC, the educational session on continued competence at the 1996 annual meeting, the Day of Discipline in August, and the Public Policy Conference planned for FY97.[106]

Former President Ruth Elliott joined the staff of NCSBN as director for Education and Practice in 1996. Her responsibilities included the management and oversight of organizational activities related to the regulation of nursing education.[107] She also served as the primary staff member for education related committees and task forces. The first NCSBN orientation session for new executive officers of boards of nursing was held in Chicago in January 1996 with 10 executive officers participating.[108] In March a workshop titled "Assessment Strategies for Nursing Educators" was held. Presented by assessment experts from NCSBN, volunteers and staff members, the workshop was attended by 68 people. Those in attendance received a comprehensive instructional manual that enabled them to continue fine tuning their assessment skills. The evaluations of the workshop were favorable and others were planned for various areas of the country. The next one was held in June in Washington, DC.[109]

NCSBN continued to offer educational opportunities for members and staff of the member boards. The next few sentences identify several of these offerings. In June 1997 the board of directors decided to continue to hold the Regulatory Day of Dialogue prior to the area meetings.[110] Lucille Baldwin of Alabama, chair of the Institute Task Force appointed to coordinate the Institute, presented the Report of the Institute, published in the 1997 *NCSBN Book of Reports*. The activities completed by the Institute during the year were: the development of a calendar of activities, a survey of the needs of the member boards, and selection of programs for the 1997 annual meeting. The Institute Task Force made several recommendations to the board of directors, including an educational offering titled "Changing Health Care Environment: Trends That Impact Member Boards," which was to be offered at the 1998 Regulatory Day of Dialogue. The Institute also recommended that NCSBN offer a program on the topic of discipline on the day before the 1997 annual meeting.[111] A series of articles on the state approval process for nursing education programs in Georgia, Oklahoma, and Utah appeared in a 1997 edition of *Issues*. There was also an article titled "U.S. Secretary of Education and Board of Nursing Recognition: Why and How?"[112]

In 1998 the report from the Institute Task Force included a recommendation, approved by the board of directors, to explore a summer institute for regulatory personnel. The board also assigned the highest priority to the volunteer program and leadership development when it reviewed the NCSBN Organizational Plan.[113] The area directors recommended that beginning in 1999, the Regulatory Day of Dialogue should follow, rather than precede, area meetings, with the program planned by the Institute Task Force.[114] The annual meeting schedule that year included a "Dialogue on Discipline," "Dialogue on Education," "and Dialogue on Impaired Practice." In addition, eight educational/research sessions were presented.[115] The orientation session at the NCSBN offices in May 1998 was attended by eight new executive officers. The Executive Officer Orientation Group met to review and revise the Executive Office Orientation Manual that was developed in 1995.[116]

At the June 1999 board of directors meeting, the president shared with the board an idea regarding the development of a leadership/fellowship program for executive officers to foster regulatory knowledge and build a leadership foundation for NCSBN. The board planned to discuss the idea further at the Executive Officer Network meeting in July.[117] An article in *Issues* reported that the popular face-to-face workshop for nursing educators, "Assessment Strategies for Nurse Educators: Test Development and Item Writing," was now available online. The article stated that more than 200 faculty members had logged on to the course and the evaluations were positive.[118]

The Board Staff Education Network planned a dialogue on education programs for the 1999 annual meeting. The focus of the presentations was the outcomes of nursing education and practice.[119] Out of eight new executive officers, seven participated in the orientation at the NCSBN offices in 1999.[120]

In February 2000 the board of directors decided to make the Executive Officer Forum an annual event with an increased focus on education, important policy, and strategic issues and management skills. The executive director worked with a team of member board presidents to plan a session for the presidents as a part of the educational forums at the annual meeting.[121] At its August meeting the board of directors recommended a March mid-year meeting during which the board would meet and forums for executive officers, a technology forum, and the area meetings would be held.[122] In October, the Executive Officer Task Force was renamed the Member Board Leadership Development Task Force, to be co-chaired by a member board executive officer and a member board president. The board of directors agreed the intent of the task force was to develop a curriculum for both groups.[123]

The delegate assembly adopted a resolution at its 2000 meeting that combined the former separate annual area meetings into a single mid-year conference at which the attendees would address issues facing the member boards. Each area would have the opportunity for a separate meeting at the conference.[124] Sharon Weisenbeck of Kentucky, chair of the Executive Officer Fellowship Program Advisory Group, spoke of the group's activities as follows:

> In recognition of the important leadership role of the Executive Officer of a board of nursing, this advisory group has been working in consultation with Dr. Patricia Benner to cull out the theoretical knowledge and highly skilled practical knowledge which informs the practice of nursing regulation. The intent of this work is to identify an effective curriculum which will serve to orient new Executive Officers to this practice and to embellish the knowledge and skill of role incumbents. Several domains of regulatory practice have been delineated and will be presented to the Executive Officers for validation during the EO Networking Group meeting.[125]

The educational offerings at the 2001 annual meeting included a forum for LPN/VNs and the Summit on Approval/Accreditation of Nursing Programs.[126] The Member Board Leadership Development Task Force, also chaired by Weisenbeck, presented a list of accomplishments for the year in its report. These activities included the following:

- Designed and implemented midyear Leadership Conference Day for executive officers and board presidents.
- Promoted and facilitated open dialogue between the membership executive officers and presidents.
- Reviewed and revised the Executive Officer Manual and the Orientation Program for New Executive Officers.
- Conducted the New Executive Officer Orientation in May and planned for a follow-up luncheon at the annual meeting.[127]

In 2002 the Member Board Leadership Development Task Force continued to work to establish an effective program to meet the needs of the member boards. In January Alicia Byrd, manager of Member Board Relations, discussed the work of the task force at the board of directors meeting. The task force recommended the development of a core curriculum for certification of nurse regulators. Byrd also presented a recommendation that the board support a Web-based orientation section that could be used for new executive officers, new members of the boards of nursing, and new NCSBN officers and board members. The board of directors supported the requests and asked for a projected plan from the Information Technology Department.[128] In May the board of directors approved the recommendations for development of future member board leadership and mentorship programs as presented by the task force.[129] At the same meeting the board of directors approved a proposal for educational programs for member boards to include an advanced regulatory curriculum. The program was planned to fulfill project work for graduate nursing credit.[130] In December Chair Joey Ridenour of the Member Board Leadership Advisory Group reported to the board of directors regarding the group's activities. The board approved several requests including a charge to plan the regulatory seminar and to select Mary Kay Sturbois, president of the Ohio Board of Nursing, as the contact person for member board presidents in FY03.[131]

At the board of directors meeting in August President Ridenour invited Polly Johnson, executive officer for the North Carolina Board of Nursing, to present a report of the Health Professions Summit of the Institute of Medicine (IOM). Johnson was a member of the Health Professions Education Committee of the IOM that was planning another meeting to engage regulators across the professions to discuss licensure, model regulations, and standards for education and to establish communication links among regulators. The board of directors approved participation by NCSBN in the planning process for the IOM Workshop. The board also heard a report of positive responses to the first annual Information Technology Conference.[132]

Marcia Rachel of Mississippi and Maris Lown of New Jersey co-chaired the Member Board Leadership Development Task Force in 2002. They reported a number of activities completed during the year, including the following:

- Arranged for continuing education credit for programs at the midyear Leadership Meeting.
- Developed a mentorship program for new executive officers.
- With NCSBN staff, implemented the NCSBN Web-based orientation program "NCSBN 101."
- Planned the 2002 orientation for new executive officers.
- Planned the regulatory curriculum for membership with core courses and electives, subsequently transferred to the Regulatory Credentialing Program Development Task Force.[133]

Debra Brady of New Mexico, chair of the Regulatory Credentialing Program Development Task Force, reported that the group had proposed to the board of directors a comprehensive multilevel education program on nursing regulation that would meet the educational needs of member boards and develop a substantive knowledge base in nursing regulation. The task force was planning a continuing education seminar on regulations for 2003 and also intended to explore the feasibility of implementing a regulatory certification program.[134]

In February 2002 the board of directors agreed to hold an Executive Officers Leadership Development Seminar in April with the title "Thrive to Survive." The seminar was designed to assist in the development of executive officers in their professional role.[135] At the April board of directors meeting, Polly Johnson reported on the IOM Health Professions Summit. The participants assembled a list of 10 recommendations with a focus on oversight bodies and five core ability areas to achieve health care competency. The board noted the importance of the continued participation of NCSBN with this group.[136]

The board of directors approved funding for an Institute of Regulatory Competence, as requested by the Member Board Leadership Development Advisory Group in July 2003.[137] Other activities of this advisory group from 2002 to 2003 included the following:

- Worked on an orientation manual for new members of boards of nursing.
- Recommended changes for the new executive officer mentor program.
- Initiated a draft business plan on the value and feasibility of a certification program.

The advisory group also drafted core competencies for member board presidents and executive officers in four main functions—knowing, leading, planning/evaluation, and communicating/relating. The draft included specific competencies in each of these categories for the president and for the executive officer. A schedule for the Institute of Regulatory Competence was included in the advisory group report as an attachment. The following topics were planned for the next four-year period:

2003   Public Policy Development and Role of Nursing Regulation

2004   Nursing Practice Violations and Discipline

2005   Nursing Competency, Evaluation and Remediation

2006   Nursing Regulatory Systems: Administration and Evaluation[138]

The group working on member board leadership development was identified both as a task force and as an advisory group in various documents used as resources for this chapter.

In 2003 The *Council Connector* reported on the educational events presented that year, revealing the continued efforts of many talented individuals who have responded to the needs of the member boards to increase their knowledge. The list of events was as follows:

- Mid-year meeting, including the Leadership Forum for member board presidents and executive officers and other educational sessions

- Educational sessions at the annual meeting

- Unlicensed Assistive Personnel Conference

- Information Technology Summit

- Investigator and Attorney Summit

- NCLEX® Invitational[139]

NCSBN announced in the April issue that starting in May 2003, the *Journal of Nursing Administration's (JONA's) Health Care Law, Ethics and Regulation* would carry a regular column from NCSBN. The first article was about the NCSBN research program and was prepared by NCSBN staff member Lynda Crawford.[140] This announcement demonstrated the ongoing effort to provide education about nursing regulation to a wide audience.

In 1988 NCSBN cooperated with the Irish Nursing Board to present a joint workshop on state boards of nursing and their functions around the world. The conference was held at Trinity College in Dublin, Ireland and its purpose was: "to increase worldwide understanding among state boards/councils on how regulatory bodies function."[141] A keynote address on the principles and future of regulation and subsequent presentations on the school approval and accreditation processes and the NCSBN DDB were made by Marsha Kelly, director of Public Policy Analysis. Jennifer Bosma, director of Testing Services for NCSBN, spoke on the examination process and CAT. The workshop was followed by the Third International Symposium on Nursing Use of Computers and Information Science where there were by more than 900 people from 28 countries in attendance. Bosma and Kelly also presented at the symposium.[142]

Over the 25 years of annual meetings of NCSBN, many distinguished individuals have addressed those in attendance. In the list of speakers below, titles and credentials have been omitted because the information was not available for all.

1979   Margretta Styles—Report of the Study of Credentialing in Nursing—A New Approach

1979   Jerome Lysaught—Implementation of Recommendations from the National Commission for the Study of Nursing and Nursing Education

1980   R. Louise McManus—State Board Test Pool: A Retrospective View

1981   Jo Eleanor Elliott—Nursing Concerns—1980s

1983   Gertrude (Trudy) Malone—Organization of NCSBN—Fifth Anniversary

1985   Michael Kane—Progress of National Council's Study of Nursing Practice, Job Analysis and Role Delineation of Entry Level Performance of RNs

1986   Barbara Nichols—Legal and Professional Responsibilities in the Regulation of Nursing Practice

1987   Martha Luzen—Mastering Change

1988   Elaine Ellibee—The First Ten Years of the National Council

1989   Lillian Gibbons—Report on the Commission on Nursing

1994   Barbara Safriet—Increasing Diversity of Types of Personnel Providing Nursing Care—from the Unlicensed Assistive to Advanced Practice

1995   Colleen Conway-Welsh—Managed Care: Regulatory Implications

1996   Jay Sanders—Telemedicine

1997   Jack Trufant, Nancy Langston, Nathan Goldman, and Ellen Deges Curl—Debate on the Regulation of Nursing Education Programs

1998   Jeffrey C. Bauer—The Future of Health Care: A Look at Nursing

1999   Andre B. van Niekerk—The Nursing Profession—Re-treading, Re-thinking or Re-inventing

2001   Timothy Porter O'Grady—Current State of Nursing and Regulation

2002   Dennis Sherrod—Strategies for Assuring Our Future Nursing Workforce

2003   Leah Curtin—The Future of Nursing Regulation

Conclusion

Since early in its history NCSBN has published books, guides, and papers as part of its continuing effort to provide information and educate the member boards, nursing students, nurses and the public. Beginning with review books for the licensing examinations and through to online courses, these references have expanded to meet identified needs. The listing of publications, courses, programs, and services on the NCSBN Web site is extensive, and the reader is encouraged to visit that site for a look at the variety of these entries. Some of the subjects of publications include: the NCLEX test plans, nurse aide registries, analyses of practice of RNs and LPN/VNs, job analysis of nurse aides, research, the *MNPA* and *MNAR*, chemical dependency, sexual misconduct, NCLEX statistics, and profiles of the member boards. The site also contains information on the availability of papers on education, advanced practice, continued competence, practice, and discipline. In addition NCSBN published *Issues* and the *Newsletter to the Member Boards* for approximately 20 years, and currently publishes the *Council Connector* and *Leader to Leader*, both of which are available online.

In recent years courses have been made available online for nursing students studying for the NCLEX-PN and -RN, and there are two levels of courses for nursing faculty on assessment strategies. Topics of the courses for practicing nurses include chemical dependency, delegation, discipline, documentation, end of life care, ethics, medication errors, nurse practice acts, professional boundaries, and critical thinking skills. There are also four video kits available: "Delegating Effectively," "Crossing the Line," "Breaking the Habit," and "Chemical Dependency Handbook."[143]

This chapter has illustrated the activities of NCSBN in the regulation of nursing education programs and the establishment of relationships with other organizations to share and obtain information related to the educational aspects of nursing licensure. Programs, meetings, and conferences sponsored by NCSBN continue to be the primary source of educational opportunities for the continued competency of the representatives of member boards. NCSBN also provides educational opportunities for nursing students, RNs, LPN/VNs, advanced practice registered nurses, and nurse aides. Perhaps one of the most valuable opportunities for learning has been one that is essentially unplanned, but occurs as the members and staff of boards of nursing meet together under the aegis of NCSBN—the informal sharing that has occurred as these representatives have gathered together for 25 years.

CHAPTER NINE
EXAMINATIONS

We urge an affiliation...between State Boards as a means of standardizing the examinations over the country, the need for which is apparent from the difference in value of the questions as they come to us.

Sophia F. Palmer, 1914[1]

Introduction

A REPRESENTATIVE of a national certifying body attending the Advanced Practice Roundtable in 1994 asked the following question: "What does the NCSBN [National Council of State Boards of Nursing, Inc.] know about developing examinations?" This chapter will answer the question in more detail than the response given by then Vice President Gail McGuill of Alaska. She explained that since its inception a major purpose of NCSBN® was to develop valid, reliable, and legally defensible licensing examinations. As shown in earlier chapters, representatives of boards of nursing have been developing and administering licensing examinations since the first laws were enacted in 1903. The need for uniform examinations that were psychometrically sound and legally defensible was identified early, and continues to be uppermost in the search for the optimal examination. The purpose of NCSBN, set forth in the 1978 bylaws, has remained the same for 25 years: "to provide an organization through which state boards of nursing act and counsel together on matters of common interest and concerns affecting the public health, safety and welfare, including the development of licensing examinations in nursing." The specific inclusion of examination development in the stated purpose gives credence to the importance of the activity to the organization.

Although most of those involved with boards of nursing saw the need for improved licensing examinations, the movement was slow until the onset of World War II, which resulted in the need to license nurses in less time and to facilitate interstate mobility for nurses. In May 1941 the National League for Nursing Education (NLNE) Committee on Nursing Tests, using volunteer assistance and loans from private sources, saw to the administration of the first pre-nursing examinations. Subsequently, the Committee on Nursing Tests began the Achievement Test Service and thereafter launched the State Board Test Pool (SBTP) Service.[2] Boards of nursing became members of the SBTP Service and representatives of boards eventually were involved in item writing, selection of items for the exams, the test plan, and the administration of examinations under specifications included in the agreement under which the boards used the examinations.

All states, the District of Columbia, and some United States territories became members of the SBTP Service. The initial examinations tested individuals for licensure as registered nurses (RNs) and soon expanded to provide examinations for the licensure of practical/vocational nurses (PN/VNs). By 1978 the licensing examination was used by all 50 states for licensure of RNs and PN/VNs except in California, and by the territories of Guam and the Virgin Islands for both. The RN examination was divided into five sections: Medical Nursing, Surgical Nursing, Obstetric Nursing, Nursing of Children, and Psychiatric Nursing, with a sixth section that tested items for use in future examinations. The PN examination was one test in two parts with a third part testing experimental items.[3] There were persistent rumors among candidates about variation in passing scores from state to state. However, all states except Hawaii recognized a standard score of 350 as the minimum passing score for the RN exam. There may have been one or more states that set a higher passing score for the PN candidates, but almost all had agreed to the standard score of 350. Eleanor Lynch, a member of the staff of the Test Services for the National League for Nursing (NLN) said:

> By 1950 all forty-eight states and the District of Columbia were using the State Board Test Pool Examination; nursing thus became the first, and at that time, the only profession in which all states cooperated in the construction and use of a uniform examination for determining the qualifications of candidates to practice the profession.[4]

National licensure examinations arose following the adoption of the following resolution by the Committee on State Board Problems in December 1942:

> That the League [NLNE] assist states in adopting machine scored examination questions, carry forward a plan for cooperatively prepared State Board Examinations for use by all states in order to have more valid and reliable sets of examination questions and have them available for more frequent administrations.

In January 1943 the NLNE Board of Directors endorsed the action and authorized its Committee on Nursing Tests to operate, for interested states, a pool of licensing tests. The SBTP Service began operation in January 1944 after a difficult year of exploration and development. During that month, four states administered one or more SBTP examinations. Within six years all 48 states and the District of Columbia used the service. Thus, for 38 years the NLNE, and since 1952 the NLN, was the test service for the licensure examinations for RNs and licensed practical/vocational nurses (LPN/VNs).[5]

Licensing Examinations for Registered and Practical/Vocational Nurse Licensure

State Board Test Pool Examination

As we have seen, the State Board Test Pool Examination (SBTPE) was the national licensing examination when NCSBN was organized in 1978 and continued as the examination until July 1982. There were two examinations—one for RN candidates and another for PN/VN candidates. At the initial meeting of the delegate assembly of NCSBN, the following actions pertaining to the examinations were taken:

> • Accepted the assignment of the American Nurses Association (ANA) Council of State Boards of Nursing rights and responsibilities with connection to the SBTPE.
>
> • Approved the form for the test service contract.

- Approved the contract form for the agreement between NCSBN and the member boards.

- Approved the contract form for the agreement between NCSBN and the NLN as the test service.

In other important actions, the delegate assembly accepted "those items and actions of the ANA Council of State Boards of Nursing which are of a continuing nature" and referred a motion "that state boards of nursing adopt testing and security requirements to accommodate individuals who, because of one or more handicaps, require special arrangements in order to be able to take the SBTPE" to the Security and Administration of Examination Committee for study and recommendation.[6]

When NCSBN assumed the ownership of the national licensure examinations in 1978 the NLN, through its Division of Measurement, became the test service for NCSBN. Dr. Lorraine Sachs, director of this division, was mentioned frequently in minutes and reports of early meetings of the board of directors, the delegate assembly, and the Examination Committee and Administration of Examination Committee. Under her leadership, division staff worked on the transition to the comprehensive examination that was implemented in July 1982.

At its first meeting, the NCSBN Board of Directors appointed two committees. The first was the Examination Committee, composed of two teams. The members were:

Team I	Team II
Eileen McQuaid, New York, chair	**Phyllis Sheridan**, Idaho, chair
Brenda Cooper, South Carolina	**Mary Aultfather**, North Dakota
Arlene Sargeant, Oregon	**Eleanor Burke**, Massachusetts
Ruth Stiehl, Florida	**Shirley Dykes**, Alabama
Sharon Weisenbeck, Wisconsin	**Nancy Wilson**, West Virginia-PN
Nancy Wilson, West Virginia-PN	

McQuaid had served as chair of the Examination Blueprint Committee for six years under the ANA Council of State Boards of Nursing. The second committee appointed at this first meeting was the Security and Administration of Examination Committee, later the Administration of Examination Committee (AEC) consisting of Marianna Bacigalupo of New Jersey (chair), Darlene Mattingly of Nebraska, Doris McDowell of Kentucky, and Dolores Milton of California-RN.[7]

At the three-day September 1978 board of directors meeting, the board spent most of one day discussing with Bacigalupo problems related to the examinations as reported from the states. These problems ranged from difficulty in obtaining examination centers, air conditioning and lighting problems, a lost test booklet and answer sheet, a candidate with a visual disability, candidates refusing to take the experimental items, and local disposition of test booklets. McQuaid notified the board of directors that the New York Board had received, anonymously, pages of questions. These pages were sent to the NLN for review and, although questions came from Series 775, there was no evidence of any lost booklet.[8] By way of explanation, numbers associated with the month and year were used to identify specific SBTPEs for a particular year as follows: February and July 1979 for RN licensure: Series 279 and 779; April and October 1979 for PN/VN licensure: Forms 479 and 079. As shown, the word "series" was used to designate the RN examination and "form" was used for the PN/VN examination.

At the last 1978 board of directors meeting McQuaid and Sheridan presented a verbal comparison of norm referenced testing with criterion referenced testing through discussion with the board. They reported on the proposal, to be presented to the member boards, for a revised test plan and an integrated examination to replace the current test plan and examination. Later in the meeting the board appointed the Committee to Develop Specifications for a Test Service with Dorothy Randell of Wyoming named as chair.[9] When Randell could not serve on the committee, the board appointed Marilyn Boyd of Virginia to the position in June 1979.[10] This committee met three times in 1980 and reported to the delegate assembly in 1981.[11] Lorraine Sachs reported that an invitational conference on the SBTPE was scheduled for January 1979 and that 90 individuals had registered to attend. Sachs discussed the comparison of the SBTPE with the Canadian Nurses Association Test Service Examination (CNATS). She reported that there was insufficient data available for comparison since only about 200 individuals had taken both. Sachs presented the first royalty check from the administration of the SBTPE in July 1978 to the board of directors in the amount of $14,996.28.[12] By way of comparison, the examination revenue for the first six months of fiscal year 2003 was reported as $14,439,538. The board of directors asked about the publication of a report that was initiated when the ANA Council of State Boards of Nursing authorized a study of the validity of the SBTPE. Sachs stated that the NLN would contact Barbara Nichols, president of the ANA, and urge early publication. As a result, in 1978 the ANA published *Critical Requirements for Safe/Effective Nursing Practice*, a report on research conducted by the American Institute for Research. The authors of the report were Angeline M. Jacobs, Grace Fivars, Dorothy S. Edwards, and Robert Fitzpatrick. The report began when the ANA Council of State Boards of Nursing appointed a research steering committee that in turn appointed a research advisory committee. This critical requirement study was a part of an overall validity study. The project was funded from a portion of the fees paid by the member boards to use the SBTPE. The purpose of the study was stated as follows: "To provide empirical performance data to be used by the NLN in developing measurement of performance, as part of its validation of the SBTPE." As a part of the study, "Approximately 14,000 critical incidents of nursing behavior were collected from 2,795 nurses at all levels of experience and responsibility." An analysis was performed on the number of incidents across clinical specialties to look for the existence of bias. Generally, the numbers were comparable. There was a tendency to report safe-effective incidents more than ineffective or "close-call" incidents across the five clinical specialties. As a conclusion, the section headed Significance of the Study stated that it should be useful not only for the research being done on the SBTPE and for the development of future examinations, but to the larger nursing community as well. The classification structure as reported in this document constituted a list of critical requirements for safe and effective nursing practice.[13]

There were other activities occurring at the same time the "Critical Requirements" study was underway related to the future test plan for the SBTPE. In June 1979 the NCSBN Board of Directors approved the distribution of a paper prepared by McQuaid titled "The Content Validity and Reliability of the State Board Test Pool Examination."[14] Earlier, at the January board of directors meeting, the Examination Committee presented its proposal for revisions to the RN test plan. The current plan was about 25 years old. Michael Kane, director of the Department of Test Development at the NLN, met with the board and discussed the development of questions to test various cognitive levels, the implications of different scoring methods, and the standardization of the examinations. The board agreed to schedule a forum on the test plan at the annual meeting and directed that the proposed test plan be mailed to the member boards as soon as possible.[15] At its 1979 meeting the delegate assembly adopted the revised test plan for the SBTPE for RNs, to be used beginning in 1982, with the proviso that some areas would be refined and presented for approval at the 1980 delegate assembly. This was done and the final test plan was adopted in 1980.[16] An interview published in the *American Journal of Nursing (AJN)*, with Eileen McQuaid, executive director of NCSBN, and Phyllis Sheridan, chair of the Examination Committee, revealed the changes in the SBTPE Test Plan for RNs. McQuaid stated,

The test plan is the initial step in developing the examination for nurse licensure. It is a guide for selecting content for the exam because it specifies the behaviors to be tested. For example the new test plan states that "nursing is perceived as deliberate action of a personal and assisting nature. The practice of nursing requires knowledge of: 1) normal growth and development; 2) basis human needs; 3) coping mechanisms; 4) actual or potential health problems; 5) effects of age, sex, culture, ethnicity and/or religion on health needs; and 6) ways by which nursing can assist individuals to maintain health and cope with health problems. Embodied in these six categories of nursing knowledge are concepts considered relevant to nursing practice, including management, accountability, life cycle and client environment." This belief and these concepts then must be integrated throughout the examination. The plan provides a summary of the content and scope of the test.

Sheridan compared the current test plan with the one to be used for the examination beginning in 1982:

The old Test Plan simply gave a list of nursing abilities by ten categories. The new test plan presents, in narrative form, the beliefs to be incorporated into the test, the nursing behaviors to be tested, and how those behaviors are tested. It also shows how items are to be weighted for scoring. In the new plan the nursing behaviors to be tested are grouped under the broad categories of assessing, analyzing, planning, implementing and evaluating. The plan then spells out how those behaviors are tested—through client-nurse situations that require decision making centered in the nurse, decision making shared by nurse and client, and decision making centered in the client. In the first type of "system," clients are in life-threatening situations that require therapeutic intervention by the nurse. In the second, clients require a therapeutic regimen to maintain life or improve health. In the third, clients are in situations that require education, guidance, or support. The plan spells out the percentage of items that will reflect each system.[17]

Interaction with the NLN

Throughout 1979 there were continuing discussions between the board of directors, and Executive Director Margaret Walsh and Lorraine Sachs, both of the NLN. These discussions included items related to royalty payments, procedures for billing and receiving funds from the member boards, and payment of expenses of item writers. In January the board of directors asked the NCSBN president to write a letter to Walsh asking that reimbursement for maintenance and travel costs for item writers and for the printing of contracts between the member boards and NLN be channeled through NCSBN by July 1, 1979.[18] There was a positive response to this request. At the final 1979 board of directors meeting, the board agreed to a resolution regarding the standard contract for the SBTPE between the NLN and the member boards as follows:

The Executive Director of the NCSBN shall be empowered to act for the Council in approving or disapproving the release of test booklets to appropriate legal offices in connection with any investigation for violation of law undertaken by such legal officials, provided, however, that the Executive Director shall require that reasonable procedures for assuring the confidentiality and security of such test booklets be made a condition of such approval.[19]

At the June 1980 meeting, the NCSBN Board of Directors raised questions about an increase in fees that was addressed in a memorandum sent to the member boards by the NLN. Following discussion the board authorized the executive director to contact the NLN to request a complete financial analysis. Further, the executive director and legal counsel were authorized to begin discussions with the NLN about the renegotiation of the fifth year of the current contract and the subsequent contract. The board noted that it recognized that an increase in fees could lead to a termination of contract.[20] In September the board of directors reviewed the correspondence with NLN and discussed the implications of potential decisions. The board decided to give notice to the NLN of termination of contract effective June 30, 1982. The board adopted a motion to prepare and circulate the specifications for a test service to the member boards with a recommendation for adoption through a mail vote. If the member boards voted in the affirmative, the board would authorize the executive director to prepare a request for proposal (RFP) for a test service and to distribute it to potentially interested services. The proposed test service specifications were approved by the member boards and the RFP was distributed.[21] In December 1980 the board accepted a proposal from the NLN for an agreement to extend the provision of examination services through the administration and reporting of Series 782 to accommodate the change to the comprehensive examination under the revised test plan.[22]

At the March 1981 meeting of the board of directors, representatives from the California Board of Registered Nursing were present and raised concerns about the adequacy of the specifications for a test service, California's occupational examinations job relatedness policy, the California procedure for filing and review of examinations, and the California adverse impact report. The board offered the visitors an opportunity to review all eight proposals, but the representatives declined due to time constraints. Subsequently, the board took the following actions:

- Issued a statement of grave concern to the California-RN board that the secure materials were used when the Central Test Unit of California used the scoring key and examination to hand score a candidate's answer sheets.

- Issued a statement of concern to the NLN Test Service that personnel did not report such a request before complying with it.[23]

In the minutes of the same meeting, the board of directors described in detail the process used by the board of directors, the executive director, the associate executive director, and the legal counsel to review and rank the proposals from eight test services, including the NLN. Three proposals clustered at the top of the ranking: The American College Testing Program (ACT), California Testing Bureau/ McGraw-Hill (CTB), and Educational Testing Service (ETS). The board of directors appointed Vice President Schowalter of Minnestoa, Executive Director McQuaid, and Legal Counsel Thomas O'Brien to negotiate further with these three services.[24] At an April conference call meeting, with Vice President Schowalter presiding, the board of directors considered a request from the NLN that NCSBN consider negotiating with it to submit a proposal to the delegate assembly as an "incumbent vendor." The board listened to the request and supporting information presented by Sachs when she joined the conference call. After hearing from Sachs, the board voted unanimously not to negotiate with the NLN for the purpose of presenting a proposal to the delegate assembly.[25]

In her report to the delegate assembly, found in the 1981 *NCSBN Book of Reports*, President Schmidt of New York, summarized the activities that led the board of directors to terminate the contract with the NLN early and issue an RFP for a new test service. She reminded the delegates that in May 1980 the NLN notified the member boards that the price of the examinations would be increased effective July 1982. Schmidt said, "The Council itself was not notified of this proposed action." When the NLN was not able to provide more detailed financial information in support of the decision, as requested, the board decided to exercise its option to give notice of termination of the agreement effective in 24 months. The test specifications from the Special Committee for that purpose were approved by a mail vote of the delegate assembly, and the board of directors issued the RFP.[26] The minutes of the June 9 to 12 board of directors meeting included the following:

The delegates voted on June 11 on the three test services with the following results on the first ballot: CTB: 52, ETS: 51, ACT: 1. CTB was elected on the second ballot on a vote of 54, with 46 votes for ETS.[27]

Three years after its organization, NCSBN took this historic action to select, by a competitive process, a new test service with two ballots necessary for the final selection.

New Test Plan

The work of NCSBN to accomplish the transition to the first examination under the new RN test plan for Series 782 began in 1980, and members of the Examination Committee attended at least 12 meetings in various states to explain the revised test plan. At the delegate assembly meeting, Chair Sheridan presented, and the delegate assembly adopted, the final form of the RN test plan and approved a standardized scoring system where the comprehensive examination would have a mean score of 2000, a standard deviation of 400, and a recommended passing score of 1,600. The delegate assembly directed the Examination Committee to explore ways to diagnose areas of deficiency for failed candidates.[28]

McQuaid's 1981 report as executive director stated that she had conducted conferences on the RN Test Plan for 10 member boards and 14 other groups. She listed the following as priorities for the coming year: begin the transition to the new test service, design a system for direct application to take the examination for use by candidates, investigate the administration of the SBTPE outside of the United States, and write a book for PN/VN candidates for licensure.[29]

An article in *Issues* by Phyllis Sheridan, "The Single Score: A Controversial Issue," presented information related to the discussion and concern stimulated by the release of information that, beginning in 1982, the RN licensing examination results would be reported as one score. Prior to that date, the SBTPE was administered in five parts with a score for each. In order to be licensed, a candidate was required to achieve a passing score on all five parts. If a candidate failed one part, only that part had to be repeated. The revised, integrated examination was presented in four parts for administration purposes and yielded one score. Sheridan listed the following reasons for the single score:

- The plan presupposes a body of nursing knowledge to be tested through nursing behaviors identified throughout the whole realm of nursing practice.

- The behaviors are categorized according to the steps of the nursing process and an integrated framework is developed for the Test Plan and the examination.

- The Committee believes that all of the nursing process steps—assessment, analysis, planning, implementation and evaluation—are equally important and should be accorded equal weighting throughout the total examination and not within the individual parts.

- The NLN Division of Measurement reports a markedly high correlation among scores achieved by individual candidates on the five tests in the present RN SBTPE. This observation suggests that, in all likelihood, the examination also is testing a body of nursing knowledge and that separate scoring by content areas may be misleading.

The article closed with the following reminder: "the licensure examination is not designed for those individuals who write it unsuccessfully. Rather, it aims to protect the public by assuring that persons who provide nursing care services have the minimum knowledge required for safe and competent practice."[30]

National Council Licensure Examinations (NCLEX®): Paper and Pencil

The Report of the Board of Directors, found in the 1982 *NCSBN Book of Reports*, referenced the change of the name of the examination from the SBTPE to the NCLEX and that the "correction for guessing" would be deleted from the examination at the earliest possible date.[31] The executive director reported that the book for the examinations for PN/VN candidates was completed and published by the Chicago Review Press.[32] An article in *Issues* described the diagnostic tool developed by Assessment Systems, Incorporated (ASI). The Diagnostic Assessment Program was designed for individuals who were interested in self-assessment in preparation for taking the examination. It was built on the instrument used to identify critical incidents from the 1977 validity study.[33] *(see fig. 9-A)*

The last SBTPE was Form 482, administered to LPN/VN candidates in April 1982. The NLN Test Service produced and distributed Series 782 for administration in July to RN candidates. This series was the first examination developed under the most recent test plan and was known as the National Council Licensure Examination for RNs (NCLEX-RN®). Several actions at the delegate assembly in Boston in 1982 related to the conclusion of the SBTPE as the licensing examination for NCSBN and the efforts of the NLN in providing testing services through the years. The delegate assembly adopted a resolution of appreciation for the NLN as the test service for the SBTPE for 38 years that read in part, as follows:

RESOLVED: That the National Council of State Boards of Nursing call attention of the profession to the invaluable service rendered both to the profession and to the public by the National League for Nursing, and its predecessor, the National League for Nursing Education in the development of the State Board Test Pool Examination.[34] *(see fig. 9-B)*

The plan for direct application by candidates to take the examination was in place in time for the administration of the National Council Licensure Examination for PN/VNs (NCLEX-PN®) in October 1982. Representatives from the member boards went to Chicago to become better acquainted with the process in late summer. The first examination with CTB as the test service was administered with minimal problems. CTB was now the NCSBN test service and a number of changes that were implemented at that time had a positive effect on the member boards. The candidates could apply directly to the test service through its data center and the member boards received the lists of candidates, computer generated seating assignments, and admission cards. Member board staff members were accustomed to preparing these items. They could now check the information against the applications for licensure, and make and report changes or corrections to the data center.

In January 1983 the board of directors authorized the NCSBN staff to enter into a contract for the development of a computer program to generate new school programs codes. Those codes in use at the time had been assigned by the NLN Test Service, which used them as identifiers for other types of tests. It was important to have these codes for identification of the nursing and practical nursing education programs from which the candidates graduated both for verification of the individual and for reporting of specific and aggregate data related to the examinations.[35] In May the board of directors also reviewed the report of the Test Service Evaluation Committee and appointed President Schowalter, Executive Director McQuaid Dvorak, and Legal Counsel O'Brien to serve on a negotiating team to extend the contract with CTB. The team was instructed to bring proposed changes to the contract for consideration by the delegate assembly in August.[36] At the annual meeting the delegate assembly agreed to retain CTB as the test service on condition that a three-year contract satisfactory to the board of directors would be negotiated. The delegates specified that the negotiations were to include the replacement of review of draft items by member boards with review by a panel of content experts to be nominated by the member boards so that each would have representation annually in either item writing or on a panel. In addition, any member board that wished to continue to review items should be allowed to continue to do so. The delegates accepted the revision of the current contract; agreed that each series of the NCLEX-RN was to contain not more than 375 items and each NCLEX-PN not more than 250 items, with not more than 75 and 60 experimental items respectively; and adopted specifications for inclusion in the contract for the data center services.[37]

In her report to the delegate assembly in 1979, McQuaid said that "there is a need to evaluate what is current practice at the practical nurse level" and she indicated that the Examination Committee had requested permission to conduct a survey.[38] The board of directors agreed at the June 1979 meeting to ask the Examination Committee to propose a method for studying and revising the test plan for the LPN/VNs.[39] Bruce Kramer, manager of Professional Examination Services for CTB, met with the board of directors in March 1982 and discussed a proposal to conduct the practical nurse validity study. The board authorized the staff to negotiate an agreement with CTB to conduct the study and to propose modifications of the test plan if necessary.[40] At the 1982 meeting of the delegate assembly many reports related to the licensing examinations were presented. Helen Ference, principal researcher under the contract with CTB, reported that the PN validity study had begun.

The board of directors received and reviewed the *Practical Nurse Role Delineation and Validation Study for the NCLEX® for Practical Nurses*, and referred it to the Examination Committee for review and for use in the revision of the PN Test Plan.[41] In August, the delegate assembly authorized the Examination Committee to develop a new test plan for PN/VNs based on the findings of the validity study and to adjust the category weightings of the current test plan in the interim.[42] The 1984 delegate assembly adopted the test plan for the NCLEX-PN based on the results of the *Practical Nurse Role Delineation and Validation Study for the NCLEX® for Practical Nurses*, to be implemented in 1985.[43]

Special Needs of Candidates

The question of policies related to special needs of handicapped candidates came to the attention of NCSBN years before the Americans with Disabilities Act (ADA) became law in the United States. In January 1979. Chair Bacigalupo of New Jersey reported to the board of directors that the most pressing work of the Committee on Security and Administration of Examinations was to develop policies for allowing handicapped individuals to take the SBTPE.[44] In June the NCSBN attorney advised that a clause should be added to the contract with the member boards to allow variations in examination administration for handicapped candidates. The board agreed that when a person has met satisfactorily all of the requirements for licensure, the person should not be denied a license solely by virtue of procedures established for administration of the licensing examination.[45] At the meeting of the delegate assembly in June, the following statement was adopted to be included in the contract with member boards as recommended by the Committee on Security and Administration of Examinations:

It is the intent of the Council and parties hereto that no handicapped candidate, as defined by federal or state statutes, otherwise qualified, shall be deprived of the opportunity to take the test solely by virtue of that handicap. The Test Service with the approval of Council will make reasonable modifications of the examination procedures prescribed herein in order to meet special needs of such candidates. A written request for modification shall be submitted by any board to the Test Service in a reasonable time, but at least 120 days prior to the scheduled examination date to facilitate the necessary modifications.[46]

The board of directors, at its June 1980 meeting, agreed to submit to the director of the Office of Compliance and Enforcement of the Department of Health and Human Services, an amended document entitled "Recommended Grievance Procedure for Handicapped Candidates." The board also approved a request to allow time and one-half for a candidate with dyslexia to complete the SBTPE Form 080.[47]

The board of directors, in 1980, addressed several other items related to handicapped candidates. One of these established "interim" standing rules that allowed staff to approve requests for modification of the administration of the examination for visually handicapped candidates based on adequate documentation from the member board. The rules required that the candidate would be seated in a room with an examiner and a proctor, separate from all other candidates; a non-medically oriented reader would be provided if necessary; and not more than time and one-half would be allowed. The board asked staff to consult with Legal Counsel Thomas O'Brien as to whether the 120 day notification requirement in the contract between the jurisdiction and the test service could be waived when medically necessary to accommodate a candidate, when the modification to the test does not involve the format of the examination, and when the candidate could be accommodated in less time.[48]

The AEC revised the policy for modifications for handicapped candidates in 1989, and the board of directors approved the revised policy and directed staff to investigate the implications of member boards charging fees to candidates for modifications.[49] In her report to the delegate assembly, AEC Chair McGuill reported that the committee had approved staff authorizations for modifications issued for handicapped candidates. These modifications were for dyslexia, learning disabilities, reading disorders, and visual and other physical disabilities. All were granted additional time and other modifications, including the use of readers, a recorder, a magnifying glass, and a ruler. Legal counsel advised that member boards have the responsibility to make the determination that the candidate has a handicap and that NCSBN must be informed of the condition in order to approve the modification.[50]

An article in *Issues* late in 1989 discussed the Bias Sensitivity Review Panel initiated by NCSBN. The panel met four times a year to review items identified in the statistical process that was used to study potential item bias. The following criteria were listed for membership on the panel:

- Representative of Black, Hispanic, Asian, Asian Indian, Native American and White ethnic groups who are assimilated into American culture and retain ties to their original cultural group. Bilingual members will be sought as appropriate to the specific cultural groups.

- Ability to empathize with persons in various socioeconomic levels and sensitivity to class and life style differences.

- Expertise in nursing and/or linguistics.

- Ability to articulate judgments and opinions using good interpersonal communication skills.[51]

The year 1992 brought new challenges to regulatory boards when the federal law known as the Americans with Disabilities Act (ADA) became effective. Previous efforts by NCSBN related to special accommodation for candidates were not driven by federal law as was the case with the passage of the ADA. In February the board of directors adopted an interim change in its policy related to disabled candidates pending action by the delegate assembly in August. The board also directed staff to prepare information for the member boards about the implementation of examination modification policies for those candidates with disabilities.[52] At the meeting of the delegate assembly the following policy statement was adopted:

It is the policy of the National Council to cooperate with Member Boards in providing appropriate examination modifications for disabled NCLEX® candidates whom Member Boards deem eligible for licensure. The National Council will do so by designing and approving procedures which ensure that such modifications are psychometrically sound and safeguard the fairness and security of the testing process for all candidates.

The AEC included procedures related to the policy in its report to the delegate assembly.[53] At the April 1993 board of directors meeting, the board accepted a statement of responsibilities of the member boards and NCSBN for disabled candidates under computerized adaptive testing (CAT) as follows:

Member Boards will continue to evaluate candidate's requests for accommodation, including evaluating the medical diagnosis and supporting documents, and to determine if an accommodation would be granted. The NCSBN shall not become involved in or review this decision other than in exceptional circumstances. The Member Boards would also continue to recommend the specific accommodation to be provided to the candidate (perhaps from a limited menu offered by ETS). The NCSBN would have the opportunity to review these recommendations and object to them on psychometric grounds. The NCSBN would not review the underlying medical diagnosis except to the extent necessary to evaluate the appropriateness of the recommended accommodation.[54]

Examination Preparation Services

In June 1982, the board of directors reviewed a proposal from ASI for the development and publication of a clinical simulation examination to be used as a diagnostic tool for readiness to take the licensing examination. The board authorized the staff to negotiate a contract with ASI for the diagnostic test, with the royalty for NCSBN to approximate 25 percent.[55] The Report of the Board of Directors in the 1985 *NCSBN Book of Reports* stated that the board had authorized the executive director to terminate the agreement with ASI and to enter into an agreement with CTB to continue a diagnostic assessment test. An item in the *Newsletter to the Member Boards* highlighted the initiation on April 19, 1997, of an interactive program on the Web to assist examination candidates to understand the information on the diagnostic profile.[56] Chapters 5 and 8 contain information on other publications and online programs developed by NCSBN to assist the candidates to prepare for the NCLEX.

Security of the Examinations

The security of the licensing examinations had been an area of concern for boards of nursing, the organized groups of the representatives from the boards, and the test service, probably since the items were written by board members in 1903 for the first administration of an examination. As the process became national in scope the risks for security breaks increased. Risk factors included the following:

- Shipment of tests from the test service to the member boards and return.

- Shipment from member boards to the testing centers and return.

- Shipment of answer sheets from the member boards to the test service.

- Repeated use of the same series or form of the examination. (series—RN examination; form—PN/VN examination).

- Varied administration dates among the member boards.

- Large number of individuals with access to the examinations.

Two of these risks were removed from the list prior to the organization of NCSBN when the decisions were made to use uniform dates for administration in all jurisdictions and to create a new examination for each administration. However, the other problems mentioned above continued along with some additional ones not listed. At each meeting the board of directors had lengthy discussions and took actions related to security breaches. For example, in 1980 the report of the AEC Chair, Geraldine Wenger of Pennsylvania, listed anomalies as follows: three instances of missing booklets in which booklets were never located and one instance where a candidate left the exam center with a test booklet under her arm, but the examiner followed her and recovered it. The AEC determined that there were two violations of Security Measures and referred them to the board of directors.[57] These types of violations were not uncommon, and the board frequently reprimanded member boards for security breaks.

Several states sought and were granted permission to destroy the test booklets locally in an attempt to remove the risk of loss on return shipment; a secondary benefit was a reduction in the cost for shipping. Corinne Dorsey, one of the coauthors of this book, recalled that one of her early assignments as a member of the staff of the Virginia Board of Nursing was to accompany a colleague to the destruction site with the driver of a truck from the Department of Buildings and Grounds for the Commonwealth. The boxes of examinations were loaded into the truck and transported to a recycling facility. Dorsey and her colleague climbed a metal rung ladder to the upper level of the plant to observe the used examination booklets as they were fed into the hopper for shredding and recycling. The local destruction was authorized through an amendment to the Security Measures included in the contract between NCSBN and the member board.

In the summer of 1979 NCSBN faced an incident at one of the examination sites in New York during the administration of Series 779 that threatened the new organization. The following headlines appeared in the *New York Times* on September 16, 1979:

STATE IS REJECTING TESTS GIVEN NURSES THROUGHOUT NATION
12,000 MUST TAKE NEW EXAMS
Education Department Is Acting Because Questions May have Been Sold In Advance[58]

This incident was first discussed by the board of directors during a conference call on July 25, 1979. Mildred Schmidt was president of NCSBN and executive secretary for the New York State Board of Nurse Examiners. She presented information that the State Education Department in New York had received 13 letters alleging that the questions on the Series 779 were available to candidates prior to the examination. The first indication of a problem surfaced on July 11 when candidate A at the New York Coliseum told the examiner at the end of the second day that she had talked to candidate B on the subway on the first day of the examination. Candidate B was reported to have said she had a copy of the examination and showed it to Candidate A. Candidate A reported that she recognized questions on the Medical Nursing test, but refused to identify herself by name. Another candidate wrote a letter stating that she had seen questions from the Nursing of Children test and, in a separate incident, one of the Psychiatric Nursing test booklets was missing. The NLN and the State Education Department of New York were involved in the investigation. The board of directors asked Elaine Laeger of Arizona, Area I Director; Marianna Bacigalupo of New Jersey, former chair of the AEC Committee; David Grams, legal counsel; and Grams' associate Rebecca Erhardt to locate and employ an investigator in New York to act on behalf of NCSBN. A decision had been reached in New York that the board there would not release any results from Series 779 until the investigation was complete. The board of directors decided to send a memorandum to the member boards stating that the allegations had been received and were under investigation.[59]

Within a week, the board of directors convened again by telephone. The New York Board had received 15 more letters regarding the security break. The NCSBN investigator had been employed at a fee of $120 per hour with a retainer of $10,000. The board of directors began the process of evaluating ways to adjust the budget to meet the anticipated costs of the investigation and appointed Laeger and Joyce Schowalter of Minnesota, the Area II Director, to an ad hoc committee to assist the attorney in monitoring the investigation. The board learned of an additional problem where a candidate from Florida intended to sue the NLN because of a keying error on Series 279, claiming "she suffered a loss of income and great humiliation."[60] Sachs had reported that there was an error in keying one question on the Nursing of Children test. Candidates in 40 states were affected as follows:

- 285 candidates reported as failing, now passed.

- 108 candidates now passed the entire examination.

- 70 candidates reported as passing now failed Nursing of Children, but may have passed other parts of the examination.

- 12 candidates from 8 jurisdictions failed only Nursing of Children.

After considering the alternatives the board of directors decided to agree to double-key the item, or accept two answers. As a result, the fewest candidates would be affected; it would allow the licensing of those previously shown as failing; and no one originally passing would fail, thus, there would be no recall of licenses.[61]

A third conference call related to the security break was held on September 11, 1979. This was the first meeting at which Eileen McQuaid was identified as the executive director. The call was initiated and paid for by the New York State Board of Nursing. Mildred Schmidt, in her role as executive secretary of the New York Board, reported that the commissioner of Education for New York had:

- Declared the July examination invalid and the results void for New York candidates and for anyone seeking licensure in New York.

- Determined that the scores would not be released to the approximately 12,000 candidates who took the examination in New York.

- Reported that statistical studies showed "there is no identifiable pattern in the answers given by domestic candidates, but a clear pattern of reducing the failure rate for the foreign candidates had occurred."

The board of directors asked Schmidt to send the information shown above with the supporting material to NCSBN Counsel David Grams, NLN Counsel Edward Spencer, and the NCSBN office.[62]

At the regular meeting of the board of directors in September, the board adopted a motion to accept the recommendations of the Committee to Monitor the Investigation regarding the administration of Series 280 as follows: to offer New York the option to purchase items from the test pool to compile a special examination for February 1980 and to identify candidates who took Series 779 in New York as "irregular (as opposed to first-time) candidates" for Series 280 in other states. In other action, two board members were asked to draft a statement for a press release to be sent to the member boards.[63] A copy of this press release was attached to the minutes of the November 26–28, 1979 meeting of the board of directors and is shown, in part, below (abbreviations have been used to reduce length of the entry):

PRESS RELEASE—For release at 2:00 CDT Thursday, September 27, 1979

The NCSBN Board of Directors at its regular meeting in Chicago, September 24–26, 1979, considered the alleged security break involving the SBTPE for RN licensure administered on July 10 and 11, 1979. The NCSBN owns the examinations and authorizes their use. The examinations are administered twice a year on uniform testing dates for RN licensure and for PN licensure in 53 jurisdictions. Even though the NCSBN owns the examination, each board of nursing is responsible for decisions regarding its use for nurse licensure.

As a result of the allegations that test questions were available to candidates prior to the July examination, a full-scale investigation is being conducted by the NCSBN in cooperation with its testing service, the NLN. On September 15, 1979, the New York State Education Department advised the NCSBN of its decision that scores from the July testing would not be used for licensure in New York State. In recognition of the fact that New York's decision is a jurisdictional prerogative, the Board of Directors of the NCSBN voted to take no official position regarding the decision. Neither the investigation nor the statistical analysis has as yet uncovered sufficient information to confirm or deny that the security of this examination was breached; preliminary information indicates that the problem appears to be localized and limited to relatively few candidates. However, the NCSBN is extremely concerned that the integrity of the examination be maintained to assure the public that individuals licensed on the basis of passing the examination are safe and competent to practice nursing. The NCSBN is vigorously pursuing the investigation and has acted to assure the security of the SBTPE.[64]

A file located in the office of the Virginia Board of Nursing contained subsequent news releases from the Virginia, North Carolina, New York, and California boards of nursing and from the New York State Nurses Association. Copies of articles from the *New York Times*, *Norfolk Virginian-Pilot* and *Ledger-Star*, *Washington Post*, *Buffalo Courier Express*, and *Buffalo News* were also found. A report of the Ad

Hoc Committee to Monitor the Investigation was attached to the minutes of the board of directors November 26–28, 1979 meeting. On October 26 President Schmidt reported that the State Education Department was issuing a press release that announced, in part, that the State Police had reported that the investigation disclosed no evidence that any part of the examination was available in advance to any candidate and no evidence of improper conduct on the part of any person connected with the preparation or administration of the examination was found. She said that the state would move quickly to distribute the results and grant licenses to those who passed. A memorandum was sent to the member boards on November 2 advising that the investigation was concluded. Interviews with candidates in New York and Illinois alleged to have access to the examination questions showed that all had taken a review course and received simulated tests, which closely resembled the SBTPE.[65]

The cost of this incident to NCSBN, a total of $28,475, resulted in a deficit in the budget. In the Report of the Treasurer in 1980, Merlyn Maillian of Louisiana-RN said that the test security investigation cost approximately $40,000.[66] Dr. Lorraine Sachs of the NLN reported that the analysis of the questions from Series 779, with material from the review course, showed 8 items were almost exactly the same. There were 13 items that showed responses too similar to have occurred coincidentally. The board of directors approved the document titled "Guidelines for Investigation of Allegations of Security Breaks Concerning the SBTPE." In 2006 Joyce Schowalter, coauthor of this book, reviewed the information that she had retained from her involvement in the investigation. The incident was one of the first tests of the examination security procedures of the new organization, particularly with a large state like New York with their many candidates. The investigators could not prove that there was a break in security despite suspicious circumstances and statistics consistent with a break. This was one of the situations that led the organization to make significant changes in the required procedures for the administration of the examinations and in the Security Measures utilized when handling examinations. Comprehensive policies and procedures were developed for investigating alleged security breaks. Although this event and the extensive investigation put a financial burden on the fledgling organization, the board of directors at the time recognized the need to take thorough and decisive action. The details of this particular security break are included because of the impact on the organization. The response to this incident reflects the strength and commitment of the leaders of the organization and the member boards.

At the March 1982 meeting the board was once again faced with problems related to the administration of examinations. Due to a winter storm in February many candidates were unable to reach the examination sites in Illinois and Missouri. The board approved the use of an alternate examination to be administered in March or April to those candidates who could not reach the examination sites.[66] The NLN Test Service reported that several booklets from various parts of the examination were missing from those shipped from Montana and North Dakota on arrival at the test service. Joyce Schowalter, vice president, and Sandra MacKenzie of Minnesota, chair of the AEC, were assigned to participate in the investigation.[67]

Chair MacKenzie reported to the board of directors at its June meeting regarding the investigation of the test booklets lost in shipment following the administration of Series 282. The board took the following actions:

- Directed the AEC to identify all times and ways security could be breached and, when possible, suggest how to deal with each.

- Directed staff to work with the test service to develop a rapid reporting system when the loss of questions is involved and to propose revision of standing rules governing investigation of alleged security breaks.

- Instructed the Examination Committee to reduce the examination to the minimum length needed to measure essential knowledge as soon as possible to reduce the volume.

- Asked CTB to keep NCSBN informed about the feasibility of testing by methods not requiring physical transportation of test questions and answer sheets.

- Took action to facilitate local destruction of test booklets.[68]

Concerns about examinations continued to occupy the meetings of the board of directors and the AEC in 1983. The board issued letters of concern and reprimands to several member boards and appointed an ad hoc committee to consider issues of security as they affected NCSBN. This committee also looked at security in relation to member boards, the test service, and the public. The board directed the committee to do a basic evaluation of NCSBN security needs and to identify proposed methods of meeting these needs.[69] In August the board of directors learned that three cartons of test booklets for Series 783 were lost during return shipment from Massachusetts.[70] At the annual meeting in August the delegate assembly approved changes in the Security Measures as recommended by the AEC.[71] In the report of the AEC in December, the chair reported that three member boards failed to follow Security Measures and failed to institute procedures to comply with the requirements for inventory, packaging, and return of examination materials.[72]

In May 1984 the board voted to reprimand the Virginia Board of Nursing for retaining 11 copies of the four booklets from Series 782.[73] The booklets had been obtained for the Virginia Board to review when questions were raised about the content of the examinations. When that activity was completed, the booklets were placed in a locked file and found again at the time of a change in board staff. At the February 1987 meeting the board of directors reprimanded the New Hampshire Board of Nursing for allowing a candidate to copy and retain the complete text of an item that the candidate believed to be faulty. This item was removed from the pool.[74]

Another potentially serious security break occurred in January 1988. During the shipment of NCLEX-RN 288 materials, one box was separated from a shipment to a California test site. CTB initiated a trace and the box was recovered. However, the box and one package of test books had been opened. NCSBN determined that a security break had occurred and implemented the disaster plan. The California Division of Investigation initiated its investigation supported by the CTB staff, printing facility staff, and McGraw-Hill corporate security officers. CTB worked with the Examination Committee to select and ensure the currency of the disaster plan alternate examination that was administered in some states in March. A retest was administered in some states in April.[75] CTB conducted an anomaly analysis on the test books of all candidates for 288 and reported to NCSBN and the affected member boards. The purpose of this analysis was to determine whether the candidates' performance was consistent through all of the books of the examination.

The Report of the Board of Directors in the 1988 *NCSBN Book of Reports* included discussion of the security break and a summary of the actions the board took, including:

- Provision to member boards of a draft letter to notify candidates that NCLEX results indicated anomaly.

- Direction to the AEC to review the disaster procedures, security break reporting procedures, and shipment security procedures.

- Authorization of treatment of flagged candidates as normal failing candidates, not identifying them individually in any way.

- Selection of the one in one hundred (.01) level of significance for flagging of anomalous performance among the passing candidates.

- Direction to the test service to rescore the flagged candidates on the basis of booklets 1, 3, and 4 using the established policy for scoring on the basis of three booklets.

- Authorization of the release of NCLEX-RN 288 indeterminate candidate's scores to the states upon written request.

- Agreement to provide member boards a summary of actions taken by states with indeterminate scores.[76]

AEC Chair McGuill also included a review of the security break in her report to the delegate assembly in 1988. She stated that a readable palm print was found in one of the test books, and the Los Angeles County District Attorney had arrested an employee of the shipper on charges of felony theft and embezzlement of the NCLEX-RN.[77] An article in the *Newsletter to the Member Boards* of February 19, reported that 12 boards would administer the alternate examination in March while 44 states had administered the examination in February as scheduled.[78] In the April 1 issue, a report stated that 14 member boards with a total of 33 candidates with indeterminate status were currently in the process of making decisions regarding the opportunity to retest on April 12 and 13, 1988.[79] In December Neil Redfern, the man charged in this matter, pled guilty to one count of grand theft and received a one-year suspended sentence, 36 months probation, 400 hours of community service, a fine of $1,000, $2,500 restitution to the state, and a $1,300 penalty.[80] Eventually all member boards agreed to accept those licensed from the compromised examination for licensure by endorsement.

On December 14, 1988, the board of directors learned that nine candidates in Missouri had received passing scores on the NCLEX-PN Form 088 that should have been failing due to "erroneous score reports." The board took the following actions:

- Determined that nine candidates should have received failing scores but did not owing to human error which caused a disaster beyond the control of the candidates and the Missouri Board of Nursing.

- Authorized the Missouri Board of Nursing to administer an alternate examination to the nine candidates prior to the 489 NCLEX-PN.

- Directed CTB to develop a financial package to compensate the involved parties for certain expenses incurred as a result of the error.[81]

Security issues continued to require the attention of the board of directors in 1989. The board of directors sent a letter of concern to the California Board of Vocational Nurse and Psychiatric Technician Examiners because of unauthorized access to the shipment of the 488 examination books.[82] At its meeting in August 1990, the board of directors learned of a security break in Indiana that involved a missing book from NCLEX-RN 790. At that time the test service was conducting a statistical analysis of the examination and appropriate investigation was in progress.[83] In a conference call in August the board of directors concluded that wide dissemination of the missing book had not occurred, and approved the release of the test results to the member boards.[84] The board subsequently reprimanded the Indiana Board of Nursing.

In 1991 the board considered a challenge by a candidate of two items on NCLEX-RN 790 and, after reviewing the content validity and psychometric soundness of the items, denied the challenges. At the same meeting the board of directors considered a request from an attorney of a candidate from Oregon. The candidate had been denied licensure on the basis of a cheating analysis performed by CTB. The board agreed to allow the candidate to review the examination under secure conditions with certain restrictions. The board also decided that NCLEX-RN 790 would not be used as a reserve examination in the future because of the possible exposure of the questions in the missing book, that the Oregon Board of Nursing must submit an addendum to its normal procedure for candidate review, and that Oregon must bear the expense of preparation of books as established by CTB.[85]

Another security break was described in the *Newsletter to the Member Boards* dated September 25, 1992. A security break occurred in New Jersey and the board of nursing there reported that two test books were missing from a box containing Book 3. When the shipment of the completed examinations from New Jersey was returned to CTB, further review disclosed that one copy each of Books 1 and 2 and two copies each of Books 3 and 4 were missing. Evidence showed that the theft occurred between the first and second day, therefore Books 3 and 4 were in circulation before administration. CTB performed an analysis to determine how widespread the exposure was and whether or not there were individuals with access to the books. The board of directors determined there was not widespread dissemination of the examination content. Individual performance anomalies were reported to the appropriate state for decision.[86] State actions were reported in December. The following listing was included in the report related to candidates with performance anomalies:

California	Licensed two passing candidates and an anomaly study was requested on all California candidates. If further evidence were to surface, appropriate action would be taken.
Florida	One candidate failed.
Illinois	One passing candidate was licensed. The investigation was continuing.
New York	One passing candidate was licensed. If definite proof was established that the candidates had access, the New York Board would reopen the case.[87]

At its meeting in October the board of directors reviewed the report of the security break investigation to date, and authorized the investigation of RN review books and courses in order to detect "leakage" of the NCLEX.[88] In a conference call on December 21, 1992, the board agreed to charge $53,273 as a financial claim to the state of New Jersey for expenses associated with the July security break. The board issued letters of concern to two member boards (states not identified in the minutes) and to CTB when the member boards failed to return test books properly and the test service did not discover this until reported by the member boards.[89]

Security breaks and problems with the shipment of examinations continued in 1993. In April material sent by the Georgia PN Board to CTB were not received. The board of directors asked CTB to score the examinations of candidates for whom all books were received and to release these scores on the normal schedule.[90] Following the administration of the NCLEX-PN in October in New York, a test book was reported missing, and in December, the board of directors issued a reprimand to the New York Board and charged it with appropriate costs of the investigation.[91]

The board issued a reprimand in 1994 to CTB for a security break during the NCLEX-PN 093 and invoiced the costs of the investigation to CTB. A second reprimand was issued to the New York State Board of Nursing as the result of a security break during NCLEX-RN 294. The costs of the investigation were billed to New York.[92] This event occurred during the last paper and pencil examination. One book from the second part of the examination was missing, but there was no evidence that the scores of the examination were jeopardized and the scores were released to the member boards.[93]

The April 21, 1995, issue of the *Newsletter to the Member Boards* reported that a NCLEX candidate was arrested for bribery. The candidate attempted to bribe a test center employee by offering $1,000 for a passing result. NCSBN and the New York State Board of Nursing participated in the investigation. The candidate failed, but had mailed $300 to the examiner and asked the examiner to call her. An investigator posed as the test center administrator and made the contact. The candidate appeared for the appointment in April and was arrested after offering $700 to the undercover investigator. The candidate faced the possibility of up to seven years in prison and a $5,000 fine.[94]

Ongoing Examination-Related Activities

At the 1979 meeting of the delegate assembly in June, the delegates adopted additional dates of future examinations as recommended by the AEC in order to have a schedule of dates available for 10 years into the future. This activity continued at each meeting of the delegate assembly until the end of the administration of the paper and pencil examination. At the same meeting, in the report of the test service, Sachs stated that the requests for hand scoring had increased following the application of a fee for the service and that a study showed that "technical language on the SBTPE was that used in textbooks."[95]

From time to time the board of directors addressed concerns about the evaluation of "experimental items." Some candidates refused to take the last booklet of the examination which was made up of new items and a part of the final step in the process of placing items into the test pool. At the 1979 delegate assembly meeting a motion was adopted to ask legal counsel for an interpretation as to whether or not to require the experimental test as part of the SBTPE.[96]

Included in the Report of the Examination Committee at the 1980 annual meeting, the following listing outlined the activities of that committee, which would recur over the subsequent years:

- Reviewed approximately 4,740 test items and adopted Series 280, Form 480, Series 790, and Form 080 and the item analysis tests for each.

- Developed confidential directions for Series 780 and 281, Form 080 and 481 and for use by RN item writers in the fall of 1979 and PN/VN item writers in the spring of 1980.

- Studied the member board reviews of 871 new items for future RN examinations and 700 for future PN/VN examinations and approved 771 and 625 respectively.

In addition, the Examination Committee reviewed the current PN Test Plan and recommended that a critical incident study be done to establish the current practice of the LPN/VN, with the results to be used for revision of the test plan.[97]

In 1980 Chair Geraldine Wenger presented the report of the AEC Committee at the annual meeting and stated some of the ongoing activities completed by the committee:

- Approved Security Measures for 19 jurisdictions regarding examination centers, seating arrangements, and storage of test booklets.

- Reviewed and approved updated Security Measures in the 1981 and 1982 review cycle.

- Reviewed and approved full Security Measures for 20 member boards.

- Reviewed reports of anomalies including defective booklets and missing booklets.

- Determined there were two violations of Security Measures and referred them to the board of directors.

A member of the AEC made a visit to observe the administration of an examination in one jurisdiction and recommended that the board of directors approve a request from Virginia to continue to destroy test booklets permanently and to revise the contract accordingly. The AEC recommended that a review of Security Measures be required if there is a major change with regard to the administration of the examination, a security problem, any other unforeseen circumstance, or an appointment of a new executive director for the member board. The delegate assembly adopted this recommendation and the proposed dates for the 1991 examinations.[98]

The board of directors, the Examination Committee and the AEC reported extensively on their activities in the 1981 *NCSBN Book of Reports* prepared for the annual meeting. In March a state senator from Illinois was present at the meeting of the board to recommend that NCSBN administer the SBTPE in other countries. The board directed staff to prepare a proposal for consideration by the delegate assembly.[99] The minutes of the meeting of the delegate assembly included a report of the board of directors with a recommendation for amendments to the contract with the member boards to require at least one RN board or staff member at the examination sites except where a test administrative service approved by NCSBN was used, and that the member board designate an RN to have administrative responsibility for compliance with the contract.[100]

The Report of the Examination Committee in 1981 presented by Chair Sheridan discussed the comparison of the CNATS to the SBTPE. The committee concluded that while the CNATS was more similar to the SBTPE than any other examination, it differed in the following ways:

- The standardization population for CNATS was different from that of the SBTPE.
- The passing score for CNATS was 350, but was not comparable to 350 on the SBTPE or the 1600 for the new test plan.
- Individual states could set a pass score for CNATS at 400 to adjust to SBTPE pass score.
- Each edition of CNATS was administered three times before a new examination while each series of the SBTPE was used only once.[101]

Based on recommendations from the Examination Committee to the delegate assembly, the delegates took the following actions:

- Requested the member boards to reevaluate rules and policies for licensure of Canadian nurses in view of recent information about the CNATS examination.
- Authorized exploration and development of a clinical simulation examination as a diagnostic tool for candidates for licensure. Such a test had been developed as part of the study "Evaluating the Validity of the SBTPE."[102]

The delegate assembly adopted the following statement presented by the AEC: "contracts with Member Boards shall permit the administration of the licensure examination to individuals whose licenses have been revoked through legal action and who are seeking relicensure."[103] In another action, the delegate assembly adopted a statement recommended by the member boards in Area IV:

Boards of Nursing will advise candidates at the time of initial release of their scores to them that the use of scores for any purpose other than licensure is not appropriate and, therefore, the board of nursing will not provide a copy of licensing examination scores to a prospective employer or to a graduate nursing program.[104]

During a conference call meeting in October 1982 the board of directors learned that the California Board of Registered Nursing had received a subpoena for copies of the SBTPE for RNs administered from July 1980 through February 1982. The California Board had review copies of Series 282 and 782 in its possession. The board authorized the president to take all steps desirable, appropriate, or necessary to obtain possession of the Series 782 booklets held by the California Board. No action would be taken in relation to Series 282 since it was the subject of an earlier security breach and was assumed to have been made public.[105]

Throughout 1982 the board of directors and the committees continued their normal responsibilities related to the examinations. In addition, the board also acted on some different agenda items during this period. In March the board of directors agreed to limit the number of items per NCLEX test booklet to

120 with a time of two hours per booklet.[106] At the meeting in June the board appointed item writers and members of a panel of judges who assisted in determining how the examinations would be scored.[107] Later a decision was reached to score all booklets for the NCLEX, even if the candidate did not write all booklets in a series or form, since it was possible to pass without completing all. The board of directors established a system for hand scoring the NCLEX with a fee of $115 for NCLEX-RN and $100 for NCLEX-PN. The board also asked the Examination Committee to again review the comparability of CNATS with the NCLEX-RN.[108]

The delegate assembly considered several reports and recommendations in 1982 and took the following actions:

- Defeated a motion to continue investigating the administration of the licensing examination in foreign countries.

- Adopted a recommendation from the Examination Committee presented by Chair Louise Sanders, Texas-RN, to include nurses who are responsible for direct care to patients as nominees for item writers and to develop a diagnostic profile for failed candidates to be initiated with Series 283.

- Adopted a recommendation from the AEC presented by Chair MacKenzie to review the member board Security Measures every four years.

- Agreed to changes to the contract between NCSBN and the member boards regarding review of the examinations.

- Referred the issue of a procedure for failed candidates to review the examination, including security, to the AEC for consideration.[109]

In other actions on examination issues at its meeting in August 1983, the delegate assembly agreed to permit member boards to administer the NCLEX to individuals whose licenses had lapsed and approved a procedure for review of a license examination by failure candidates. The delegates also adopted a motion to provide to schools of nursing, upon request, aggregate performance profile data on its candidates for each examination series or form in relation to the test plans. The cost of this service was to be paid by the schools requesting the service.[110]

In the Report of the Examination Committee in the 1983 *NCSBN Book of Reports*, Chair Sanders reported on the study of the comparability of CNATS and NCLEX-RN. The information received from CNATS was limited, but the following areas were compared: test plans, job relatedness, item development and review, statistics, bias, security, testing dates, and content validity. The committee reported some similarities and some differences but stated, "To the knowledge of the Examination Committee, there is no way to determine comparability of the two examinations without a research study."[111]

At its December 1983 meeting, the board of directors directed staff to express "extreme displeasure" to CTB regarding an error in the examination key sent to the California Board of Registered Nursing for review of Series 783 of the NCLEX-RN. The board asked for an apology to the California Board and a report of how CTB would prevent a recurrence of this error.[112]

Comprehensive articles in *Issues* in the spring and summer of 1983 presented clear and concise information about the development, construction, and scoring of the NCLEX.[113] Another article, also in the spring issue, "Diagnostic Profile for Failure Candidates," presented a general description of what is included in the profile of the performance of the candidate in relation to the components of the test plan and how it was to be interpreted.[114]

The biweekly *Newsletter to the Member Boards*, first issued in January 1983, was used extensively for sharing information about the NCLEX. Almost every issue contained reminders about such issues as deadlines for hand scoring, correcting program codes, distribution of scoring reports, nominations for item writers, filing late applications, contacting American Express International regarding the return of test booklets, instructions for item review, packing booklets for shipment, sample letters, manuals and revisions, guides for reporting unusual incidents, damaged container forms, examination preparation checklists, and the return of the jurisdiction control file from member boards to CTB. One issue, which contained a statement regarding the hand scoring of examinations, noted that all examinations with scores close to the cut score (score that determines pass/fail) were automatically hand scored as part of the quality assurance procedure. At that time, none of the hand scores had resulted in the changing of any scores.

The board of directors continued to devote a large amount of time to issues related to the examinations in 1984. However, with the adjustment to the new test service and the new test plan accomplished, the board was able to increase its focus on other matters. In April the board asked President Schowalter, Executive Director McQuaid Dvorak, and Legal Counsel O'Brien to negotiate a contract with ACT to conduct research of a job analysis, role delineation, and nursing practice. The board authorized the president to sign the agreed contract. In response to a proposed disaster plan, the board of directors agreed that 90,000 secure copies of the NCLEX-RN and 40,000 of the NCLEX-PN would be printed to create a reserve examination. The plan included a process to continue to add to the reserve each year and to discard six-year old booklets each year.[115] CTB sponsored an Invitational Conference in Monterey, California, in 1984 to provide the opportunity for member boards to learn more about the processes involved in the NCLEX. The conference was well attended and became an annual event for ensuing years.[116]

In other actions in 1984, the board directed the AEC to develop guidelines for use in emergencies during an examination when the collection of test booklets is required. In addition, the board authorized McQuaid Dvorak to explore with the California Board of Vocational Nurses and Psychiatric Technicians Examiners (California-VN), membership issues and possible purchase by NCSBN of the examination questions owned by that board.[117] The board also discussed questions related to licensure by endorsement to other states for California LPN/VNs who had been licensed from 1974, until such time as California-VN would begin the use of the NCLEX-PN. California-VN became a member of NCSBN in 1986. Many states required those licensed by the California-owned examination prior to 1986 to take the SBTPE and later, the NCLEX-PN in order to be licensed in the new state.[118]

Sandra MacKenzie of Minnesota, chair of the AEC, reported on that committee's activities at the meeting of the delegate assembly in 1984. The AEC developed three options for member boards to use for candidates who needed to have the NCLEX read to them. These options were to use a professionally prepared tape, a non-professionally prepared tape, or a reader.[119] McKenzie also reported that the committee examined the question of changing the time of year for administration of the PN examination. A survey of member boards on this question showed no overwhelming support for the change.[120] The delegate assembly gave special recognition to MacKenzie for her contributions to the organization and her service as a member and chair of the AEC from 1979 to 1984.

The Report of the Nursing Practice and Standards Committee in 1984 included a statement on rewriting the NCLEX in which it made the following recommendation: "To place no limitation on the number of times a candidate may rewrite the examination or on the time period within which a candidate may make repeated attempts." The delegate assembly adopted the statement and asked the member boards to give favorable consideration to its adoption.[121]

In 1985 the board of directors approved a confidentiality agreement developed by the AEC to be signed by all persons who work with confidential examination material. The board approved language for a contract with the California Board of Vocational Nurses and Psychiatric Technician Examiners to enable membership in NCSBN and authorized the executive director of NCSBN to purchase items in the item bank of that board.[122]

Leola Daniels of Idaho chaired the AEC in 1985. In February the board of directors accepted a recommendation to send a letter of concern to a member board when an unauthorized person had access to a locked area containing test booklets. At that same meeting the board of directors denied additional time for a candidate with a learning disability related to "a cultural deficit and a language barrier."[123] Louise Sanders, chair of the Examination Committee, reported that the board of directors had approved a recommended policy to use the term "form" in future editions of the NCLEX-RN and -PN rather than the current terms "series" and "forms" respectively. Further, the booklets would be designated "parts" rather than "books."[124]

In February 1986 the board of directors met in an executive session during a conference call for the purpose of discussing potential litigation against NCSBN by The Mosby Company regarding NCSBN's pretest. Although the discussions regarding the potential litigation occurred in executive session, the basis was largely centered around potential conflict of interest regarding the development and sale of a pretest for examination candidates. The board adopted the following motion:

That the National Council of State Boards of Nursing authorize the release of NCLEX® data, other than the text of individual questions, at a commercially reasonable rate to any interested party for its use to perform linkage studies for pretests upon similar conditions to those upon which such data have been made available to CTB/McGraw-Hill, including the requirement that consent of any individual candidate and the state board be obtained prior to the release of individual data.[125]

Subsequently, at meetings late in February, early March, and again in April, the board of directors continued to discuss the threat of litigation by The Mosby Company regarding the pretest. In April, the board learned that litigation had been filed by Mosby against NCSBN, CTB, and the NLN. The board gave direction to legal counsel and staff related to negotiations for a possible settlement.[126]

At its April 1986 meeting the board of directors appointed a primary negotiating team composed of Joyce Schowalter, Executive Director Jennifer Bosma, and Legal Counsel Thomas O'Brien to negotiate with CTB as the test service and data center for NCLEX for the period of October 1988 through September 1991.[127] At the July meeting the negotiating team made its report and the board agreed to recommend to the delegate assembly that CTB continue as the test service and data center.[128] The delegates approved the recommendation.

Harriet Johnson of New Jersey, chair of the Examination Committee, presented a recommendation to the delegate assembly in 1986 to initiate a policy for reporting the results of the examination with "pass" for a passing score and a numeric score for failure. The committee had addressed this issue because of questionable uses made by employers and educational institutions of numeric scores when considering applications from nurses. The only proper use of these scores was the decision of whether or not to issue a license. The recommendation was referred back to the committee.[129] The delegate assembly directed the Examination Committee to revise the NCLEX-RN® Test Plan as needed based on the *Study of Nursing Practice and Role Delineation and Job Analysis of Entry Level Registered Nurses* completed in 1986.[130] The board of directors authorized ACT to conduct a job analysis of entry level LPN/VNs during FY87–88. The delegate assembly adopted a resolution entitled "Future Direction for Development of New Licensure Examinations."[131] The board appointed a task force "to explore and plan for the development of new licensure examinations that address the competencies of evolving levels of nursing practice," to respond to the intent of the resolution. An article in *Issues* reported that "the first computer adaptive administration of NCLEX items was demonstrated to participants at the 1986 delegate assembly."[132]

The board of directors, several committees, and the delegate assembly devoted a significant amount of time to reports and actions related to both current and future examinations in 1987. At the February meeting the board authorized the use of the assumptions related to NCSBN as a test service that had been developed by staff and revised by the board for continuing study of the feasibility of NCSBN becoming its own test service.[133] However, when the delegate assembly met in August, it adopted a resolution stating that all consideration of NCSBN becoming its own test service was to be discontinued. The rationale for this resolution was, in part, that resources were needed to continue experimental test development and the opportunity for objective comparison of proposals to produce the examination would be lost.[134]

Rosalie Seymour, executive director for the Delaware Board of Nursing, had met with the board of directors in May to propose that the Delaware Board be allowed to administer NCLEX-PN in Germany to 400 U.S. Army personnel with the military occupational specialty (MOS) of 91C. The designation 91C refers to a U.S. Army course to prepare personnel for the specialty. (The education for the MOS was generally equivalent to that required for licensure as a PN/VN and most member boards admitted the graduates of the course to the licensing examination.) The Army had assigned these soldiers to duty overseas prior to the time that the Army established rules requiring that they be licensed. The board agreed to refer the question to the delegate assembly.[135] At its meeting, the delegate assembly authorized the Delaware Board of Nursing to administer NCLEX-PN to a maximum of 105 eligible U.S. Army 91C's in Germany in October 1987 and the same number five more times over 36 months, after evaluation of the first administration by the Delaware Board.[136]

The 1987 *NCSBN Book of Reports* used at the annual meeting also reflected activities related to examinations by the various groups within NCSBN. In the Report of the Test Service, there was mention of the number of tests administered from July 1986 through April 1987 as follows: to RN candidates: 108,981 and to PN candidates: 47,084.[137] Chair Johnson of the Examination Committee Team I presented a recommendation to adopt the proposed revisions to the RN test plan.[138] Renatta Loquist of South Carolina, chair of Examination Committee Team II, presented a policy of reporting scores on the NCLEX as pass/fail effective in October 1988, with failing candidates receiving enhanced diagnostic profiles.[139] The delegates agreed to the recommendations from both teams.[140] The Examination Committee had been divided into two teams because of the increasing work assigned to it.

The 1987 issues of the *Newsletter to the Member Boards* continued to include much information related to examinations. There were two papers related to the pass/fail score reports. One was written by Kara C. Schmidt, director of the Office of Testing Services, Michigan Department of Licensure and Regulation. She supported reporting "pass" to successful candidates to avoid "abuses" of numeric score reporting, but she advocated that failing candidates receive numeric scores with diagnostic information. The second paper was prepared by Thomas O'Brien, legal counsel for NCSBN. He spoke to misuse of numeric scores that could result in litigation, impair the security or validation processes, increase expenditures for legal fees, and bring about unfavorable publicity.[141]

The paragraphs that follow will illustrate the magnitude of the work of the committees and the board of directors as NCSBN became more involved in CAT. At the 1988 meeting of the delegate assembly, Chair McGuill presented recommendations from the AEC. The delegates authorized the committee to develop the policies and procedures for computerized testing and adopted the crisis management plan for the examinations.[142] Chair Johnson presented the Report of the Examination Committee and the delegates authorized the committee to prepare a revision of the NCLEX-PN® Test Plan.[143]

Joan Bouchard of Oregon, chair of the Task Force on Examinations for the Future, presented a task force report to the delegate assembly in 1988. She recommended that the delegates authorize the Nursing Practice and Education (NP&E) Committee to review data relative to LPN/VN competencies, synthesize these competencies, and determine their relationship to the competencies synthesized by the task force in FY88. Details of the task force report were printed in the 1988 *NCSBN Book of Reports*.[144]

At its meeting from January 29 through February 1, 1989, the board of directors learned that an increase in the frequency of the NCLEX-RN would require an additional per candidate cost of seven dollars. The board decided to survey the member boards about the need to increase the frequency.[145] In May the board decided that the result of the survey did not support presenting a recommendation to the delegate assembly.[146] The delegate assembly adopted a resolution requiring NCSBN to explore the feasibility of the administration of a third NCLEX-RN and -PN annually and to report the findings to the 1990 delegate assembly.[147]

In April 1989 Meredith Mullins, NCLEX project director for CTB, presented to the board of directors an unsolicited proposal for a contract extension for both the test service and the data center. The board referred the proposal for extension of the contract from 1991 to 1993 to the delegate assembly, with the condition that the test service evaluation be completed in time for consideration by the board at its July meeting. The board selected Dumond and Associates as the independent firm to assist with the evaluation and appointed Treasurer Donna Dorsey, Executive Director Jennifer Bosma and Legal Counsel Thomas O'Brien to discuss definitive terms of the proposal with CTB.[148] The delegate assembly acted on the matter in August, deciding that in lieu of issuing a request for proposals in the fall of 1989, the test service and data center contract with CTB be extended from 1991 to 1993.[149] The complete name of the CTB was changed in 1989 to "CTB, a division of Macmillan/McGraw-Hill School Publishing Company."[150]

There were no major problems with the administration of examinations in 1989, but the board of directors did send a letter of concern to the California-VN Board because of unauthorized access to the shipment of the 488 examination books.[151] At the request of the AEC the board agreed to incorporate the critical incident approach in the FY90 job analysis study, and appointed two external individuals to NCSBN to meet two times, first to evaluate the methodology for the study and again at the end to evaluate the interpretation of the results.[152] Subsequently, Michael Kane from ACT and Angeline Jacobs from Azusa Pacific University were named to this External Job Analysis Panel.[153]

In August 1989, the delegate assembly adopted the revisions of the NCLEX-PN® Test Plan as developed by the Examination Committee. The delegates also adopted a motion to conduct the RN and PN job analyses on a regular schedule, but no less frequently than every three years on a rotating basis so that the analyses would not occur simultaneously.[154] Further, the delegates adopted a resolution that NCSBN continue to utilize industry standards such as the guidelines of the American Educational Research Association, the American Psychological Association, and the National Council on Measurement in Education in the preparation of valid, current, and legally defensible licensure examinations.

In 1990, the Examination Committee again attempted to compare the CNATS examination with the NCLEX-RN. The board of directors reviewed a draft report of the comparison in January and agreed to send the report to the CNATS for review.[155] Examination Committee Chair Dorothy Chesley of Texas-RN prepared an attachment to an April *Newsletter to the Member Boards* to provide information for the comparison of the CNATS examination to the NCLEX-RN. She said that the report was based only on information provided by the CNATS and that some material requested, such as statistics and the passing rates, was not provided because it was classified as confidential. Chesley stated that another limitation of the comparison was that only a paper comparison was done. A direct psychometric comparison would require research such as obtaining CNATS and NCLEX-RN results for a selected groups of candidates and thereby equating the two. The conclusion presented by the Examination Committee was that it could not conclude the equivalency of the two examinations. The major factors leading to this conclusion were the lack of a job analysis and the norm referenced scoring of the CNATS examination. Finally, the report stated that without extensive research and additional information, no further comparison could be done by the committee at that time.[156]

Lucille Joel, president of the ANA, was present for the open forum session on April 30, 1990, during the board of directors meeting, Joel discussed the view of the ANA on the development of an examination for graduates of baccalaureate in nursing programs. She reported that the ANA had approved a business plan for a free-standing credentialing center and said she believed that differentiated practice (by educational preparation) with different licensure would not occur until the ANA, other nursing and health care organizations, and the public brought it about in the workplace. She inquired about the acceptability of the ANA's examination for graduates from a generic baccalaureate program for licensure if and when statutory change occurred. She also offered to provide information on additional sites where individuals might be engaged in differentiated practice, and could be surveyed for a job analysis. The Task Force on Examinations for the Future was having difficulty in locating individuals for such a survey.[157] At its July meeting, the board of directors accepted a recommendation for the AEC to explore the feasibility of decreasing the administration time of NCLEX-RN.[158]

The delegate assembly adopted revisions to the NCLEX-PN® Test Plan in 1989. The board of directors set a new passing standard for the examination in 1990. The minutes stated that past experience showed that a new standard would require candidates to answer three or four more questions in order to pass the examination. The board directed the staff to distribute a news release for use by the member boards in sharing the action with PN/VN educators and others. The delegate assembly adopted a resolution to authorize the Washington State Board of Practical Nursing to administer the NCLEX-PN in Germany to qualified 91C applicants for the Big Bend U.S. Army contract beginning in April 1991 and ending in October 1996.[159]

In February 1991 the board of directors asked the AEC and the staff to survey member boards regarding any interest in a project to track candidates who were repeating the NCLEX and to develop specific procedures if there was an interest.[160] A flyer describing this service was attached to an October *Newsletter to the Member Boards*. The service allowed the member board, for a fee of five dollars per candidate, to search the six previous examination cycles to determine whether or not an applicant had previously taken the NCLEX.[161] With the CTB contract due to end in 1993, the board appointed the treasurer and the chair of the Committee for Special Projects to serve as a resource for the staff in developing the RFP for a test service.[162] At the August meeting the board reviewed the draft of the RFP, made suggestions to staff, and approved it to be issued on September 1, 1991.[163]

In other action in August, the board agreed to add items to collect information on three topics to the cover of the test book beginning in February 1992. As a result, the candidates would provide data related to (a) the study of English as a second language, (b) certification from the Commission on Graduates of Foreign Nursing Schools (CGFNS), and (c) whether or not RN candidates have been LPN/VNs. In addition, the board decided that its Coordinating Committee would act as a steering committee to monitor and coordinate the work of the other teams appointed to implement CAT.[164]

The delegate assembly continued to act on motions related to examinations in 1991. The delegates authorized the Delaware Board of Nursing to continue to administer NCLEX-PN in Germany to qualified 91C personnel from October 1991 through October 1993. The delegates also agreed to a resolution calling for analysis of future NCLEX-RNs and NCLEX-PNs for the relationship between time, English proficiency, and performance on the examination. The Examination Committee chair, Karen Brumley of Colorado, reported that the committee recommended that no changes be made in the NCLEX-PN® Test Plan and the delegates agreed.[165] The Job Analysis Monitoring Committee, an ad hoc committee of the board of directors chaired by Louise Sanders Waddill of Texas-RN, reported on its review of several research projects underway in 1991. In addition to reviewing the work of the Research Services staff, this committee also received the information submitted by Drs. Kane and Jacobs, members of the External Job Analysis Panel. Projects reviewed in 1991 that were related to one or more examinations were as follows:

- Job Analysis of Nurse Aide Practices in Nursing Homes, Home Health Care Agencies and Hospitals
- Job Analysis of Newly Licensed, Entry Level LPN/VNs
- Pilot Study: Use of Content Analysis of Critical Incident Descriptions to Differentiated Practice
- Definition of Time Frame for Demarcating Entry-Level Practice[166]

The delegate assembly also adopted a resolution to study the issues related to the administration of the NCLEX in Manitoba, Canada, and other similarly situated countries or provinces.[167] An article in the *Newsletter to the Member Boards* in February noted that the Commonwealth of Puerto Rico Board of Nurse Examiners had fulfilled all of the requirements for membership in NCSBN. The first administration of the NCLEX in Puerto Rico was scheduled for July 1991.[168]

In February 1992, after reviewing the responses to the RFP for a computerized test service issued in September, the board of directors agreed to negotiate with the following potential test services with the agency for CAT administration of each: ACT with the National Computer System and Insurance Testing Corporation; CTB/Macmillan/McGraw-Hill with the Roach Organization; and Educational Testing Service (ETS) with Sylvan-Kee Systems. Joyce Schowalter, Donna Dorsey, and Executive Director Bosma served on the negotiating team.[169] At the August meeting the board of directors endorsed ETS as the CAT vendor of choice for the NCLEX.[170] At the meeting of the delegate assembly, after lengthy presentations and deliberation, the delegates voted by ballot to select the vendor for the test services and administration of NCLEX by CAT. As a result, ETS received 66 of the 116 votes cast and the president declared ETS and Sylvan-Kee as the test service to implement CAT administration of NCLEX in 1994.[171]

The 1992 delegate assembly declined a request from Manitoba, Canada, and other similarly situated provinces or countries that might make a request for access to the NCLEX-PN. They also increased the time by 10 minutes per book for both NCLEX-RN and NCLEX-PN starting in October 1992. In addition, they agreed that the board of directors would stop evaluating the adequacy of the sample size and appropriate instrumentation for a limited scope job analysis of nurses in evolving levels of nursing practice until further direction was received from the delegate assembly regarding future examinations.[172] AEC Chair Betty Clark of Maine, reported to the delegate assembly that a screened area with the word "NCLEX" had been added to the background on reports of results because a candidate had altered a report from NCLEX-PN 491 to indicate "pass."[173]

NCLEX Using Computerized Adaptive Testing

In September 1982 the board of directors directed the staff to work with the test service to develop a proposal for funding to enable testing a new electronic system for the administration of examinations.[174]

Two items included in the 1983 *NCSBN Book of Reports* for the annual meeting began a 10-year process that was to become one of the outstanding accomplishments of NCSBN in its first 25 years. The first was included in the Report of the Board of Directors and stated that the board had approved the preparation of proposals for funding a study of a system of electronic testing as a prototype of the administration of the licensure examination.[175] The second entry was in the Annual Report of the Test Service in a section headed Application of New Technology to NCLEX®:

An initial investigation was made into the research issues that surround the computer administration of NCLEX® examinations. While the use of machine-scorable test books has enhanced both security and ease of administration, distribution, and collection of over seven-million pages of secure copy each year, technologies exist that can considerably improve the process without significantly increasing cost. Through adaptation of existing psychometric and computer technology, it would be possible to administer NCLEX® at local sites on continuous, year-round basis. Research must be conducted to find optimum methods of implementing this technology, but it is conceivable that within five years most or all NCLEX® examinations would be scheduled by individual appointment, administered on a highly simplified computer terminal, and yield pass/fail information and diagnostic profile information at the end of the administration.[176]

The board of directors took several other actions in 1983 related to the NCLEX, including the following:

- Directed the Item Writer Selection Committee to explore the use of LPN/VNs as item writers for NCLEX-PN.

- Received a report from the Examination Committee regarding an update of the NCLEX-RN® Test Plan and directed staff to revise the RFP for the *Study of Nursing Practice and Role Delineation and Job Analysis of Entry Level Registered Nurses* to include nurse aides, LPN/VNs and RNs including those in advanced practice and those holding certification.

- Authorized revision of both of the study guides published by the Chicago Review Press.[177]

Bruce Kramer, manager of Professional Examination Services for CTB, authored an article in Issues in 1984 titled "An Appointment for NCLEX®." Kramer described a scenario where a young woman kept an appointment at a computer center to take the licensing examination for nursing. His description of her experience there emphasized the uniqueness of the examination, the possibility of completing with relatively few questions, the minimal computer skill that was required, and speed with which the results were offered. While a good deal of research was still needed, Kramer said that the technology was available and that implementation of CAT for all member boards was possible. He concluded that, in addition to assuring valid and reliable testing, other advantages included "examination by appointment, immediate scoring and vastly improved security of the item pools—and from CTB's standpoint, well, the seven million pages of NCLEX examinations in our scoring center will be no more than a pleasant memory."[178]

At the May 1985 meeting Kramer presented a summary of a study of the computerization of the NCLEX. The board of directors authorized the staff to define the requirements and costs, and to explore possible funding sources for research, planning, and development of a CAT model for the NCLEX.[179] In August the board heard reports of the Computer Based Testing Group of The Psychological Corporation and the National Board of Medical Examiners regarding testing using computers. The board authorized the staff to develop a grant proposal for funding for research and development of CAT.[180] The proposal was presented to the board in November and then submitted to the W. K. Kellogg Foundation.[181] At its August 1986 meeting, the board of directors directed staff to prepare a proposal for internal funding of the CAT Project and supported a continued search for external funding.[182] In November 1986 the board approved an additional expenditure in FY87 of $44,830 to provide a budget for special projects, which in this case would be CAT.[183]

In February 1987 the board authorized the appointment of a second team comprising three members to relieve the workload of the Examination Committee. The board learned that external funding had not been forthcoming for CAT and allocated an additional $132,170 to complete the funding of Phase I of the CAT Project. Anthony R. Zara joined the staff as Director for Special Projects. In that capacity he served as project director for CAT.[184] Also in 1987, the board of directors directed that full payment be made to the CAT software developer in order to retain full ownership rights even if Phase II of the CAT Project was not approved. The board ratified the criteria for selection of judges for establishing the passing score for the NCLEX and authorized staff to solicit nominations for participants in this process from the member boards.[185]

Joan Bouchard of Oregon, chair of the Task Force on Examinations for the Future, reported to the delegate assembly in 1987 that the purpose of the task force was to explore how NCSBN could best meet the needs of individual member boards for licensure examinations should they enact statutory or regulatory changes that redefine the legal scopes of practice and minimum competencies.[186] She proposed, and the delegate assembly authorized, the task force to implement the first step of the plan of action in FY88, and to recommend a testing model to the delegate assembly in 1988.[187]

The *Newsletter to the Member Boards* in November 1987 reported that CAT software pilot testing was in progress. RNs and LPN/VNs from the Chicago area made appointments to go to a computer testing facility to interact with CAT-NCLEX and give their reactions to the experience.[188]

Much of a 1987 edition of *Issues* was devoted to discussion of CAT. An article described the reasons for the interest in CAT as follows:

- Examination environment was conducive to optimal performance.

- Candidates could schedule at any test site, receive results faster, and retake, if necessary, sooner.

- Member boards would no longer need to obtain facilities, proctors, etc.

- Integrity of the examination was better guarded.

- Individualized examinations assured users of results of the precision of measurement for each individual.

Critical features of CAT were enumerated:

- The computer program selects from a pool of items the optimal question for measuring a given examinee's competence.

- As each item is answered, the computer scores it right or wrong, updates the current estimate of the examinee's response and selects the next item.

- Each examinee's response provides more information about his or her "true" level; the computer selection of each next item, therefore is based on an increasingly precise estimate of the examinee's competence level.

- At some point, the score estimate becomes sufficiently precise to determine with a known degree of confidence whether or not the examinee possesses the minimum competence necessary to practice safely and effectively.

The progress of the project was described in another section of the publication. Phase I consisted of the development of computer software and pilot testing of the software. Phase II was expected to be authorized by February 1988 to include the activities anticipated for the following years included detailed studies of operational, cost/benefit, legal, and psychometric implications; large scale field trials; and a recommendation to the delegate assembly regarding the implementation.[189]

The development of CAT required the close attention of the board of directors, the Special Projects Committee, the Examination Committee, and the AEC in 1988. *Issues*, Volume 9, Number 2, published in 1988, is a good source of information on Phase I and II and the planned activities to complete Phase II.[190] In February 1988 the board of directors received the final report on Phase I of the CAT Project and the budget for Phase II. The board created a designated fund of $318,042 for Phase II through August 31, 1988.[191] At the meeting of the delegate assembly in August the delegates voted to proceed with Phase II of the CAT Project along the timeline developed by the Committee for Special Projects, except that only RN items would be developed and field tested at that time and the NCSBN portion of the candidate fee would be increased by five dollars effective with the October 1988 examination.[192] In other action, the board presented and the delegate assembly adopted a recommendation that an RFP for the test service beginning in 1991 be issued in the fall of 1989.[193]

In her report in the 1988 *NCSBN Book of Reports*, Chair Haynes included information on issues needing study as part of the plan for completing Phase II of the CAT Project:

- Operational issues—member board computer needs, staff needs, and costs for administration.

- Security Measures.

- Legal analyses—to be done by the University of Illinois Office of Social Science Research and Vedder, Price, Kaufman and Kammholz.

- Psychometric equivalence of CAT and the paper-and-pencil examination.

- Addition of items to the test pool.[194]

In April 1989 the board of directors approved the criteria for selecting the states and sites for CAT field tests and adopted the Security Measures for the conduct of these tests.[195] The board approved the CAT field test states and the alternates in July, and agreed that no single computerized test service vendor would be selected for the field tests. The Committee for Special Projects determined the most appropriate vendor in each state.[196] The report of the Committee for Special Projects, presented to the delegate assembly by Chair Billie Haynes of Califonia-VN, identified the states selected for the CAT Feasibility Study Field Tests as follows: Area 1—Oregon and California; Area 2—Illinois and Missouri; Area 3—Mississippi and Texas; and Area 4—New York and New Jersey. The alternates were Idaho, Ohio, Georgia, and Maryland, from Area 1 through Area 4 respectively.[197]

The board of directors took several actions in 1990 related to CAT, including the following:

- Approval of a new database program for CAT at an estimated cost of $31,000.[198]
- Agreed to at least one field test on the PN/VN population, preferably in four states with approximately 400 candidates in conjunction with the NCLEX-PN® 092.
- Revised a questionnaire on jurisdictional legal issues to be sent to the executive directors of member boards.
- Appointed a communication team to coordinate and supervise a staff effort to develop a CAT Communiqué column for member boards.
- Appointed a planning/administration team to receive and review proposals submitted by the external audit committee.
- Selected Ernst and Young as consultants on CAT equipment and security.[199]

The president, in her report to the delegate assembly in 1990, mentioned the creation of partnerships for the CAT Project. This project was designed to determine if the licensing examination could be administered using a computer. One of these partnerships was with the American Board of Orthopedic Surgeons for the use of NCSBN software for CAT and brought $100,000 to NCSBN. The second partnership was with the American Society of Clinical Pathologists to provide valuable research information for both organizations.[200] An excellent source for the activities leading to the development of CAT and other information about NCLEX in 1990 can be found in *Issues*, Volume 11, Number 4.[201] Selected activities will be found in the paragraphs that follow.

The member boards; the board of directors; and most of the NCSBN committees, staff, legal counsel, consultants, and volunteers were intensely involved in the activities related to the final steps to prepare the information needed for action by the delegate assembly in August 1991. The several paragraphs that follow describe some of these activities. At the 1991 meeting the delegates were scheduled to act on a motion to adopt CAT as the method of examinations by NCSBN. The board held work sessions on CAT at its February and April meetings. Some of the activities of the board are listed below:

- Agreed to conduct an additional validity study with a simulated NCLEX assembled according to CAT procedures.
- Heard a report in February that the field testing for CAT was underway and that candidate participation goals had been fulfilled.
- Reviewed computer equipment, configurations, security, and facilities and heard presentations from two organizations about nationwide computer centers.
- Reviewed legal analyses and the results of jurisdictional legal issues questionnaires.
- Studied ways to estimate the cost for NCLEX administration by CAT.[202]

In June the board of directors reviewed joint recommendations from the Committee for Special Projects, the Examination Committee, and the AEC regarding CAT technology issues and adopted more than 30 of these recommendations, including the following: the minimum and maximum number of items, the maximum testing time, the number of tryout items included within the first 60 items, scoring method, item selection, and warm up items. Others approved were related to the issue of reporting results on-site, member boards, proctors, floor space, the use of calculators, handicapped candidates, and identification of candidates.[203]

Throughout the period leading up to the meeting of the delegate assembly in 1991, a regular column called CAT Communiqué was published as a part of the *Newsletter to the Member Boards*. The purpose of these articles was to provide information to the member boards as they prepared for decision making at the annual meeting. A list of the CAT Communiqués was included as part of the Report of the Board of Directors in the 1991 *NCSBN Book of Reports* as follows:

- Progress Report and Questionnaire Regarding CAT
- Working Assumptions and Facts Pertinent to Potential Implementation of CAT
- Answers to Initial Member Board Questions About CAT
- CAT: What Information Can I Expect and When?
- Legal Issues in CAT
- Security of CAT Examinations
- Area Meeting Update
- Results of the CAT Field Testing[204]

Chair Haynes reported on behalf of the Committee for Special Projects to the delegate assembly regarding the CAT Feasibility Study. She stated that the field tests showed CAT and paper and pencil testing were psychometrically comparable, and that computer experience had no effect on candidate performance. She reported further that the legal analysis showed CAT was legally defensible, field testing showed that the security could be maintained, and CAT could be delivered under various scenarios with proper staff training.[205]

On August 1, 1991, Helen Kelley of Massachusetts, secretary of NCSBN, on behalf of the board of directors, moved that CAT be the examination method for the NCLEX. The motion was adopted. The following four related motions were then adopted:

- That NCSBN contract with national vendors for CAT administration of NCLEX in all jurisdictions.
- That the conversion from paper-and-pencil to CAT will occur at one point for all jurisdictions.
- That the transition timeline be established following receipt of proposals from qualified vendors so that implementation occurs at a point mutually agreed upon between NCSBN and related vendors, but no sooner than November 1993.
- That the board negotiate a contract extension with CTB for paper-and-pencil administration, if necessary, to provide services during the transition between July 1993 and the implementation of CAT.[206]

These actions by the delegate assembly led Delegate Joyce Schowalter of Minnesota to address the group as follows:

I ask the Assembly to take a moment to reflect on the "momentousness" of the decision to move from a paper-and-pencil testing modality to CAT.[207]

The statement was met with general applause from those present. In the President's Message in *Issues* following the action of the delegate assembly, President Carolyn Hutcherson of Georgia-RN said the following:

Consistent with the organizational goal adopted by the membership, to "develop, promote, and produce relevant and innovative services," the National Council is demonstrating initiative in creating an environment to make nursing regulation the best it can be. The Annual Meeting encompassed the feeling of progress by showing strong support for computerized adaptive testing (CAT) as delegates overwhelmingly voted to implement administration of NCLEX® via CAT.[208]

The Report of the Board of Directors and the reports of the examination related committees in the 1992 *NCSBN Book of Reports* provided an overview of the activities of NCSBN as those concerned took the necessary steps for the transition to CAT. The board adopted a master plan for the transition and selected the jurisdictions for the PN field tests.[209] The three teams that had been appointed made reports to the delegates. One of these was the CAT PN Field Test Team chaired by Barbara Kellogg, of South Carolina. The team acted to affirm the design for their study, and assure candidate recruitment and adequacy of the item pool. In addition, the team reviewed test sites and administrative services.[210] In December the board received a report that 911 candidates participated in the PN field tests in October.[211] In addition, the board of directors authorized five and a half full-time equivalent positions through June 1993 for the work required to implement CAT, and added $457,078 to the CAT designated fund.[212]

The activities of the CAT Education/Information Team, chaired by Charlie Dickson of Alabama, included the following:

• Prepared a general brochure on CAT.

• Submitted articles to external publications and Issues and began a "CAT Corner" in the *Newsletter to the Member Boards*.

• Published the CAT Communiqués for the member boards.

• Developed a fact sheet on legal issues for the member boards.

• Made 22 presentations to various groups between January and May of 1992.

• Provided exhibits at national meetings.

• Developed "prepared speeches" for use by member boards.

• Developed an informational video about NCLEX® CAT that was distributed to the member boards in June 1992.[213]

The CAT Implementation Team, chaired by Renatta Loquist, was charged to:

• Plan, coordinate, and monitor activities to enable member boards to implement CAT in their jurisdictions.

• Identify and focus on resolving questions related to implementation in such a way that no jurisdiction was disadvantaged or compromised.

• Work closely with staff and other teams with specific focus on providing direction for the comprehensive plans for components of the implementation.[214]

After one meeting the team had responded to work of the other two teams, reviewed vendors' proposals and reported to the negotiating team, and reviewed a draft of a new member board contract.

In June 1992 the board of directors approved four regional workshops (one in each area) and designated funds to cover these workshops.[215] The following month the board established a designated fund of $334,800 to purchase common computer capabilities for the member boards. The board also established another designated fund of $50,000 and agreed to add 20 percent of the examination revenue over expenditure, not to exceed $50,000 each year, as a fund to pay legal costs associated with the defense of any challenge to the validity of the licensing examinations.[216]

The delegate assembly adopted motions to use fingerprints for candidate identification, to charge a candidate fee of $88 for CAT, and to approve the substance of the revised contract between NCSBN and the member boards.[217] At the December meeting the board of directors acknowledged Idaho as the first member board to submit the signed contract for NCLEX delivered by CAT administration.[218] Following the annual meeting, the Examination Committee continued to work as two teams to accommodate the work of the coming year. Zara, the director for CAT, moved into the position of director of Testing Services for NCSBN.[219]

An article in *Issues* late in 1992 described the plan for beta testing, crucial to the effective implementation of CAT. Beta testing was to be preceded by a complete alpha test in March 1993 where individual system components, the entire system, and system security would be tested. The beta test was scheduled for June and July. Candidates would be identified, the examination fee for that group would be free, and failing candidates would be offered one CAT retest free. The expectation was to test 5,000 RN candidates and 4,000 PN candidates who would be divided so that specified numbers would be tested via CAT, via paper and pencil over two days, and via paper and pencil over one day instead of two (a test that would be administered to a smaller number of RN candidates).[220]

The year 1993 was one of decision for NCSBN. After several years of study and hard work by the staff of NCSBN, the test service, the board of directors, the committees, and the member boards, it was time to examine the results of the efforts and decide as to whether or not all was ready to begin the administration of the NCLEX by CAT. Before the decision could be made, however, other matters related to the examination required attention. The board of directors took action in March to affirm the decision of the Examination Committee Team I that an item on the NCLEX-RN 792 that had been challenged was psychometrically sound, valid, and correctly keyed. The board also approved a statement developed by the AEC to be read to candidates regarding the confidentiality statement included on the examination. On the recommendation of Team II of the Examination Committee, the board agreed to reimburse the participants in the beta test at the time of the examination. In other action, the board accepted 180 as the maximum number of real items for the NCLEX-PN with a maximum time of three hours for test taking. The number of tryout items was to be 15 to 25 depending on the need of the item pool. The board also agreed to proceed with the CAT implementation timeline subject to meeting the readiness criteria.[221]

In May 1993 the board adopted a policy that candidates could take the NCLEX by CAT four times a year but not more than once in any three-month period.[222] At the August meeting the board of directors agreed to inform the delegate assembly that telephone registration would be available to the NCLEX candidates, contingent upon acceptable quality service standards being negotiated with ETS.[223]

At the meeting of the delegate assembly in August 1993, the delegates adopted the readiness criteria to be met in order to implement CAT.[224] The criteria were developed by an expert panel chaired by Joyce Schowalter of Minnesota. The members were Billie Haynes of California-VN, Marie Hilliard of Connecticut, Louise Waddill of Texax-RN, and Sharon Weisenbeck of Kentucky. The criteria adopted by the delegate assembly were used by the board of directors to evaluate progress.[225] The process began in October 1993 and was completed in time for the board of directors meeting on October 25. At that meeting the board determined that the CAT readiness criteria were met and unanimously adopted a motion to proceed with the implementation of CAT-NCLEX beginning April 1, 1994.[226] Once again, NCSBN celebrated another of its "finest hours" when the member boards were notified of the decision.

The delegate assembly considered several reports and took the following actions based on recommendations at the annual meeting:

- Approved the following policy recommended by the AEC: "It is the policy of the National Council to cooperate with Member Boards in providing appropriate opportunities for their review of newly developed NCLEX® items or simulated computerized adaptive examinations. The National Council will do so by developing procedures which ensure that the review of the material will be under conditions which do not adversely affect the security of the test items."[227]

- Adopted a resolution authorizing NCSBN to contract with the Maine State Board of Nursing to develop a psychometrically sound and legally defensible supplemental licensure examination for use by Maine in licensing baccalaureate level candidates to measure unique minimal competencies required of these graduates.[228]

- Authorized the Delaware Board of Nursing to administer NCLEX-PN in Germany in October 1993 to qualified 91C personnel stationed in Europe.[229]

Information included in several of the issues of the *Newsletter to the Member Boards* in 1993 reported that Member Board Office Software (MBOS) had been developed to facilitate the transfer of information to and from the member boards and ETS.[230] A news release attached to the July 16 *Newsletter to the Member Boards* reported on the completion of the NCLEX beta test, in which 44 member boards participated. The boards made great effort in this endeavor, showing their dedication to the project. Nursing educators across the country were instrumental in recruiting the participants.[231]

An article in *Issues* early in 1994 reported on the two major conclusions resulting from the beta test of CAT. The conclusions were that NCLEX administration using CAT was psychometrically comparable to the paper and pencil NCLEX, and that the administration of the NCLEX using CAT on an ongoing basis in numerous sites across the United States and its territories was logistically feasible. The participants in the beta test included 5,902 RN candidates and 1,566 LPN/VN candidates. Within 48 hours, 99 percent of the candidates' results were transmitted to the member boards.[232] The member boards administered the last NCLEX-RN with paper and pencil in February 1994. Administration using CAT began on April 1, 1994.

Examination Activities Continue

Even as it made the momentous transition to CAT, NCSBN continued to address new issues facing member boards. At its March 1994 meeting, the board of directors exempted Puerto Rico from the requirement that NCLEX be the sole and exclusive licensing examination in English for the licensure of RNs and LPN/VNs because of a change in the law in Puerto Rico.[233]

The delegate assembly once again adopted a revision to the NCLEX-RN® Test Plan in 1994.[234] In the 1994 *NCSBN Book of Reports*, Alta Haunsz of Kentucky, chair of the AEC, reported to the delegate assembly that the committee reviewed and ratified 376 authorizations for modifications issued to candidates with disabilities taking NCLEX-RN 793, 294 and NCLEX-PN 093 and the beta test.[235] Executive Director Bosma reported to the delegate assembly that NCSBN staff "successfully coordinated the April 1, 1994, transition to computerized adaptive testing for NCLEX with the member boards, testing-related committees, ETS and the Sylvan Learning Systems." Bosma included a partial list of activities by these groups in her report. Some of these were beta testing, retesting and reporting, analysis of readiness criteria, preparation of numerous communications to a variety of audiences, work on MBOS training, development of policies and procedures, and multiple presentations on CAT.[236]

The delegate assembly adopted a resolution of appreciation for the invaluable service rendered both to the profession and to the public by CTB/McGraw-Hill in its 14 years of involvement with the development of NCLEX.[237] *(see fig. 9-C)*

The committed volunteers and staff members of the nursing regulatory boards and NCSBN repeatedly demonstrated the positive outcome of a unified commitment to accomplish a goal. In 1994 NCSBN became the first health-related profession to offer a licensing examination administered by CAT in every U.S. state and territory. Member boards saw a drastic change in their role in examination administration. Candidate registration to take the examination and receipt of results were significantly improved, employers had licensed personnel sooner, and unsuccessful candidates had the opportunity to retest sooner. Even the board of directors of NCSBN saw a change as the result of CAT. The amount of time devoted to issues and questions related to NCLEX decreased significantly. In the fall of 1994 an article in Issues reported that the NCLEX passing rate was consistent. During the first six months of testing, the NCLEX-RN was administered to 70,321 candidates with a 91.1percent passing rate among those taking the examination for the first time who were educated in the U.S. This performance was consistent with the passing rate for the previous paper and pencil NCLEX. The NCLEX-PN was taken by 33,326 candidates. First time, U.S. educated candidates achieved a 91.2 percent passing rate. This rate was also consistent with the paper and pencil NCLEX-PN.[238]

Early in 1995 the board of directors asked the staff and legal counsel to investigate the legal, fiscal, and logistical implications of establishing a mechanism to facilitate the release of individual candidate identification information and examination results among jurisdictions that permit such release and desire the information.[239] At a meeting in August the board approved a proposal for ETS to provide services allowing member boards to share NCLEX candidate data across jurisdictions.[240]

The board of directors took several other examination-related actions in 1995, including the following:

Upheld an Examination Committee decision that a challenged NCLEX-PN item was psychometrically sound, valid, and had only one correct answer that was the keyed option.[241]

Changed the passing standard for NCLEX-RN.[242]

Voted not to authorize testing sites in Canada at this time.[243]

The delegate assembly considered and took action on three motions related to examinations at its August meeting. Paulette Worcester of Indiana, chair of the Examination Committee, presented the revisions to the NCLEX-PN® Test Plan, which the delegates adopted. The delegates heard a recommendation from the board of directors, adopted the NCLEX® Administration Stabilization Criteria, and authorized the board to apply the criteria to specific geographic sites as the need arose. The delegates adopted a resolution that NCSBN identify a commonality of language regarding "assessment" as a component of the nursing process that could be incorporated and reflected in the NCLEX-PN® Test Plan after approval by the delegate assembly in the normal cycle of test plan revision.[244] The Report of Staff Activities, presented to the delegate assembly by Executive Director Bosma, noted that the staff of NCSBN had monitored the implementation of CAT for NCLEX to approximately 187,000 candidates. The staff also recruited, screened, and confirmed 144 item writers and 50 item reviewers.[245]

At its November 1995 meeting, the board of directors approved an amendment to the contract with ETS for assignment of the contract to the newly formed ETS subsidiary, Chauncey Group International (CGI).[246] The test service report from CGI and Sylvan Prometric in the 1996 *NCSBN Book of Reports* summarized changes in its organization to advise that on January 1, 1996, CGI, a wholly owned subsidiary of ETS was established. Other changes to Sylvan Learning Systems meant an expansion in the number of sites where the NCLEX would be administered. In the fall of 1995, Sylvan acquired DRAKE Prometric and was subsequently called Sylvan Prometric; and in March 1996, Sylvan acquired the National Association of Securities Dealers (NASD) site.[247]

A dramatic change in the level of activities related to examinations was evident in the review of the board of directors minutes, the delegate assembly minutes, the *NCSBN Book of Reports*, and other NCSBN publications in 1996. In May the board of directors asked the NCLEX® Evaluation Task Force, chaired by Deborah Feldman of Maryland, to explore the production of a video or other media format exploring the purpose and use of the diagnostic profiles to be made available to constituents.[248] In August the board decided to extend the contract with the NLN for the NCLEX® Diagnostic Readiness Test through 1999.[249] After reviewing the evaluation of the test service and identifying aspects of good performance and items where improvement was needed, the board appointed a negotiating team to develop contract terms for discussion with CGI and Sylvan Prometric. Members of this team were Donna Dorsey of Maryland, Sheila Exstrom of Nebraska, and Faith Fields of Arkansas.[250] The board also raised the passing standard for the NCLEX-PN.[251]

At the meeting of the delegate assembly in 1996 the report by Terry DeMarcay of Louisiana-PN, a member of the Subcommittee on Practical Nurse Assessment, was included in the Report of the Examination Committee. After studying the scope of the LPN/VN in assessment, the subcommittee developed the following statement:

That the term used to categorize assessment-related activities performed by LPN/VNs be "data collection." The term data collection is defined as: The LPN/VN collects information, observes the patient, records and reports to the appropriate person signs and symptoms and other pertinent data which may indicate that the client's condition deviates from normal and/or that there is a change in the client's condition. LPN/VNs contribute to the assessment of clients through data collection. The term "contribute to" denotes an active role on the part of the LPN/VN based on the LPN/VN's knowledge, skills and abilities.

The delegate assembly adopted the statement.[252] Renatta Loquist, chair of the Examination Committee, reported that the committee reviewed issues related to examination administration including the interstate sharing of data. Loquist stated that 42 member boards had elected to share data.[253]

On the recommendation of the Examination Committee through its chair, Lynn Norman of Alabama, the 1997 delegate assembly adopted revisions to the NCLEX-RN® Test Plan. In addition, the delegates approved language for inclusion in the member board contract to facilitate the provision of qualified readers for NCLEX candidates who had been granted accommodation related to disabilities.[254] Chair Norman reported to the delegate assembly that the members of the Examination Committee had met with members of the Computerized Clinical Simulation Testing (CST) Task Force to set guidelines for developing CST cases, examinations, scoring mechanisms, and standard setting procedures in preparation for the 1998 CST Pilot Study.[255] The delegate assembly selected CGI as the NCLEX test service for the period of October 1999 through September 2002. The delegates agreed to set the candidate fee at $120.[256]

Two articles appeared in *Issues* in 1997 that reported on examination-related activities. The first reported that the Examination Committee structure was changed by amendments to the bylaws. A Subcommittee on Item Review was named to review new, referred, and base pool items and to recommend the disposition of these items to the Examination Committee.[257] A later article reported that the 1997 Job Analysis of Newly Licensed LPN/VNs was completed and would be used to determine the need to revise the NCLEX-PN® Test Plan.[258]

At its February 1998 meeting the board of directors concurred with a conclusion reached by the Examination Committee that a policy of providing NCLEX results on-site at the examination centers not be considered at this time. This conclusion was reached due to the need to incorporate the safeguards and quality control measures currently in place to verify the validity of the results.[259] There were some technical problems with the NCLEX-RN® Test Plan in April 1998. The board of directors authorized the release of the results that were on hold because of the technical problems and confirmed the validity of the results for candidates testing since April 1, 1998.[260] At the 1998 meeting of the delegate assembly, the delegates adopted the revision to the NCLEX-PN® Test Plan as presented by Chair Norman. The Nursing Practice and Education Committee recommended that member boards conduct criminal background checks on applicants for licensure. The delegates concurred with the recommendation.[261] In order to find a way for candidates to know the results of the examination earlier, eight states volunteered to participate in a pilot study for candidates to receive their unofficial examination results by telephone for a fee of $7.95 charged to the telephone bill.[262] In February 1999, the board of directors agreed to a proposal to make the NCLEX results available in all jurisdictions by telephone as a part of the NCSBN Special Services Division.[263] During a telephone conference call meeting in June, the board learned of a shut down of the Results-by-Phone service on May 24 following incidents of incorrect results given. The board directed the staff to continue the shut down and communicate with CGI regarding the issue.[264] The board agreed to restart the Results–by-Phone service at its October meeting.[265]

At the annual meeting in 1999, the board of directors recommended that the delegate assembly select National Computer Systems, Inc. (NCS) as the new test service for NCLEX for the period from October 1, 2002 through September 30, 2009, according to the terms arrived at by the negotiating team.[266] The delegate assembly adopted the recommendation and the contract was signed by August 1999.[267] The delegates also adopted two resolutions with implications for the licensing examinations. The first resolution called for NCSBN to explore opportunities, including possible partnerships, for the development of a legally defensible English proficiency examination or examinations for minimal practice competencies. The second asked that NCSBN conduct research to determine the feasibility of development of appropriate and legally defensible cut scores for currently available examinations of English proficiency. The study was to determine if the relationship of the examination to competency in English proficiency was needed for safe practice.[268]

In other action, the board decided to add mouse and calculator options to the current NCLEX administration, but no sooner than April 1, 2002.[269] In July, the board of directors decided to recommend that the delegate assembly set the fee for NCLEX candidates at $180.[270] At the meeting of the delegate assembly the delegates set the fee at $200 and adopted "enhancements" to the NCLEX-RN® Test Plan.[271] Chair Norman explained that the Examination Committee had reviewed the most recent job analysis and other resources and determined that there was no need to propose revisions to the test plan. However, the enhancements proposed were designed to improve readability and provide clarity to the plan.[272]

In October 2000, the board of directors asked for a comparison study of the Canadian Registered Nurse Examination (CRNE), formerly known as CNATS, and the NCLEX-RN with a report ready for presentation to the delegate assembly in 2001. At the same meeting the board considered a letter from the governor of Guam. He asked for assistance in certification of the U.S. Embassy in the Philippines as a testing site for the NCLEX-RN.[273] At a meeting in November the board asked the Examination Committee to explore the topic of international testing and provided a list of elements for the committee's consideration. The board also considered a question related to the increase in the NCLEX fee as it would impact those individuals who had registered before the effective date of the new fee. The board expressed interest in establishing a date when the candidate must take the examination to prevent an influx of registrations prior to the increase.[274]

NCSBN initiated a publication titled the *Council Connector* in 2000. In the November issue an article noted that a test service transition newsletter was to be introduced that month. This newsletter was distributed electronically to member board offices monthly to keep the member boards up-to-date on the transition to the new test service.[275] Another article asked the question "Who Owns NCLEX® Exam Data?" The article reminded the reader that individual candidate data was the property of the individual member boards, that NCSBN may legally release aggregate statistics, and that NCSBN does not endorse or recommend the use of NCLEX results for research conducted by any third party not previously authorized by NCSBN.[276]

The delegate assembly took only one action related to the NCLEX in 2001 when it adopted "enhancements" to the NCLEX-PN® Test Plan.[277] However, the board of directors considered and acted on several examination matters. In January Anita Ristau of Vermont, chair of the Examination Committee, discussed the issue of international testing with the board of directors. The Examination Committee planned to begin exploration with the move to the new test service.[278] Ristau again reported to the board in May regarding its effort to compare the CRNE with the NCLEX-RN for entry level testing. The report was to be presented to the delegate assembly in August.[279] In June the board of directors expressed concerns about candidates registered with CGI but not tested at the time of the change to the new test service. The board requested that an attempt be made to ascertain the testing intent of the candidates.[280] In one of the few cited incidents involving the testing centers, the board heard a report of an incident when a candidate was refused testing because of failure to remove a head covering. The board was assured "that the policy did not fail, but the implementation at the test site did." The Examination Committee was reviewing the incident and related policies. Later, the board agreed to revise the testing policy to extend the registration period for NCLEX from 180 days to 365 days and approved a new NCLEX-PN passing standard to be effective on April 1, 2002.[281]

In addition to work with the enhancements to the NCLEX-PN® Test Plan and the comparison of the CRNE with the NCLEX-RN in 2001, Chair Ristau reported that the committee continued to investigate the feasibility of the international administration of NCLEX, monitored all aspects of examination development and administration, and monitored the activities related to the transition to the new test service.[282]

In 2001 NCS was purchased by Pearson plc., a company based in the United Kingdom specializing in media and publishing, and the name was changed to NCS Pearson. Virtual University Enterprises (VUE), a company with expertise in test delivery solutions, was purchased by NCS to assist in its efforts to enter the computerized testing business. VUE continued to be the computerized testing entity within NCS that would "provide the backbone for the NCLEX testing services." By 2003 the name Pearson VUE was found in all references to the test service in the NCSBN meeting minutes and the *NCSBN Business Book*.[283]

The *Council Connector* reported in May 2001 that a pilot study for the NCLEX of the future was completed. RNs and LPN/VNs were administered 15 test questions each using innovative formats via CD-Rom at the offices of member boards in Arkansas, Colorado, Illinois, Louisiana-PN, Missouri, Nebraska, New Hampshire, Pennsylvania, and Vermont. Participants responded to a survey about the item format. In general, the responses were positive about format, clarity, and the comparison to multiple-choice questions. Respondents expressed concern about technical difficulties with the mouse interface, scrolling, and scoring some of the item formats.[284] Member boards in Alabama, California-RN, California-VN, Kentucky, Maryland, and Missouri began participation in the alpha test in preparation for the transition to Pearson VUE. These member boards tested the VUE registration, eligibility, and scheduling systems. The beta test was scheduled to start in January 2002.[285]

A report of a study found in the *Council Connector* in December showed the passing rate for persons repeating the examinations. With CAT the passing standard had been raised three times for both RN and PN examinations. With each increase in the standard, there was an expected decrease in the passing rate and an increase in the number of candidates subsequently repeating the examination. This raised the question of the success rate of repeaters. An analysis of NCLEX data from April 1994 to December 1999 showed that a large proportion of both RN and PN repeat candidates did pass. Candidates were more likely to pass in few attempts, "although a small number of candidates have passed at extreme numbers of administrations." Repeating candidates educated in the U.S. were far more likely to pass at any given attempt, compared to those educated in other countries.[286]

While the Examination Committee continued its ongoing activities, the 2002 delegate assembly, the board of directors and Examination Committee spent some time on the question of international testing. The board of directors heard a report in January that NCS Pearson was capable of delivering the test in 123 countries. The board identified test security and candidate service as key considerations. The Examination Committee was exploring security issues, cost, and best practices related to the subject.[287] In May the board of directors accepted a recommendation from the Examination Committee to present to the delegate assembly in August.[288] The delegates adopted the following motion:

> To proceed with negotiations for a contract amendment with the test service for purposes on international administration of NCLEX®. As part of this contractual negotiation for international administration for purposes of domestic licensure, the Board of Directors will utilize criteria developed by the Examination Committee and establish jurisdiction-specific candidate examination fees for NCLEX® delivered outside current Member Board jurisdictions. International administration not to occur before August 1, 2004.[289]

Later in the meeting a motion was made to reconsider the motion and the following proviso was added and adopted, stating that the motion:

> will not go into effect and cannot be implemented until the following conditions have been met:
>
> 1. Acceptable criteria for selection of countries, including NAFTA [North American Free Trade Agreement] countries and comprehensive needs assessment determine the necessity for international testing.
>
> 2. Security Measures to be utilized in international countries are developed or identified.
>
> 3. Fiscal analysis including direct costs and staff resources is considered by the appropriate committees of the NCSBN.
>
> 4. Report made to the Delegate Assembly no later than 2003.[290]

In March 2003 the board of directors heard reports of comments of concern from various sources regarding alternative item formats for the NCLEX. Educators and students raised concerns that there was inadequate notice of change, was lack of understanding about the change, and fears regarding the potential negative impact on passing rates. The director of Testing reported that new formats were being pretested and would not influence candidate performance. The board asked that a fact sheet be posted on the NCSBN Web site.[291] An article in the September *Council Connector* discussed the addition of a practice drill containing 40 innovative item types to NCSBN's review for the NCLEX-RN. The format used was different than standard multiple-choice items and included the following features:

> • Hot spot items—the candidate was asked to identify an area of a picture or graph.
>
> • Multiple choice with more than one correct answer.
>
> • Fill-in-the-blank items.[292]

The 2003 delegate assembly adopted changes to the NCLEX-RN® Test Plan. After amendment, a recommendation regarding extension of the time limit for the NCLEX-RN was agreed to as follows:

> that the Delegate Assembly authorize the NCSBN Board of Directors to negotiate and enter into a contract amendment with Pearson VUE to implement a time limit extension for the NCLEX-RN examination supported by the data and the analysis of the Examination Committee.[293]

In July the board of directors learned that the governor of the Northern Mariana Islands had suspended the NCLEX as a requirement for licensure. The board listed concerns to be used in a response to the governor as follows: the member board contract and testing center privilege would be jeopardized and the CGFNS examination is a predictor examination and not an equivalent replacement for the NCLEX. The board also requested advice from legal counsel in the matter.[294] At the next meeting, the board of directors was advised that the governor met with the Northern Mariana Islands Commonwealth Board of Nursing and revised his directive to support the current language in the nursing practice act regarding the NCLEX. He decided to require the CGFNS predictor examination for employment of foreign nurses in the public health system. The NCSBN legal counsel expressed his concern to the board that this lends the perception that the CGFNS test rather than the NCLEX was the interim public protection device.[295]

Another change in the administration of NCLEX in 2003 was reported in the *Council Connector*. The "wait period" between taking the same type NCLEX was reduced from 90 to 45 days, beginning in January 2004. The report stated that 50 member boards would participate, while 9 would continue to follow the 90-day retake policy.[296]

Competency Evaluation for Nurse Aides

At the February 1988 meeting of the board of directors the Area II Director, Leota Rolls of Nebraska, reported on questions raised at the area meeting regarding Public Law 100-203. This law, passed by the United States Congress, was also known as the Nursing Home Reform Act (NHRA) and was a part of the Omnibus Reconciliation Act of 1987 (OBRA 87). The board of directors asked staff to disseminate the information to the member boards[297] and appointed the Task Force on the Evaluation of Nurse Aides, with Sharon Weisenbeck of Kentucky as its chair. The name of the task force was later changed to the Nurse Aide Competency Evaluation Program (NACEP) Committee. The following is an excerpt from the information distributed by NCSBN staff to the member boards regarding the implications of the new law:

As a part of the Omnibus Budget Reconciliation Act of 1987, PL 100-203 was enacted with the President's signature on December 22, 1987. The law is of particular interest to nursing because of its provisions for nurse aide training, competency evaluation and a registry of trained nurse aides.

Specifically, the bill outlines the minimum content requirements for the establishment of the programs, state by state, to train nurse aides for use in nursing homes in order to receive Medicare and Medicaid funding for operation of a nursing home. It further delineates the establishment of a registry system and competency evaluation programs. The law does not specify who the agency within each state will be, it just specifies that the state will provide for a training, competency evaluation and registry system with target dates of September 1, 1988 for the former two and March 1989 for the latter.

State Boards of Nursing need to strategically consider any role they will play in carrying out the mandates of this law based on a concern for the public's health, safety, and welfare. As the law reads, boards of nursing could potentially assume program approval, competency evaluation, and/ or registry roles in enacting the provisions of the law.

Each role would have very specific issues that would need to be considered in the decision to seek legislative authority to enact the provisions of the law. Though all those considerations have not been evaluated, the Nursing Practice and Standards Committee of the National Council is presently considering those issues and plans to have a concept paper available for circulation to Member Boards as soon as it is feasible to address some of those concerns.

In the meantime, boards of nursing need to be alerted to the fact that various health related state agencies will be seeking legislative authority to carry out the mandates of this law. These legislative initiatives will have implications for Boards of Nursing related to how these agencies will seek to define the minimal knowledge, competencies and registry system for the nurse aide who will be carrying out designated nursing functions.[298]

In June the board of directors authorized staff to distribute an RFP to test services for development of a nurse aide competency evaluation.[299] At the annual meeting in August, the delegate assembly adopted a recommendation from the task force and the board of directors that NCSBN proceed with the development of a competency evaluation program for nurse aides with a projected cost of $182,500 in FY88 and $165,500 in FY89. The delegate assembly authorized the board to proceed with actions, including selection of the test service and approval of the test plan.[300]

The board of directors selected The Psychological Corporation (TPC) as the test service for the Nurse Aide Competency Evaluation Program (NACEP) at the November meeting. The board also approved the process for appointment of item and task development writers.[301] In December the board accepted the *Blueprint for NACEP* as developed by the task force and modified by the board.[302]

In 1989 the board of directors agreed to publish and send to the member boards and other agencies a summary of the nurse aide job analysis process, the major categories of care, tasks with weights, and a bibliography.[303] In November the board reviewed the report from the NACEP Committee and agreed to the following:

- That an incumbent job analysis with provisions to include a survey of frontline supervisors would be conducted and nurse aides would be surveyed in all major settings where they work.

- That the selection criteria for item writers, task developers, item reviewers, and the standard setting panel would include representatives from a range of relevant experiences.

- That the final form of NACEP should be reviewed by an NCSBN representative and that the NACEP Committee chair and program manager establish a process to review the forms that have been modified in response to state requests.

- That the board of directors establish the NACEP pass score based on information from the Standard Setting Panel.

- That a procedure for review of potentially biased items be accepted.

The board decided to conduct a logical job analysis for home health aides. This group of aides was also included in the NHRA.[304] An article in the *Newsletter to the Member Boards* reported that 77 individuals in 37 states assisted in item writing, item review, and task development during the initial work on the NACEP prior to the field testing.[305] The first administration of the NACEP occurred on July 22, 1989, in 4 states. By November 23 states were using NACEP as the sole examination.[306]

At its April 1990 meeting, the board of directors accepted the report of the NACEP Committee and agreed to publish aggregate statistics from NACEP, approved the release of results of the home health aide logical job analysis, and approved TPC to market the NACEP for home health aides on the basis of the match between the results of the job analysis and the NACEP Blueprint.[307]

In its first report to the delegate assembly, TPC included a report of NACEP results from July 1989 through February 1990. Results were stated as follows:

Written Evaluation: Total Tested—65,422 with a pass rate of 94.2 percent

Manual Skills: Total Tested—40,001 with a pass rate of 90.1 percent[308]

An article in *Issues* in 1990 reported on the first Nurse Aide Conference in Seattle in May. Many topics were discussed and those in attendance heard from the division director of Administration from the

Health Care Financing Administration (HCFA) regarding financing of training programs and the competency evaluation program.[309]

At its February 1991 meeting, the board of directors requested that the staff and TPC develop a plan to provide diagnostic information to candidates who failed the NACEP. The board also determined that, based on results of study and statistical analysis, the NACEP remained a secure and accurate assessment. The board agreed to conduct a job analysis every five years.[310] In October the board agreed to some minor revisions to the NACEP Blueprint and approved a new list of manual skills.[311] The delegate assembly adopted a motion in August to allow the board of directors to select and contract with a test service for the NACEP for the period beginning at the expiration of the current contract in 1993.[312]

The NACEP Committee reported to the board of directors in May 1992, and the board adopted a passing standard on both the written and manual skills portions of the NACEP.[313] In October the board agreed to negotiate with TPC for a three-year extension of the contract for the NACEP.[314]

In 1995 the board of directors approved a recommendation from the NACEP Committee to conduct a nurse aide job analysis every three years instead of every five years.[315] The Report of the NACEP Task Force in the 1995 *NCSBN Book of Reports* showed that Cindy M. Lyons of Oklahoma was chair, replacing Sharon Weisenbeck who had completed six years in that position.[316] *Insight*, an NCSBN publication with information related to the regulations of nurse aides, reported in the summer/fall issue that a recent job analysis had been published. The committee recommended no changes in the current blue print for NACEP.[317]

In April 1996 the board of directors authorized the president to execute the documents involving TPC and ASI for interim and long term agreements for the NACEP.[318] There were changes in the organization of the NACEP test service reported in the *NCSBN Book of Reports* in 1996. TPC announced in May 1996 the acquisition of ASI, leading to the transition of TPC's credentialing and licensure program including NACEP, to ASI.[319] Chair Lyons reported that the user survey showed an increase in satisfaction with the NACEP over the past year.[320]

The Report of the National Nurse Aide Assessment Program (NNAAP™) in 2002 described the program as jointly owned and operated by NCSBN, CAT*ASI (formerly known as ASI), and a nationally administered certification examination program. It was the product of the combination of the NACEP and the National Nurse Aide Examination. The integration of the two was completed in 1999 with exclusive administration of NNAAP in FY01.[321] In 2001 ASI was acquired by Computer Adaptive Technologies, a Haughton-Mifflin Company, and the name CAT*ASI was used for a year to maintain marketplace recognition. The name Promissor was adopted in August 2002.[322] At its meeting in March 2003 the board of directors received the completed Nurse Aide Practice Analysis and forwarded it to Promissor to support the next test plan for the NNAAP.[323]

NCSBN recognized a role it could play to facilitate the legislative mandate for states to register nurse aides who had been educated in approved programs and had successfully completed a competency evaluation. This recognition provided another valuable service to those member boards that subsequently became involved in the regulation of another type of health care worker. While many individuals contributed to the success of this venture, the early leadership of the NACEP Committee by Sharon Weisenbeck and the support of the program managers, Barbara Halsey and Ellen Gleason, who succeeded Halsey, deserve special note.

Computerized Clinical Simulated Testing

CST offered the test taker a simulated clinical nursing situation that had the potential of evaluating problem solving and decision making skills in a way different from paper and pencil tests and other forms of computerized tests. The first step taken by NCSBN related to CST occurred in 1986 when the board of directors agreed to explore the feasibility of entering into an agreement with the National Board of Medical Examiners (NBME) for that purpose.[324] In 1987 the staff of NCSBN developed and submitted a funding proposal to adapt the software technology and databases developed by the

NBME for CST in nursing. The proposal included possible use of CST as part of the NCLEX.[325] At the February 1988 meeting the board of directors charged the CST Steering Committee to:

- Oversee the design of CST software modifications and the form and extent of database and case development.

- Select and recommend appointment of the members of the case development and scoring committees.

- Provide information regarding legal and psychometric issues.

- Design and implement a plan to promote CST as a part of NCLEX.

- Monitor and evaluate outcomes and make recommendations to the board of directors.[326]

At the 1988 meeting of the delegate assembly, the CST Steering Committee recommended that NCSBN investigate the feasibility of using CST for initial and continued licensure. The delegates adopted the recommendation.[327] In her report to the delegates President Ruth Elliott noted that funding to explore the feasibility of using CST for nurse licensure examinations had been received from the W. K. Kellogg Foundation.[328]

The following year the board of directors named Shirley Dykes of Alabama as chair of the CST Steering Committee and the committee established goals, objectives, and strategies for the project.[329] The board heard in April that negotiations were continuing with the NBME for a contract for CST development by NCSBN.[330] In 1990 NCSBN entered into a contract with the NBME to enable access to service and object codes for the CST Project.[331]

At its February 1991 meeting the board of directors asked the CST Steering Committee to address questions related to the marketing of CST, its availability to educators, and potential applications for measuring continued competence using CST. Legal counsel reported to the board on financial obligations of NCSBN to the NBME under the contract for the licensing and software maintenance agreement for CST.[332] In October the board of directors agreed to fund the CST Project staff through June 1992 and designated $102,625 to cover staffing and NBME license fees.[333]

At the annual meeting in 1991 the delegate assembly adopted a motion, as recommended by the board of directors, to continue research and development of CST within a three to four year time frame, with annual reports to the delegates to include an evaluation of progress and implications for future development.[334] Chair Shirley Silverman's (formerly Dykes) report on the CST Steering Committee, presented to the delegate assembly, listed the following goals:

- Adapt the technology for the development and delivery of computer based clinical simulations for initial licensure.

- Develop a pool of computerized clinical simulation cases.

- Examine the validity and reliability of CST as a basis for making nursing licensure decisions.

- Develop and implement a plan for promoting the use of CST in nursing licensure examinations with member boards and the nursing community.[335]

The board of directors continued to add funding to the CST Project in 1992 by agreeing to requests for $21,879 for the second phase and $75,000 for a market analysis survey for FY93. The board also asked staff and legal counsel to review the contract with the NBME and to negotiate appropriate changes.[336] The Report of the CST Steering Committee for 1992 was presented to the delegate assembly by Debra

Brady of New Mexico, the current chair of the committee. She reported that field tests planned for 1992 were cancelled and discussed plans for studies of alternative uses of CST, such as discipline, continued competency, reentry to practice, and licensure. The CST Steering Committee made presentations and demonstrations at national and regional meetings.[337]

Chair Brady authored an article in a 1993 *Issues* that gave a succinct summary of the project to date. NCSBN had received a $1.9 million grant from the W. K. Kellogg Foundation in 1988 to study the feasibility of developing and administering a CST of nursing competence. Chair Brady wrote that the "use of performance assessment is the wave of the future for evaluating competency to practice in a profession. CST has potential for assisting boards of nursing to make more valid assessments about who is competent to practice nursing." The article stated that potential uses of the results of the work of the CST Steering Committee included the following:

In conjunction with CAT, for initial licensure.

As an assessment tool for reeducation planning or reentry for the RN out of practice for a period of time and evaluation of clinical competency of RNs who have been disciplined.

As a teaching tool or an assessment/evaluation mechanism within formal education programs or as a component of continuing educational offerings.[338]

Following the receipt of a grant of $100,000 in April from the W. K. Kellogg Foundation to assist in defraying the cost of additional research and development of CST, with limited additional funding forthcoming, the board of directors established a designated fund of $2,965,817 for additional research and development of CST for the period from FY94 through FY98.[339] In her report to the delegate assembly, Chair Brady reported that the CST Steering Committee had decided to focus on research related to initial license to more efficiently provide the evidence necessary to determine whether or not CST could be used for evaluating competence in nursing problem solving and decision making. The evidence obtained could then be used as a foundation for investigating other potential applications for CST.[340]

Dorothy Fiorino of Alaska presented the report of the CST Steering Committee to the delegates in 1994. She discussed the negotiations with schools of nursing for the purpose of investigating the construct validity of CST, exploring the use of CST as an educational tool, and identifying the type of technical support needed by the students who would participate in the next large scale CST pilot study.[341]

In June 1996 the board of directors selected the jurisdictions to participate in the pilot study. The board also authorized NCSBN to enter into a contract with the NBME for the third phase of CST.[342] Chair Brady reported to the delegate assembly that the CST Task Force, formerly the CST Steering Committee, developed and programmed the specifications of a new simulation system. The next step for the group was the pilot study to evaluate the psychometric soundness and legal defensibility of CST as a potential component of the NCLEX-RN. In addition, the task force met with the Examination Committee to discuss how the two groups could work together on the project.[343]

The CST Project continued to appear in the NCSBN minutes and reports in 1997. In February the board of directors approved Colorado as a participant in the pilot study of member board use of CST for applications other than initial licensure.[344] The board selected the jurisdictions in May to participate in an initial evaluation of member board use of CST for RN education and evaluation. Those chosen were Arizona, Delaware, Mississippi, Oklahoma, Oregon, Washington, and West Virginia-RN.[345] In her 1997 report to the delegate assembly Chair Brady reported that 215 nursing education programs submitted applications expressing interest in participating in the pilot study. Of these, 95 were selected (65 participants and 30 alternates.) Individuals at the schools were to receive CST orientation and practice software for the 1997–1998 academic year. The schools were to recruit the students as study participants and provide them with practice using the CST software.[346]

The CST Project received increased attention in 1998. In May the board of directors deferred marketing activities for CST software until future relationships with the NBME were more clearly defined. The board also decided to delay a decision by the delegate assembly on CST as a component of NCLEX-RN to no later than 2000. Further, the board approved the delay of an external technical evaluation of CST software developed by the NBME until the fall of 1999.[347] In June, the board of directors discussed the presentation of information on CST to the delegate assembly in August. A question emerged: "Should CST research and development continue given operational and other defined issues?" The board decided to schedule a forum where the issues would be summarized and responses requested from the delegates.[348] At the annual meeting the delegate assembly decided to continue with research and development of CST as a component of the NCLEX-RN.[349] A 20-page overview of the CST Project was included in the 1998 *NCSBN Business Book*. In November the board of directors received and approved the steps for coordination between the CST Task Force and the Examination Committee to complete the research study on the potential use of CST as a component of NCLEX-RN.[350]

After more than 10 years of research and development, the board of directors presented the following recommendation to the delegate assembly in 1999: "that the National Council discontinue activities related to computerized clinical simulation being considered as a possible component of the NCLEX-RN® examination." The following rationale and fiscal impact were presented to support the recommendation:

At its May 1999 meeting, the Board of Directors reviewed comprehensive information from multiple sources about the CST project. Based on its careful consideration of reports from the Finance Committee, Examination Committee and the CST Task Force, and its evaluation of the organization's fiscal resources and program priorities, the Board of Directors determined that the most responsible and prudent action was to suspend the CST project activities and to bring the question of the future of CST to the Delegate Assembly for a decision at this time. The Board action is not inconsistent with last year's Delegate Assembly direction to continue the CST pilot study and bring a report back to the Delegate Assembly *no later* than August 2000.

On the basis of its review of the issues addressed in the Finance Committee Examination Committee, and CST Task Force reports, the Board of Directors believes that ample evidence has been developed to suggest that it is not viable for the National Council to implement CST, as it has been operationalized, as a potential component of the NCLEX-RN® examination. Also, based on the committee reports, its consideration of Member Board concerns raised at the Area Meetings, and its fiduciary responsibility to the organization, the Board of Directors believes that the appropriate action which provides for the best stewardship of organizational resources would be to end the CST project and discontinue investing National Council resources in CST at this time.

The fiscal impact for discontinuing the CST project at the 1999 Delegate Assembly is estimated to be approximately $650,000, which will be saved from the FY99 and FY00 budgets. These savings have been estimated to account for all outstanding payments to NBME and outstanding costs to discontinue the CST project. It is important to realize that these savings are related *only* to this phase of the CST pilot study project. If the CST project were continue, additional significant fiscal resources would need to be budgeted to finance future work.

Other documents presented showed that $5,776,691 was budgeted for CST for FY88 through FY00, W.K. Kellogg Foundation grants had been received in the amounts of $1,968,954 between 1988 and 1993, and the projected costs for entry-level implementation were $5,500,000 to $6,600,000. The Finance Committee recommended that the CST Project be discontinued immediately. The Examination Committee reported a vote of no confidence for using CST as a component of the entry-level examination program. The CST Task Force had asked the board to withhold a decision until completion of the CST Pilot Study, but no later than August 2000.[351] The recommendation was adopted by the 1999 delegate assembly and the CST Project was discontinued at that time.[352]

Despite the fact that the CST Project was discontinued, those who were directly involved gained a great deal of new knowledge about innovative testing and important steps were taken to ensure that NCSBN was a part of ongoing developments in the examination process. It is important to recognize the leadership of Shirley Silverman and Debra Brady as chairs of the CST Steering Committee, later the CST Task Force, and Anna Bersky, CST project director throughout the existence of the project.

Conclusion

This chapter is a review of the studies, activities, and actions related to examinations by many board and staff members from the boards of nursing and NCSBN. Some of these individuals have been identified, but space limitations prohibit the listing of all who have participated in this vital function of the organization. Those persons listed below include those individuals who have chaired the committees, task forces, and teams related to the SBTPE, the NCLEX, the NACEP, the NNAAP, and CST during the first 25 years of NCSBN.

Examination Committee

1978–1979	Eileen McQuaid (later Dvorak), New York
1980–1981	Phyllis Sheridan, Idaho
1982–1988	Louise Sanders (later Waddill), Texas-RN
1986–1988	Harriet Johnson, New Jersey
1989–1991	Dorothy Chesley, Texas-RN
1992	Karen Brumley, Colorado
1993	Patricia Earle, Minnesota, then Gwen Hinchey, California-VN, Team I
1993–1994	Renatta Loquist, South Carolina, Team II
1994–1995	Paulette Worcester, Indiana
1996	Renatta Loquist, South Carolina
1997–2000	Lynn Norman, Alabama
2001–2003	Anita Ristau, Vermont

Security and Administration of Examination Committee

1978	Marianna Bacigalupo, New Jersey

Administration of Examination Committee

1979–1981	Geraldine Wenger, Pennsylvania
1982–1984	Sandra MacKenzie, Minnesota
1985–1987	Leola Daniels, Idaho
1988–1989	Gail McGuill, Alaska
1990–1992	Betty Clark, Maine
1993	Alta Haunsz, Kentucky

Special Projects Committee

1987–1991	Billie Haynes, California-VN

CAT Field Test Team

1992–1993	Barbara Kellogg, South Carolina

Cat Education/Information Team

1992	Charlie Dickson, Alabama

CAT Evaluation Task Force

1995	Deborah Feldman, Maryland

Task Force on Examinations for the Future

1987–1988	Joan Bouchard, Oregon

CST Steering Committee, later Task Force

1988	Sherry Smith, Indiana
1989–1992	Shirley Dykes Silverman, Alabama
1992–1993	Debra Brady, New Mexico
1994	Dorothy Fiorino, Alaska
1995–1999	Debra Brady, New Mexico

Task Force on Evaluation of Nurse Aides, later NACEP Committee

| 1988–1994 | Sharon Weisenbeck, Kentucky |
| 1995–1998 | Cindy Lyons, Oklahoma |

As stated at the beginning of this chapter, examinations have continued to be at the center of the activities of NCSBN since its inception, and had been the primary focus of the groups of representatives of boards of nursing that preceded NCSBN. This chapter has described the work of the various parties involved in the continuation of the SBTPE from 1978 until 1982, and the development of NCLEX since that time. The outstanding effort on the part of so many individuals and groups that led to the administration of NCLEX by CAT has been described. The beginnings of the next steps in the evolution of examination for licensure are apparent at the end of the first 25 years of the organization as NCSBN begins to take the steps toward international administration of the examinations, and to study innovative formats for the examinations. Leadership of people like Eileen McQuaid Dvorak, Jennifer Bosma, Tony Zara, and Casey Marks, from the staff of NCSBN, and the farsighted individuals from the NLN, CTB, CGI, and Pearson VUE who worked with the volunteers who served on the examination-related committees deserves far more recognition than has been received. However, the effort was never for recognition, rather for the commitment to public protection that drives those associated with the regulation of nurses. The outstanding work accomplished in these years answers the question stated in the first paragraph of this chapter, "What does the NCSBN know about developing examinations?" We can say, with confidence, "The NCSBN does indeed know a great deal about developing examinations."

CHAPTER TEN
INTERSTATE MOBILITY

Nurses are the wandering spirits of the Earth; their training teaches them to be ready to march, like a soldier, at a moment's notice; they seldom become deeply rooted in one place, seldom accumulate cumbersome belongings; they divest themselves of everything which may impede flight, and a change of residence becomes...easy for them.

M. Adelaide Nutting, 1904[1]

The National Council of State Boards of Nursing, Inc. (NCSBN®) was organized to provide a forum where its member boards could meet together to discuss "matters of common interest and concern that impact the health, safety and welfare of the public." Several of the original objectives of NCSBN related to the facilitation of the licensure of nurses as they moved from one state to another, and later, as they practiced across state lines. These objectives included the provision of national licensing examinations and the identification of "desirable and reasonable uniformity in standards and expected outcomes in nursing education and nursing practice." By 1984 NCSBN adopted new test plans for registered nurses (RNs) and licensed practical/vocational nurses (LPN/VNs), contracted with a new test service, and adopted the *Model Nursing Practice Act and Model Nursing Rules and Regulations*. The member boards had long recognized the importance of reasonable uniformity in legal standards of practice and requirements for licensure as well as national psychometrically sound and legally defensible examinations as the basis for interstate mobility for nurses.

Background

Within a year of the passage of the first nursing practice acts, statements related to "reciprocity" began to appear in the *American Journal of Nursing (AJN)*. For example, in the 1904 section of the Official Reports of Societies, the following statement was included:

An entry from the Virginia State Nurses reported on a meeting of the Graduate Nurses Examiners Board of Virginia ...at which the Board decided "that we recognize the requirements of the boards of New York and Maryland and that North Carolina be recognized for one year."[2]

In 1915 a speaker at the American Nurses Association (ANA) Convention "emphasized the differences among the laws of various states and problems thus inherent in the movement of nurses from state to state."[3]

The term "reciprocity" was used for many years to describe the process through which a nurse licensed in one state would become licensed in another state. Anna Jamme, chair of the ANA Committee on Legislation in 1917, made the following statement about reciprocity:

> The basis of reciprocity has been founded on the wording of the law "requirements equivalent to." The laws of twenty-five states demand equivalent requirements; the interpretation of equivalent requirements should mean equivalent preliminary educational entrance requirements and equivalent minimum course of instruction in the training school. It is the opinion of this committee that upon the above interpretation only, can a rational basis of reciprocity be established.[4]

Webster's New World Dictionary defines reciprocity as "mutual exchange, especially of special privileges; the act of reciprocating." Reciprocate is defined as "to move alternately back and forth" and [Archaic] to be correspondent or equivalent."[5]

Some nursing practice acts provided for reciprocity, but some did not. In New York a representative of the board of nursing surveyed, and the board of regents subsequently approved, schools of nursing in other states. An entry in the minutes of the Virginia Board of Nursing in the 1920s reported that a representative from New York had visited several schools in Virginia that were later recognized by New York. The term "reciprocity" usually indicated that there was a mutual agreement or acceptance of something. Many boards of nursing required that the applicant entering a new state must have transcripts of pre-nursing and nursing education as well as verification of the original license sent to the receiving state where all documents were reviewed for equivalency with the requirements of the receiving state. At the meeting of the Legislative Committee at the ANA Convention in 1930, Mary M. Roberts said that she believed the profession would soon find it necessary "to set up standardizing machinery that all states will recognize." This would enable the graduates of accredited schools to be eligible for examination by a national board of nurse examiners "whose findings would be acceptable to all states and thus abolish the problem of reciprocity for graduates of schools in this upper level."[6]

In the 1930s the NLNE published its *Curriculum Guide* that led to improved consistency in the standards for nursing education, and in the early 1940s the national licensing examinations became available. There was increased effort to arrive at suggested language for nursing practice acts. All of these events had an impact on interstate mobility for nurses and the term "endorsement" came into common use to replace "reciprocity." Webster's definition for "endorsement" is "the act of endorsing something." "Endorse" is defined as "to write on the back of a document; to give approval to; support; sanction…"[7] The endorsement process, for the most part, required the nurse to file an application with the receiving board of nursing and to request the original (and sometimes the current) board of nursing to endorse the license to the new state by attesting to education, examination, and current status of the license in most states. However, the application was still reviewed to assure that there was conformity with the requirements of the receiving state. The process was an improvement over that for reciprocity. However, significant differences between the state laws remained and the process could be slow at times. NCSBN continued to look at ways to improve interstate mobility for nurses throughout its first 25 years.

An Early Look at Interstate Mobility

Eleanor J. Smith, executive secretary for the Virginia Board of Nursing from 1971 to 1983, told her board members in the late 1970s that she thought nurses must make up the largest number of migrant workers in the Untied States. She based this statement on the large number of address changes the board staff processed daily. Smith's comment reinforced the magnitude of the mobility of nurses.

As early as 1979, representatives from the ANA National Accrediting Board met with the NCSBN Board of Directors to discuss "the issue of recognition of a national accreditation system for continuing education." The basis for the concern that led to this meeting was a belief that mandatory continuing education could be a threat to interstate mobility. The group asked NCSBN to support the ANA National Accreditation Board to maintain mobility.[8] Two years later at the annual meeting the delegates adopted a motion that the NCSBN Board of Directors provide a mechanism to study the problems of continued education requirements and interstate mobility of RNs and LPN/VNs.[9]

The Ad Hoc Committee on Verification of Licensure Forms developed a form in 1982 that was reviewed by the board of directors. The board approved the form and asked the area directors to present it at the area meetings to be considered for adoption by the member boards.[10] In the 1983 *NCSBN Book of Reports*, Area III Director Merlyn Maillian of Louisiana-RN reported that the verification of licensure form was reviewed and the group added "name in which originally licensed" and "social security number," which were to be provided by the member boards. Area IV Director Lois O'Shea of Delaware reported that at the Area IV meeting the group decided to study the form and make suggestions for change to send to the board of directors by January.[11] The same year the board of directors approved a verification form, in principle. The board asked the area directors to submit additional information to the president by October 1983. The final form would then be offered to the member boards for their use.[12] In a somewhat related matter, among the list of NCSBN activities for 1983 was a plan to "explore liaison with other North American countries of Canada and Mexico for purposes of maximizing beneficial resources and intercountry endorsement of nurses' licensure."[13]

In 1984 Area IV Director O'Shea reported again that discussion at the area meeting included the topic of endorsement generally, and endorsement for advanced nursing practice in particular. The group also discussed problems when a licensee held both the RN and the LPN/VN license.[14] The following year, the Area IV Task Force to Study Commonalities of Licensure Requirements of the Member Boards reported on a comprehensive response to a survey of all member boards, led by Elizabeth Richard from the Maine State Board of Nursing. Of 61 member boards, 58 responded. While some commonalities were identified, there were substantial differences among the responses. Some of these differences included educational, age, and citizenship requirements for licensure.[15]

Information System to Support Mobility

In 1985 a survey of the needs of the member boards was conducted. The survey supported the need for a national nurse licensee database. The board of directors authorized staff to seek external funding for a feasibility study relative to the development of a national computerized database of all licensed nurses. Upon receiving a positive response the board authorized the staff to prepare a grant proposal.[16] This entry in the minutes was the beginning of a lengthy period and extensive work by many people to achieve the goal of this action by the board of directors in 1985. By the end of the first 25 years of NCSBN, an information system with participation by the majority of the member boards was in operation. The next pages will describe the actions during the following years to reach that level of participation.

In January 1986 the NCSBN staff proposed the appointment of a committee to examine the feasibility of establishing a computerized national licensee database. The board of directors authorized $4,500 in FY86 for a Database Committee of five members to begin the feasibility study. The board also authorized $37,562 for FY87 to continue the work of this committee.[17] In her report to the delegate assembly, President Sharon Weisenbeck of Kentucky said that a Nurse Licensee Data Base Committee had been appointed. The committee was subsequently called the National Nursing Licensee Data Base (NNLDB) Committee. Members of the committee with data system experience were selected from the four areas. They were Walter (Pete) Bailey of South Carolina, chair; Charles Barner of Florida; Linda Coley of Idaho; Elizabeth Jensen of Michigan; and Bertha Mugurdichian of Rhode Island. The committee was charged "to explore operational issues and to recommend strategies for future potential implementation of a national nurse licensee data base system."[18] At the 1987 meeting of the delegate assembly Chair Bailey presented the report of this NNLDB Committee. The delegates adopted a motion to implement activities to establish a national nursing information system.[19] The Report of the National Nurse Licensee Data Base Committee listed the following as benefits of a national nursing database:

- General statistics about nurses in aggregate form.

- Central clearinghouse and linkage where member boards could access disciplinary and license data provided by other member boards and present a quick and efficient method of verifying the information on an endorsement application.

- Detailed statistical analysis for planning for the profession and educational institutions and to study trends data, activity levels, gains and losses, attrition, etc.

The committee concluded that an information system would be beneficial to the member boards and/or national agencies. The committee identified a long-range goal of full participation by the member boards, but decided to begin with a sample for testing purposes.[20] In an October *Newsletter to the Member Boards* the NNLDB Committee reported on its plan for a pilot study. Several member boards offered data for use in the study and more member boards were to be asked to participate.[21]

The report of the NNLDB Committee in 1988 stated that 11 states participated in the pilot study. The following summary was included:

The NNLDB Committee has found interest on the part of Member Boards in creating a National Nursing Information System (NNIS). However, there are practical, fiscal, technical and other limitations for many Boards wishing to collect nursing data to contribute to the national data base. Also, there is substantial variation in the type and amount of data collected by those states already surveying nurses.

The Committee proposes to continue collecting data from those Boards which have a system already established. To assist other Member Boards to participate in the NNIS, the committee recommends seeking outside funding to plan and design a model survey instrument which would be available for Member Board use.

The Committee recognizes that, in its early stages, the NNIS will not be the ideal comprehensive data base because not all the states will be able to participate. However, it is the hope of the committee that a well-designed survey could serve as a prototype which could eventually result in more states being able to collect data and in greater comparability of data collected for nurses in the United States.

The delegate assembly adopted the recommendation from the committee to continue to work with the member boards to identify data currently available in a computerized format for inclusion in a national information system, and to pursue a grant or other external funding to assist member boards in setting up systems to collect the information.[22]

The NNLDB Committee met in the fall of 1988 and revisited the original intent to develop a nurse information system that would facilitate an accurate count of the number of individuals holding active RN and/or LPN/VN licenses. The committee identified the data elements needed to "unduplicate" a list of all licenses, listed the major elements to be included in a funding proposal, and planned for sharing the information with the member boards.[23] Subsequently, the board of directors changed the name of the NLDB Committee to the Nurse Information System (NIS) Committee, and Judie Ritter of Florida was named chair.[24]

In 1988 the Report of the Nursing Practice and Standards (NP&S) Committee included in its objectives for 1988–1989 "to prepare a model set of endorsement standards."[25] This action was the result of a 1987 resolution from the delegate assembly that asked the NP&S Committee to:

Document and distribute the requirements of each Member Board for licensure by endorsement of RNs and LPNs,

Study the differences in the requirements, and

Recommend to the Delegate Assembly desirable and reasonable standards, which, if implemented would facilitate endorsement yet assure public protection.[26]

At the 1989 meeting of the delegate assembly, the delegates adopted the Uniform Standards for Endorsement, as amended.[27] The requirements were as follows:

---

1. A completed application including the following identifiers:
    A. Name at birth and all other previously used names and aliases;
    B. Passport picture;
    C. Birth date
    D. Social Security number
    E. Name of high school and year of graduation, or date of GED;
    F. Name of basic nursing education program;
2. Verification and date of completion of the educational requirements for licensure.
3. Verification and documentation of licensure status:
    A. The original jurisdiction of licensure to include the following information:
        1. Type of examination;
        2. Date and series/form;
        3. Result of scoring;
        4. Number and date of original license;
        5. Disciplinary action;
        6. Current status of license;
        7. All jurisdictions to which the license has been verified.
    B. The jurisdiction of most recent nursing employment to include the following information:
        1. Number and date of license;
        2. Disciplinary actions.
4. Submission of the required fee(s).

The document also listed the requirements for a temporary license or permit, and there were comments provided in a second column beside each requirement. Prior to its adoption, a final statement was added as an amendment by the delegates: "Uniform models and standards are intended as guidelines for use by jurisdictions in carrying out their regulatory charge of monitoring nursing practice and education."[28]

A more comprehensive report of the NIS Committee was published in the 1989 *NCSBN Book of Reports*. Chair Ritter included a review of the premises of the project. The committee identified data elements needed to unduplicate lists provided by the member boards as follows: name; date of birth; zip code of mailing address; Social Security number; type of license; license number in reporting state; and original license information (type, date, jurisdiction, number, and basic nursing education program). The committee also reviewed several approaches to data collection to accommodate the unique characters of different member boards. Carolyn Yocom and William Lauf were the NCSBN staff members assigned to the committee.[29] In November the board of directors authorized a $7,000 increase in the budget for the NIS Committee. The funding was for a pilot study to demonstrate that license data from three jurisdictions could be combined into one database and that licensee entries could be unduplicated.[30]

At the first board of directors meeting in 1990 the board approved a demonstration project for the NCSBN Network (NCNET), an electronic network for the delivery of a variety of software services between NCSBN and the member boards. The project included the placement of a licensure verification form on the system, the creation of new and improved promotional materials, and a demonstration of the system at the 1990 annual meeting.[31]

The NIS Committee report to the 1990 delegate assembly included discussion of a meeting with representatives from the Robert Wood Johnson Foundation; the Health Resources and Services Administration of the Department of Health and Human Services (Division of Nursing); and the ANA to discuss potential funding for NIS. Subsequently, the committee:

- prepared and submitted a grant proposal to the Robert Wood Johnson Foundation;

- obtained a commitment from the Division of Nursing to provide $15,000 to help defray the cost of the feasibility study; and

- obtained a commitment from the ANA to provide "in kind services," valued at $17,000, to help defray costs.

In addition, the committee selected the Georgia-RN, Nebraska, and South Carolina member boards to participate in the study and worked with representatives from these member boards and from National Computer Systems to develop a scannable survey form.[32]

Thomas Neumann of Wisconsin, the Nursing Practice and Education (NP&E) Committee chair, reported that the committee had developed a Statement on Endorsement Issues Related to Peer Assistance/Alternative Programs. The purpose of this action was:

to explore issues and make recommendations regarding endorsement of licensees who are participating in confidential peer assistance/alternative programs. Member Boards need to address whether or not information regarding participation in peer assistance/alternative programs can be required of endorsement applicants and how to give notice to licensees that self-disclosure may be required if the nurse moves to another jurisdiction.[33]

The delegate assembly adopted the statement at the 1990 annual meeting.[34]

An article in *Issues* late in 1990 announced that NCSBN had received a Robert Wood Johnson Foundation grant in the amount of $117,000 to examine the feasibility of establishing a National Nurse Information System that would facilitate an accurate count of both RNs and LPN/VNs, and be a resource for data about selected nurse characteristics.[35] At the November board of directors meeting the board approved an adjustment to the capital acquisition budget of $7,000 for furniture and computers for the director and staff of the NIS Project.[36] With the funding and a structure for its work in place, the term "NIS Project" was used to designate the effort to achieve the information system for NCSBN.

The Projects Committee of the board of directors presented a uniform licensure verification form to the board in February 1991. The board agreed to introduce the form to the member boards by distributing it with a *Newsletter to the Member Boards.[37] (see fig. 10-A)*

At the 1991 annual meeting the delegates received the Report of the Nurse Information System Committee. Judie Ritter continued as chair and Melanie Neal was identified as project director. The pilot study on license verification was continuing. The committee surveyed the member boards regarding the availability of data, constraints on release of data, and the cost of supplying the data to NCSBN. Of the

62 boards, 60 responded to the survey. The results showed that most could comply, but that the Social Security number and date of birth elements were likely to be restricted. The committee was also working with the ANA to conduct a market analysis survey to identify potential uses of NIS and to determine specific needs.[38]

At the August meeting of the board of directors, the board accepted the recommendation from the NIS Committee to increase the FY92 budget by $126,800. The purpose of the increase was to allow for the completion of the study to determine the feasibility of establishing the NIS and the negotiation of contracts with member boards for their participation in the NIS.[39] In December the board of directors adopted the proposed contract with the member boards for the NIS, and authorized its issuance to the first two in January 1992.[40]

The *Newsletter to the Member Boards* on November 22, 1991, included an update on the project. The feasibility study was completed and a final report had been sent to the Robert Wood Johnson Foundation, the Division of Nursing, and the ANA. Based on the results of the study, the member board survey and the market analysis, the decision was made to begin Stage I of the project's implementation. Stage I included finalizing the contracts with the member boards and seeking external funding to support data collection and further development of NIS. Key statements from the executive summary of the "Final Report on the NIS Feasibility Study" were the following:

- The Member Board survey showed that most Boards would be able to provide most of the information necessary to produce the NIS.

- Analysis of the pilot study data indicated that it was possible to produce an unduplicated, multi-state file containing licensee data.

- More than half of the potential users questioned in the market analysis survey indicated an interest in purchasing a comprehensive list of nurse licensees.

- Selection characteristics that respondents indicated would be most desirable in constructing a partial list of licensees were employment status, type of employment, practice area, and level of education. The most frequently identified uses for the lists were research, staff recruitment, and marketing products and services.

- Based on the results of the feasibility study, the National Council concluded that the NIS is both technically and financially feasible.

A fact sheet also accompanied this issue of the *Newsletter to the Member Boards*. This document included the background and plans for the implementation of NIS. The following uses and benefits of NIS were listed:

- Through the NIS, Member Boards would have access to data on their own licensees that they may be unable to collect, or that are not included in their umbrella agency's computer system.

- The NIS would provide regional data on the supply of licensees, and the characteristics of those licensees, for Member Boards and others concerned with the geographical distribution of nurses.

- Member Boards would be able to obtain comparative data on licensees in other states and regions.

- The NIS would be able to be linked with the Disciplinary Database (DDB) in order to provide Member Boards with information on the states in which an applicant for licensure/endorsement has been or is currently licensed.

- The National Council could fill requests for data and labels and provide a licensee data back-up system for Member Boards.

- An up-to-date NIS would be the most accurate and accessible source of information on licensed nurses, and would provide Congress and state legislatures with the data they need to make informed decisions on the funding of existing educational programs, provision of scholarship and loan funds to nursing students, and needs for additional education programs.[41]

At its meeting in May 1992 the board of directors heard a request from the Area I meeting that the board present the concept of NIS and its actual implementation to the delegate assembly at such time as the information was available to make the decision to begin the NIS.[42] In July the board of directors decided to recommend to the delegate assembly that NIS be implemented, contingent on receipt of substantial external funding for development and initiation of the system. The board also instructed the staff and legal counsel regarding the inclusion of a "hold harmless" clause, for intentional or negligent acts of NCSBN, in the contracts with the member boards for NIS.[43] The recommendation was adopted by the delegate assembly in August.[44]

Marie Hilliard of Connecticut was chair of the NIS Committee in 1992. Her report to the delegate assembly described the activities for the year, including the development of a model contract with member boards, the pursuit of funding sources, and the preparation for implementation contingent on positive action by the delegate assembly.[45] The report of the NP&E Committee mentioned a meeting with Melanie Neal, NIS program manager, to discuss the possibility of the interchange of information in the DDB with information in the NIS, particularly to look at all of the states in which an individual was licensed.[46] The NIS Committee report to the board of directors informed the board that funding had been received from the Robert Wood Johnson Foundation in the amount of $530,110. The board approved a designated fund of $250,654 for NIS with $177,319 to cover the NCSBN portion of the grant and $73,335 to purchase an optical scanning device and computer hardware.[47]

In 1993 the board of directors charged the NIS Committee "to recommend policies regarding use of, access to, and security measures for the NIS, and to provide input on other aspects of the project as necessary to the second project year or until policies are in place." The board also approved nine policies developed by the committee including those for data transfer, unduplicated count, file backup, release of data, and data security.[48] The board of directors appointed the Technical Advisory Panel, required by the Robert Wood Johnson Foundation as a condition of the grant. The members of the panel follow:

Helen Hayes-Thomas, Manager, Data Administration, Loyola University Medical Center

Barbara L. Jones, Director, Data System Development, Michael Pine and Associates, Inc.

Dale C. Jones, Principal Scientist, Research Triangle Institute

William D. Marder, Director, Health Labor Market Research, ABT Associates, Inc.

Evelyn Moses, Chief, Nursing Data and Analysis Staff, Division of Nursing

The panel was charged to provide advice on technical matters related to the NIS Project.[49] In September the NIS Committee reported that it was collecting data from the Arizona, Connecticut, West Virginia-PN, Georgia-RN, Texas-RN, and Oklahoma member boards. The committee expected the addition of data from Iowa, Idaho, Massachusetts, and Texas-VN boards by the end of the year.[50]

The report of the NIS Committee that Chair Hilliard included in the 1994 *NCSBN Book of Reports* was optimistic in that it projected that most or all member boards would send data and programming would be in place to produce the preliminary unduplicated file by the end of the year.[51] In September the NIS staff members met with the senior program officer of the Robert Wood Johnson Foundation to provide an update on the project. A representative from the Division of Nursing was also present. Those at the meeting reacted favorably to the report and made suggestions for a NIS continuation grant proposal. The proposal was submitted at the end of September.[52]

In her report to the delegate assembly in 1995, Executive Director Jennifer Bosma talked about NIS activities and said that NCSBN had received a grant of $499,995 from the Robert Wood Johnson Foundation in continued support of the project.[53] Chair Patricia Brown of Washington reported for the NIS Task Force (formerly the NIS Committee) and said that policy development continued, and that she had participated in the NIS Technical Advisory Panel meeting. She anticipated that NIS would be available on a limited basis after March 1996.[54] At its October 1995 meeting the board of directors approved the pricing structure as presented by the NIS Task Force. The minutes of the meeting stated, "At present policy contains no specific prices and the board of directors expressed its expectations in terms of the need to consider the amount of information requested when actual prices are to be considered." The board also contributed information to the task force regarding the pricing structure for member board access to data other than its own data. Carolyn Yocom, director of Research, provided the board of directors with an update about programming for NIS and the difficulties experienced with the contractor, Strategic Technology Research (STR).[55] In the spring of 1995 the NIS Task Force conducted a pilot test of a user screen with 24 member boards participating. There was a positive response to the test.[56]

Vicky Burbach of Nebraska was chair of the NIS Task Force in 1996. There were no reports of activity related to NIS in 1996, except in relation to the Electronic Licensure Verification Information System (ELVIS). ELVIS was developed as a part of the continuing effort to facilitate licensure by endorsement. The objective was to establish a computerized system that would maximize the use of technology for transmittal of licensee information from one member board to another. The information in NIS was important to the success of ELVIS. In June, the board of directors stated that fees for ELVIS should be calculated to cover present costs and to build a reserve for future operating needs of the system. This fee should be based on the number of queries a member board makes to ELVIS.[57] The Report of the Licensure Verification Task Force, chaired by Mark Majek of Texas-RN, included a review of previous work toward the development of an electronic licensure verification system, including the pilot tests and surveys done earlier in the 1990s. This task force reviewed verification forms from the member boards and identified essential information. The task force also made plans for the future and discussed ELVIS at the area meetings.[58] At the annual meeting the delegates adopted a resolution to continue toward full development of ELVIS. The resolution also directed NCSBN to explore funding to support ELVIS and to encourage the member boards to evaluate the cost of endorsement using ELVIS.[59] In August the board adjusted the FY97 budget to include a capital acquisition of $119,000 to purchase the equipment necessary to implement ELVIS.[60]

Beginning in May 1996 and continuing through the June, August, and November meetings of the board of directors, the board members, staff, and legal counsel met in executive session to discuss issues related to programming services for NIS provided by STR. At each meeting the board gave direction to staff and/or legal counsel for action to be taken on behalf of NCSBN. At a January 1997 meeting of the board of directors, legal counsel discussed with the board in executive session regarding negotiations with STR. At its February meeting the board of directors voted to direct staff to accept the $80,000 settlement offer from the STR.[61]

At the same meeting the board approved a change in the wording on the *NCLEX® Candidate Bulletin* in order to allow the use of data for the purposes of ELVIS. The Candidate Bulletin accompanied the application sent to the candidate and provided necessary information about the examination. The new language read as follows: "The information provided in this application may be used in all licensing related activities and for other purposes authorized by applicable state and federal laws."[62] In August the board of directors discussed potential vendors for NIS and ELVIS, and gave direction for the process of vendor selection and the appointment of an advisory committee of member board representatives. The board stated that the charge for ELVIS was not to exceed $15 per candidate and could be lower.[63]

At the annual meeting in 1997 the Report of the Licensure Verification Task Force advised that the task force had recommended language for the Candidate Bulletin, as cited above and for the member board contracts to provide data for ELVIS. The task force also developed three payment models. Most of the member boards preferred the model where the applicant would send the license application form and fee to the board of nursing and the separate ELVIS request form and fee to NCSBN. However, it was impossible for one member board to use this model. The other two models specified that the applicant would forward all fees (a) to the member board or (b) to NCSBN, and the fee would be distributed to the other entity by the receiver of the fees and forms.[64] The delegate assembly approved the language for the member board contracts to facilitate the provision of ELVIS.[65]

Work on the information system increased in 1998. In April the board of directors selected several vendors for the project:

- Data Base America, Inc. as the data collection vendor.

- Client Servers, Division of Systems Automation Corporation as the software application vendor.

- Oracle Corporation for database software, with the database housed in the NCSBN offices.

- Sysix Technologies to provide hardware.

In addition, agreements were reached with various consulting services, including Process Management Group, Ltd., as a software acceptance testing agent. The board of directors adjusted the budget for the current fiscal year to support the project in the amount of $170,183 for the operating budget and $1,751,644 for the capital budget.[66]

Licensure Verification

Another major activity related to interstate mobility of nurses in 1992 was reported in an article in the *Newsletter to the Member Boards* early in the year. The licensure verification project using NCNET was completed. The report stated that the Arizona, Georgia-RN, Iowa, Louisiana-RN, North Carolina, Nevada, South Carolina, and Texas-RN member boards participated. The board of directors decided to share the report with all of the member boards and requested that future use of NCNET licensure verification be studied within the larger issue of electronic communication and information access. The report was distributed with the *Newsletter* and included a description of the study, background information, and participant evaluation. Of the six member boards responding, five agreed that the idea should be pursued. Problems encountered during the pilot study included:

- Lack of cross-trained individuals in each board to perform as back-up in case of emergency.

- Lack of sufficient computers. Many of the boards had to share a computer with other individuals or departments. Many times, the person responsible for doing verifications and the person responsible for endorsements were located in separate rooms and it was difficult to share a common dedicated computer system.

- Some boards had developed a computer system to print out their own request or response forms with data from their own computer systems at the touch of a button. In order to participate in using electronic forms, these were required to re-type their responses.

- Inconsistent responses from other participating boards. Individuals were trained to expect certain results, and when some of the boards failed to respond, this introduced a lack of confidence in the functionality of the system.

The study showed the following advantages: the process was faster than sending the forms through the mail and the applicant had a shorter waiting period. The primary disadvantage identified was stated as follows:

With the present flow of information and the use of forms, information from a verifying board must be keyed directly into the NCNET form (i.e., it cannot be electronically transferred from a board's existing computer files.)

The following "other" findings were listed:

- It has been shown that it is possible to walk a board through the installation of the program and train staff in the usage of forms and messaging directly over the phone rather than having to send a technical representative from NCSBN   to be on site.

- Five of the eight boards participating in the project were initiated to NCNET with favorable/positive experiences.

- There is much difference from one board to another. Financial payment is one concern, but there is also the difference in approach with regard to the type of information and the means of storing and reporting this information.

- Member boards are at varying levels of computerization, making licensure verification on NCNET difficult for some and a backward step for those with more sophisticated computer systems already in place.[67]

A recurring question that the member boards raised was how each board would be reimbursed equitably. The current process required the endorsement applicant to pay one board for the application and new license and the other board for verification. All possible options were discussed by the participants in the study. Among these options would be an increase in the application fee to offset the loss of revenue from the verification fee. The report closed with the following considerations:

- The first priority should be to promote and train all boards regarding the benefits of NCNET.

- More work needs to be done to move each board in the direction of using the same data items, thus a National Licensure Verification Form.

- If uniform system data elements were identified, it would be possible to download the specific data from a board's existing computer files into a generic format and transmit this data in an approved file format to other boards. Each participating board would incorporate a routine in their system to "dump" the data items into a file. The board would then use NCNET to transmit this data file to the endorsing board.

- A master plan for implementation would have to be introduced that would identify, among other things, the incentives or resources for all member boards to use NCNET, training and service needs, technical and communications support, and fiscal impact.[68]

Provider Identification Numbers

At the March 1994 meeting of the board of directors, the board heard a report of a contact from the ANA, on behalf of the Health Information Standards Planning Panel, relative to proposed health care reform plans that would require health professionals to have unique provider identification numbers (PINs). The board authorized the staff to develop, in collaboration with the ANA, plans for using NIS to generate unique provider numbers for all licensed nurses. Further, the board directed that the plan outline fiscal impact, funding sources, and the promotion of the capability of selected member boards to collect and provide essential NIS data necessary to generate unique provider numbers.[69] At the annual meeting of the delegate assembly, the delegates considered and defeated a resolution that called for

NCSBN to monitor activities in the development of unique provider numbers and report yearly to the delegate assembly, and decided that the NIS data not be used in the construction of a unique provider identification system until authorization to do so was given by the delegate assembly.[70] At the October meeting the board of directors adopted the following approach to the matter of PINs:

1. National Council would explore the technological, fiscal and legal implications of using the NIS to generate PINs and provide the required information directly to the designated national repository.

2. National Council would provide ANA with a list of those jurisdictions where the provision of key licensee data and data elements essential for 100 percent unduplication is problematic. Included would be information as to the nature of the problem contributing to the inability to provide this data. Prior to its release to ANA, Member Boards would be requested to verify jurisdiction-specific information.

3. ANA would develop and propose state specific strategies for addressing the identified problem areas. These strategies would be submitted to the National Council's Board of Directors for approval.

4. National Council would communicate with each Member Board for the purpose of sharing the jurisdiction-specific state nurses association (SNA) strategies and to request Member Board input regarding whether: (1) they would work collaboratively with the SNA, (2) they could not work in a collaborative relationship with the SNA but wouldn't oppose their activity, or (3) they would request that no SNA action be undertaken in their jurisdiction.

5. Following receipt of Member Board input, National Council would authorize ANA and the SNAs to proceed with implementation of the identified state-specific strategies in those jurisdictions where this is not opposed by the Member Board.[71]

The March 1995 *Newsletter to the Member Boards* reported that a task force had been appointed to study the mobility of advanced practice registered nurses (APRNs). A questionnaire to the member boards was developed to compile a reference document related to APRN regulation that could be updated annually for the member boards. The following information was to be included: regulatory environment (i.e., who regulates?); scope of practice regarding prescriptive authority; and requirements for licensure/legal recognition in the jurisdictions. The objective was to assist member boards in evaluating APRNs who have practiced in other jurisdictions as they move to a new state.[72]

Nur*sys*®

At its meeting in August 1998 the board of directors received a report of the NCSBN Information System User Group. For the first time the name "Nursys" appeared in relation to the NIS, and eventually the name was changed to Nur*sys*. The board took several actions related to the report that included the following:

- Approved the addition of data into Nur*sys*™ [At the time of this board meeting, Nursys was not yet a registered trademark as it is now] from multiple sources including the Member Boards, Chauncey Group International (CGI), National Change of Address (NCOA), NIS data scan forms, the Disciplinary Data Bank, and CTB data tapes.

- Determined the schedule for including data:

  1. Design and develop Nur*sys*™ to accept data from multiple sources.

  2. Include data from only the Member Boards, CGI and NCOA in the initial production readiness.

  3. Test other sources of data after Nur*sys*™ is in production and problems are prioritized and resolved.

  4. Set a date for inclusion of other data after testing the original sources and Nur*sys*™ is in a stable production environment.[73]

An article in *Issues* in 1998 discussed the development and implementation of Nur*sys*. The article provided a broad and encompassing description for the nurse data system and the supporting business applications and services. The first applications of Nursys were the nurse licensure verification program and the discipline reporting services. The plan for the second phase was to provide service for the mutual recognition of licenses.[74]

At a March 1999 conference call meeting, the board of directors reviewed a letter from the attorney for Systems Automation Corporation, the software application vendor selected for the information system in 1998. The letter had been sent in response to correspondence from NCSBN indicating its intent to initiate a 60-day period for remediation of serious concerns regarding the work of the company on the Nur*sys* project. The board considered options presented by Executive Director Eloise Cathcart and Legal Counsel Thomas Abram, and directed Abram to begin negotiations with attorneys for Systems Automation to sever the contract.[75] The board continued to discuss this issue in another conference call later in March.[76] In May the board of directors approved the selection of Crockett and Associates to begin work on the Nur*sys* project and approved an increase in the capital budget for FY99 of $255,679 and a decrease in the operating budget of $137,585.[77] At the end of 1999 the board directed that APRNs be included in the Nur*sys* database and that a specific screen for APRN information be developed.[78]

At the February 2000 meeting the board of directors decided that the member boards with nurse licensure compacts in place would be added to the pilot test for Nursys. The board asked Abram to draft an interim agreement to allow for participation of these states. The board also agreed to engage Value Enhancements Strategies, Inc., to conduct a comprehensive evaluation of Nur*sys* with a special focus on the revenue system.[79] In June the board of directors received the report from Value Enhancements including options to fund the Nur*sys* project.[80] The board voted in August to increase the Nursys verification fee from $15 to $30 effective on January 1, 2001.[81] An article in the *Council Connector* in December 2000 reported that North Carolina, Ohio, Idaho, Missouri, Texas-RN, Texas-VN, Arkansas, and Iowa member boards were providing data to Nur*sys* on a regular basis. The article noted major enhancements to the system including the ability to support mutual recognition and several improvements to the licensure verification process.[82]

An article in the Council Connector in March 2001 included comments from Mark Majek of Texas-RN and Susan Boone of Ohio. Majek and Boone reported that the Nur*sys* pilot test met expectations. Favorable comments related to the process of log in and retrieval of data and the "Speed Memo" feature of Nur*sys* enabled access to other member boards to answer questions. The time required to issue temporary and permanent licenses was reduced. There were fewer telephone inquiries and less time required of the member staff. Majek and Boone also commented on the increased speed in updating discipline data. The opportunity to clear and remove duplicated information was an unexpected result.[83] In another article in May there was a description of enhancements to Nur*sys* related to the member boards with interstate compacts. The enhancements allowed the compact member boards to view, edit, and delete investigative and alternative program contact information. Nur*sys* did not store actual details of this information but stored the name and telephone number of a person at the member board who could answer questions.[84]

The board of directors discussed a report from the Nur*sys*™ Advisory Panel at its meeting in June 2001. The panel was exploring the possibility of public access to the program. Items under consideration included what data to make available, costs, and whether a fee should be applied. The board asked the director of Finance to develop a business plan for Nur*sys*. The report also stated that verifications of licensure had doubled in May. The staff was processing 100 to 250 per day.[85]

In January 2002, 15 member boards were participating in Nur*sys* and 8 were expected to be added in the near future. The Nur*sys*™ Advisory Panel, chaired by Faith Fields of Arkansas, planned an Information Technology Summit for July 2002.[86] Also in January, the board approved public access to Nur*sys* according to the limits identified by the individual state agreements.[87] In March the board asked staff to develop a transition plan and have the Finance Committee review the proposal for in-house data collection.[88] In

May the board of directors approved a 24-month contract with Donnelly Marketing for data collection services and for the development of an RFP to establish in-house data collection for Nur*sys*.[89]

The board of directors decided in April 2003 that the Nur*sys*™ Advisory Panel was an internal organizational committee and not a committee of the board. The board noted progress toward daily updates for Nur*sys* and projected that it would be in place by the end of August 2003.[90] The Report of the Nur*sys*™ Advisory Panel found in the 2003 *NCSBN Business Book* stated that the Utah, Wisconsin, Arizona, and Delaware member boards were participating, with three others pending. Nur*sys* was launched during the year for both online verification submission and public access to the section known as Nurse Licensure Quick Confirm. The panel reported on its other activities, including the completion of enhancements for the discipline section; updated forms; and the process for member boards to remove disciplinary data, which had been documented and distributed.[91]

There was an informative article in the January 2003 *Council Connector* that described public access to Nur*sys* as limited to license verification information for RNs and LPN/VNs in the jurisdictions that chose to participate. The article also described the process by which the nurse sent an application and a $30 fee to NCSBN. Other aspects of the program were also discussed.[92]

The effort to produce a computerized system of nurse information in response to a stated need of the member boards began in 1986. At the end of the first 25 years of NCSBN in 2003, there were 27 participating states in the program. Some of the original goals of the system can be achieved only when all members boards participate, but it is an important asset for the member boards with nurse licensure compacts. The process of licensure by endorsement when a nurse moves to a new state was greatly improved with Nur*sys*. In addition the availability of information was important to practice across state lines.

Telecommunications and Practice Across State Lines

The second major development related to interstate mobility of nurses began in 1995 when the members of the delegate assembly adopted the following resolution:

That the Board of Directors form a special committee to:

1. study the issues related to telecommunications practice across jurisdictional lines, and

2. develop guidelines to assist Member Boards in the regulatory issues related to interjurisdictional telecommunications practice.[93]

For several years before this action was taken the member boards had been confronted with many questions as to whether a nurse licensed in another state could practice, using one or more forms of telecommunications, in the state of the member board. It may be more appropriate to say the actions that followed the resolution above have facilitated interstate practice, rather than interstate mobility. However, the issue is appropriately discussed in this chapter because of the impact on other facets of interstate mobility.

The board of directors appointed Libby Lund of Tennessee to chair the Nursing Regulation Task Force in 1995. Carolyn Hutcherson was assigned as the primary staff to the task force. At its first meeting in 1996 the board received a report from the task force and provided overall direction for the role of NCSBN in activities related to regulatory reform. The board stated that NCSBN should take a leadership role in proposing regulatory models for the future and in "championing discussion" of the evaluation of models with nursing groups and other health professional regulatory groups.[94]

At the same time an NCSBN task force was looking at telecommunications issues. The Telecommunications Issues Task Force was chaired by Lonna Burress of Nevada, and Carolyn Hutcherson served as staff to this group. The board of directors approved a request from the task force to invite various telecommunications vendors to display their technologies for delivery of health care on an informal basis at the annual meeting in 1996.[95]

In April, the board of directors authorized the expenditure of up to $43,800 for a maximum of 67 participants to attend a conference for member board representatives to work on a proposed revised model for nursing regulation. The board also agreed to highlight the leadership role of NCSBN in this area by issuing a news release.[96] Another report from the Nursing Regulation Task Force was received by the board of directors in June. The board approved funding for a focus group to meet to review and refine the models that the task force was developing. In addition, the board funded an extra meeting for the task force to enhance and finalize its report to the delegate assembly at the annual meeting.[97]

Chair Lund presented a comprehensive report of the Nursing Regulatory Task Force, which can be found in the *NCSBN Book of Reports* for the delegate assembly in August 1996. As background, the task force examined existing models of regulation including endorsement, reciprocity, drivers' license, mutual recognition, federal license, and others. A hybrid system was developed calling for the creation of a multistate license for persons who met specified criteria. This model was designed to allow practice by the nurse licensed in one participating state to practice in all participating states. Focus groups discussed disciplinary questions and the impact on revenue for the member boards. The task force reported other activities including a special conference where 59 representatives of the member boards were present and the task force discussed its work with external groups. A conference cosponsored by the Citizens Advocacy Council and NCSBN, titled "Crafting Public Protection Practice for the 21st Century," was scheduled for December 1996. The task force asked the board of directors to provide direction about the selection of a revised model for nursing regulation that would meet the regulatory objective of protecting the public.[98]

The Telecommunications Issues Task Force reported to the delegate assembly in 1996. During the year the task force defined telenursing as "the practice of nursing over distance using telecommunications technology." In other activities, the task force identified a number of technology modalities used in telenursing and, to assist the member boards, a telecommunications hotline was developed to disseminate pertinent information to the member boards.[99]

At its meeting in 1997 the delegate assembly adopted the definition of telenursing and the accompanying position paper on telenursing. The definition follows:

> Telenursing is the practice of nursing over distance using telecommunications technology. The nurse interacts with the client at a remote site, using this technology, to electronically send and receive client health status data, initiate and transmit therapeutic interventions and regimens, monitor and record client responses and nursing care outcomes.[100]

The examination of telecommunication as it relates to practice across state lines was an important step in the search for another model for the regulation of nurses.

Multistate Licensure

At the 1996 annual meeting the delegate assembly adopted a recommendation from the board of directors as follows:

> That the Board of Directors be charged to continue developing the concept of a regulatory model which incorporates the characteristics of a multistate license by directing activities including: evaluate the magnitude of the needs of consumers, nurses and health care delivery systems for multistate practice; evaluate the impact of state level regulatory processes on multistate license concept; identify core licensure requirement; evaluate potential future implications for Board of Nursing role and functions; identify mechanism for effective cross state disciplinary processes; analyze

current laws and regulations for potential impact on multistate practice; explore the feasibility of a demonstration or pilot project with possible external funding. Nothing in this recommendation shall preclude the investigation of potential options which would facilitate multistate practice. A report of these activities shall be presented to the 1997 Delegate Assembly.[101]

An article in *Issues* following the annual meeting reported that Joan Bouchard of Oregon had been named to chair a Multistate Regulation (MSR) Task Force. The other members of this task force were Charles Bennett of California-VN, Iva Boardman of Delaware, Shirley Brekken of Minnesota, Faith Fields of Arkansas, Patty Hayes of Washington, Mary Kinson of New Hampshire, Celinda Kay Leach of Indiana, Libby Lund of Tennessee, Carol Osman of North Carolina, Ida Rigley of North Dakota, and Sharon Weisenbeck of Kentucky. Jennifer Bosma, executive director, and Susan Williamson, director of Credentialing and Practice for NCSBN, provided staff support to the task force. The charge to the task force was "to continue developing a regulatory concept which incorporates the characteristics of a multistate license." The following statement was developed as the vision for nursing regulation:

Regulation supports the public's protection and access to nursing care within a seamless practice arena on a national scope. Competent nurses can care for clients wherever they are, based on the best care delivery methodology. States' rights to determine who does and does not practice are respected.

A state nursing license recognized nationally and enforced locally[102]

The task force also identified the functions of a desirable system as follows: state-based authority, license linked to state of residence, central database, core standards, revenue (cost) neutral, and expedient processing of licensure applications. In addition, the task force identified 13 criteria for the evaluation of models of regulation. To be considered favorably, any proposed model should:

- require anyone practicing nursing to be accountable for complying with all laws governing practice;
- delineate source of legal authority for scope and location of practice and discipline;
- assure licensed nurse has demonstrated the knowledge, skills and abilities to provide safe and effective nursing care;
- establish standards for education, licensure and discipline;
- promote an expeditious discipline process while ensuring protection of due process for all parties;
- provide effective monitoring of the practitioner's competency and professional conduct;
- provide for the protection of the public by dissemination of information about disciplinary action within and across the jurisdictional boundaries;
- provide for an open system of information exchange;
- be compatible with state sovereignty;
- eliminate the barriers to interstate practice;
- facilitate interstate commerce;
- be administered in a cost-effective and cost-conscious manner; and
- generate revenue to support operations.[103]

Mutual recognition was emerging as the focus for further action by NCSBN in the search for a means to resolve the question of practice across state lines, interstate mobility and a new model for regulation. The board of directors asked the NP&E Committee to address the question of and issues related to competence requirements for multistate regulation as part of its activities for 1997.[104]

Mutual Recognition

In June 1997 the board of directors received the report of the MSR Task Force and decided to recommend the following plan to the delegate assembly at the annual meeting: "To endorse a mutual recognition model of nursing regulation and authorize the Board of Directors to develop strategies and services including an interstate compact and an information system needed to assist the Member Boards with implementation." At the same meeting, the board of directors charged the NP&E Committee to continue work on uniform core licensure requirements.[105] In July the board of directors adopted two motions related to mutual recognition:

1. To endorse a mutual recognition model of nursing regulation for all levels of nursing with appropriate time lines.

2. To direct the APRN Task Force to study issues surrounding implementation of a mutual recognition model for APRNs and develop strategies for consideration by the Delegate Assembly in 1998.[106]

At the annual meeting in 1997 the delegate assembly adopted the following motion: "That the National Council endorses a mutual recognition model of nursing regulation and authorizes the Board of Directors to develop strategies for implementation to be adopted by the Delegate Assembly."[107] Following the close of the annual meeting, President Thomas Neumann of Wisconsin said, "The delegates of the National Council accomplished a historical initiative by unanimously endorsing a mutual recognition model of nursing regulation in 1997."[108]

At the September board of directors meeting, the board authorized a call for a special meeting of the delegate assembly from December 14 to 15, 1997. The purpose of the special meeting was to consider the interstate compact for a mutual recognition model of nursing regulation.[109] At a November meeting the board of directors reviewed a report on the mutual recognition project received following the October 21, 1997 meeting of nursing leaders, cosponsored by the ANA and NCSBN. The board also reviewed correspondence from the National Association of Pediatric Nurse Associates and Practitioners (NAPNAP). Both documents contained inaccuracies and the board of directors gave direction for a response for dissemination to the member boards and responses to the ANA and the NAPNAP.[110] Again, a week later, the board of directors reviewed and discussed comments from the ANA on the interstate compact and directed that a copy of the formal response be forwarded to the member boards.[111]

The delegate assembly of NCSBN reached another milestone when it held a special meeting in Chicago on December 14 and 15, 1997. After several hours in forums and discussion, the following motion was considered: "To approve the Nurse Licensure Compact for the mutual recognition model of nursing regulation." A substitute motion was introduced as follows: "To postpone action on the motion until the next regularly scheduled meeting of the Delegate Assembly in August, 1998 with provisions for additional development and information to the Member Boards." The substitute motion failed on a vote of 55 yes votes and 61 no votes. The original motion was then amended as follows: "To approve the proposed language for an interstate compact in support of a standard approach to a mutual recognition model of nursing regulation" and was adopted on a vote of 72 votes in favor and 40 votes in opposition.[112]

Next the delegate assembly adopted motions to approve the strategies for implementation of the *Mutual Recognition Model of Nursing Regulation*. The following is a listing of those strategies:

Strategy 1.   Provide assistance to Member Boards regarding the transition process.

Strategy 2.   Provide support to Member Boards who choose to implement mutual recognition.

Strategy 3.   Disseminate materials to support education and communication of the mutual recognition model to consumers, licensees, regulatory groups, employers, nursing and other professional organizations.

Strategy 4.   Implement a planned approach to demonstration projects on various aspects of the model.

Strategy 5.   Confirm data elements and policies, and implement the coordinated information system as it relates to mutual recognition.

Strategy 6.   Determine a governance structure and funding mechanism for the Compact Administrators Group.

Strategy 7.   Develop model compact administrative rules to facilitate and coordinate implementation of the compact.

Strategy 8.   Establish model compact administrative procedures.

Strategy 9.   Seek external funding resources for activities such as discipline demonstration projects, information system, telecommunications, and educational resources.

Strategy 10.   Collaborate with consumers, professional organizations, and governmental entities external to the National Council to implement the mutual recognition model.

Strategy 11.   Develop additional strategies for implementation of the mutual recognition model deemed necessary and appropriate by the Board of Directors by the time of the 1998 Delegate Assembly.

Strategy 12.   Identify the additional incremental cost to the Member Boards and the National Council for implementing the coordinated licensure information system and strategies for the implementation of the Mutual Recognition Model by the time of the 1998 Delegate Assembly.[113]

The delegates took a final action at its special meeting as follows:

To strongly recommend that states who adopt the interstate compact include an implementation date no earlier than January 1, 2000. Prior to implementation, the coordinated licensure information system and all necessary supporting services are to be fully operational.[114]

Nurse Licensure Compact

The Nurse Licensure Compact is the model for mutual recognition chosen by NCSBN. In the September 5, 1997, *Newsletter to the Member Boards* Polly Johnson, executive director for the North Carolina Board of Nursing, reported the following:

Not only was North Carolina the first state to pass laws related to the practice of nursing in 1903, but in August 1997, it is the first state in which the Board of Nursing is empowered by statute to enter into interstate compacts.[115]

Although North Carolina was not the first state to have a Nurse Licensure Compact in place, it was the first to be empowered to do so.

Beverly Malone, president and Argeno Carswell, staff member, both from the ANA met with members of the NCSBN staff on January 30, 1998, to discuss mutual recognition and the Nurse Licensure

Compact. The ANA representatives raised questions about how mutual recognition would affect the structure of NCSBN and its the relationship to the DDB and to ELVIS. In addition, they listed the following major areas of concern for the ANA: discipline, state resources, impaired nurses, and the involvement of the SNAs.[116]

In February 1998 the board of directors named the MSR Task Force as the lead group on all issues related to the impact of the transition to the Nurse Licensure Compact on the member boards individually. The board retained the lead for all issues having to do with organizational impact and relations outside NCSBN. The board sent a letter of commendation to the task force and directed a letter to the ANA inviting collaboration with respect to addressing certain transition issues.[117] In April, the board of directors approved the transition plan and the accompanying budget with an adjustment for FY98 of $240,470 added to the operating budget and an additional $155,000 to be expended from October 1998 through December 1999. The board also authorized the expenditure of $20,000 from the discretionary fund to complete capital expenditures associated with the project for material that would have utility beyond the project.[118] The following month the board of directors reviewed the MSR Task Force report and agreed to sponsor a one-day meeting, in conjunction with the annual meeting, that would focus on legislative strategies and opportunities for discussion of operational and fiscal issues.[119]

The board of directors considered the possibility of discussions with the ANA on the topic of mutual recognition. The board decided that when "the appropriate time and conditions" were identified, Joey Ridenour of Arizona, Laura Poe of Utah, Katherine Thomas of Texas-RN, and one staff person would be the appropriate group for such discussions.[120] In June President Neumann reported to the board of directors about a meeting with representatives of the ANA and about contact with the president of the American Nurses Credentialing Center (ANCC). The board agreed that it would:

> entertain the prospect of a joint resolution with the ANA provided that (1) the ANA House of Delegates does the same, (2) no negative or inaccurate information is contained in any resolution passed by the ANA House of Delegates, and (3) any joint resolution cannot impede the implementation of mutual recognition.

The board of directors appointed six members to enter discussions with the ANA on identified issues related to mutual recognition.[121]

In other action, at the June meeting the board of directors affirmed its role by stating, "the aim is that the National Council may be the choice for supplying the needs of the official Compact Administrators Group (CAG), based on quality and cost advantages." The board also approved the objectives and structure of the Interim Compact Administrators Group (ICAG): to develop suggested policies and procedures; to solicit input from future party and non party states; and to develop the official CAG structure, relationships, decision-making processes, and funding mechanisms.[122]

At the meetings of the board of directors immediately prior to and after the annual meeting in 1998, the board received a number of reports and acted on several issues related to mutual recognition. These actions included:

- The appointment of a coordinating group of approximately eight members drawn from the MSR Task Force and the board of directors to coordinate oversight of the implementation of the NCSBN Mutual Recognition Master Plan. This group was known at the Mutual Recognition Master Plan Coordinating Group and Joan Bouchard of Oregon served as chair.

- Funded the Interim ICAG for two meetings to deal with various items.

- Agreed that NCSBN would hold a meeting for member boards and SNAs from states where intent has been expressed to introduce Nurse Licensure Compact legislation in 1999.

The board planned that this meeting would be held prior to another meeting with the ANA representatives to discuss the compact.[123] At the annual meeting the delegate assembly adopted a resolution that NCSBN reaffirm its commitment to continue dialogue with professional and consumer organizations to address concerns about mutual recognition through the interstate compact.[124] In his president's report Neumann noted the following:

We are positioned to optimistically view the new curves ahead of us, ready to leap beyond the danger zones, and evade the death which awaits those who ignore strategic planning and decision making. Just like the visionaries of 1978, we must be willing to take the risks in changing the face of regulation to reflect the current needs of Member Boards and the public we purport to protect.[125]

The *NCSBN Business Book* for the delegate assembly meeting in August of 1998 reflected the many activities related to mutual recognition through a nurse licensure compact. The Report of the Mutual Recognition Master Plan Coordinating Group stated that a master plan to implement mutual recognition with three levels—phases, activities, and tasks—had been developed. Several other work groups had accomplished their charges and the strategies set forth in the action of the delegate assembly in December 1997. The work groups reporting included the following: MSR Operations, MSR Fiscal, Multistate Discipline Process, and MSR Alternative Programs.[126]

The board of directors' Committee on Compact Administration report stated in its conclusion that the committee felt that the ICAG was crucial to the goal of establishing the CAG as a semi-autonomous entity operating within the general framework of NCSBN. "The aim is that the National Council may be the choice for supplying the needs of the official Compact Administrators Group, based on quality and cost advantages." The board also stated its belief that, as the transition goes forward, frequent, open communications among future compact administrators and non-party state member boards was essential.[127]

The fact of the extraordinary effort to reach the 1998 position of NCSBN in the development of an alternate model for nurse regulation—the Nurse Licensure Compact—was reinforced by a listing in the 1998 *NCSBN Business Book*. This list identifies those 57 volunteers from member boards and the board of directors, and the 12 attorneys who were counsel to NCSBN and to the member boards who worked on the project.[128]

Articles in Issues in 1998 also provided information about the progress of the Nurse Licensure Compact. In his message in an early 1998 issue, President Neumann stated that on March 14, 1998, Utah Governor Michael Leavitt signed into law a Senate bill, the Nursing Regulation-Interstate Compact Bill, with an effective date of January 1, 2000.[129] Neumann continued by saying that Utah was the first state to adopt mutual recognition compact legislation for nursing.

Another article in *Issues* reported on states moving forward to implement mutual recognition as the result of meetings at the national and state level. NCSBN and the ANA participated in sessions on July 20, August 25, and September 9 and 10, 1998, that focused on the ANA House of Delegates resolution on mutual recognition. Each of the 14 points from the house of delegates was discussed. NCSBN agreed to provide clarification of language of the compact. The ANA reported that its constituent state associations within the organization had three views on mutual recognition, as follows: those states that were opposed to the compact and would not go forward, those states that were ambivalent and desired more information, and those states that desired to move forward. At the end of the last meeting the ANA announced that it had developed and was sending alternate compact language to the SNAs. NCSBN expressed disappointment and questioned whether this action by the ANA would be supportive to those states choosing to move forward.[130]

Approximately 18 member boards had indicated plans to introduce mutual recognition licensure compact legislation in 1999 and 2000. Representatives from these states met, along with their SNA counterparts, at three "in-person" meetings and two conference calls. The Texas-RN and Utah member boards and the Texas Nurses Association took leadership with their respective groups at these meetings. As a result, clarifying but nonsubstantive changes were made to the compact language and the enabling language was developed. An article in *Issues* about the meeting concludes with this statement: "The proposed compact language represents substantial collaborative work by the state boards of nursing and the state nurses associations to finalize language that could be supported by the various states and thus introduced into the legislature."[131]

At its meeting in November the board of directors approved the revision of the compact language and expressed support for the substantial work done by the member boards and the SNAs. The board of directors urged the ICAG to convene soon to address the issues before it. The board agreed that the financial structure for the CAG should be based on a "dues concept." The board also reminded ICAG that approval of policies and structures of the compact was shared with the board and the ICAG with final approval belonging to the CAG when it comes into existence on January 1, 2000. The minutes of the November meeting included the "final agreed" policy goal for mutual recognition as follows: "Simplify governmental processes and remove regulatory barriers to increase access to safe nursing care."[132]

The board of directors, in May 1999 decided that the proposed rules developed by the ICAG should be brought to the delegate assembly for review and comment during a forum. There were 19 members of the ICAG at that time.[133] Early in June the board of directors discussed counter proposals to mutual recognition received from the ANA. The response of the board was to be finalized and sent to all member boards and to the executive directors of the SNAs prior to the meeting of the ANA House of Delegates.[134]

Continuing in June, the board of directors heard a report of the status of the development of the Nurse Licensure Compact. The report emphasized the relationship of the Nurse Licensure Compact Administrators (NLCA) to NCSBN. The board asked legal counsel to develop possible reporting structures for discussion by the board in July. The board also reviewed the proposed bylaws for the CAG as developed by the ICAG, and agreed to work closely with the ICAG over the next few months in order to remain a united group working toward implementation of mutual recognition. Further, the board said that it must seek information from the member boards that were not moving toward mutual recognition in order to identify all concerns.[135] At the July meeting the board of directors reviewed the revised articles of affiliation for NLCA and the Nurse Licensure Compact draft rules and regulations.[136] On August 1, 1999, after reviewing the NLCA Articles of Organization and other relationship documents, the board approved affiliation status with the NLCA. Further, the board agreed to serve as the secretariat for that group and to collect, administer, and disburse the fees of the NLCA.[137] Although not stated in the minutes of these meetings, the assumption is made that the name of the CAG was changed to the NLCA.

Chair Shirley Brekken of Minnesota presented the Report of the Mutual Recognition Master Plan Coordinating Group that included the activities for the past year in the 1999 *NCSBN Business Book*. The report discussed the progress on activities to achieve each phase. As of June 1999, action on compact legislation had been completed in five states and was pending in four others.[138]

In February 2000 the board of directors received its first report from Chair Laura Poe of the NLCA. Poe reported that there were seven states participating in the compact and that the members of the NLCA were meeting bimonthly via conference calls. The group had adopted articles of organization. The Finance Committee recommended that the board of directors support a contractual relationship with the NLCA. The board directed the staff to continue to develop specifics for an agreement and to present the finalized proposal to the Finance Committee.[139]

President Joey Ridenour of Arizona and Executive Director Cathcart met with ANA President Mary Foley and Executive Director David Hennage on February 29, 2000. The minutes of the March 9 meeting of the board of directors do not state that mutual recognition was discussed at the meeting with the ANA representatives. However, there was discussion about a joint board meeting in the fall. On March 1, Vickie Sheets, a member of the NCSBN staff, visited the ANA where the staff expressed an interest in implementing quarterly joint conference call meetings to foster mutual sharing of issues and concerns.[140] In June the board learned that Ridenour, Cathcart, and Sheets participated in a conference call with their ANA counterparts to address outstanding concerns as well as the potential discussion of mutual recognition at the meeting of the ANA House of Delegates.[141] Subsequently, the board heard a report of another conference call with representatives of the ANA during which the discussion included the ANA's 14 points regarding mutual recognition and other topics.[142]

The NCSBN documents for the year 2001 show very little activity related to the Nurse Licensure Compact. In October the board of directors approved the assessment of $3,000 from each NLCA member for the secretariat to be provided to the members by NCSBN beginning in October 2002.[143]

ANA Vice President Patricia Underwood and Executive Director Linda Stierle met with the NCSBN Board of Directors in January 2002. The discussion focused on current and future "partnerships," based on the mission of each organization. Stierle stated that the ANA supported each state making its own determination on participation in mutual recognition.[144] In June 2002 the board of directors approved tactics to be included under the mutual recognition outcome in the NCSBN Strategic Plan as recommended by the NLCA. These tactics were as follows:

1. In collaboration with NLCA, the NCSBN will develop a communication plan for education regarding the mutual recognition model and

2. In collaboration with NLCA, the NCSBN will participate in planning of and implementation of technology solutions that provide post implementation support to assure compliance with the provisions of the *Nurse Licensure Compact*.[145]

The delegate assembly adopted a licensure compact for APRNs at the annual meeting in 2002.[146] In the Summary of Recommendations to the 2002 Delegate Assembly in the *NCSBN Business Book*, the supporting statement for the recommendations showed that the APRN Compact Development Subcommittee was charged to develop the compact. The APRN compact was built on the 2000 Uniform APRN Licensure/ Authority to Practice Requirements that had been developed in order to promote quality, consistency, and accessibility of Advanced Practice Nursing Care within states and across state lines.[147]

The February 2002 *Council Connector* reported that the Nurse Licensure Compact section of the NCSBN Web site was accessible to all who visit the site. The visitor had access to much information including about the Nurse Licensure Compact, the enabling provisions, rules and regulations, the status of compact legislation in the states, and frequently asked questions.[148]

The final reference to the Nurse Licensure Compact in the documents related to the first 25 years of NCSBN appeared in the minutes of the December 2003 meeting of the board of directors. The board agreed to join with the NLCA in writing a letter addressing the remaining concerns of the ANA about the Nurse Licensure Compact. The letter was to be posted on the NCSBN Web site and used in the future to combat any negative articles regarding the compact.[149]

Member board revenue is an issue that has persisted beyond decisions related to a change in nursing regulation. Faced with a declining number of fees for licensure by endorsement, verification of licensure, and renewal of licenses because of the mutual recognition model, the member boards have carefully weighed decisions for change. In many instances, remaining sources of revenue have been increased to maintain adequate revenue to meet expenditures.

Conclusion

Once again, NCSBN attained a major achievement through the untiring efforts of a large number of volunteers from the member boards as well as the NCSBN Board of Directors and the NCSBN staff. This accomplishment began with the Nursing Regulation Task Force following the 1995 resolution of the delegate assembly to study interjurisdictional practice, continued through the adoption of the language for an interstate compact in support of a mutual recognition model of nursing regulation in

1997, and concluded with the implementation of the first Nurse Licensure Compact. As of August 2003 there were 15 states in the compact, with several others in process. These states and the effective date of their entry into the compact are listed below:

1999	Maryland
2000	Arkansas, Delaware, Iowa, North Carolina, Texas, Utah, and Wisconsin
2001	Idaho, Maine, Mississippi, Nebraska, and South Dakota
2002	Arizona
2003	Tennessee

While there are still steps that need to be taken, interstate practice has been facilitated, and interstate mobility is far easier to accomplish than it was at the time NCSBN was organized. Lavinia Dock, writing in 1900, called for a pragmatic approach to the problem when she said, "Such questions as moving one's residence are easily arranged for on common sense principles."[150] Over the succeeding 100 years the member boards have tried to solve the problems of interstate mobility for nurses. Nursys was a giant step to facilitate licensure by endorsement. The Nurse Licensure Compact has the potential to achieve Dock's 1900 statement of the need to find a "pragmatic approach" through the use of "common sense principles."

CHAPTER ELEVEN
ADVANCED NURSING PRACTICE

A judge of an appellate court in Kentucky recently rendered the decision that a nurse who gives an anaesthetic under the direction of a physician [and] who receives her remuneration from him is not practicing medicine. The decision will doubtless help to solve the question in other states.

American Journal of Nursing, *1917*[1]

Background

As seen in an earlier chapter, regulation of advanced nursing practice began prior to the organization of the National Council of State Boards of Nursing, Inc. (NCSBN®), with the earliest regulation in Idaho. At the annual meeting of NCSBN in 1982 a program session on advanced nursing practice was held. At that session a report of a survey of the member boards showed that 30 to 35 states had laws or enabling statutes to regulate advanced practice. There were many variations and more were developing. Subsequently, at the same meeting the delegate assembly adopted a motion that authorized the board of directors to assign an existing committee or appoint a new committee to study the issues surrounding the implementation of advanced nursing practice statutes.[2] The board of directors referred the study to the Nursing Practice and Standards (NP&S) Committee. Chair Therese Sullivan of Montana was present when the board of directors charged the committee to develop a position paper addressing the regulation of advanced nursing practice by boards of nursing and report on its work to the delegate assembly in 1984.[3]

First NCSBN Position Paper on Advanced Nursing Practice

Because of the complexity of its ongoing work in 1982 following the adoption of the *NCSBN Model Nursing Practice Act (MNPA)* and its continuing work in 1983 on the proposed model nursing rules and regulations (MNRR), the NP&S Committee did not begin the study of advanced nursing practice until 1984. That year the committee sent a questionnaire to the member boards to collect the current data on advanced practice. In addition, one of the objectives for 1984 was to develop a liaison with the

Cabinet on Nursing Practice of the American Nurses Association (ANA) relative to common interests and goals for advanced practice.[4] In the 1985 report of the NP&S Committee the following statement was made: "two members of the Nursing Practice and Standards Committee and two representatives from the Cabinet on Nursing Practice served on an ANA/NCSBN Ad Hoc Committee on Advanced Practice." The ad hoc committee met twice and began work on a joint statement on advanced practice.[5] However, the minutes of the NP&S Committee in 1985 show that a paper was developed, but consensus between the two groups was not achieved and the NP&S Committee decided to continue to refine the paper alone.[6]

The "Position Paper on Advanced Clinical Nursing Practice" was presented to and adopted by the delegate assembly of NCSBN at the annual meeting in 1986.[7] It was distributed widely to nursing organizations, member boards, and other interested parties. The following are excerpts from the introduction to this paper:

Advanced clinical nursing practice is a concept varying greatly in interpretation and regulation. Nursing practice statutes and administrative regulations range from no provision to detailed statutory and regulatory control. At the present time, approximately 42 jurisdictions give legal recognition to some level(s) of advanced clinical nursing practice.

The profession, on the other hand, has endeavored to recognize advanced nursing practice through the mechanism of voluntary certification. Currently there are at least 16 nursing organizations offering 35 certification programs each with specific education and practice requirements.

The paper also contained the following definition of advanced clinical nursing practice:

Advanced clinical nursing practice is the practice of nursing at a level which requires substantial theoretical knowledge in a specialized area of nursing practice and proficient clinical utilization of this knowledge in implementing the nursing process. The competencies of specialists include the ability to assess, conceptualize, diagnose, and analyze complex problems related to health. Credentials for a specialist require current licensure as a registered nurse, at least a master's degree in nursing, current national certification in the advanced practice area, and approval by the board of nursing.

The NP&S Committee described implications to be considered in selecting an approach to advanced practice regulation including legal implications, limits to mobility, costs, effects of statutes and of regulations by other administrative agencies, effects on generic nursing practice, and relationship to other professionals. Alternate methods of regulation were described and the paper concluded with the following position:

Boards of nursing have the responsibility to assure the health, safety, and welfare of the public by verifying that nurses practice safely and effectively. If the public health, safety, and welfare is not assured by other means, boards of nursing have a responsibility to promulgate regulations for entry into and the practice of advanced clinical nursing. These regulations should be based on the following:

1. Regulations should be in response to a clear statutory mandate.

2. A minimum of master's preparation in a clinical nursing practice specialty should serve as the basis for advanced clinical nursing practice.

3. Boards may use recognition of national certification to identify nurses with the special credentials necessary for advanced clinical nursing practice if it is based on the acquisition

of additional knowledge and skills attained through at least master's preparation in a clinical nursing specialty.

4. The preferable method of regulating advanced clinical nursing practice is designation/recognition because it is the least restrictive means for assuring the public health, safety and welfare.

In March 1984 Toni M. Masaro, assistant professor of law at Washington and Lee University in Lexington, Virginia, prepared a legal opinion on advanced practice for NCSBN. Masaro was formerly associated with Vedder, Price, Kaufman and Kammholz, the firm that represents NCSBN. Masaro's legal opinion was cited as a reference for the work of the NP&S Committee on the position paper cited above, and proved valuable to subsequent groups that examined advanced nursing practice regulation in later years.[8]

Second Position Paper on Advanced Nursing Practice and Language for Model Laws and Regulations

Four years passed before there was another mention of advanced nursing practice in the minutes or reports of NCSBN. At the fall planning retreat of NCSBN in October 1990, those in attendance identified significant trends and issues in the regulation of nursing. Every breakout group identified advanced nursing practice as an important and timely issue. The issue was referred to the Nursing Practice and Education (NP&E) Committee (formerly the NP&S Committee) where it was discussed at length.[9] The board of directors agreed to a recommendation from the NP&E Committee to appoint a subcommittee "to study regulation of advanced nursing practice."[10] The five-member Subcommittee to Study the Regulation of the Advanced Nursing Practice appointed by the board of directors comprised two executive directors and three members of boards of nursing. Corinne Dorsey of Virginia, served as chair. One of the subcommittee members was an nurse practitioner (NP) and another was a clinical nurse specialist (CNS). Activities accomplished by the subcommittee in 1991 included the following:

- Completed a comprehensive survey of member boards regarding the current regulation of nurses in advanced practice and published the result of the survey in *Issues*.

- Hosted the first Leadership Roundtable for Advanced Practice for the purpose of communication with representatives of the American Nurses Credentialing Center; the Council on Certification of Nurse Anesthetists; the National Certification Board of Pediatric Nurse Practitioners and Nurses (NCBPNP/N); the National Certification Corporation of the Obstetric, Gynecological and Neonatal Nursing Specialties; and the American College of Nurse Midwives.

- Researched definitions for terminology commonly applied to regulation and advanced practice and reviewed literature on advanced practice and on regulation in general.[11]

The report of the survey of the 53 member boards that regulated registered nurses (RNs) showed that 46 of the member boards addressed advanced practice in some way. The method ranged from definitions to separate chapters in the law. The report also showed that 40 member boards had responsibility for regulatory oversight; 16 had oversight by medical boards (some jointly with the nursing board); and in 10 jurisdictions a regulatory department had oversight. As to method of regulation the report showed; 9 issued a second license in addition to the RN license; 18 issued a certificate of advanced practice; 1 recognized national certification as a basis for prescriptive authority; and there were 12 other methods reported. Nurses in advanced practice roles had prescriptive authority in 24 jurisdictions, with the nurses in 4 of those states holding DEA numbers which were issued by the United States Drug Enforcement Administration (DEA) to authorize the prescription of controlled drugs. The most liberal regulations were found in Washington and Oregon where those in advanced practice had prescriptive authority, independent practice, no required physician collaboration/supervision, and no required written protocols. In summary, the survey showed that whether advanced practitioners should be regulated was not an issue in a majority of jurisdictions. The "what and how" was being developed by many boards with variations that might impede mobility and cause frustrations. The high percentage of states that had addressed advanced practice reflected both the changing roles of nursing in response to consumer health-related needs and the boards of nursing response to these changing roles.[12]

The subcommittee discussed interstate mobility, continued competence, and economic factors as they related to regulation and determined the need to identify areas of potential risk to the public, including the risk that occurs when the opportunity to utilize fully the services of advanced nursing practitioners is threatened. The subcommittee hosted a roundtable attended by representatives of several agencies that certified nurses in advanced practice as well as organizations with an interest in the question of regulation of these nurses. Corinne Dorsey, coauthor of this book and chair of the subcommittee, recalls that an interesting outcome of this first roundtable was consensus among the certifying organizations that their examinations were not intended to be used as the basis for regulation by boards of nursing, and the representatives expressed some concern that this was occurring. The work of the Subcommittee to Study the Regulation of the Advanced Nursing Practice during this first year was not without question or controversy. Some of the nursing organizations and certifying agencies were uncertain as to the purpose and activities of the subcommittee and raised questions and concerns on the basis of this uncertainty among their members and constituents. At the board of directors meeting in December 1991 President Carolyn Hutcherson of Georgia-RN reported on a conference call with the ANA president and executive director, and stated that a meeting was scheduled for February where the issue of advanced practice would be one of the topics for discussion.[13] In its report to the delegate assembly in the summer of 1991, the subcommittee stated its belief that open lines of communication between the organizations and the certifying bodies would assist both in the work of the subcommittee and in the acceptance of that work.[14]

The subcommittee completed a preliminary draft of a position paper in early 1992. The board of directors approved a plan for sharing the material with the member boards and with the organizations that were represented at the roundtable in 1991.[15] In a cover letter, the subcommittee requested that the recipients of the mailing limit its distribution by not forwarding it to other groups. By April it was evident, from questions raised to member boards and received at the NCSBN office, that there had been widespread dissemination of the information. The item that raised the greatest concern was the paper's conclusion, which stated that:

Boards of Nursing should regulate advanced nursing practice by licensure of advanced nursing roles due to the nature of the practice which requires advanced knowledge, clinical proficiency, independent decision-making and autonomy. The risk of harm from unsafe and incompetent providers at this level of complex care is high.[16]

The main reason for the concern was that the proposed licensure of nurses in advanced practice roles was a significant change from the position of the 1986 paper that stated that designation/regulation was the appropriate level of regulation. As a result of the widespread discussion and questions, NCSBN initiated a broader mailing of the most recent draft of the position paper to many groups and organizations. While this mailing may not have answered all of the questions, it was an attempt to get the information to more individuals and groups directly from NCSBN.

At its May meeting the board of directors authorized another roundtable meeting.[17] Two sessions were held on June 15 and 16. The purpose of these meetings was to provide an opportunity for presentation of the work of the subcommittee and for response to questions regarding the proposed position paper and model legislative language. At the first meeting President Hutcherson joined two members of the subcommittee and members of the NCSBN staff to meet with representatives from the National Certification Corporation, the Council on Certification of Nurse Anesthetists, the American Nurses Credentialing Center (ANCC), and the NCBPNP/N. On the second day the same individuals from

NCSBN met with representatives from the American Association of Nurse Anesthetists, the National Association of School Nurses, the National Association of Neonatal Nurses, the ANA, the National Alliance of Nurse Practitioners, the American College of Nurse Midwives, the American Academy of Nurse Practitioners, the National Organization of Nurse Practitioner Faculties, the Nurses Association of the American College of Obstetrics and Gynecology, and the National Association of Nurse Practitioners in Reproductive Health.[18] Comments received by mail from the member boards at area meetings and those in attendance at the roundtable in June were considered and incorporated into the proposed position paper and the subcommittee completed work on a draft of language to be added to the *MNPA*. Both documents were included in the material presented to the delegate assembly at the annual meeting in August.

In the period between the convention of the ANA in June and the annual meeting of NCSBN in August there was considerable activity regarding the proposed recommendations from the subcommittee nationally in correspondence, nursing publications, and at a variety of meetings. In late June Chair Dorsey attended a meeting at the NCSBN offices with President Hutcherson, members of the NCSBN staff, and, from the ANA, President Virginia Trotter Betts, Second Vice President Beverly Malone, and staff members Karen O'Connor and Winifred Carson. The representatives from the ANA conveyed concern from the recent ANA Convention related to the proposed position paper and proposed language for the *MNPA*. They implied that nurses in large numbers would react in opposition if NCSBN went forward with the proposal. Subsequently, the ANA urged representatives at the state nurses' association level to visit the offices of the member boards in their states and to contact individual members of those boards to request that their delegates vote against the proposal at the annual meeting.

At the meeting of the delegate assembly in August Chair Dorsey introduced the motion to "adopt the position paper on the Licensure of Advanced Nursing Practice." The delegate assembly adopted an amended motion to refer the position paper and the language for the *MNPA* back to the subcommittee to review the comments received from the delegates and the representatives of the nursing organizations and to develop proposed model rules.[19]

At its next meeting the board of directors authorized the subcommittee to continue its work for another year, and also agreed that three NCSBN representatives would participate on the ANA Ad Hoc Committee on the Review of Credentialing Advanced Practice. In the August 1992 issue of *Nursing Management* Leah Curtin, in her editorial, "Advanced Licensure: Personal Plum or Public Shield," paraphrased a well-known nursery rhyme as follows:

Little Nurse Horner sat in the corner
Eating her Practice pie
NCSBN put in its thumb
And pulled out a plum
And frightened Nurse Horner away!

Curtin said, further, "Heaven forbid that advanced practitioners be legitimized: it could mean control… some states are too restrictive…it's a state plot to oppress nurses or divide them or…they might think they're special." In her conclusion she suggested that it would be in the best interest of all concerned to work together to "iron out the kinks" in the proposal. She stated,

---

That is true self-governance. Demands for "control of practice," in the absence of visible mechanisms for exercising such self-control, are geared only to nurses' convenience. To leave the people unprotected—and demand proof of malfeasance before we act—is directly contrary to every value nurses have espoused in the last 30 years: education, accountability, patient advocacy, differentiated practice. The NCSBN is giving us the chance to realize those values. So, let's do it.[20]

The following month in the same publication Nancy Sharp of Sharp and Associates, a nationally known NP and advocate for nurses in advanced practice, wrote an opposing view in "Second License for the Advanced Practice Nurse." Sharp listed some reasons why nurses believed they should "watch out" for the proposal, including the idea that its roots were found in the influence of other providers of health care in state regulatory agencies or those outside influences whose aim was to "divide and conquer" the nursing profession. She implied that NCSBN might be circumventing the question of the baccalaureate degree for entry to professional practice by requiring the master's degree for licensure for advanced nursing practice. Sharp suggested that individual nurses write to state legislators to tell them about the issue.[21] In January 1993 NCSBN submitted a letter to the editor of *Nursing Management* to provide clarification of points raised by Sharp in her article. The letter explained the purpose of NCSBN and its relationship with the member boards and stated that those boards determine what if any part of position papers or models might be useful for individual state purposes. In this letter President Rosa Lee Weinert of Ohio corrected some of the information in the article and concluded with support of Sharp's "call for action."

The subcommittee resumed its work on refining the position paper and the proposed language for the *MNPA*, and began work on the language to be added to the *NCSBN Model Nursing Administrative Rules (MNAR)*, formerly the *NCSBN Model Nursing Rules and Regulations (MNRR)*. A survey was sent to member boards asking for information on disciplinary action involving nurses in advanced practice in the categories of Certified Registered Nurse Anesthetist (CRNA), Certified Nurse-Midwife (CNM), CNS, and NP. The survey was prompted by questions raised at the NP&E Forum at the annual meeting in 1992. The results of the survey showed that 43 of the 56 member boards that regulated RNs responded. The information varied by category. Complaints about the CRNAs were more often chemical dependency/drug related where practice complaints made up the highest number of complaints for the others. However, 70 percent of the practice-related complaints involving NPs were dismissed, and almost 40 percent of the total complaints against nurses in all four categories were dismissed. In addition, 67 complaints resulted in action by boards ranging from reprimand to revocation of license. A comment at the end of the report, however, indicated that because of the small sample, "continued study over time may be useful."[22]

At two of its meetings the subcommittee set aside one afternoon as an open forum to offer the opportunity for representatives from interested nursing organizations and certifying bodies to attend, be updated on the work of the subcommittee, and share information and comments. Individuals from several organizations, including the National Organization of Nurse Practitioner Faculties, the National Association of Pediatric Nurses in Advanced Practice, the National Certification Corporation, the National Association of Neonatal Nurses, the National Alliance of Nurse Practitioners, the American Association of Nurse Anesthetists, and the American College of Nurse Midwives attended these forums, raised helpful questions and presented suggestions. Several of the groups submitted written suggestions, many of which were incorporated in the final drafts of the proposed position paper and the language for the *MNPA* and the *MNAR*.[23] The subcommittee reviewed and commented on the document prepared by the ANA Ad Hoc Committee, and in March the board of directors agreed to forward the suggested changes from the subcommittee to the ad hoc committee.[24]

The subcommittee completed the draft of model rules for advanced nursing practice, and the document was distributed to the member boards for discussion at the area meetings. In April the subcommittee hosted the third annual roundtable for the representatives of the certifying bodies and the organizations concerned with advanced nursing practice. Those attending this meeting had the opportunity to discuss the drafts for a final time before they were to be considered by the delegate assembly. During the session the group discussed the possibility of an examination of core competencies for NPs that might be developed by NCSBN should member boards find that available certifications were not sufficient for regulatory purposes. The subcommittee was surprised when a representative from one of the certifying bodies asked what NCSBN knew about developing examinations. Vice President Gail McGuill of Alaska was present and responded with an explanation of how NCSBN was involved in the development of licensing examinations for RNs and licensed practical/vocational nurses (LPN/VNs).

The final report of the subcommittee with the proposed position paper and language for the *MNPA* and for the *MNAR* was included in the 1993 *NCSBN Book of Reports*. At the meeting of the board of directors in August, just prior to the meeting of the delegate assembly, the president reported that NCSBN had submitted an article on the proposed position on the regulation of advanced nursing practice for publication in the September issue of the ANA publication *The American Nurse* alongside an article stating the position of the ANA. The article from NCSBN, written by Vickie R. Sheets, director for Public Policy, Nursing Practice and Education at NCSBN, stated that its proposal offered a blueprint for Advanced Practice Registered Nurse (APRN) regulation and further, that legal regulation is the clearest, most unequivocal authorization of such practice. The following statement was included to rebut the frequent reference made in arguments against the proposal that physicians did not have to have a second license to practice a specialty:

Physicians were the first health professionals to become licensed, and they carved out a scope of practice without fixed boundaries. Thus in medicine, specialty certification can be issued without consideration of additional legal authority. However, registered nursing's scope of practice has boundaries that exclude certain additional aspects of care, such as diagnosing and prescribing, which APRNs are qualified to perform. The question therefore becomes how best to expand the legal boundaries for those nurses qualified to practice at an advanced level. It is for this reason that licensure for advanced practice nurses is being discussed.[25]

The article with the ANA position was written by Beverly Malone, second vice president of the ANA, and included a statement about the ANA's belief that the premise for advanced practice nursing is "a common foundation of nursing education and understanding of the nursing process." Therefore, the ANA was opposed to second licensure and advocated that other alternatives short of a second license were needed to regulate and recognize advanced practice nurses. In addition to the argument regarding physician licensure, questions were raised about the economic factors of a second license and how boards of nursing would investigate and discipline holders of two licenses. Malone speculated on 53 variations on second licensure with 53 pharmacy and medical boards interjecting their authority over nursing. She concluded the article with the following statement: "Nursing can and must develop institutions and processes to protect its right to regulate itself. Nursing draws its strength from unity and sheer numbers. To fracture the profession at this critical juncture will be detrimental to all of nursing."[26]

With all of the controversy surrounding the work of the Subcommittee to Study the Regulation of Advanced Nursing Practice, the members of the subcommittee recognized that their activities had brought national attention to NCSBN. It was an experience that both raised concerns about the controversy and brought positive rewards from the support expressed by many to the group.

The delegate assembly at its 1993 annual meeting took the following actions:

1. Adopted the Position Paper on the Regulation of Advanced Nursing Practice with the proviso that the Board of Directors continue collaboration with the American Nurses Association, the American Association of Nurse Anesthetists, the American College of Nurse-Midwives, and other nursing organizations including nurse certifying bodies.

2. Adopted the Model Legislative Language and Model Administrative Rules for Advanced Nursing Practice, to be incorporated into the existing *Model Nursing Practice Act and Model Nursing Administrative Rules*.[27]

A number of delegates and representatives from various organizations spoke while the motions were pending, as there was still some controversy about the proposals. The documents included requirements for educational preparation based on a graduate degree with a major in nursing or in the designated practice area, criteria for reviewing certifying programs if a member board chose to require certification, prescriptive and dispensing authority, independent practice, and grandfathering for those nurses practicing at an advanced level at the time of legislative implementation. Also included were clear authority for advanced nursing practice, a definition of scope of practice, predetermined requirements, title protection, and provisions for discipline. The position paper recommended the use of the title "Advanced Practice Registered Nurse." The three documents provided the basis for boards of nursing to regulate advanced nursing practice by licensure of advanced nursing roles due to the nature of the practice, which requires advanced knowledge, clinical proficiency, independent decision making, and autonomy. In addition, the subcommittee had found that the risk of harm from unsafe and incompetent providers at this level of complex care was high and licensure would prevent practice by those who did not meet the requirements set forth in law and regulation within the various states. The report of the subcommittee included future considerations, three of which follow:

1. Assist member boards in evaluating professional certification requirements and examinations to determine if the examinations are developed psychometrically to serve as a sound basis for regulation and are legally defensible for use in the regulation of advanced nursing practice.

2. If existing examinations do not meet all criteria for legal defensibility:

    a. work with certifying organizations to promote the meeting of these criteria; and, if needed,

    b. give consideration to other means for providing member boards with examinations which would provide a sound basis for licensure of advanced nursing practice categories.

3. Continue the liaison relationship with the advanced nursing practice professional certifying organizations and other nursing organizations in order to provide current information regarding credentialing processes and advanced nursing practice issues.[28]

Assisting Member Boards to Review Agencies Certifying APRNs

In October the board of directors agreed to create a document known as the Clearinghouse on Advanced Practice to assist member boards in reviewing professional certification. It would address recertification as well as initial certification and would include legal analysis and public policy reviews. The document would also include descriptions of the legal and psychometric characteristics of certifying examinations, and describe how educational requirements and other credentials are congruent with a specified area of practice. NCSBN identified that information about the five following certifying bodies be distributed to the member boards: the ANCC, the Council on Certification of Nurse Anesthetists, the NCBPNP/N, the National Certification Corporation, and the American College of Nurse-Midwives Certification Council.[29] An article in the February 1994 *Newsletter to the Member Boards* reported that NCSBN had developed the information for the Advanced Practice Clearinghouse.[30]

The ANA had established an Ad Hoc Committee on Credentialing in Advanced Practice. To ensure representation of NCSBN, President Hutcherson, Vice President McGuill, and Associate Executive Director Doris Nay attended the meetings of this committee. In January 1994 they attended the final meeting of the ANA Ad Hoc Committee on Credentialing in Advanced Practice. A paper titled "Advisory on the Regulation of Nurses in Advanced Practice," which was distributed with the *Newsletter to the Member Boards*, called for collaboration between boards of nursing and state nurses' associations with regard to legislative and regulatory activities surrounding advanced practice.[31]

Core Competencies for Examinations for Nurse Practitioners

In August 1994 issues related to advanced nursing practice continued to be discussed, and the delegate assembly adopted three resolutions relative to APRNs:

1. That the National Council perform a study exploring the regulatory, fiscal, and political implications of developing a "core" competency examination for nurse practitioners with a report to the 1995 Delegate Assembly.

2. That the National Council perform a study to identify core competencies of nurse practitioners with a report to the 1995 Delegate Assembly.

3. That the National Council establish a task force to (1) develop a data base of advanced practice credentialing requirements (licensure, recognition, certification, authority to practice, etc.) for each Member Board with enough specificity for other Member Boards to make credentialing decisions, and (2) study whether additional mechanisms could be developed to facilitate interstate mobility of advanced practice nurses with a report to the 1995 Delegate Assembly.[32]

The board of directors subsequently appointed the Task Force to Identify Core Competencies for Nurse Practitioners (Core Competencies Task Force), chaired by Carla Lee of Kansas. The task force was charged to define standards for NP practice. After reviewing and discussing multiple documents and background materials, and drawing upon their own experiences as NPs, the task force members drafted a document containing a description of a NP's core roles, essential functions, characteristics, and essential competencies. The group determined that validation should be sought from two sources: NPs and members and staff of member boards familiar with NP practice. The draft document and the final version were shared with the Task Force to Study Feasibility of a Core Competency Examination for Nurse Practitioners (Feasibility Task Force).[33] Katherine Thomas of Texas-RN served as chair of this second task force. The board of directors established a third task force related to advanced nursing practice in 1995, known as the Task Force to Study Advanced Practice Nurse Mobility (APRN Mobility Task Force), with Judi Crume of Alabama as the chair.

The 1995 *NCSBN Book of Reports* for the annual meeting included reports from all three groups, and their work was the subject of discussion at a roundtable held in June. In May the board of directors established an Advanced Practice Registered Nurse (APRN) Coordinating Task Force with Katherine Thomas as chair. This group hosted the Advanced Practice Leadership Roundtable.[34] NCSBN representatives attended a special meeting of the certification organizations held in conjunction with the Keystone Nurse Practitioner Conference. The purpose of the meeting was to "achieve the goal of effectively responding to NCSBN's concerns."[35]

The Core Competencies Task Force completed its work and identified 21 competency statements that were categorized within three domains: management of client care, management of health care delivery systems, and management of professional relationships. These were described in a statement titled "Nurse Practitioner Core Competencies." In addition to providing information for the Feasibility Task Force, the Core Competencies Task Force believed that the statement could be used by member boards when evaluating the educational preparation of NPs applying for legal recognition within a jurisdiction.[36]

The Feasibility Task Force concluded that there was enough content to produce measurable core competencies for NP practice; that member boards needed entry-level core competency measurement and entry-level specialty content measurement; that it would be acceptable to create a core competency measurement, and then make a subsequent determination regarding the development of specialty measurements. The task force developed five possible models and reported the regulatory strengths and weaknesses and the fiscal and political implications of each. The task force recommended to the board of directors that NCSBN proceed with the development of an entry-level core competency examination for NPs using a model where NCSBN would develop and offer to member boards a core competency examination, while the specialty groups would continue to develop and offer their specialty content examinations.[37] The delegate assembly at the annual meeting in 1995 adopted the following recommendation from the board of directors:

- That the National Council collaborate with nurse practitioner specialty certification organizations to make significant progress toward legally defensible, psychometrically sound nurse practitioner examinations, which are sufficient for regulatory purposes.

- That the bench mark for progress shall be established and evaluated by the Board of Directors.

- That the Board of Directors shall report to the 1996 Delegate Assembly specific recommendations regarding future actions including the potential creation of a core competency examination.

- That if at any time, the Board of Directors determines that significant progress is not being made, the Board is authorized to conduct a job analysis of entry-level nurse practitioners.[38]

The delegate assembly also adopted a resolution requiring NCSBN to gather data on the current state of the CNS from a regulatory stand point, identify regulatory needs of member boards with respect to the CNS, and initiate relationships with specialty certification organizations for the CNS.[39]

Continued Discussion of Certifying Bodies

Once again, 1996 was a year of controversy among nursing organizations, bodies that certified NPs, and NCSBN, as the latter worked to carry out the resolutions from the 1995 session of its delegate assembly. In January the board of directors reviewed correspondence and a report of a conference call with four NP certifying bodies. In order for it to deem that satisfactory progress was being made toward meeting the terms of the delegate assembly's resolution, the board of directors concluded that plans for site visits and an acceptable procedure for document review must be in place by March 1. The certifying bodies requested a non-compete agreement, while NCSBN preferred using a third party to perform the document reviews and site visits.[40] The certifying bodies met on January 24 and, in February, sent correspondence that included a review mechanism, standards, and report components acceptable to them. The acceptable components for the report included new limitations to the job analysis that would involve the executive summary only and limits on notes made during the site visit. In addition, there were further requests for specific insufficiencies and for a commitment that NCSBN would not develop or administer a generic or specialty examination for NPs. NCSBN President Marcia Rachel of Mississippi and staff member Carolyn Hutcherson attended a meeting with the certifying organization representatives on February 26. Following this meeting NCSBN reviewed the correspondence regarding the outcomes of this meeting where the certifying bodies presented new issues to be addressed.[41] The board of directors continued its efforts to establish a means to respond to the actions from the 1995 delegate assembly. During a conference call meeting on March 5, the board discussed the report of correspondence received and the issues raised at the meeting in February. The board then provided direction for items to be included in a letter to the certifying bodies agreeing that:

- All documents involving the process and schedule must be complete by March 13.

- The standards and categories presented by the bodies were acceptable with minor clarification.

- The NCSBN will provide an advance copy of the final report for review, comment and suggestion by the bodies, but will not agree to approval or unilateral modification right for the certifying bodies.

- All document reviews, site visits and certifying information must be completed and received by the NCSBN by May 1, with two weeks then allowed for NCSBN to produce the draft report and two weeks allowed for the certifying bodies to review and a completion date of June 11.

- The Board of Directors would review the final report at its June meeting and distribute the report to the Delegate Assembly as a supplement to the *Book of Reports*.[42]

The response to the letter referenced above, received from the certification organizations on March 13, included a proposed memorandum of agreement and a confidentiality agreement with substantial changes from terms proposed by NCSBN. This counterproposal included the following recommendations: to keep the memorandum of agreement itself confidential; to bind all NCSBN persons including volunteers to confidentiality regarding the reports; and to return all documents prior to the completion of the report and presentation at the annual meeting.[43]

Executive Director Jennifer Bosma made an initial response stating that it was unacceptable for the bodies to have the right to make modifications in the final report "in any way they deem appropriate at their sole discretion." In a telephone conversation the certifying bodies agreed to consider alternatives regarding the final report and proposed a meeting in Chicago on March 20, 1996. Three days later the executive director relayed a proposal to Mary Jane Schumann, who represented the certifying bodies. The proposal included provision to allow any of the bodies that had serious irresolvable concerns about the report to have the option to decline publication of any report, with that action reported to the delegates. She also indicated support for a meeting on March 20, provided there was a viable proposal for the approval of the report and all participants understood that all issues must be resolved at this meeting in order to proceed further with the collaborative process. Schumann requested any additional points raised in the legal review in writing, and suggested that the meeting on March 20 be conducted by telephone rather than face-to-face. The legal counsel for NCSBN prepared language for an alternative report and it was sent to the certifying bodies on March 20, at which time Schumann indicated that they wished to delay the conference call to consider the comments. Later that same day, she called to say that a written response would be delivered. This written response continued to bind volunteers to confidentiality; newly limited report distribution to "official representatives of each state Board of Nursing registered and in attendance at the 1996 Annual Meeting"; and provided that if and when an agency declines publication of the agency's report, this decision would be announced as follows: "the parties could not reach mutual agreement regarding the content of the report." A new sentence related to report content was included: "The draft report shall not include any information that adversely affects the legal defensibility or integrity of any test or testing process."[44]

The board of directors, in response to being polled by President Rachel, decided to initiate the job analysis of entry-level NPs. This decision was conveyed to the certifying bodies on March 25, 1996, advising that the basis for the decision was the lack of significant progress in collaboration between the parties toward legally defensible and psychometrically sound NP examinations sufficient for regulatory purposes. Specific barriers listed included the limitations on reporting the findings, on the ability to openly discuss the findings, and the process used. On March 28 a correspondence from the certifying bodies stated that they were "at a loss to understand how Council has reached the conclusions…" and that they "remain open to dialogue if the National Council believes this would be beneficial." A request for proposals (RFP) for the performance of an entry-level NP job analysis study was issued by NCSBN on March 29. On April 4, after reviewing the correspondence from the certifying bodies and comments from the APRN Task Force, the board of directors directed that a reply to the March 28 letter from the bodies be sent reiterating the NCSBN commitment to the job analysis, and offering the opportunity for any of the agencies to approach NCSBN for further dialogue.[45] In early April, the board of directors authorized the distribution of information related to the current status of the issue including copies of a chronology of events and activities, relevant correspondence to and from the certifying bodies, and the RFP.[46]

At its May 1996 meeting, the board of directors agreed to a contract with the Chauncey Group International (CGI), the test service for National Council Licensure Examination (NCLEX®), to conduct the entry-level NP job analysis. The board of directors also considered the report of the APRN Task Force and agreed to a timeline for receipt of the results of the NP job analysis and the development of recommendations for the delegate assembly. In addition, the board of directors supported forwarding two other recommendations to the delegate assembly:

1. For authorization from the delegate assembly for the board of directors to give final approval of the family nurse practitioner curriculum guidelines and regulatory criteria for evaluating nurse practitioners applying for prescriptive authority, with prior review and comment by member boards, indicating organizational support as a model for use by the member boards.

2. To encourage member boards to promote the use of similar criteria for recognition of CNS and NP.[47]

An article in the May 3 *Newsletter to the Member Boards* noted that member boards were being asked to respond to questions related to the activities and/or recent negotiations between NCSBN and the four certifying bodies. Further, correspondence had been sent to NPs by the bodies directing them to contact the executive officer of their board of nursing and legislators to voice their opposition to the development of an examination. A fact sheet was distributed by the four groups: the American Academy of Nurse Practitioners, the NCBPNP/N, the ANCC, and the National Certification Corporation for the Obstetric, Gynecologic and Neonatal Nursing Specialties. The following is a quote from that fact sheet regarding the release of an RFP by NCSBN:

> Based on NCSBN's most recent actions, the certifying organizations, in retrospect, can only conclude that the NCSBN was not negotiating in good faith regarding the review process. The timing of the release of the RFP, only four days after negotiations were halted by NCSBN, causes the certifying organizations to conclude that the NCSBN had prepared these materials while the negotiations were in progress.

However, the *Newsletter to the Member Boards* article states that the RFP was only four pages long and was developed by the director of Research for NCSBN, who had extensive research experience and had successfully written many RFPs within a similar time frame.[48]

In a letter dated April 23, 1996, ANA President Virginia Betts wrote to NCSBN President Rachel stating that she was "dismayed, disappointed and at a loss" to understand the "impasse in negotiations" that led to NCSBN issuing the RFP. Next, Betts questioned why "NCSBN continues to premise its movement toward APN [advanced practice nurse] licensure upon unproven allegations that the existing nurse practitioner certifying examinations are psychometrically unsound and legally indefensible." She said, "This is simply not true…it borders on libel to the affected credentialing organizations." Betts gave some examples of attempts at collaboration by saying that the ANA supported the national clearinghouse as a means of providing information about the certifying agencies to the member boards. She continued by saying that NCSBN had not compiled the information for a national clearinghouse to assist boards of nursing or maintained it in an accessible form for review. A second example of collaboration cited by Betts was that when the two organizations discussed the possibility that NCSBN would, or planned to, develop an independent certifying examination, NCSBN had assured the ANA and others that it did not desire to develop another examination. She said that the issuance of the RFP within four days after the negotiations reached an "impasse" was a short time. "All of this," Betts said, "reinforces the appearance of a less than good faith intention to negotiate your proposal for advanced practice competency examinations, in lieu of another NCSBN sponsored examination." The final paragraph of Betts' letter read as follows:

> Through your continued public statements reflecting a vague apprehension about the ability and safety of APNs (especially in light of rapidly changing health care delivery systems) your organization undermines the long standing trust and reliance of the public upon nursing and may well facilitate the subsequent demise of advanced professional nursing through perpetuation of the medical model and narrow, authoritarian control of nursing practice.[49]

President Rachel responded to Betts on May 1, 1996, and invited her to meet with the NCSBN Board of Directors on May 10 either in person or by conference call, because of the "breadth of the issue and level of misunderstanding." She reminded Betts that the concern of NCSBN about the certifying examinations "is whether or not they are sufficient for regulatory purposes and suitable to measure entry into advanced practice." She also referenced the 1991 Leadership Roundtable for Advanced Practice Nurses where representatives from some of the certifying bodies, including the ANCC, said "that their examinations were not designed for entry-level use and that any board that used the examination in such manner was doing so inappropriately." This was of concern to boards of nursing, mainly because this could leave the NP vulnerable to challenges that legal authorization to practice was based on a measure without validity for this specific use. Rachel said further:

> Let me reiterate that at no point has the National Council alleged that the nurse practitioner certifying examinations are not psychometrically sound and legally defensible. The regulatory issue is whether or not these examinations meet industry standards for use as an entry-level measure upon which legal authority for practice can be granted. In order for states to comply with their mandate to identify standards upon which authority to practice is granted, a measurement valid for this specific purpose must be established. Either the current nurse practitioner certification examinations fill this need or the National Council must respond to the needs of its membership by providing the resources needed by the state boards.

President Rachel concluded her letter with the following paragraph:

> The actions of National Council, rather than "undermining the long-standing trust and reliance of the public upon nursing," are intended to provide consumers with the absolute certainty that persons who call themselves nurse practitioners have met certain standards. Rather than being a part of the "demise of advanced professional nursing through the perpetuation of the medical model," boards of nursing are the single most important entity in ensuring that nurse practitioners can practice with solid legal authority and without fear of legal reprisals by the medical community.[50]

The APRN Coordinating Task Force met again in May. During that meeting the task force hosted the Sixth Annual Advanced Practice Leadership Roundtable. Pat Bielecki, president of the National Association of Clinical Nurse Specialists (NACNS), was guest speaker. The group discussed the distinctions and value of the roles of the CNS and NP. The afternoon session was devoted to discussion of the negotiations between NCSBN and the four NP certifying organizations. The executive director provided information on the negotiation process and supporting documents related to the issue were disseminated to those in attendance.[51] Later in May representatives of NCSBN, the NP certifying bodies, and the affiliated professional associations met in Washington, D.C. The outcome of the meeting was positive progress toward a third-party review of each of the examination programs to determine their sufficiency for member boards' regulatory uses. An article in the *Newsletter to the Member Boards* stated:

> The third-party review is likely to be the National Commission for Certifying Agencies (NCCA) process sponsored by National Organization for Competency Assurance (NOCA). Those present at the meeting agreed to seek every possible means to expedite the process and all indicated commitment to full approval as the end result.[52]

At its meeting on June 26 to 28, 1996, the board of directors reviewed the issues related to the NP certifying examinations and continued planning for a meeting for third-party review. The certifying bodies, their affiliated professional organizations, NCSBN, and the two consultants who were to conduct the initial review would establish the groundwork and mutual expectations at that meeting.[53] By its meeting in mid-July, the board of directors noted that all four bodies had committed to NCCA review.[54]

The board of directors met from August 4 to 10, 1996, and heard a report of the preliminary findings of the nurse practitioner job analysis from Denny Way of the CGI. Katherine Thomas, chair of the APRN Task Force, commented that the job analysis revealed sufficient common content across the NP specialty areas to support a possible core competence examination. President Rachel reported on a conference call among the representatives of the certifying bodies, professional organizations, and NCSBN. Chair Thomas spoke to the task force opinion regarding the benefits of NCSBN creating an NP examination. She cited as a basis for this the member board confidence in NCSBN, the ability of the member boards to monitor an NCSBN-created examination, wide availability of such an examination, meeting state needs when unable to delegate examination development to outside groups, and alignment with states' unique role in granting legal authority and scope of practice. The board of directors decided not to proceed with the second phase of the nurse practitioner job analysis at that time, but to wait until the final evaluations of the examinations of the certifying bodies were received and significant progress toward mutually acceptable plans for correction were made.[55]

At the annual meeting of NCSBN in Baltimore from August 6 to 10, 1996, a session providing an open dialogue and a forum on advanced practice issues were held.[56] Subsequently, the delegate assembly adopted the following recommendation from the board of directors:

In order to assure that Member Boards have psychometrically sound and legally defensible nurse practitioner examinations available for their regulatory purposes and pending receipt of the final examination evaluations and mutually acceptable plans for corrections, the Board continue to negotiate with the nurse practitioner certifying organizations. If at any time, the Board determines that significant progress is not being made, the Board of Directors is authorized to proceed with Phase II of the nurse practitioner job analysis. Furthermore, the Board shall determine a mechanism for assuring continuing adherence with established standards for psychometrically sound, legally defensible nurse practitioner examinations used for regulatory purposes.[57]

Next, the board directed staff to notify the CGI not to proceed with Phase II of the job analysis for NPs, but to retain the existing data. Further, the board of directors appointed Marcia Rachel of Mississippi, after she had completed her term as president, to continue negotiations with the certifying bodies on behalf of NCSBN during FY97.[58]

An *Issues* article published in early 1997 had a comprehensive summary of the activities of NCSBN related to NP issues and the role of the certifying bodies and NCSBN. Following the meeting of the delegate assembly in August, the four certifying bodies underwent NCCA review. At the time of publication of the article, ANCC was awaiting the NCCA report. The American Association of Nurse Practitioners (AANP) and National Certification Corporation (NCC) had completed the NCCA review and received certification, but were awaiting the final report that addressed the examination-related requirements outlined by NCSBN. In July the NCBPNP/N underwent NCCA review, received full NCCA recognition, and the final report was forwarded to NCSBN in November 1996. The article went on to report that NCSBN was in the process of discussing with member boards and the certifying bodies, a mechanism to be used to assure ongoing regulatory sufficiency. The article concluded with the statement that "at present, the NCSBN is not pursuing a job analysis or any form of test development related to any category of APRNs."[59]

In May 1997 the board of directors reviewed the report of the APRN Task Force and agreed to discontinue the Advanced Practice Clearinghouse and replace it with the APRN Certification Organization Annual Report.[60] In June, after reviewing the status of negotiations and the reports from the NP certifying bodies, the board of directors determined that current progress in demonstrating regulatory sufficiency of the NP certification examinations was adequate.[61] A news release issued on July 11, reported that the American Academy of Nurse Practitioners Certification Program; the National Certification Corporation for the Obstetric, Gynecologic and Neonatal Nursing Specialties; and the NCBPNP/N had received accreditation from the NCCA. Further, boards of nursing were advised that these examinations were suitable for regulatory purposes based on the information contained in the reports. The NCCA was in the process of reviewing the ANCC. In August 1996 the ANCC submitted a report by independent consultants that addressed the same criteria and resulted in a positive overall evaluation of the appropriateness of ANCC's NP certification examinations for regulatory uses.[62]

The year 1998 brought a less hectic experience for the APRN Task Force and the NCSBN Board of Directors in relation to APRN issues. On a recommendation from the task force, the board of directors agreed to provide a letter of support for removing supervision requirements for CRNAs as stated in proposed rules from the Health Care Financing Administration (HCFA). This support was based on the belief that state authority was appropriate for such decisions.[63]

Two meetings sponsored by NCSBN were held during 1998 with representatives from over 20 advanced practice organizations attending for the purpose of discussing uniform licensure/authority to practice guidelines. The organizations were supportive of the effort. At the annual meeting in Albuquerque in August, the Report of the Board of Directors stated that all four organizations that certify NPs had attained the NCCA accreditation. A series of forums were held by the APRN Task Force to discuss the uniform licensure/authorization to practice guidelines.[64] The reason for developing these guidelines was related to a model for including the APRNs in mutual recognition that had been developed for RNs and LPN/VNs. Mutual recognition was the model of regulation adopted by NCSBN to facilitate practice across state lines. Other specifics related to the APRN and mutual recognition are discussed elsewhere in this chapter.

A report of the fourth and last of the APRN forums held in 1998 appeared in a January 1999 *Newsletter to the Member Boards*. Representatives from 20 organizations attended the forum to discuss and reach consensus on the uniform licensure requirements for APRNs. Of the nine major elements of the requirements, the group achieved consensus in seven and reached a "sense of group" in the remaining two. The article quotes several of the attendees at the forum. Jan Towers of the American Academy of Nurse Practitioners Certification Program said she was "glad for the opportunity the forum is providing for the stakeholders to discuss and work to consensus on very difficult issues." Geraldine Felton, from the National League for Nursing (NLN) Accrediting Commission expressed enthusiasm and said, "It allowed us to see that this is a good time and place for nursing to be." Nancy Sharp of Sharp and Associates was also quoted as follows: "Through the consensus building process, the group was able to come to agreement about the key elements of uniform criteria."[65] At its meeting in May 1999 the board of directors initially agreed to the following statement: "That the Delegate Assembly approve the APRN Licensure/Authority to Practice Requirements and recommend that states move toward incorporation of the requirements at the state level." The board of directors immediately rescinded the previous motion pending further discussion at the meeting in June.[66] The APRN Task Force hosted a forum at the annual meeting in August with the focus on discussion of the Uniform APRN Licensure/Authority to Practice Requirements document as it appeared in the 1999 *NCSBN Business Book*.[67]

The board of directors reviewed the report of the APRN Task Force in June 1999 and agreed that NCSBN, after collaboration with the advanced practice certification bodies, would develop a policy and procedure for evidence-based monitoring and review of all examinations used by member boards for legal authorization of advanced practice. Further, the board of directors directed that the director of testing review the standards of the American Board of Nursing Specialties as a potential accreditor and requested consultation with legal counsel regarding any potential conflict of interest of an accrediting body whose membership may include an organization it is accrediting.[68] In October the board of directors reviewed the history of NCSBN and the APRN certification examinations, and the process by which they were determined to be psychometrically sound and legally defensible. At the same meeting legal counsel advised the board of directors that individual APRN boards created in some states were ineligible for membership in NCSBN due to the bylaws requirement that members must use one of the NCSBN licensing examinations.[69] At the December meeting the board of directors heard from Katherine Thomas and Marcia Rachel regarding the history of NCSBN's use of NCCA accreditation of certifying bodies in the regulation of NPs. The board agreed to appoint the Blue Ribbon Task Force, under the aegis of the NP&E Committee, to develop recommendations for the next generation of criteria for approving examinations used to regulate APRNs.[70]

In April 2000 the board of directors named the members of the Special Advanced Practice (AP) Task Force, with Katherine Thomas and Marcia Rachel as co-chairs. The board requested that this task force examine the method for determining the regulatory sufficiency of the certifying examinations; determine criteria for eligibility as an APRN, especially for member boards that waive certain requirements; and establish the availability of examinations for developing advanced practice categories.[71] The task force refined the charge to include determining a method of assuring consistency in the process for certification that will support the boards in protecting the public.[72] An article in the December *Council Connector* reported on the Special AP Task Force meeting where the group developed "second generation" criteria and discussed a process to evaluate national accreditors of APRN certification programs.[73]

Several other activities related to advanced practice occurred in 2000. In June the board of directors met with the president and executive director of the ANCC to discuss issues of mutual concern, specifically APRN certification. When the representatives from ANCC asked about the availability of components of computerized clinical simulation testing (CST), they were reminded that the work on CST done by NCSBN was not based on advanced practice. Both groups expressed interest in cooperating on continued competency initiatives.[74] At the August meeting of the delegate assembly, the delegates considered a recommendation from the board of directors and adopted the "Uniform Advanced Practice Registered Nurse Licensure/Authority to Practice Requirements."[75] These requirements included:

- Unencumbered RN license;

- Graduation from a graduate level advanced practice program accredited by a national accrediting body;

- Current certification by a national certifying body in the advanced practice specialty appropriate to educational preparation; and

- Maintenance of certification or evidence of maintenance of competence.[76]

The Special AP Task Force continued its work in 2001. An update from the task force published in the July *Council Connector* included a report on the annual Advanced Practice Leadership Roundtable held earlier, with 40 representatives of the various organizations in attendance. The co-chairs of the task force met with representatives from ANCC and discussed new certification examinations; the use of the title APRN, BC (board certified); waivers of or appeals to eligibility criteria; and application of eligibility to APRN candidates.[77] Another meeting was held later in the year with representatives from the ANCC who reported that waivers allowing psychiatric/mental health CNSs to qualify for the psychiatric/mental health NP examinations would expire on December 31, 2001. Those present also discussed the waiver-exceptions process and scope of practice issues as related to numerous specialty examinations being developed by the ANCC and other certifying bodies.[78] In the *NCSBN Business Book* for the delegate assembly in August, the Report of the Advanced Practice Task Force list of activities for the year included the following:

1. Developed "second generation" criteria in order to increase the specificity of the NCSBN criteria to assure that the criteria more closely address the regulatory needs of boards of nursing and recommended that the "second generation" criteria apply to all licensed categories of APRNs.

2. Developed a process to evaluate and develop a reporting mechanism for national accreditors of advanced practice certification bodies seeking deemed status for state regulatory purposes.

3. Explored the development of alternate mechanisms for approval of applicants for whom a certification examination has not been developed that are equivalent to the requirements for APRN license.[79]

In August 2001 the board of directors agreed to a request from the American Association of Nurse Anesthetists to send a letter of support to the federal Center for Medicaid and Medicare Services for a proposed rule that would defer to the states the matter of supervision of nurse anesthetists.[80] This action was consistent with the premise that the regulation of nurses at any level is the responsibility of the state, not the federal government.

Consensus on Certification Examinations

The APRN Task Force had a busy year in 2002 with Katherine Thomas again serving as chair. In January 2002, following the presentation of the report of the APRN Task Force, the board of directors approved the second-generation criteria for the evaluation of advanced practice certification examinations. In addition, the board of directors agreed to recommend that the delegate assembly adopt the revision of the alternative mechanism element of the "Uniform Advanced Practice Registered Nurse Licensure/Authority to Practice Requirements." The alternative mechanism element was designed to provide an alternative to a certification examination in a specialized area where none was available.[81] At the meeting in May the board of directors approved a process for implementing the NSCBN APRN Certification Examination Review Program, approved the American Board of Nursing Specialties as a participating accrediting agency for the program, and decided to continue the APRN Task Force for two years to monitor the implementation of initiatives.[82] During the year the board of directors endorsed several documents including *National Consensus-Based Core and Specialty Competencies for Primary Care Nurse Practitioners, A White Paper for Consortium of Quality Nurse Practitioner Education*, and "Criteria for Evaluation of Nurse Practitioner Programs," prepared by the National Organization of Nurse Practitioner Faculties.

In its comments in support of the revision to the alternative mechanism element of the "Uniform Advanced Practice Registered Nurse Licensure/Authority of Practice Requirements," the task force reported that it:

did not support recognition without examination. Further, there were concerns regarding the proliferation of examinations that may not be psychometrically sound. The intent is to move toward a broad, generalist preparation as opposed to a subspecialty preparation. Certification in a subspecialty could be obtained after credentialing in a generalist category has been completed.

The delegate assembly adopted the revision as follows:

For applicants for whom there is no appropriate certification examination available, the state may develop alternative mechanisms to assure initial competency until January 1, 2005. Evidence of an equivalent mechanism to certification examinations will not be accepted after January 1, 2005, and initial licensure as an APRN will no longer be issued without an appropriate certification examination.[83]

Third NCSBN Position Paper on the Regulation of Advanced Practice Nursing

In May the board of directors approved the 2002 NCSBN "Position Paper on the Regulation of Advanced Practice Nursing," which acknowledged the two previous papers and maintained many of the premises of both. This paper continued to reflect the statement that "boards of nursing should regulate APRN practice by licensure due to the nature of the practice, which requires advanced knowledge, clinical proficiency, independent decision-making and autonomy." The paper also reflected the work of the APRN Task Force since the 1993 position paper was adopted, as well as the current state of APRN education, certification, and practice. The conclusion of the paper stated,

---

Failure to regulate advanced nursing practice creates potential risks for the public. Without licensure, complex activities requiring a high level of specialized knowledge and independent decision-making may be performed by individuals without sufficient preparation and skill. Without licensure, professionals are not held legally accountable for their practice. Without licensure, the public does not have the benefit of an unbiased forum to resolve complaints regarding issues of safety and competence.

For most boards of nursing, the current approach to licensure involves reliance on educational credentials, certification examinations and the information provided by the applicant. Thus, cooperation of educational institutions, accrediting bodies, credentialing organizations, regulators and licensees is essential to produce the best result for the health care of the public. Support for communication among these organizations for the sake of public protection is an ongoing goal of NCSBN.[84]

The board of directors continued to address issues of advanced nursing practice in 2003. Following review of the report of the APRN Task Force in February, the board of directors approved a draft of a document designed to assist member boards in determining the regulatory sufficiency of the advanced practice certifying examinations.[85] In April the board of directors acted to continue the APRN Task Force for another year with Katherine Thomas as chair.[86]

Clinical Nurse Specialists and NCSBN

At the July meeting of the board of directors, the executive director reported on recent testimony before the Federal Trade Commission (FTC) in which the NACNS implied antitrust violations on the part of NCSBN in regard to the regulation of CNSs. The board of directors requested that legal counsel draft a response that might be sent to the FTC.[87] Dr. Brenda Lyons, speaking on behalf of the NACNS, presented testimony to the FTC on June 11, 2003. Her testimony referred to Noerr-Pennington, which is a doctrine of United States antitrust law set forth by the United States Supreme Court in two cases. The doctrine suggests that under the First Amendment of the United States Constitution, it cannot be a violation of federal antitrust laws for competitors to lobby the government to change the law in a way that would reduce competition. The following are excerpts from that testimony:

Noerr-Pennington/anticompetition question:

Is it appropriate for the association to develop the policy which would require the use of uniform standards for licensure, and the use of the standardized exam and subsequently, force the state boards of nursing to use its product by limiting access to a national disciplinary database or alternatively, work to undermine other competency certification products?

We do not believe the Noerr-Pennington exemption was created for this purpose.

We believe that:

1. The NCSBN exceeded the boundaries of the exemption when it developed policy inconsistent with state goals related to regulation—*protection of the health and safety of the public while not creating barriers to block the public's access to needed services.*

2. The NCSBN has exceeded the boundaries of the exemption through its development of policy that would support NCSBN products for sale to State Boards of Nursing.

a. State licensure boards, not the NCSBN, were designed to address the health and safety of the public.

b. Policy developed by an association with ties to state boards of nursing that can be anticompetitive, discriminatory and is unrelated to the primary standards of licensure (policy established for administrative ease rather than evidence of harm) subject to antitrust challenges.

Anticompetitive concerns:

Changing the scope of CNS practice and/or creating insurmountable barriers to practice substantially limits the economic and professional opportunities of this practitioner, without providing a clear scientific or legal basis to do so. We believe that is anticompetitive.[88]

NCSBN President Donna Dorsey of Maryland responded to the testimony cited above in a letter to the FTC dated July 31, 2003. Dorsey cited the two NBSBN initiatives that were central to the concerns raised by the NACNS in the testimony. The first of these was the endorsement of minimum requirements for a nurse to obtain legal authority for advanced practice in order to promote the mobility of APRNs while maintaining consistent standards critical to protecting the public health. Dorsey argued,

In particular, the [APRN] Task Force found that the proliferation of specialty designations presented a clear potential risk of harm to the public due to confusion or misimpressions over the meaning of the various subspecialty designations and the competence of nurses who adopt these titles to undertake direct responsibility for patient care.

The second initiative that caused concern to the NACNS was the development in 2002 of the Model Advanced Practice Registered Nurse Compact to provide that participating member states authorize the practice of an APRN in their state based on licensure in the APRN's "home" state without the necessity of obtaining a separate license in each state in which the APRN practices. Dorsey emphasized that the model compact called for each state to adopt the above-described minimum requirements for advanced practice authorization, which would be essential to enactment of the compact, and facilitate interstate practice. At the end of the letter President Dorsey refuted the claim of the NACNS that the task force was advocating the development of a standardized "generalist" examination to "evaluate safe advanced practice nursing" and that NCSBN had a "vested economic interest in doing so since it would develop the exam." Dorsey said,

This assertion is particularly galling and inaccurate in its claims that the NCSBN has been acting out of self-interest. Rather than developing one "generalist exam" for APRN licensure, the NCSBN for the last ten years has been working with the various APRN certification organizations to enable state boards of nursing to use APRN certification examinations as a basis for APRN licensure decisions. As a result of these efforts, there are a wide range of broad-based certification examinations available to CNSs who wish to practice at an advanced level.[89]

The Report of the Advanced Practice Task Force found in the 2003 *NCSBN Business Book* for the annual meeting in August reflected the varied activities of the task force, including hosting the annual APRN Roundtable in April. The task force also began working with the Veterans Administration (VA)—Department of Defense Task Force regarding federal guidelines for nurses working in the VA system. In the listing of future activities, the task force included the development and implementation of a plan for member board education about APRN regulation.[90]

President Dorsey and Executive Director Kathy Apple reported that they had met with the CNS representatives early in September 2003. The board of directors decided to monitor the situation and directed the staff to write a letter to the editor of the CNS journal responding to the errors about NCSBN in a recent article with a request that the NCSBN letter be published in the journal. The board of directors also directed that the NCSBN request the CNS leaders to send a letter to the FTC retracting their statement regarding NCSBN. In other action at the September meeting, the board of directors endorsed the Psychiatric-Mental Health Nurse Practitioner Competencies from the National Organization of Nurse Practitioner Faculties and added a charge to the task force for the coming year to develop a vision paper addressing the future of APRN regulation.[91]

Conclusion

In just over 20 years NCSBN, through the commitment and efforts of many representatives of its member boards, has devoted a considerable effort to the issues surrounding advanced nursing practice. None of the accomplishments would have occurred without the continued dialogue with the various organizations and certifying bodies related to the APRNs across the country. The continuing proliferation of subspecialties of areas of practice still presents regulatory problems and will need to be resolved at some point in the near future. Although interstate mobility and practice remain problematic for APRNs, a continuation of the collaboration of individuals and groups holds the promise of benefits both to the public and to APRNS.

CHAPTER TWELVE
NURSING ASSISTIVE PERSONNEL

The type of illness, not the pocket book, should determine the kind of care the patient should have...there are innumerable cases that could be adequately cared for by the attendant...

Annie Goodrich, 1917[1]

THE QUOTE CITED ABOVE was a part of the discussion that followed the presentation of two papers at the American Nurses Association (ANA) Convention in 1917. In the first paper, "Is There a Need for Another Class of Sick Attendants Besides Nurses?" Author Frances Stone concluded that the answer was "yes," but seemed to say that attendants should care for those who could not afford the services of the registered nurse (RN).[2] Edith Ambrose presented the second paper, "How and Where Should Attendants be Trained?" and concluded that a plan should be worked out for the cooperation of hospitals for chronic diseases, and that visiting nurses and health associations should be involved in the training of those nurses. She said,

This plan, if developed, would do away with the awful bugbear of "invasion of our rights" and "lowering of our standard" for it would give the control of the entire field into the hands of the nursing profession and would work for the common good of the registered nurses, the attendants, and the public.[3]

One impetus to train attendants to assist nurses at the time these papers were presented was World War I. This fact was illustrated when Sophia Palmer noted, in an editorial comment in the *American Journal of Nursing (AJN)*, that the Graduate Nurses Association of Virginia, "through its legislative committee, working with the Virginia State Board of Nurse Examiners, had a bill to train and license attendants introduced and passed by the legislature." The stated purpose of the act was to alleviate the serious shortage of nurses resulting from the demands of the war.[4] While these attendants were licensed in Virginia, more assistants to nurses began to appear in other states and all were not licensed. These individuals were identified by several different titles such as nurse aide and nursing assistant. They did a variety of tasks in the care of the patients.

Administration of Medicines by Unlicensed Personnel

The first reference to unlicensed personnel appeared in the minutes of the National Council of State Boards of Nursing, Inc. (NCSBN®) Board of Directors meeting on July 6 to 8, 1978, the first meeting after the convention at which the organization was established. President Elaine Ellibee of Wisconsin reported that she had received a telephone call from Faye Abdellah, assistant surgeon general of the United States, regarding a public hearing to be held in Chicago on July 11 to 12, 1978. The subject of the hearing was the federal regulations for skilled and intermediate care facilities participating in the federal Medicaid and Medicare programs. One item to be considered at the hearing was the administration of medicines by unlicensed personnel.[5]

No further entries regarding assistive personnel were found in the NCSBN minutes, reports, or publications until 1981 when Kathleen Dwyer of Rhode Island, the Area IV director, reported on discussion and actions taken at the area meeting, including a discussion on the administration of medicines by unlicensed personnel. The Area IV representatives requested that NCSBN consider this issue and posed the question, "could the NCSBN develop a policy statement that would help state boards in dealing with the problem?" Those attending the same meeting "voted to refer to the NCSBN, as it is a national, not a regional problem, the certification of nurse's aides by state boards of nursing."[6]

The following year the reports of the area directors in the *NCSBN Book of Reports* again mentioned discussion and reaction to unlicensed personnel. Merlyn Maillian of Louisiana-RN, the Area III director, listed scope of practice for unlicensed personnel among the agenda items for the area meeting.[7] Lois O'Shea of Delaware, the Area IV director, reported that the same item appeared on the agenda for her area meeting in the fall of 1982. The member boards represented at the Area IV meeting formed an ad hoc committee to study the problem of the "illegal practice" of unlicensed personnel and to make recommendations to the 1983 delegate assembly. Area IV met again in the spring of 1983. The ad hoc committee reported that 47 member boards responded to a questionnaire on the subject and that a report of the findings should be ready for the 1983 annual meeting.[8]

Prospective Pricing and Hospital Staffing

Nursing organizations and NCSBN examined with concern a related event that occurred in 1983 with the beginning of the phase in of prospective pricing for Medicare services on October 1. In an article in *Issues*, Roger C. Nauert, a recognized leader in health care management, described the difference between the traditional third party program that paid hospitals for costs or charges for services provided and the prospective pricing system. The latter paid the hospital a flat rate for each case covered by Medicare. The rate of payment did not change because of length of stay or the complexity of the care required by the patient. The rate was based on the admitting diagnosis and related medical and surgical diagnoses. The diagnosis was assigned to one of 467 possible diagnosis related groups (DRGs), a new acronym that became a pervasive term in health care in the United States. Some hospital costs, including direct teaching costs, were fully reimbursed as in the past and "until congress changes the payment formula." Nauert continued the article with the following:

> Prospective pricing, Washington's massive scheme to slow spiraling health care costs, will have profound, long-term effects on the way that hospitals treat the sick and injured. And, because nursing is the heart of hospital care, this new payment system will radically transform the practice of nursing, and indirectly, the academic preparation for the profession.

As the reimbursement for services changed, the money available to operate the health care institutions changed and managers looked for ways to reduce costs, including the cost for the nursing staff. The following was another quote from the article that described the effect of DRGs on nursing:

Exacerbating the nurse's challenge is the fact that many hospitals are and will continue to cope with the stringent cost-cutting demands of the new payment plan by paring overhead wherever they can. Hospitals, as everyone knows, are labor-intensive organizations; thus staffing has been the logical, if painful place to slash costs. As a result, fewer nurses will be treating patients who need more care.

Nauert also said, "nurses will need to be consummate diplomats" to help patients who may believe they are being discharged before they are ready to go. He stated that nurses needed new management skills, and he emphasized the need to develop standards of care and to measure nursing actions against these standards. Nauert concluded the article as follows:

The history of American healthcare delivery has been a story of nurses dedicating themselves to providing the best possible care for the sick and injured. Although the economic environment may complicate the nurse's job, we may be certain that nurses will continue to give the best care they can. For the nurse who is prepared to make the most of the challenges the profession faces, the future can be a time of exciting professional growth.[9]

The above discussion has been included here because of the resulting changes in the United States health care system following the implementation of DRGs. The acronym DRGs became commonly used as a shortened name for prospective pricing. Two major factors that have had a substantial impact on the issue of nursing assistive personnel have been the economics of health care and a recurring shortage of nurses.

At the 1985 meeting of the Delegate Assembly, the delegates adopted the following motion:

That the Board of the National Council provide for an investigation into the degree of problems present in each jurisdiction concerning assistance with medications by unlicensed personnel and if the problem is a major consequence to the public health, safety and welfare, the Board will then appoint a committee to prepare a position statement on this issue to present to the Delegate Assembly.[10]

A questionnaire on the activity of unlicensed personnel was attached to the *Newsletter to the Member Boards* that was mailed on December 27, 1985.[11]

After several years of discussion at the area meetings, in 1986 NCSBN became more active in the area of exploring unlicensed personnel with an emphasis on their role in the administration of medications. The Nursing Practice and Standards (NP&S) Committee, chaired by Therese Sullivan of Montana, reported that they had completed a report on the activities of unlicensed personnel following a survey of the member boards in January. The committee planned to develop a position statement on the activities of unlicensed personnel, particularly the administration of medications, if directed to do so by the delegate assembly.[12] The report of the activities of unlicensed personnel was included in the *NCSBN Book of Reports*. The findings included the fact that administration of medicines by unlicensed personnel was legal in 23 jurisdictions and not legal in 22. Some exceptions were noted: in New Hampshire, the activity was legal in maximum security and state prison hospital systems; in Colorado, physician extenders could administer medications; and in New York, attendants at the Department of Mental Health institutions could administer with adequate MD or RN supervision. The jurisdictions listed their sources of authority related to unlicensed personnel as one or more of the following: public health law in 5 jurisdictions; an exception to the nurse practice act in 9 jurisdictions; and the medical practice act in 4 jurisdictions. This authority was reported as "other" in 16 jurisdictions.[13]

The NP&S Committee also found little or no reporting of problems, and those reports that were made were to a variety of agencies. As a result there was little or no accountability for the actions of these individuals with no clear means to report, investigate, and take action when the worker had posed a risk to the health and safety of the patients. The most common settings where unlicensed personnel administered medications were residential centers, foster and group homes, and nursing homes. Other sites included day centers for adults or children, extended care locations, and prisons. Other findings showed that 12 jurisdictions had "certified medication aides" and 34 did not. In those jurisdictions where these aides were certified, their regulation was done by the Department of Health, the Department of Mental Health, or the Department of Aging. In addition, 40 jurisdictions reported the use of unlicensed personnel to administer medications and 23 reported that there were problems with unlicensed personnel performing other types of nursing activities. The report concluded with the following statement: "A specific concern relative to the administration of medications by unlicensed persons or certified/uncertified personnel was also clearly documented by the survey results." The findings led to the recommendation that the delegate assembly prepare a position statement on the subject.[14] At its 1986 meeting, the delegate assembly adopted a motion to approve the formulation of a position statement on activities of unlicensed personnel, particularly the administration of medications, for consideration by the delegate assembly in 1987.[15]

NCSBN Statement on the Nursing Activities of Unlicensed Personnel

The NP&S Committee completed and published the "Statement on the Nursing Activities of Unlicensed Personnel" in 1987. The statement examined the various concerns that had existed since the early 1900s. The changes in the practice of nursing and the availability of health care for more and more people were discussed. The statement also addressed the increasing costs of health care and the public policy changes that led to attempts to restrain these costs by reducing the price of the delivery of care. The recurring nursing shortage was identified as another contributor, but the statement also acknowledged that more recently the driving force to hire unlicensed personnel was "largely financial in nature." The dangers of this approach were described in the statement as follows: "The inappropriate use of unlicensed persons to perform nursing acts at a lesser cost than nursing care provided by nurses is placing the public health, safety and welfare at risk." The statement continued by saying that boards of nursing have legitimate concerns and the legal responsibility to monitor any and all nursing activities. In addition, the statement clarified that when RNs delegate selected nursing tasks, the RN retains the responsibility and accountability. The burden of determining the competency of the person who will perform the tasks and of evaluating the situations rests with the licensees. The following are the conclusions included in the statement:

1. Performance of non-nurse delegated and non-nurse supervised nursing activities by unlicensed persons constitutes practicing nursing without a license and is not in the interest of the health, safety, and welfare of the public.

2. Language in Nursing Practice acts that allows for supervision of nursing activities by non-nursing persons in inappropriate.

3. The interpretation of physician delegation clauses in Medical Practice acts that allows for physicians' delegation of nursing acts is inappropriate.

4. Pieces of care should not be provided in isolation by unlicensed persons functioning independently of the nurse if the health, safety and welfare of the public is to be assured.

5. Boards of Nursing need to monitor guidelines and regulations of federal and state regulatory agencies with the understanding that the state's Nursing Practice act has the higher legal authority.

6. Boards of nursing need to work to assure evidence of adequate nurse involvement where nursing services are being provided.

7. Boards should promulgate clear rules on the utilization of unlicensed persons in all settings where nursing care is delivered.

8. Boards need to clearly define delegation in regulation.

9. A limited supply of nurses is not an excuse for the inappropriate utilization of unlicensed persons.

10. Boards must set standards based on the health, safety, and welfare of the public regardless of cost containment arguments for lowered standards.

11. Regulations regarding the delegation of nursing functions must be linked to the disciplinary process.

12. Boards need to pursue criminal prosecution when there is clear evidence that unlicensed persons are performing nursing activities.[16]

The delegate assembly approved the statement after minor amendments.[17]

Tri Council for Nurses Statement on Assistive Personnel to the Registered Nurse

In February 1990 Executive Director Jennifer Bosma reported to the board of directors on meetings with representatives from the ANA where the nursing shortage and unlicensed personnel were discussed.[18] At the meeting in April the board considered a request from the Tri Council for Nursing—comprising the ANA, the National League for Nursing (NLN), the American Organization of Nurse Executives (AONE), and the American Association of Colleges of Nursing—for an endorsement of a statement on assistive personnel. The board decided to present the request to the delegate assembly for consideration after a decision was reached on guidelines for responding to requests for endorsement of position statements.[19] In August the delegate assembly endorsed the January 1990 "Statement on Assistive Personnel to the Registered Nurse" developed by the Tri Council for Nurses.[20] This endorsement of a position statement from another group was a first for NCSBN, and the statement follows in its entirety for that reason:

Nursing is an essential component of health care, and the consumer of health care needs to be assured of the availability, accessibility, and quality of nursing care. It is in the spirit of this responsibility that this statement related to the use of assistive personnel has been developed. Historically, unlicensed personnel have assisted registered nurses in the delivery of patient care. However, in recent years, with economic demands driving the delivery system, there have been increasing concerns about the role of assistive personnel. It is extremely important to use assistants in a manner that assures appropriate delegation or assignment of nursing functions and adequate direction and supervision of individuals to whom nursing activities are delegated.

Patient care is delivered today by a staff mix of Registered Nurses (RN), Licensed Practical/Vocational Nurses (LPN), and unlicensed personnel in assistive roles. The term "assistive personnel" is used to recognize the trained/unlicensed health care worker who is employed within the continuum of acute hospital care to home health, ambulatory and long term care. Two categories of assistive personnel are generally recognized; the patient care assistant to whom the RN delegates or assigns aspects of nursing care and who functions under the supervision of the Registered Nurse, and the unit assistant who supports the nursing care system through a variety of non-nursing activities.

Many clinical settings are revising the staff mix needed for the delivery of patient care because of changing patient needs, the economics of reimbursement, and demand driven shortages of nursing personnel. A variety of manpower models are being explored and refined as the industry strives to balance quality and cost issues. The ultimate aim is to reallocate nursing and non-nursing activities to enable the registered nurse to focus on the patient. Specific models are best crafted at the point of delivery of care.

The nursing profession is accountable for the quality of the service it provides to the consumer. This includes the responsibility for developing nursing policies and procedures and setting the standards of practice for the nursing care of populations being served. It is further incumbent on the nursing profession to define the appropriate educational preparation and role of any group providing services within the scope of nursing practice. The State Board of Nursing is responsible for the legal regulation of nursing practice for the RN and LPN and should be responsible for the regulation of any other category of personnel who assists in the provision of direct nursing care. Professional and statutory provisions require that when the RN delegates and assigns direct nursing care activities to LPNs and assistive personnel, appropriate reporting relationships are established and the RN supervises all personnel to whom these activities have been delegated. In all situations, registered nurses and licensed practical nurses are responsible and accountable for their respective individual nursing activities. These relationships should be made explicit in workplace policies.[21]

Delegation of Nursing

Another important action at the 1990 meeting of the NCSBN Delegate Assembly was the adoption of a concept paper on delegation.[22] The Nursing Practice and Education (NP&E) Committee, chaired by Thomas Neumann of Wisconsin, developed the paper. Excerpts from the paper are shown below:

The purpose of the National Council in formulating this concept paper is to provide to Member Boards a conceptual basis for delegation from a regulatory perspective. It is the position of the National Council that licensed nurses, in accordance with board of nursing requirements, determine the appropriateness of delegating acts from their scopes of practice. Each person involved in the delegation process is accountable for his/her own actions in this process. There is potential liability if competent, safe care is not the outcome of the delegation.

The first 8 of 12 premises included in the NP&E paper were from the 1987 "Statement on Nursing Activities of Unlicensed Persons." The last 4 premises read as follows:

9. While tasks and procedures may be delegated, the functions of assessment, evaluation and nursing judgment should not be delegated.

10. While non-nurses may suggest which nursing acts may be delegated, it is the licensed nurse who ultimately decides the appropriateness of delegation.

11. The unlicensed person cannot redelegate a delegated act.

12. Boards of nursing must develop clear rules on determination of competence of persons to perform delegated nursing tasks or procedures, the level of supervision necessary, and which acts may be delegated.

Delegation was defined in the paper as "transferring to a competent individual authority to perform a selected nursing task in a selected situation." Employing the regulatory perspective, the committee developed a framework for managerial policies and listed the following as the basis for delegation:

• Determination of the task, procedure or function that is to be delegated.

• Staff available.

• Assessment of client needs.

• Assessment of potential delegate's competency.

• Consideration of the level of supervision available and a determination of the level and method of supervision required to assure safe performance.

The conclusion of the paper stated,

> From a regulatory perspective, the nurse is held accountable for both acts directly carried out and acts delegated. This regulatory perspective should serve as the framework for managerial policies related to the employment and utilization of nurses. They may be involved in either delegation or assignment, depending upon interpretation of the definitions of these terms. Both the delegating nurse and the delegate are accountable for their own actions in the delegation process. Furthermore, the delegating nurse has a responsibility to determine that the delegate is indeed competent to perform the delegated act. Finally, the delegating nurse must provide appropriate supervision. The nurse must be the person who ultimately decides when and under what circumstances delegation is to occur. Non-nursing and managerial persons must not coerce the nurse into compromising client safety by requiring the nurse to delegate. While tasks and procedures may be delegated, the nurse should not delegate practice pervasive functions of assessment, evaluation and nursing judgment.[23]

In 1991 the delegate assembly adopted the paper "Nursing Care in the School Setting: Regulatory Implications," as developed by the NP&E Committee.[24] This paper discussed the recent expansion of the role of school nurses and the increasing complexity of the care required. With the "mainstreaming" of children with disabilities and chronic illnesses the demand for care had increased. In most jurisdictions direct nursing care in schools was delegated to unlicensed personnel, but the RN retained the responsibility for care. Additionally, the delegating nurse was required to comply with the licensing laws of the state. The NCSBN paper on delegation was referenced for guidance in developing "Nursing Care in the School Setting: Regulatory Implications." The following statement is the concluding paragraph:

> In addition, it is recommended that policies and procedures be developed to guide the educational preparation and practice of school nurses, and that those policies and procedures specifically address delegation and supervision issues. Consideration also needs to be given to the development of protocols for action in specific situations, including the identification of the qualifications of individuals who are authorized to initiate and implement those protocols. Finally, it is recommended that school districts consider establishing maximum student/nurse ratios; such ratios should take into consideration the health needs of the student population being served, the availability of licensed practical nurses and unlicensed personnel to provide direct services, and the need to assure adequate supervision of those individuals. Administrative personnel in school districts should consider their own liability in observing and supporting safe nurse/student ratios.[25]

The delegate assembly adopted a recommendation from the NP&E Committee in 1992 to accept the "Joint Statement on Maintaining Professional and Legal Standards During a Shortage of Nursing Personnel." This statement was developed in collaboration with the ANA and the National Federation of Licensed Practical Nursed (NFLPN) and is discussed in Chapter 7.[26]

At the 1994 annual meeting the Report of the NP&E Committee was presented by Chair Karen Macdonald of North Dakota. Two of the items listed among future considerations for NCSBN were (a) the exploration of how the essential competencies studies could be used to assist decision making regarding which nursing functions can and cannot be delegated, and (b) the development of strategies for addressing issues related to the provision of nursing care by unlicensed assistive personnel (UAP).[27]

The delegate assembly adopted two resolutions related to UAP at its 1994 meeting. The first resolution directed that NCSBN collect and analyze the results of current and past studies of the utilization of licensed and unlicensed nursing personnel with a report to the 1995 delegate assembly. The analysis was to focus on the quality of nursing care delivered to the consumer, and on cost effectiveness. The second resolution directed that NCSBN write a letter to a large number of health-related organizations (a list of more than 16 was included in the resolution) to express the position of NCSBN in unequivocal terms regarding the inappropriate use of unlicensed personnel in lieu of licensed nurses for the delivery of quality nursing care for the consumer. The letter was to be an expression of the commitment of NCSBN to the protection of the public health, safety, and welfare. President Marcia Rachel of Mississippi began the letter with a reference to the resolution. Excerpts from the letter, dated August 24, 1994, follow:

> The National Council and all of its member boards of nursing hold as their highest goal the protection of the public health, safety, and welfare. In keeping with this commitment, the National Council urges you to consider the meaning of licensure, and the assurance of quality that it provides to patients, residents, and clients to whom nursing care is provided.

She spoke to the dramatic increase in the use of unlicensed personnel with the projection of continued increase, and reminded the reader of the necessity for nursing supervision of unlicensed personnel performing nursing tasks:

> Delegation is an appropriate means, and a useful tool, to maximize the contributions of various members of the health care team to the well-being of the patient/client/resident when performed according to self-reasoned principles. The National Council's delegation paper sought to set out such principles. First, nurses should avoid delegating the practice-pervasive functions of assessment, evaluation and nursing judgment. Second, the delegating nurse assumes responsibility for determining that the delegate is indeed competent to perform the delegated act and provides appropriate supervision. Third, boards of nursing must clearly define delegation in regulation, promulgate clear rules for its use, and follow through with disciplinary action when there is evidence that the rules are violated.
>
> Underlying all of the above principles relative to delegation is a central tenet of professional regulation: that a license is a mechanism to assure the public of the competence of the licensee to practice safely and effectively. The process leading to licensure is therefore rigorous, including requirements for education and examination. Such assurance cannot be replicated by training programs typically provided to unlicensed personnel. Nor can the accountability of unlicensed personnel match the accountability of the licensed nurse. The licensee is accountable not only to the employer, but also to the state authorities issuing the license. The licensee stands to lose not only his or her job, but also license, should the care provided not meet the standards for safety and effectiveness.
>
> The National Council urges all who participate in the provision of health care to the public to consider and endorse the value of a license as an essential mechanism to assure the delivery of quality nursing care for the consumer.[28]

This letter was consistent with the intent of the delegate assembly when it asked that the position of NCSBN be expressed in unequivocal terms.

Vicky Burbach of Nebraska authored an article in *Issues* in 1994 entitled "Delegation in Nursing." She discussed definitions, delegation as a concept, accountability, and responsibility. Burbach also looked at limitations to delegation; authority and assignment; and delegation as an art and skill, and as a process. She concluded with the following:

When defining delegation, it is important to remember that delegation principles are based upon autonomy and individual development. Nursing is a process discipline and cannot be reduced to a list of tasks. Job descriptions and state and federal regulations that list activities identifying hierarchical divisions of labor based upon tasks discourage autonomy and decision-making by the nurse, and diminish the significance of nursing judgment. Only nursing judgment can determine when a bath is not a simple task, and when providing the right medication to the right client at the right time is not a complex activity.[29]

The delegate assembly authorized the board of directors to review and approve a 1995 paper on delegation following revision by an assigned task force.[30] In November the board of directors approved the final version of *Delegation: Concepts and Decision Making Process*.[31] The following is quoted from this paper:

Nurses who are uniquely qualified for promoting the health of the whole person by virtue of their education and experience, must be actively involved in making health care policies and decisions; they must coordinate and supervise the delivery of nursing care, including the delegation of nursing tasks to others.[32]

This document updated the earlier paper on delegation with an addition and expansion of information. Perhaps the most quoted portion was the following "Five Rights of Delegation":

- RIGHT TASK
  One that is delegable for a specific patient.
- RIGHT CIRCUMSTANCES
  Appropriate patient setting, available resources, and other relevant factors considered.
- RIGHT PERSON
  Right person is delegating the right task to the right person to be performed on the right person.
- RIGHT DIRECTION/COMMUNICATION
  Clear, concise description of the task, including its objective, limits, and expectations.
- RIGHT SUPERVISION
  Appropriate monitoring, evaluation, intervention as needed, and feedback.

The paper ended with this conclusion:

The guidelines presented in this paper provide a decision-making process that facilitates the provision of quality care by appropriate persons in all health care settings. The National Council of State Boards of Nursing believes that this paper will assist all health care providers and health care facilities in discharging their shared responsibility to provide optimum health care that protects the public's health, safety and welfare.[33]

The board agreed to a request from the ANA for minor adaptations and use of the section of the NCSBN delegation paper on the "Five Rights of Delegation." The ANA planned to use this excerpt in a paper on community health.[34]

Unlicensed Assistive Personnel

In October 1994 the board of directors assigned the Subcommittee on Unlicensed Personnel to the NP&E Committee.[35] At the annual meeting in 1995 the delegates reviewed the Report of the Unlicensed Personnel Subcommittee presented by Chair Harriett Clark of New Jersey. The subcommittee summarized its activities and reported that member boards had responded to an outline statement with the following themes emerging from those responses:

- Quality and safety concerns are the same for the client, regardless of the qualification of the provider.

- Preparation and training for all Unlicensed Assistive Personnel (UAP) should be augmented and standardized.

- Only persons with authority to perform nursing can delegate and supervise nursing.

- Delegation must be based on sound clinical judgment and regulatory principles.

- Consumers are confused about qualifications of providers.

- Research data must be gathered to ascertain the impact of substitution of unlicensed providers for licensed providers.

- Protection of the public must be paramount in all decisions regarding patient care.

The subcommittee accepted the premise that when an unlicensed person is performing a nursing task, the performance must meet the same standards as if performed by a licensed nurse. Variations in title added to confusion in the health care system and the subcommittee suggested that except where external regulation required otherwise, the title "UAP" should be used. The subcommittee was in the process of developing a concept paper.[36]

The 1996 Report of the Unlicensed Assistive Personnel Task Force, formerly a subcommittee, included four attachments reflecting its recent work. The attachments were entitled *Premises, Use and Regulation of UAP in the Continuum of Care, Board of Nursing Enforcement Options in the Utilization of Unlicensed Assistive Personnel*, and a draft for delegation education outlines.[37]

At its November 1996 meeting the board of directors discussed the urgency of the topic of UAP as reported by the board members and NCSBN staff from conversations with member board representatives. The board agreed to have staff obtain more information about studies by the ANA and AONE that were in progress. The board identified the most recent Role Delineation Study by NCSBN which described the roles of the different nursing care providers, and the development of a continuum of unlicensed personnel as potentially helpful resources for the member boards in their policymaking related to UAP.[38]

Executive Director Bosma addressed items related to UAP in her Report of Staff Activities in 1997. One of these items was the report, "Current Research Addressing the Impact of Using Licensed vs. Unlicensed Nursing Personnel on the Quality of Client Care." She discussed the limited amount of research on the subject that was available, and that it was difficult to draw conclusions about the impact of changes in the skill mix. Bosma also referred to a 1996 Institute of Medicine report, "Nursing Staff in Hospitals and Nursing Homes—Is It Adequate?" which included the following statement:

Based on the expert discussions, the Institute of Medicine Report and a review of the published literature, the overarching questions to be addressed by research related to nurse staffing and quality of care in hospitals are: What is the contribution of nursing to the quality of care in hospitals, and what are the cost implications of this contribution? Within this area, *a high research priority continues to be identifying patient outcomes that are sensitive to nursing care* [emphasis added].

Bosma also reported that the *Federal Register* for November 13, 1996, presented a request for comments on and suggestions of priority research topics related to the impact of nurse staffing on the quality of care in hospitals. Responses to the request were to be considered in planning for future research initiatives to benefit health care for the public. Bosma stated that the ANA provided funding for a pilot study to explore the impact of staff mix on quality care indicators. The ANA had also funded planning grants to state nurses associations in Arizona, California, Minnesota, North Dakota, Texas, and Virginia to move nursing's quality indicators into broader use.[39]

The Unlicensed Assistive Personnel Task Force, chaired by Marie Fisher of Maine, reported on its activities at the annual meeting in 1997. The task force developed and pilot tested resources and tools to provide strategies for addressing the UAP issues. Two of these were in draft stage: "Role Development: Critical Component of Delegation, Curriculum Outline," and "A Continuum of Care: Roles of the Licensed Nurse and Unlicensed Assistive Personnel." The task force completed the nursing tool, "Delegation Decision-Making Grid," to assist nurses in making delegation decisions. The task force also presented information on its activities at the Annual Nurse Aide Conference.[40]

The publication *Insight* presented several related articles in its 1997 winter/spring issue. These included a description of how UAP could be used in school settings, a delegation decision tree from the Ohio Board of Nursing, a report from the Oklahoma Board of Nursing, as well as its plan to regulate UAPs.[41]

In May 1998 the board of directors received a report from the Unlicensed Assistive Personnel Task Force, and agreed to the described plan for reorganization of the task force for the next year. The task force suggested a collaboration with the American Association of Critical Care Nurses (AACCN), a joint oversight group, and a partnership with a publisher for disseminating key resources related to the interface between licensed nurses and assistive personnel.[42] In a move to protect the public's right to know their nursing care personnel's licensure status, the delegate assembly adopted a resolution at the 1998 annual meeting endorsing the practice of nursing personnel displaying their license credential on their employment identification badges.[43]

The description of one of three 1998 NCSBN studies, Client Care Outcomes of Delegating Nursing Activities to Unlicensed Assistive Personnel, appeared in an article in *Issues*. The purpose of the study was stated as follows: to describe and evaluate the impact of factors influencing client outcomes following licensed nurse delegation to and supervision of UAP who perform nursing activities. The article listed these research questions:

- How do the characteristics of the practice setting influence the outcomes of delegated nursing activities?

- How do the educational and experiential backgrounds of the licensed nurse and unlicensed assistive personnel influence the outcomes of delegated nursing activities?

- How do factors related to supervision influence the outcomes of delegated nursing activities?

- How do factors related to delegation decisions influence the outcome of delegated nursing activities?

- Is there a pattern among critical factors related to practice, education and supervision and the outcome of delegated nursing activities?

At the time of publication of the article describing the study, a pilot study was underway to evaluate the data collection and analysis procedures to be used in the overall study. Following any needed modifications, a contract would be signed for data collection and analysis of activities for the main study.[44] In a later edition of *Issues*, NCSBN announced that the contract was awarded to Dr. Mary Anthony at Frances Payne Bolton School of Nursing at Case Western Reserve University in Cleveland, Ohio.[45]

In March 1998 NCSBN launched a new section on its Web site titled "Delegation and UAP Issues."[46] The Unlicensed Assistive Personnel Task Force reported in the January *Newsletter to the Member Boards* that it had created a profile of issues related to UAP. The profile included types regulated, practice settings, state fees for regulation, types of certifications, training programs, and competency testing.[47] In July the task force posted its revision of the paper, "The Continuum of Care: A Regulatory Perspective," on the Web. The member boards were urged to review it prior to the forum at the annual meeting.[48]

In May 1999 the board of directors discussed the certification examination for UAP of the AACCN in light of previous discussion of collaboration with the AACCN. The NLN also expressed interest in pursuing a similar collaboration with NCSBN. The board asked staff to explore the fiscal impact of the project for the certifying examination for review by the Finance Committee and for further consideration by the board.[49] The following month the board decided not to pursue a business relationship with the AACCN based on the results of market research. The board of directors affirmed the importance of the topic of UAP to the member boards and voted to continue the annual conference on nurse aide/UAP issues.[50]

Articles in *Insight* continued to provide information on UAP and nurse aides in 1999, including a report of the U.S. Supreme Court decision related to nursing care for the disabled in public schools. The decision called for continuous one-on-one nursing care for these students, but said school districts should decide who provides care using state law, including the nursing practice acts.[51]

In 2001 the North Dakota Board of Nursing asked the NCSBN Board of Directors for an *amicus curiae* brief to support an appeal of a judgment by the Department of Health Services related to nursing home bed makers. The North Dakota Board was concerned about the judgment because it questioned the authority of that board to define the practice of nursing in that state. The North Dakota long term care association and two nursing homes offered to partner with the North Dakota Board of Nursing to support its position. The board of directors agreed to provide the requested brief.[52]

When the board of directors approved committees in 2003 for the coming year, it established a subcommittee of the Practice, Regulation and Education (PR&E) Committee to be known as the Subcommittee on Delegation and Assistive Personnel.[53] Nursing assistive personnel and the nursing shortage remained among the 16 issues in the nursing environment identified by the board of directors that would guide strategic planning discussions in 2003.[54] In September 2003 the board of directors discussed a preliminary request from Promisor, the test service for the National Council Licensure Examination (NCLEX®), to consider endorsing a medication aide certification examination. The board agreed to discuss this request further at a subsequent meeting. The board also talked about collecting discipline data on nursing assistive personnel. The board decided to ask the Subcommittee on Delegation and Assistive Personnel to include in its report a recommendation to capture data on nursing assistive personnel and to use the states doing this for a beta test.[55] At the December 2003 meeting of the board of directors, the board added the role of medication technicians to the issues for strategic planning discussion.[56]

The Nursing Home Reform Act

The Nursing Home Reform Act (NHRA) included provisions for education and registration by the states of nurse aides employed in Medicare and Medicaid funded health care facilities. Details about this act are included in Chapter 9. This act was frequently referred to as OBRA 87, an acronym for the Omnibus Budget Reconciliation Act of 1987 that included the NHRA. President Renatta Loquist of South Carolina, speaking in her President's Message in *Issues* in 1988, said,

Passage of the Nursing Home Reform Act requiring nurse aides to complete state-approved training programs and pass a competency evaluation examination required many boards of nursing to begin planning to implement various requirements of the law. In response to the Member's needs, the Council has embarked on a new service to Members and others charged with the implementation of the federal law in their states, through the development of a competency evaluation program for nurse aides.[57]

The first mention of the potential involvement of boards of nursing in the regulation of nurse aides appeared in the minutes of the February 1988 meeting of the NCSBN Board of Directors. Leota Rolls of Nebraska, the Area II director, reported on concerns from the member boards in the area relative to PL 100-203 (also referred to as the NHRA and OBRA 87) requiring the registration of nurse aides in nursing homes and in home health care. OBRA 87 was an act of the United States Congress, and PL 100-203 was just one of the public laws included in it. However, the designation OBRA 87, through common usage, became the term that many used as the shortened name for the individual law. The law applied to those nurse aides employed in agencies and facilities receiving funds from Medicaid and Medicare. These nurse aides who completed the required education and passed the competency evaluation were placed on a state registry. In some states the title certified nurse aide (CNA) was used to identify these individuals. In other states the nurse aides were said to be registered and other designations were used. The board of directors directed staff to disseminate existing information about PL 100-203 to the member boards, and to work with the NP&S Committee to provide information on implications for the member boards.[58]

The discussion related to the work of NCSBN to provide a reliable competency evaluation for nurse aides was covered in Chapter 9 and will only be mentioned incidentally in this chapter. Both NCSBN and the member boards that were assigned the responsibility for the nurse aide registry in the states were at a disadvantage because the federal regulations for implementation of the law were not final until September 1991, almost a year after the date the registries were to be in place. A fact sheet published by NCSBN in 1991 listed the basic requirements of OBRA 87 as amended by Congress, with which the state must comply in its process to implement the registries and the competency evaluation program. These requirements were as follows:

- Effective implementation date: October 1, 1990.

- Approved training programs require a **minimum** of 75 hours divided between skills training and classroom instruction.

- Core curriculum content is specified.

- Training performed by or under general supervision of a registered nurse who has two years experience, at least one of which is in the provision of care in long term care facilities.

- Determination of competency can be by successful completion of a training and competency evaluation program or a competency evaluation program.

- Competency Evaluation:

  - Must address each area in the core curriculum.

  - Includes a written or oral examination and a skills demonstration component.

  - Skills demonstration component must be evaluated by a registered nurse with two years experience in caring for elderly and/or chronically ill of any age.

  - State establishes standard for satisfactory completion of the competency evaluation.

- Requires states to establish and maintain a nurse aide registry and indicates what information must and may be included, when the **registry** must be accessible, and guidelines for disclosure of registry information.

- Includes three deeming provisions for previous experience or training.

- Prohibits states from charging nurse aides for the costs associated with training, materials, competency evaluation or the registry.

- Applies to temporary or per diem aides effective January 1, 1991.

- Requires checking by facilities of out-of-state registries if they have reason to believe a nurse aide worked in another state.[59]

The fact sheet referenced above summarized the involvement of member boards in relation to the regulation of nurse aides as follows:

Many Boards of Nursing are not involved in the regulation of nurse aides. Some boards of nursing are involved in various aspects of implementation of OBRA 87 requirements:

- Approximately 14–17 boards have responsibility to implement one of the required provisions, i.e., approve training programs or maintain the registry.

- Approximately 11–14 boards have responsibility to implement all provisions of OBRA 1987 relating to nurse aides employed in long term care settings except investigation of complaints.

- Approximately 7–10 boards have responsibility to implement all provisions of OBRA 1987 relating to nurse aides employed in long term care and home health care settings except investigation of complaints.

- Approximately 5–6 boards have responsibility under state law for aspects of training, competency evaluation, and/or registry for nurse aides employed in acute care settings.[60]

NCSBN endeavored to provide information needed by those member boards with any level of involvement in implementing the requirements.

The NCSBN Board of Directors appointed the Task Force on Nurse Aide Evaluation with Carolyn Ace of Pennsylvania, Lonna Burress of Nevada, Edda Johnson-Foster of Maryland, and Christine Zambriki of Michigan as members, and Sharon Weisenbeck of Kentucky as chair.[61] By August the NP&S Committee reported to the delegate assembly that a concept paper on PL 100-203 had been prepared. The following is a list of relevant points from the concept paper:

- The philosophical belief of a board of nursing regarding the appropriateness of establishing a training and competency evaluation method for nurse aides has no bearing on the reality of PL 100-203's existence.

- Boards of nursing need to work to assure evidence of adequate nurse involvement where nursing services are being provided.

- Boards should promulgate clear rules on the utilization of unlicensed persons in all settings where nursing care is delivered.

The paper further stated,

If the board of nursing chooses to be the state entity to enact any or all of the provisions of PL 100-203, regulatory control over nurse aides, who deliver nursing care will remain in the domain and control of the board of nursing. If the board chooses not to be the state entity to enact any or all of the provisions of PL 100-203, the control of the board of nursing over this level of nursing practice will be diluted.[62]

An article in the November 1988 *Newsletter to the Member Boards* referenced correspondence to and from the Health Care Financing Administration (HCFA). The correspondence included information and clarification of OBRA 87 provisions and demonstrated what was to become an ongoing positive relationship between NCSBN and the HCFA that assisted in providing meaningful information to the member boards.[63]

In 1989 the board of directors decided that NCSBN would not develop language related to implementation of the requirements of OBRA 87 in the form of a model law and regulations. Instead the board decided that NCSBN would serve as a clearinghouse for member boards needing information on model language.[64] Language developed by one or more member boards was generously shared with others where laws or regulations were being developed. Later in the year the board decided that NCSBN would maintain a list of state agencies responsible for the nurse aide registry.[65] Subsequently, this listing was helpful to the member boards that made provision for certification by endorsement and facilitated information sharing between the states.

At the 1989 annual meeting, the delegate assembly adopted a resolution on the regulation of nurse aides with the following requirements:

- That the National Council of State Boards of Nursing and its member boards work cooperatively with federal and state agencies in the implementation of the mandates of PL 100-203 relating to the regulation of nurse aides to insure coherence and coordination among their parts.

- That the Delegate Assembly direct the Nursing Practice and Education Committee to develop standards for the regulation of nurse aides through 1) the approval of programs preparing such nurse aides and 2) the maintenance of a list or registry of those persons who have successfully completed an approved program and a competency evaluation for inclusion in the NCSBN MODEL NURSING PRACTICE ACT and NCSBN MODEL NURSING ADMINISTRATIVE RULES.

- That the NP&E Committee present recommendations on revisions to the model act and model rules for consideration by the 1990 Delegate Assembly.[66]

Nurse Aide Competency Evaluation Program Committee

Within a year of its appointment the Task Force on Nurse Aide Evaluation, became the Ad Hoc Nurse Aide Competency Evaluation Program Committee. Sharon Weisenbeck remained as chair. In 1992 the ad hoc designation was removed form the name of the committee. The major responsibilities of the committee, under its various names, were the planning and implementation of the competency evaluation and to provide information to the board of directors and the member boards related to the implementation of OBRA 87. In 1989, Chair Weisenbeck reported on the activities of the Ad Hoc Nurse Aide Compctency Evaluation Program (NACEP) Committee at the annual meeting. She outlined the OBRA 87 basic requirements including the requirement to include adverse findings of investigations conducted by the state related to abuse, neglect, and misappropriation. (This provision brought about a significant increase in investigations and case adjudication activities by the member boards that had responsibility for the registries.) Weisenbeck also included information on the efforts for the development of a NACEP examination in cooperation with The Psychological Corporation. The first examinations of NACEP, referred to as "forms", were administered in July 1989.[67] As with many other programs and activities of NCSBN over the years, it is not possible to identify all of those who contributed outstanding amounts of time, energy, and expertise to make this test available so quickly and to provide important and timely information for the member boards. However, it seems important to recognize the leadership of Sharon Weisenbeck, chair of the committee, and Barbara Halsey, program manager for NACEP, when looking at these early accomplishments.

The Subcommittee on Nurse Aide Language, chaired by Joyce Smyrski of North Carolina, worked in 1990 to develop a model nurse aide regulation act and model nurse aide administrative rules for consideration by the delegate assembly in August. In an introductory statement for the models, the subcommittee stated its belief that all nurse aides, regardless of practice setting, should be regulated by boards of nursing. Nurse aides were described as assistive personnel to nurses, and the reader was reminded that the licensed nurse who delegates or assigns tasks to aides is accountable for the delegation and for provision of supervision of the personnel performing the activities. The model act was presented in a format that related the sections to the requirements of OBRA 87 and to the *NCSBN Model Nursing Practice Act (MNPA)*. The model administrative rules were presented with the knowledge that the federal rules to implement OBRA 87 were not yet final, and addressed four areas of responsibility in order to:

- Establish standards for training and competency evaluation programs,

- Establish standards for approval of training and competency evaluation programs,

- Establish review and approval process of programs, and

- Establish and maintain a registry of nurse aides including documentation of validated complaints.

The model nurse aide regulation act and the model nurse aide administrative rules appeared as attachments to the Report of the Subcommittee on Model Language for Nurse Aides in the 1990 *NCSBN Book of Reports*.[68] The delegate assembly adopted both documents.[69] In April 1990 the board of directors agreed to comment on the proposed federal regulations for the implementation of OBRA 87 and directed the staff to provide a suggested comment letter for use by the member boards.[70]

The Ad Hoc NACEP Committee reported on its activities in the 1990 *NCSBN Book of Reports*. These activities included monitoring test development, informing the member boards about federal- and state-related activities, maintaining a list of state agencies responsible for the nurse aide registries, commenting on proposed rules and legislative changes, and reviewing the language for the proposed models. The committee also took a lead role in the first NCSBN-sponsored Conference on Nurse Aides. The conference was developed in cooperation with the Washington State Board of Nursing. Held in May in Seattle, representatives from 17 states and officials for HCFA were in attendance. A second conference was held in Baltimore in September.[71] A later report of this conference indicated that 22 states were represented and HCFA leaders attended for a "good interchange of information."[72]

In February 1990 the first *Directory of Nurse Aide Registries* was distributed. The individual nurse aide registries were under the jurisdiction of a variety of state agencies including boards of nursing, departments of public health, and others. This directory was useful to those agencies when there was a need for communication between states.[73] In August the NACEP Committee reported that a letter from the secretary of Health and Human Service to a senator from Colorado had confirmed that HCFA regulations would no longer prohibit the states from assigning the responsibility for investigations of complaints and the conduct of hearings involving nurse aides to a state agency of their choosing. Before this, these activities were specifically assigned to the survey agency that was charged to regulate nursing homes in the state.[74]

Executive Director Bosma, at the meeting of the board of directors in April 1991, reported to the board about ongoing discussions with the AONE on its concerns over the involvement of NCSBN in the regulation of nurse aides. The board reviewed and accepted a draft letter, the fact sheet about OBRA 87, and information about related actions taken by NCSBN. The letter and the fact sheet were shared with the member boards and distributed to the major nursing organizations, including AONE.[75] That same year, the *NCSBN Book of Reports* included the Report of the Ad Hoc NACEP Committee in which Chair Weisenbeck listed the activities of the committee for the year. In addition to continuing its oversight of the testing program, the committee shared information in the form of fact sheets, updates, and a list of state agencies; conducted another conference; and identified the need for an educational session at the annual meeting on the regulation of nurse aides and on the ANA Task Force on Unlicensed Assistive Personnel to the Registered Nurse.[76]

Weisenbeck continued to report on activities of the NACEP Committee in 1992. She noted that the final rules for nurse aides employed as home health aides were issued in July 1991 and for those employed in long term care facilities in September 1991. The committee continued to update the list of registries. Ellen Gleason became the program manager when Barbara Halsey moved to the position of computerized adaptive testing (CAT) program manager. The year 1992 also marked the initiation of the newsletter *Insight*.[77] The publication contained articles tracing the history of OBRA 87 and the involvement of NCSBN. In the Chair's Forum Weisenbeck said, "Our goal in creating this publication is to provide current information affecting nurse aides, [*sic*] discuss topics that impact those who work with nurse aides or who have an interest in nurse aide roles and responsibilities."[78] At the 1992 meeting of the delegate assembly the delegates adopted a resolution to conduct a feasibility study regarding the inclusion of nurse aide disciplinary information in a disciplinary data bank.[79]

In 1993 the delegate assembly voted not to establish a disciplinary data bank for nurse aides after considering the request from some member boards.[80] Another conference was held and *Insight* was published three times during the year with more than 500 copies distributed.[81] Following the receipt of the Report of the NACEP Committee at its June 1994 meeting, the board of directors agreed to explore the benefits of a comprehensive study of the effects of nurse aide/assistant training on the care provided in nursing homes.[82] The Fifth Annual Nurse Aide Conference was held in 1994, with 75 people attending. The theme was "Nurse Aides in a Decade of Change," and some of the topics presented were nurse aide certification, disciplinary action and nurse aides, and the survey process as it affects nurse aides.[83] *Insight* continued to present a variety of articles on topics of interest to nurse aides and those involved with regulation and practice. These topics included elder abuse, delegation to assistive personnel, and restraint in special circumstances.

The 1995 *NCSBN Book of Reports* included the report of the NACEP Task Force. Cindy Lyons of Oklahoma was chair of the task force at this time. The report stated that the Sixth Annual Nurse Aide Conference drew more than 60 attendees when the main topics for discussion included UAP and the ramifications of using UAP for those who supervise and regulate nurse aides. The *NACEP Study Guide* had been developed to assist candidates who were preparing to take the test, and *Insight* was distributed to more than 800 individuals during the year.[84] The spring issue of *Insight* included an article on "delegatory issues" for school nurses. Its circulation grew to more than 800 in its second year of publication, and exceeded 1000 in 1996.[85]

The board of directors approved a plan to revise the *Model Nurse Aide Regulation Act* and the *Model Nurse Aide Administrative Rules*, pending action by Congress on the federal budget and OBRA 87.[86] A November 1996 *Newsletter to the Member Boards* in reported that Nancy Chornick was assigned to NACEP responsibilities when Ellen Gleason assumed responsibility for NCLEX item development recruitment.[87]

The Competency Evaluation Program for Nurse Aides and the Annual Conference on Nurse Aides and Unlicensed Assistive Personnel continued to be offered at the end of 2003. Publication of *Insight* was discontinued with the final issue in 1999. At the board of directors meeting in March 2003 the board reviewed the Report of Findings of the Nurse Aide Practice Analysis that showed that nurses were not delegating to nurse aides, but were assigning tasks. These nurses did not view their role in this situation as delegation. Board members expressed concern about the use of assignment vs. delegation as it affected patient safety. The board asked the PR&E Committee to follow up in the process of developing regulations on delegation in the next year.[88]

The Registered Care Technologist

In addition to the impact of OBRA 87 on NCSBN and on the member boards in 1988, another item demanded a substantial amount of time and discussion for the nursing regulatory community as well as for the nursing organizations when the American Medical Association (AMA) published a proposal related to the supply of nurses. The *Newsletter to the Member Boards* dated April 15, 1988, included the following as an attachment:

AMA PROPOSED IMPLEMENTATION PLAN FOR NURSING EDUCATION
AND THE SUPPLY OF NURSING PERSONNEL IN THE UNITED STATES

A report outlining a proposed implementation plan for nursing education and the supply of nursing personnel in the United States was presented to the Board of Trustees of the American Medical Association in February. According to information received, the report has been distributed to State Medical Boards. It contained the following salient points:

1. Background statement which referred to the planned phasing out by nursing of hospital based bedside care programs (LPNs and Diploma nurses by 1992 and 1995 respectively);

2. Statement of concern about the shortage of bedside nurses, particularly LPNs in the long term care settings;

3. Description of program requirements, scope of practice and curriculum for the implementation of two new levels of bedside care personnel; with the program being offered through technical and community colleges in cooperation with hospitals and agencies;

4. Description of the scope of the two new levels "Registered Care Technologist (RCT) and Advanced Registered Care Technologist (RCT-Advanced)," who would be licensed at the registered level and certified at the advanced level, to be responsible for "the execution of medical protocols at the bedside with special emphasis on technical skills;"

5. Description of the care settings of RCTs: "care for the chronically ill and frail elderly and also the less critical patients in acute care settings;"

6. Description of the care settings of RCT-advanced: "care in all types of critical care units;"

7. Description of the licensing process as being implemented through state statutes;

8. Statement of support of efforts by nursing profession to recruit and retain nurses at the bedside and the belief that the RCT system is a "technical role" in contrast to "professional nursing care that is labeled as autonomous, managerial and holistic;" and

9. Statement that the RCT system will "assist business and administration to access interchangeable pools of bedside technologists and nurses for acute and long term facilities."

The report ends by recommending that the board of trustees of AMA approve the:

---

1. Organization of a task force of interested associations to solve the shortage of bedside care personnel;

2. Promotion of the development of educational programs for RCTs that can be accredited and certified;

3. Promotion of development of continuing educational programs for RCTs; and

4. Coordination of the programs of education for bedside care technologist with other associations affected by the shortage of personnel at the bedside.

The attachment continued with a statement that this brief analysis was being distributed to the member boards primarily for information and also to raise some thoughtful questions for consideration. It concluded by asking the member boards to be alert to any related initiatives within their states and asked for thoughts about (a) the impact the implementation of the proposed RCT roles could have on the practice of nursing in the individual states; and (b) the response to this report, if any, NCSBN should prepare.[89]

At its June 1988 meeting the board of directors discussed the "AMA Proposal on Development of the Registered Care Technologist Role" (AMA RCT Proposal). The board, in its discussion, raised questions about legal implications related to safe care. Carolyn Hutcherson of Georgia-RN, the Area III director, was asked to attend the AMA Panel of Nursing Consultants meeting on August 7 to 8, 1988.[90] In August the president reported that NCSBN had received a position on the AMA RCT Proposal from the National Association for Practical Nurse Education and Service (NAPNES).[91] The board directed that a concept paper from NCSBN be distributed at the annual meeting to the member boards, health-related organizations, and others, as requested.[92] The following is a summary of the concept paper titled "Response to the American Medical Association's Proposal on Development of the Registered Care Technologist Role (RCT)." In the introduction the reader learned that the AMA approved the plan at its house of delegates meeting in June. The proposal, as approved, was essentially as it was described in the "AMA Proposed Implementation Plan for Nursing Education and the Supply of Nursing Personnel in the United States" shown above. The plan was to be regulated by state boards of medicine, but the RCTs would be supervised by nurses. The paper looked at the relevance to boards of nursing and questions were raised regarding lines of authority, delegation of nursing functions, and disciplinary processes. The concept paper ended with the following conclusions:

1. The regulatory questions raised about lines of authority, delegation and discipline should be addressed carefully by any state legislature considering the implementation of the RCT role.

2. The regulatory questions about lines of authority, delegation and discipline clearly identify the nurse as legally vulnerable in choosing to or choosing not to supervise an enacted RCT role. Such vulnerability appears to place an undue legal burden on the nurse role and should be carefully evaluated by any state legislature considering the implementation of the RCT role.

3. The philosophical belief of the nursing community regarding the appropriateness of establishing the RCT role has no bearing on the reality that legislative bodies in each state have the ultimate authority for the establishment, regulation and supervision/delegation authority for any role deemed necessary or appropriate by that body. This reality provides the framework for any strategy for opposing the enactment of the RCT role.

4. The RCT role could significantly contribute to role confusion for the public about the difference between the RCT and the nurse; and if both roles will be enacting a similar role, it is unclear how establishing this role, when the general populace is not choosing the role of nurse currently, will assist with the nursing shortage. It is even feasible it will compete with the same population for recruitment into the nurse role.[93]

The delegate assembly adopted a resolution at the annual meeting in 1988 directing the following actions in response to the AMA RCT Proposal:

- That the National Council of State Boards of Nursing strongly oppose the AMA Registered Care Technologist Proposal; and

- That the National Council support all efforts in concert with its Member Boards and the nursing community to prevent its implementation; and

- That the National Council send the message of strong opposition to the RCT Proposal to the American Medical Association's Board of Directors; and

- That National Council's Delegate Assembly support working cooperatively with AMA's Advisory Nursing Consultant Panel to resolve the critical issues of the nursing shortage.[94]

The delegates urged that a copy of this resolution be widely disseminated by the member boards within their jurisdictions.

A *Newsletter to the Member Boards* in August 1989 included an article titled "Update on the RCT Proposal," which stated that Joan Bouchard of Oregon, vice president of NCSBN, had attended a meeting of the Panel of Nurse Consultants of the AMA and reported that the AMA Board of Trustees was directing the implementation of the RCT Proposal. The curriculum for the RCT nine-month program had been developed, and development of the advanced RCT program curriculum was in progress. There was a task force developing methods for evaluating the cost effectiveness and quality of care delivered by RCTs. Bouchard also reported that sites had been identified for demonstration projects. Questions raised by those in attendance at the meeting and responses given by representatives of the AMA included the following:

- Will AMA certify RCTs? The task force was looking at this question.
- Who will teach the program? A multidisciplinary team.
- Who will supervise the RCTs? Legal counsel was reviewing state practice acts.

The article concluded by stating that boards of nursing should expect to be the focus of much attention as the issue continued to be discussed and debated. Nursing organizations were expected to take a strong stand in opposition to the proposal. The AMA said that it was willing to allow for strong disagreement and that it would take whatever action was necessary to ensure the implementation of the demonstration projects.[95]

The nursing organizations did indeed convey messages of strong opposition to the AMA RCT Proposal. On the positive side, the issue united nurses and nursing organizations in a more cohesive way than any other single issue in many years. No one knows exactly what impact this unity in opposition had on the final outcome of the issue. However, at the June 1990 meeting of the AMA House of Delegates, the delegates took action to discontinue the RCT program. An article in *Issues* published soon after this action included two statements made at the AMA convention. Donna Miller of the AMA staff said, "AMA believes that the program increased the national awareness of the nurse shortage and helped stimulate new approaches to dealing with the problem." M. Ray Schwarz, senior vice president of Medical Education and Science for the AMA stated that "the AMA has not forgotten the nurse shortage issue."[96]

Conclusion

As NCSBN reacted to concerns about nursing assistive personnel, federal mandates to regulate nurse aides employed in facilities receiving Medicare and Medicaid funds, and delegation of nursing acts, the focus of the response continued to be consistent with the role if its member boards—to protect the health, safety, and welfare of the public.

CHAPTER THIRTEEN
ENFORCEMENT

The object of such legislation is unmistakable even to the most casual observer. It is for the protection of that great body we call the public, but it is especially designed as an aid to those not well favored by education or fortune or experience or knowledge. Its intent is to promote their welfare by securing to them the means of knowing to whom they may safely apply for skilled help in their extremity. It enables them to determine by the only feasible means who are the educated and intelligent nurses, and who are not; who are entitled to the trust that must of necessity be reposed in them, and who are not; who are true and may truly "walk in the light," and who are pretenders; who are deserving of esteem, and who are presumptuous and often woefully ignorant.

Mary M. Riddle, 1907[1]

GEORGIA MANNING, a member of the Louisiana State Board of Nursing-RN, wrote an article for *Issues* in 1995 titled "Surviving Disciplinary Hearings: A New Board Member's Primer." With this article, Manning presented to board members a thorough look at the gamut of emotions and the role change that occurs when a board member moves from being one of the "protected public" to a "protector of the public." The National Council of State Boards of Nursing, Inc. (NCSBN®) offered support to the member boards in their responsibility to impose sanctions on those licensees found to be in violation of provisions of the nursing practice act. Manning described her initial experience in a disciplinary hearing as follows: "I felt well prepared educationally and professionally to be a board member—until I sat in on the first disciplinary hearing. What I experienced that day left an indelible impression on my very being." After concluding the article with a reflection on the magnitude of the other matters that come before boards of nursing, she said, "Disciplinary hearings cause board members the most grief. It is ironic that the board members experience some of the same emotions as the licensees called before them."[2] Those who have served as either members or staff members to boards of nursing can, no doubt, identify with the words of this article.

Limited License

The first action related to discipline occurred at the meeting of the delegate assembly of NCSBN in 1979 when the delegates adopted a motion related to "limited licenses." The action required the board of directors to appoint an ad hoc committee to study the current statutory and regulatory provisions for a limited license, and the need for and conditions in which a limited license should be utilized, including situations involving handicaps and discipline, and to suggest procedures for initiating, verifying, and endorsing such a license.[3] The first report on the progress of the study was made to the board of directors in March 1981.[4] In June Lynne Illes of Iowa, chair of the Ad Hoc Committee to Research Limited License Provisions, reported to the delegate assembly that the committee had defined limited license as follows: "Limited license shall mean a license issued by the board to an individual to practice nursing in a restricted capacity, with the restrictions relating to the manner or the setting in which the new graduate or licensee may practice." Further, the committee recommended the adoption of guidelines to be used by each member board when considering the issuance of a limited license. These guidelines were included in the report as follows:

Basic essential standards must be met in each educational program; however, special adaptations may be made to accommodate specific behavioral objectives, provided that these adaptations correlate with reasonable modifications in the licensure examination procedure that can be instituted by the Board of Directors of the NCSBN.

The legal procedure within each jurisdiction for initiating limitations should be followed by the Board of Nursing, and should provide the applicant or licensee with due process.

All Boards of Nursing participate in reporting action taken to the Disciplinary Data Bank of the NCSBN.

Questions which will establish information regarding limited license should be included on the initial application for licensure, renewal application, and verification form.

Limited licensure provisions should be noted in some manner selected by the Board of Nursing on the license issued to the individual.

When limited licensure has been imposed on a licensee by one jurisdiction, the legal procedure within other jurisdictions for initiating the same or similar limitations should be followed by other jurisdictions in which the licensee is either licensed or seeking licensure by endorsement.[5]

The committee also reported on the results of a questionnaire regarding statutory and regulatory provisions for a limited license. The results showed that 12 member boards had statutory authority, 5 provided for limited licensure in administrative regulations, and 1 member board relied on case law or attorney general opinion for authority. Member boards made use of the limited license for discipline, continued licensure and specialty practice, and to permit practice while the applicant was taking a refresher course to regain a full license. Of the member boards using a limited license, 7 noted the limit on the license and 7 did not.[6] The delegate assembly referred the report of the committee to the Nursing Practice and Standards (NP&S) Committee for incorporation into the model nursing practice act (MNPA) and the model nursing rules and regulations (MNRR) that were in progress.[7]

The NP&S Committee incorporated a section on limited license into the proposed MNPA that was presented to the delegate assembly in 1982. The delegates adopted the MNPA at that meeting. The provision allowed a limited license to be used for applicants or licensees with a handicap or those who had been found guilty on any grounds for discipline. The provision also stated that the parameters of practice would be defined in writing and the limitation was to be noted on the license. In addition, the provision included suggested terms and conditions of limitation, and the consequence of compliance or noncompliance.[8]

An article in *Issues* in 1984 described the use of the limited license in Kentucky. Authors Kathleen Bellinger, board president, and Sharon Weisenbeck, executive director, discussed proposed regulations to provide for limited licenses. The regulations proposed the use of the limited license for two types of applicants for licenses: those with a physical or mental handicap that restricted or impaired their ability to practice the full scope of nursing and those subjected to disciplinary action by the board of nursing. The article provided an extensive and comprehensive review of the subject.[9]

NCSBN Disciplinary Data Bank

Early in the history of NCSBN the member boards and the board of directors identified the need for access to information about disciplinary action taken by the member boards. As seen in Chapter 10, nursing licensees often hold licenses in several states. In some instances licensees have been found to move from one state to another and have failed to report pending or completed disciplinary action to the new state. With this as background, in April 1980, the board of directors directed the staff to pursue the development of a data bank that would list the names and other information of licensees against whom the member boards had taken disciplinary action, to be maintained in the office, and to bring proposals to the board for action as soon as possible.[10] In June 1980 the board authorized the staff to implement the Disciplinary Data Bank (DDB) on September 1, 1980. The plan was to maintain a listing of the disciplinary actions taken by the member boards.[11] In her report to the delegate assembly in June 1981 Executive Director Eileen McQuaid Dvorak reported that 58 of 59 member boards were participating in the DDB, and that the information received had been compiled and reported monthly to the member boards since September 1980.[12] These reports have continued to provide information to the member boards since that time, although the format and availability have changed with changes in technology. The early reports used the nurse's name as the primary identifier and reporting resulted from the submission of written reports by the member boards on a voluntary basis. The member boards received the monthly report and searched them, looking for nurses licensed in their states who had been disciplined in another jurisdiction.

The board of directors decided in 1983 to release the DDB reports to the Council on Recertification of Nurse Anesthetists and to other certifying organizations, on request, provided the member boards would permit such dissemination. The board also asked the Finance Committee to develop criteria for release and to establish a subscription fee for the service.[13] Prior to this action the board had limited distribution of the DDB to the member boards and to appropriate federal agencies because of the variation among the jurisdictions related to public information.[14] NCSBN acquired the ability to enter and retrieve the data from its computers in 1984. A December 1984 *Newsletter to the Member Boards* reported that the conversion of 7,000 cumulative reports to the computer had been completed. The first computer-generated monthly DDB Report was distributed on December 24, 1984.[15]

National Practitioners' Data Bank

Executive Director McQuaid Dvorak briefed the board of directors in July 1988 on a request from the United States Department of Health and Human Services for a proposal to establish a national disciplinary data bank for health care providers. The board decided not to respond.[16] At a board meeting the following month Marsha Kelly, director of Public Policy Analysis, discussed the DDB and the implications of the recently enacted federal legislation to establish the National Practitioners' Data Bank (NPDB). At the same meeting Bruce Douglas from the Steering Committee of the Council on Licensure, Enforcement and Regulation (CLEAR), met with the board. He presented information on the intent of CLEAR to obtain a federal grant to implement the NPDB. The board agreed to recommend to the delegate assembly that it adopt a resolution in support of the proposal from CLEAR.[17] The delegates adopted the resolution in August.[18] A 1988 *Newsletter to the Member Boards* provided detailed information about the NPDB. One article noted that the Health Care Quality Improvement Act passed by Congress in 1986 established the specific requirements for reporting and releasing the information. The two areas of required reporting were payments made for the benefit of physicians, dentists and other health care practitioners as a result of medical malpractice actions and claims, and certain adverse actions taken regarding the licenses and clinical privileges of physicians and dentists. The reporting of adverse action on the licenses of nurses was to be implemented later.

Subsequently, in 1987 the act was amended to require mandatory reporting on all health care practitioners, including malpractice claims and adverse actions against clinical privileges and license status. The amendment also established fees to cover the cost of access to the information in the system, which led the NCSBN staff to study the impact of compliance with the law on the member boards.[19] A list of data to be deposited in the NPDB appeared in another article later in 1988. A partial list follows:

- Malpractice, disciplinary licensure data (medicine and dentistry only at that time); adverse clinical practice data, adverse membership data; (required from medical and dental societies, optional for others).

- Health care entities and societies must report to state medical and dental boards.

- Hospitals must query the NPDB every two years for staff members and at the time of negotiation for additions to the medical staff or when granting privileges.

- Licensing boards may query.

- All state boards of licensed health practitioners must eventually submit requisite data to the NPDB.[20]

The board of directors selected Marsha Kelly, from the staff of NCSBN, to serve on the Executive Committee and the Technical Advisory Group for the NPDB.[21] In 1990, when Kelly resigned from the staff, the board replaced her on the NPDB Executive Committee with Vickie Sheets, also a staff member.[22] In May the board of directors again discussed the DDB and the NPDB and decided to recommend that the delegate assembly decide whether NCSBN should be the agent of the member boards to report to the NPDB.[23] At the meeting of the delegate assembly in August the delegates did not take this action, but did adopt two motions related to the subject of disciplinary data. The first motion stated that the DDB would be maintained and converted to be consistent with the NPDB report forms. The second motion said that upon implementation of the NPDB for nursing licensure actions, member boards would be urged to send to NCSBN copies of the adverse licensure action forms submitted to the NPDB. In another action, the delegates directed the board of directors to implement a pilot study for access to the National Council Network (NCNET) for disciplinary data.[24] NCNET was an electronic network for member boards on which a variety of software services were delivered, including information related to testing.

The board of directors approved a timeline at its meeting in April 1991 for a project related to electronic access to the DDB to determine if and how the member boards could access the DDB through NCNET. The board also discussed fees for electronic access to the DDB.[25] The delegates adopted the recommendation from the board of directors that NCSBN provide computer linkage allowing member boards access to the NCSBN DDB.[26] Once again, the *Newsletter to the Member Boards* provided information about NCSBN activities and those of other groups. In February 1991 an article reported that the NPDB began operation on September 1, 1991. All required reports for physicians, dentists, and malpractice payments for all health care practitioners had been reported. In the first month there were more than 9,800 reports received and over 300,000 inquiries made.[27] In April a fact sheet on the NCSBN DDB was distributed as an attachment to the *Newsletter to the Member Boards*. According to the fact sheet, the fee schedule for member boards to access the DDB was stated as follows: For member boards per inquiry: first five—free; subsequent inquiries: mail/telephone—$5.50 per name, fax—$5 per name, NCNET—$4 per name and for a list of 10 or more names at once—$2 per name. The member boards were to be billed quarterly for these fees.[28]

At the August 1992 meeting of the delegate assembly, the delegates adopted a resolution to conduct a feasibility study to include nurse aide disciplinary information in a database such as the NCSBN DDB.[29] In April 1993 the board of directors reviewed a staff report on the possible nurse aide disciplinary database. The report included the results of a member board survey, a survey of other agencies, and the technical requirements and costs for such a database. Based on the report the board decided to recommend that a nurse aide disciplinary database not be developed at that time.[30] The delegate assembly agreed to the recommendation in August.[31]

Another interesting report in a 1992 *Newsletter to the Member Boards* discussed a survey of the member boards regarding the NPDB. The member boards had begun to receive reports of malpractice payments to patients on claims against nurses. The staff of the NPDB said "not many nurse malpractice payments were reported." The NCSBN staff conducted a survey of the member boards about these reports. It was noted that in the responses from 45 member boards, 29 received one or more reports. The member boards had taken a variety of actions in response to receipt of the reports including investigation, referral to legal counsel or another department, opening a file and waiting, and filing the reports.[32]

In 1994 the board of directors authorized the staff to explore and prepare a plan for expanded access to the NCSBN DDB in response to a request from the American Nurses Credentialing Center.[33] Of the 62 member boards, 53 were reporting to the DDB in January 1994. The member boards that were not reporting at that time were the District of Columbia, Guam, Hawaii, Louisiana-PN, Massachusetts, the Northern Marianas, Puerto Rico, Utah, and the Virgin Islands.[34] In July 1995 the board of directors considered a staff plan for expanded access to the DDB and reaffirmed the 1983 board action to approve dissemination of disciplinary data reports to certifying organizations whose certification was required by states as a condition for practice. The board then adopted a detailed plan for increased access to the DDB and authorized staff to obtain formal authorization for expanded access to the DDB information from each member board, to promote the service among APRN certification agencies, and to implement the approved services.[35]

A *Newsletter to the Member Boards* in November 1996 reported that the NCSBN staff participated in a conference call with representatives of the Health Resources and Service Administration (HRSA) to discuss progress on issues of common concern and possible collaboration between the NPDB and NCSBN. The NPDB was expected to require the reporting of disciplinary actions of "other health care providers" in the near future, including nurses as specified in Section 5 of the Health Care Quality Improvement Act that established the NPDB. NCSBN was prepared to assist with a variety of activities in preparation for beginning this aspect of reporting to the NPDB.[36]

Health Integrity and Protection Data Bank

The year 1997 brought several actions related to disciplinary reporting. In March the board of directors endorsed preparation and publication of an *Emerging Issues* dedicated to the NPDB and the Fraud and Abuse Data Bank.[37] The Fraud and Abuse Data Bank was another provision in federal law that required the reporting of fraud and abuse incidents by licensees to a national bank. Later in June the board of directors decided to forward to the delegate assembly a resolution requiring that NCSBN serve as an agent on behalf of the member boards for reporting disciplinary actions to the NPDB.[38] At the board meeting in August Vickie Sheets reported on the status of the DDB and the current rules for the NPDB and the Healthcare Integrity and Protection Data Bank (HIPDB), known previously as the Fraud and Abuse Data Bank. The board gave direction that NCSBN provide the service of generating lists of disciplinary actions from 1992 to present by state, at no charge to the member boards, to assist them in fulfilling the federal mandate for reporting actions dating starting January 1, 1992.[39] The delegate assembly adopted the resolution to "empower the NCSBN to act as reporting and querying agent for the Member Boards to the NPDB and the HIPDB created by Congress."[40] At the annual meeting in 1997, the Report of the Disciplinary Data Bank Task Force was presented by Dorothy Fulton of Alaska, who was chair of the task force, with Sheets serving as staff. The task force determined that the DDB should be maintained regardless of the status of the NPDB and HIPDB.[41]

A March 1997 issue of the *Newsletter to the Member Boards* provided up-to-date information about the NPDB. The pending federal rules to implement Section 5 were still in development. These rules would set the requirements for reporting disciplinary actions against health care practitioners in addition to physicians and dentists. Boards of nursing would be required to report to the NPDB in order to meet the requirements of Section 5. The directive for the federal Fraud and Abuse Data Bank was also in process. The purpose was to establish data collections for reporting final adverse actions including civil judgments, criminal convictions, adverse licensure, and certification actions; other negative actions or findings; federal and state exclusions, and those sanctions required by the Health Care Financing Administration (HCFA). The expectation was that the required reporting would be accomplished with reports to the NPDB.[42] An article a 1998 *Newsletter to the Member Boards* reported additional information about the HIPDB. The proposed rules had been reviewed by the DDB Advisory Committee, and the stated purpose of the HIPDB was to provide a resource to assist in the prevention and tracking of health care fraud and abuse. This database was broader in scope than the NPDB. The DDB Advisory Committee was identifying comments on the proposed rules to be submitted by NCSBN, and asked for comments from the member boards.[43]

At the June 1999 board of directors meeting Sheets and Legal Counsel Thomas Abram reviewed issues surrounding the HIPDB. The member boards were notified that historical disciplinary data (legacy data) must be completed by August 30, 1999, and that ongoing reporting would begin on October 1, 1999.[44] The board of directors discussed the advantages and potential liabilities of having NCSBN assume an agent role for the member boards. The board also talked about whether the activity would be a member board service or if a charge would be made. The board decided that NCSBN should assume the agent role for member boards in reporting legacy data to the NPDB and HIPDB and continue to explore other issues. This decision was conveyed to the member boards and to the HRSA. The board also agreed to discuss the issue further with the member boards at the delegate assembly meeting. Later in June Dr. Vivian Chen from HRSA met with the board and discussed HIPDB, the federal mandates, and expectations. The large majority of the member boards had expressed interest in having NCSBN serve as the agent for reporting.[45] In July the board of directors approved the language for the contract with the member boards for reporting the HIPDB legacy data.[46] In October the board of directors agreed that NCSBN would continue to serve as the agent for the member boards for ongoing reporting and/or inquiry for the NPDB/HIPDB for registered nurses (RNs), licensed practical/vocational nurses (LPN/VNs), advanced practice registered nurses (APRNs), and nurse aides.[47] The board of directors further discussed the sharing of DDB information with other organizations. Abram informed the board that the policies governing data sharing must be based on the principle that data are shared only as authorized by the member board providing the data. The board of directors asked staff to update the contracts with the member boards to obtain specific authorization regarding the sharing of disciplinary information with certification agencies.[48] In December the board of directors accepted a draft contract for the member boards to authorize NCSBN to act as the agent for mandated reporting to the HIPDB/NPDB. NCSBN would report on RNs, APRNs, LPN/VNs, and nurse aides in the jurisdictions where the member boards maintained the nurse aide registry without additional fees for the term of the contract. NCSBN also agreed to serve as the agent for reporting information on other health providers regulated by the member boards at a fee to be determined.[49] The reporting of the legacy data was completed by the end of February 2000.[50]

The *NCSBN Business Book* for the annual meeting in 2001 contained the Report on Agent Role—Health Integrity and Protection Data Bank Reporting. The report stated that the majority of the member boards were reporting data to Nur*sys*®, and ongoing reporting by NCSBN to the HIPDB had begun and was continuing. Other information of interest in this report included the following:

- Four member boards had no discipline entries on Nursys or the DDB. These were the member boards of the Northern Marianas, American Samoa, Puerto Rico, and the Virgin Islands. The NCSBN staff understood that no disciplinary action had been taken.

- Twelve member boards had not entered data or submitted written reports for Nursys. These were Alabama, the District of Columbia, Georgia-PN, Guam, Hawaii, Kansas, Illinois, Indiana, Louisiana-PN, Montana, New Hampshire, and New York.

- There were twenty-nine member boards with ongoing HIPDB Reporting Agreements.

The report closed with a complete chronology of the work of NCSBN on disciplinary data from 1980 to 2001.[51] At the board of directors meeting in September 2003 the board discussed collecting disciplinary data on nursing assistive personnel and deferred the activity until such time as it would become feasible.[52]

Imposters

As NCSBN expanded its activities, efforts increased to meet the needs of the member boards in the area of discipline. When Kathleen Dwyer of Rhode Island, the Area IV director, made her report to the delegate assembly in 1981 she included a reference to action taken at the Area IV meeting that year. This action requested NCSBN to support the efforts of the member boards to secure funding to deal with unprofessional conduct, to have a data bank on "nurse imposters," and to hold a national conference on unprofessional conduct and disciplinary action against licensed nurses.[53] The term "nurse imposter" has been used to describe an individual who is unlicensed but is pretending to be a licensed RN or LPN/VN. Most member boards have had interesting experiences with imposters over the years and a number of issues of the *Newsletter to the Member Boards* contained information about imposters. One of the earliest references to an imposter was reported in the *American Journal of Nursing*, which cited an issue of the *Pacific Coast Journal of Nursing* in 1929 as follows: "A person using the credentials of a registered nurse represented herself as a registered nurse when, in fact, she was not. She was arrested and arraigned in San Diego and at trial she pled guilty and was fined $100."[54]

An article in the January 2003 *Council Connector* reported on the first conference call arranged by the Disciplinary Resources Task Force, held in December 2002. The conference call included 65 disciplinary professionals from 25 member boards. Items discussed included an increase in imposter cases ranging from LPN/VNs forging licenses to reflect RN status to individuals who presented fraudulent records to obtain licenses. The group also discussed cases involving the diversion of drugs by nurses and the increasing use of methadone by licensees.[55]

Assisting Member Boards with Disciplinary Procedures

In December 1983 the board of directors discussed discipline as a function of the member boards. The board decided to establish a task force of five members to propose methods for NCSBN to assist the member boards in fulfilling their responsibilities in regard to disciplinary action.[56] At the annual meeting in August there was a program session titled "Protecting the Public: The Role of the Board in Disciplinary Procedures."[57] The 1983 *NCSBN Book of Reports* included a report of a review of the objectives and strategies of NCSBN. Several areas of further study were identified, including disciplinary action with attention to the definition of unprofessional conduct, effectiveness of probation, reporting of colleagues, reinstatement of licenses, and impaired nurses.[58]

The Disciplinary Task Force, chaired by Vivian DeBack of Wisconsin, made a report to the board of directors in 1984 describing the activities for the past year including a model disciplinary procedure and flow chart for the disciplinary action procedure. The board referred these documents back to the task force, approved the plan to hold workshop with a model disciplinary hearing, and approved the task force's recommendation to conduct a survey of the member boards regarding their use of the DDB.[59] At the annual meeting in August the Disciplinary Task Force presented its report to those present. The task force had continued to work on a model disciplinary procedure, developed a workshop to be held in 1985, and examined other ways to assist the member boards with their discipline-related responsibilities.[60] At the same meeting the delegates adopted a resolution that encouraged NCSBN to continue to expand its services to the member boards in the area of disciplinary issues.[61]

Phyllis Sheridan of Idaho was chair of the Disciplinary Task Force in 1985 when the task force completed a second draft of the model disciplinary procedures.[62] In April 1986 the board of directors reviewed the work of the task force including the model guidelines for disciplinary procedures and the accompanying flow chart, which would be presented in the *NCSBN Book of Reports* for the annual meeting. In addition, the board authorized the compilation and maintenance of a list of current references related to disciplinary procedures of regulatory boards. The board also directed that the development of standards for disciplinary actions and guidelines for rehabilitation of impaired nurses be referred to the NP&S Committee. Finally the board directed that any guidelines developed by member boards for handling the impaired nurse or for selecting types of disciplinary action appropriate for certain violations be submitted with the annual report data.[63] The Report of the Disciplinary Task Force in the 1986 *NCSBN Book of Reports* reflected a busy year for the group. Activities included those mentioned above as well as the completion of the "Model Guidelines for Disciplinary Process and Flow Chart." The report restated the basic premise of the task force: "Professional misconduct, incompetence and illegal nursing practice should be reported to the appropriate regulatory agency in order to protect the health, safety and welfare of the public." Other influences that impacted the charge to the task force during its existence included the following:

- The "Analysis of Membership Needs Study" by Touche Ross.
- DDB Research Project conducted by Elliott and Heins of the Tennessee Board of Nursing.
- Work of the NP&S Committee on issues related to the impaired nurse.
- Increased number of national and regional conferences dealing with the disciplinary responsibilities of regulatory boards.

The key steps in the procedure contained in the model guidelines, as accepted by the board of directors, were the following: reporting, investigation, formulation of charges and notice of hearing, hearing, administrative adjudication, notification of action, appeal, follow-through, and final action. The Disciplinary Task Force completed its work at the close of the annual meeting in 1986.[64] One of the programs at that meeting was entitled "Disciplinary Issues: Defining Unprofessional Conduct." The presenter was Mary Snyder of Boston, Massachusetts.[65]

At the 1993 annual meeting the delegates adopted a resolution calling for NCSBN to develop a nursing practice disciplinary case analysis example in a single practice area to present to the delegate assembly in 1994. The resolution also asked that the work include recommendations, with cost analyses, for further disciplinary case analyses that could be available for member board review and use in investigative and adjudicative processes. In another resolution the delegates asked that NCSBN conduct a pilot study focusing on collaboration among individuals in nursing education, service, and regulation to identify strategies for prevention of common nursing practice deficiencies.[66] Over the years that *Issues* was published, there were often articles about studies and other activities of individual boards of nursing related to the discipline process from reporting and investigation through to adjudication.

As a result of the resolutions above, the Disciplinary Case Analysis Process Focus Group, chaired by Harriet Johnson of New Jersey, reported in 1994 that it had developed a Disciplinary Process Flow Sheet and Criteria. This was an extension of the 1986 flow chart. The delegates adopted a motion that the Disciplinary Flow Sheet and Criteria be promoted as a resource for new board members and staff and as a framework for analysis that the member boards could use with their disciplinary cases. *(see fig. 13-A)* The delegates adopted a recommendation from the board of directors that resulted from the work of the Literature Review Focus Group as follows: that NCSBN conduct a survey of disciplinary issues on member board actions, decisions, positions, and opinions on the six issues identified by the focus group and to request information on the common practice issues that bring nurses to their boards for disciplinary action. The six issues were dishonesty/ethics, abandonment, abuse (physical/verbal), sexual misconduct, psychiatric disorders, and practice outside of scope.[67] The September 1994 *Newsletter to the Member Boards* reported that a study of the effectiveness of nurse disciplinary actions by boards of nursing had begun.[68] The following year an article in *Issues* provided more information about this study as follows:

With little available data on the effectiveness of licensee discipline and no comprehensive studies across jurisdictions that address disciplinary trends and the outcomes of selected remedies, the NCSBN sought funding for a study in this area. The Division of Quality Assurance, HRSA, United States Department of Health and Human Services, awarded a contract to NCSBN for the study. The NCSBN staff is performing the study in collaboration with the staff of the CAC [Citizens Advocacy Center]. The study examines the relationship between substantial charges against nurses and the disciplinary action taken against their licenses by boards of nursing, and evaluates the effectiveness of disciplinary interventions as they relate to remediation of nurse licensees.[69]

At the annual meeting in 1996 the delegate assembly adopted another resolution related to assistance for member boards in the area of disciplinary action. The resolution stated that NCSBN would develop resource modules that would assist the member boards in decisions involving chemical dependency and criminal/fraudulent behavior.[70] At the same meeting the Nursing Practice and Education (NP&E) Committee, chaired by Dula Pacquiao of New Jersey, reported to the board of directors on its recommendations, developed by the Complex Discipline Cases Subcommittee, chaired by Ann Torres of Arizona.71 This subcommittee report recommended that:

- two copies of the *Discipline Resources Notebook* containing information developed by the subcommittee be distributed to each member board and that the response to and use of the "notebook" be reviewed in 1997.

- the Complex Discipline Survey be repeated in FY98.

- NCSBN explore how member boards' access to criminal records could be facilitated.

- NCSBN facilitate national reporting of disciplinary action.

- the revision of the *NCSBN Model Nursing Administrative Rules (MNAR)*, formerly the *NCSBN Model Nursing Rules and Regulations (MNRR)*, and the *NCSBN Model Nursing Practice Act (MNPA)* include suggestions for approaches to informal and alternative resolution of cases.

- NCSBN develop educational materials to assist member boards to educate nurses regarding the responsibility to report violations; to raise public awareness of the purpose and role of nursing regulation; and to assist consumers in reporting to boards of nursing.[72]

A "Day of Discipline," an educational program, preceded the annual meeting in 1996. The content of the program included setting complaint/case priorities; time management strategies; the informal process for case resolution; and financing, including the use of fines and recovery of costs. The program also included a session on sexual misconduct cases.[73]

In 1997 the Disciplinary Modules Task Force, chaired by Nan Twigg of New Mexico, reported that it had asked the board of directors to approve the task force plan for a chemical dependency module and to authorize continued work on the criminal/fraudulent behavior module. These modules were to be available for the education of member board staff and others.[74]

The delegate assembly adopted a policy recommendation from the NP&E Committee in 1998 that would require the member boards to conduct criminal background checks on applicants for nursing licensure.[75] In another action related to public protection, the delegates adopted a resolution to endorse the protocol that nursing personnel clearly display on their employment identification badges their licensing credential.[76] The same meeting included two educational sessions entitled "Dialogue on Discipline" and "Dialogue on Impaired Practice."[77] The Report of the Discipline Resources Subcommittee, presented by Chair Jane Werth of Arizona, included information on the *Criminal Behavior Handbook*" for boards of nursing developed by the subcommittee. The report also included a supporting paper, "Criminal Convictions and Nursing Regulations," by Gregory M. Cooper, Chief of the Provo, Utah Police Department, and Vickie R. Sheets, NCSBN staff.[78]

Later in 1999 the *Study of Effectiveness of Nursing Discipline* was included in an attachment to the *Newsletter to the Member Boards.* Also included was an article from the CAC's *News and Views* titled "Boards of Nursing Releases *Study of Effectiveness of Disciplinary Actions of Nursing*," which stated that the primary goal of the study was to take a first step toward determining the effectiveness of disciplinary actions imposed by boards of nursing. The study included the development of a disciplinary grounds and a disciplinary actions lexicon based on a content analysis of statutes and administrative law documents. The methodology and findings along with areas of possible future research were also included in the report. The report stated that actions by boards of nursing "resulted in the encumbrance or loss of license in over seventy percent of all cases included in the study." In an editorial note the CAC commented that it "finds the NCSBN study to be of great importance." Other comments included: "The study should help all licensing boards—not just boards of nursing—evaluate their disciplinary programs and show them the value of recording and analyzing data about the impact of their disciplinary interventions." The CAC went on to say, "the findings of the study confirm what many observers have noted—nursing boards are more willing than many other professional boards to hand out tough punishments."[79]

Taxonomy of Error Root Cause Analysis and Practice Responsibility

The Disciplinary Issues Task Force, chaired by Patricia Uris of Colorado, presented an extensive report in the *NCSBN Business Book* for the annual meeting in 2000. Earlier the board of directors had directed the task force to develop new knowledge about the causes of nursing practice breakdown. This study, conducted by the task force, built on the findings of the *Study of Effectiveness of Nursing Discipline.* The task force proposed delving deeper into the factual content of cases by using more complete information obtained from a variety of materials ranging from the initial complaint to witness statements, investigatory reports, hearing transcripts, and staff interviews. Such a study could be considered a root cause analysis of the cases in order to determine whether there are particular elements that could identify nurses at risk. Nurse and patient identifiers in the cases used in the pilot study were redacted. The aim of the pilot study was to determine if sufficient information was available in reports of disciplinary cases to conduct a phenomenological study.[80]

In 2001 the Report of the Practice Breakdown Research Advisory Task Force discussed the collection and analysis of documents and the phenomenological methodology used to discover individual and workplace factors associated with each instance of practice breakdown. The data from the analysis of the first 12 cases resulting from the study were used to develop an audit instrument—The Taxonomy of Error Root Cause Analysis and Practice Responsibility (TERCAP). Subsequently, 24 cases were analyzed using TERCAP. A grant application was submitted for funding for further study and the task force developed an outline for a monograph based on the pilot case studies.[81]

At a 2002 board of directors meeting the board approved the Discipline Resource Plan and agreed to appoint a Discipline Task Force for FY03–FY04 to assist in its implementation.[82] In the Annual Progress Report on the achievement of strategic initiatives, the research study, *An Epidemiology of Nursing Error,* was discussed and the following achievements were listed:

- Six states had entered into participation agreements for study and eleven more were interested.

- TERCAP Coding Protocol was completed.

- A training workshop was held for fifteen participating member boards.[83]

The Report of the Discipline Curriculum Advisory Panel, chaired by Valerie Smith of Arizona, reported on the development and preparation for implementation of a plan to update and create information in several categories including disciplinary resources, communication/networking, consultation/collaboration, and education/training. The plan included proposals for written, electronic, and interactive resources. There were also plans for increased opportunities for member board staff and attorney networking, consulting, and methods of collaborating with other organizations.[84]

In 2003 the board of directors continued the Disciplinary Resources Task Force for the purpose of implementing the Disciplinary Resources Plan, and agreed to ask the Bylaws Committee to explore making the task force a standing committee.[85] Later in the year the decision was made to continue the Practice Breakdown Focus Group for a year and to expand it to seven members. The board charged the expanded focus group to do the following:

- Develop plans for and promote the use of the TERCAP as a data collection strategy for boards of nursing.

- Continue the consulting services of Dr. Patricia Benner for project continuity and her expertise related to competence.

- Work with a subgroup of the focus group to complete the qualitative analysis of the 106 nursing narratives portion of TERCAP collected for the *Epidemiology Study of Nursing Error*.

- Publish the TERCAP tool and coding protocol.

- Work with a freelance writer to finish the planned monograph, *Lessons from Boards*.

- Explore the use of TERCAP by health care facilities to further collect risk factors for practice breakdown.

- Make recommendations for a more extensive epidemiological study.[86]

The *NCSBN Business Book* for the 2003 annual meeting included the Report of the Disciplinary Resources Task Force. Chair Uris listed committee activities in the following three categories:

- Disciplinary Resources—developed additional resources and commented on the discipline lexicon developed by staff.

- Communication/Networking—gave guidance to developing discipline staff/attorney networking, began quarterly discipline conference calls, and gave advice regarding tracking and analysis of multistate disciplinary cases.

- Consultation/Collaboration—discussed possible collaboration with the Federations of Associations of Regulatory Boards.[87]

In other related activity, the Practice Breakdown Research Focus Group, chaired by Patricia Uris, reported on its activities in the 2003 *NCSBN Business Book*. The group, formerly known as a task force and then a focus group, reviewed study findings, provided expert analysis of data, and reviewed the usefulness of the TERCAP instrument for data collection. The report stated that 14 member boards collected data on 10 to 20 cases each. The epidemiological methodology was determined to be appropriate when identifying causes of error and searching for disease determinants. Disease determinants were defined as "the risk factors or antecedent events that are associated with the appearance of a disease or condition (error)." The study provided comprehensive data related to the study of person, place, and time.[88]

Reports to Boards of Nursing by Federal Employers

Another discipline issue of concern to the member boards surfaced in 1982. The delegate assembly adopted two motions related to the receipt of information by boards of nursing about nurses employed in the federal government. The first motion was to request the board of directors to establish a Joint Military/Civilian Nursing Practice Committee to address the issue of loopholes in the military reporting of discipline action. The motion also specified that the NCSBN members of the committee should include both RNs and LPN/VNs, and NCSBN should invite the federal services to appoint members representing the military and other agencies. The second motion asked that the federal nursing leaders be asked to contribute to the NCSBN DDB in relation to discipline for unprofessional conduct and/or drug abuse among licensed nurses employed by federal agencies.[89] The majority of member boards had an exemption clause similar to that found in the 1982 *MNPA*, Article XII: Exemptions, which read as follows:

> No provision of this Act shall be construed to prohibit…the practice of any currently registered nurse or licensed practical nurse of another state who is employed by the Untied States government, or any bureau, division, or agency thereof while in the discharge of official duties.[90]

However, very few, if any, of the federal agencies that employed licensed nurses reported incidents that might require investigation and possible action by the member boards of the state where the nurse was licensed.

The 1983 *NCSBN Book of Reports* contains the Report of the Committee on Disciplinary Case Reporting by Federal Agencies. Ann Petersen of Utah was chair of this committee, which met with representatives from the Veterans Administration (VA), the United States Public Health Service (USPHS), and the Army Nurse Corps (ANC). The USPHS supported the concept of local reporting and a memorandum of support was to be sent to the chief nurse at various installations. Additionally, the Office of Personnel Management of the United States Department of Health and Human Services had a policy that a current license was not required for practice by nurses not engaged in direct patient care. The VA suggested that boards of nursing request necessary information directly from the VA Hospitals. The ANC representative attended the meeting on behalf of the Military Services, and reported that the Military Services had their own substance abuse prevention and treatment program. The Military Services reported physicians to the Federation of State Medical Boards DDB and indicated a willingness to consider the same for nurses. NCSBN subsequently contacted the Department of Defense urging the addition of regulation specific to nurses and expressing its willingness to share the information in the NCSBN DDB provided the Defense Department reciprocated. No further meetings were planned.[91] At the annual meeting in 1983 the delegates adopted the following resolution:

> That the United States Federal Government, and any subdivision of said government, institute a requirement that all nurses employed by said government and its subdivisions must hold valid and current licenses issued by legally recognized state jurisdictions empowered to regulate nurses and nursing practice.[92]

In 1984 the Committee on Disciplinary Case Reporting by Federal Agencies stated that it was continuing to work with the Defense Department to develop regulation requiring the reporting of discipline by the branches of the Military Services.[93]

Enforcement and the Chemically Dependent Nurse

The first mention of chemical dependency found in the documents of NCSBN appeared in a *Newsletter to the Member Boards* in 1983. An article announced a seminar in California titled "Interdisciplinary Approaches to the Issues of the Chemically Dependent Nurses."[94] In addition to the increasing number of drug-related discipline cases faced by the member boards, several states were beginning to explore alternatives to discipline in resolving and, when possible, preventing these cases from coming to the member boards. Part of the impetus for these alternative programs came from the state nursing associations following discussions and concerns raised at meetings of the American Nurses Association (ANA) and other organizations. Delegates at the 1984 NCSBN Annual Meeting heard a discussion of alternative programs in Georgia and Kentucky when Evelyn Polk from the Georgia-RN Board of Nursing and Melva Jo Hendrix from the University of Kentucky presented information on their respective programs designed to aid nurses impaired through substance abuse.[95] The same year the board of directors approved a request for $2,700 to fund a descriptive study of disciplinary action involving nurses from the NCSBN DDB. The majority of the actions taken by member boards related to substance abuse. The principal investigators, both from the Tennessee Board of Nursing, were Ruth Elliott, executive director, and Margaret Heins, president.[96] In August 1985 the board of directors received the preliminary report of the study,[97] and at a program session at the annual meeting, Heins discussed an analysis of actions taken by the Tennessee Board of Nursing between 1976 and 1984 and data from the study of the NCSBN DDB.[98] The study was published as *The NCSBN, Inc., Disciplinary Data Bank: A Longitudinal Study.*

Chaired by Therese Sullivan of Montana, the NP&S Committee began a study in 1985 of the role of boards of nursing in their responsibility to protect the public health, safety, and welfare in relation to the impaired nurse. The committee was also working on guidelines to assist the member boards as they dealt with cases involving the impaired nurse.[99]

Sister Lucie Leonard, the nursing practice consultant for the Louisiana-RN Board of Nursing, wrote an article for *Issues* in 1986 in which she described the Louisiana Network for Impaired Professionals, which was established through a memorandum of agreement between the board of nursing and the Louisiana State Nurses Association. Leonard said,

> A formal agreement between the professional association and the regulatory agency…seems to be an effective method for protecting the public…while permitting an RN to maintain licensure and pursue treatment for the disease of chemical addiction. The safety of the public is further enhanced by the vigilance of both the association and the agency.[100]

At the annual meeting in 1987 the delegate assembly approved a monograph developed by the NP&S Committee entitled *The Regulatory Management of the Chemically Dependent Nurse.*[101] The monograph was used extensively as a reference by states looking for effective ways to manage a growing problem. The NP&S Committee listed as contributing authors to this monograph Sister Lucie Leonard of Louisiana-RN, Chair Elnora Daniel of Virginia, Judy Gillium of New Mexico, Joann Griffin of New York, Rena Lawrence of Pennsylvania, and Ann Mowry of Iowa. Marsha Kelly, the staff member assigned to the committee, was also listed as a contributing author. The major chapter headings included in the monograph are the following:

- Chemical Dependence
- Legal Implications Related to Chemically Dependent Nurses
- Philosophical Differences between the Disciplinary Approach and Preventive Approach
- Methods of Treatment for the Chemically Dependent Nurse

The Conclusions and Recommendations from the monograph are listed below:

Conclusions:

1. Chemical dependence is a phenomenon with multiple causative factors.

2. The primary theory for chemical dependence currently is the disease of addiction theory, which is based on the general genetic theory.

3. Chemical dependence is a progressively declining process beginning with drug use, evolving into misuse and abuse and finally dependence.

4. Charges of addiction to alcohol and drugs, or misuse or abuse of the same, must be related to the practice of nursing unless the statute provides specifically that addiction or misuse are violations of the statute in and of themselves.

5. The public has a right to expect protection from harm by the police power of the state, from nurses who are impaired due to chemical misuse or dependence.

6. The nurse has a property right of continued licensure, the right to freedom from invasion of privacy, the right to seek employment in another state and the right to due process when allegations are brought against the nurse.

7. Personal rights of the nurse are negated when the actions of the nurse place the public welfare at risk.

8. The preventive approach to chemical dependence among nurses is based on the rationale that chemical dependence is a process which can be prevented as well as treated.

9. A combination of the preventive and disciplinary models for action by boards of nursing in dealing with the chemically dependent nurse can provide for public protection while having a rehabilitative impact on the chemically dependent nurse.

10. The effects of the different treatment modalities for chemical dependence vary greatly with their predictability of success.

11. Treatment programs (both inpatient and outpatient), though not totally predictable in success, have more positive than negative effect.

12. Abstinence as a treatment modality is based on the belief that chemical dependence is a progressive and potentially fatal disorder that cannot be modified except by total abstinence from mind-altering substances.

13. Recovery for the dependent person can include periods of relapse.

14. Continued treatment, after initial treatment for chemical dependence assists in long term success.

15. Alcoholics Anonymous, because of its widespread availability, its applicability to drug dependencies other than alcohol, and because of its lack of cost, is ideal for continued care for any person recovering from chemical dependence.

16. The nurse recovering from the process of chemical dependence should not be allowed to take on a therapeutic role with other chemically dependent nurses for a significant period of time following the beginning of the recovery process.

17. The selection of a treatment program to be required of nurses facing discipline should be determined by the likelihood for successful recovery rather than cost.

18. Continued employment in nursing by the chemically dependent nurse can have a therapeutic effect on the recovery state of the nurse.

19. Recidivism endangers the public health, safety and welfare, and increases the cost to the chemically dependent nurse, to the board of nursing and ultimately to the public.

Recommendations:

1. Pursuant to the responsibility of the board in implementing the discipline function, boards of nursing should thoroughly educate themselves in theories of treatment, the characteristic

behavior patterns of the chemically dependent nurse, and the expected outcomes of any required screening test or treatment modality as required of the chemically dependent nurse in disciplinary actions.

2. Boards of nursing should develop a written philosophy, based on a conceptual framework of chemical dependence, to use in implementing discipline management plans for chemically dependent nurses.

3. Boards need to consider the following criteria to decide when discipline should be initiated: a) the nurse is a risk to the public or to herself; and b) the nurse poses a threat to the public's health, safety and welfare.

4. Boards of nursing should use limited licensure and probation with stipulations only with nurses who are in the recovery stage of dependence.

5. Boards of nursing should allow nurses to continue active employment if the public's health, safety and welfare are not a risk.

6. When dealing with the chemically dependent nurse, boards should explore disciplinary models.[102]

In 1988 the delegate assembly adopted a motion that asked the NP&S Committee to develop a research proposal to be submitted to an outside agency for funding to study the effectiveness and cost implications of the various regulatory models of intervention presented in the monograph cited above.[103] Lois Scibetta of Kansas was appointed to chair the Subcommittee to Study Regulatory Models for Chemically Dependent Nurses, but was replaced by Melinda Sanders of Missouri in 1989 following Scibetta's resignation from her position with the Kansas Board of Nursing. The *NCSBN Book of Reports* for the 1989 annual meeting included the report of this subcommittee, which stated that there had never been a comparative study to determine which of the various approaches was more successful in terms of the rehabilitation of nurses, their return to work, recidivism rates, and cost. The list of activities of the subcommittee included the following:

• Searching for funding.

• Identifying a theoretical framework for the study.

• Identifying types of regulatory models to include in the study.

• Determining the need for a member board survey to learn the types of approaches in use.

• Developing the mechanism for identification of the population to be studied.

• Identifying relevant data collection instruments to be reviewed.

• Determining that the study participants should be followed for two years.

• Deciding that, in order to obtain full cooperation, there was a need to subcontract data collection to an outside group or in collaboration with another group, e.g., a university, research center or other.

The NCSBN staff member assigned to the subcommittee was Carolyn Yocom, and Mary Haack from the National Institute of Alcohol Abuse served as a consultant.[104]

In November 1989 the subcommittee asked the board of directors to consider funding for a pilot study to examine the co-occurrence of chemical dependency and psychiatric disorders in nurses. This study was needed to support a funding request to the federal government for the larger study. The board directed that an inquiry be sent to the member boards to determine if they were willing to share such data on dual diagnoses as an alternate to a pilot study.[105] At its next meeting the board of directors approved the expenditure of $10,800 during FY90 to conduct the pilot study.[106] In the next several years numerous attempts were made to obtain external funding for this study.

The delegate assembly adopted a resolution at the 1989 annual meeting to study the issues and concerns involved in the referral of nurses involved in peer assistance programs from one jurisdiction to another.[107] In 1990 the delegates approved the *Statement on Endorsement Issues related to Peer Assistance Alternative Programs*.[108]

When the Subcommittee to Study Regulatory Models for Chemically Dependent Nurses made its report to the delegate assembly in 1993, Jean Sullivan of Washington-RN stated that funding for the study of regulatory models had still not been obtained. The members of the subcommittee believed the need for the study continued to exist. Further, it was believed that the study could be designed and implemented in a fiscally prudent manner that would address the member boards' information needs within the next three years. The subcommittee also identified other activities as follows:

- Development of model guidelines for a non-punitive regulatory approach.

- Presentation of comparative information about the cost to member boards of various regulatory approaches.

- Provision of assistance to member boards relative to collection, storage and retrieval and analysis of data about chemically dependent nurses under their jurisdiction for program evaluation within and across the member boards.[109]

In August, five years after the original resolution that led to the activities of the Subcommittee to Study Regulatory Models for Chemically Dependent Nurses, the board restructured the subcommittee as the independent Ad Hoc Committee on Chemical Dependency Issues. The charge to this committee was as follows:

1. Develop model guidelines for disciplinary diversion programs (FY94)

2. Conduct an internally funded research project to compare and evaluate the effectiveness of regulatory approaches for management of chemically dependent nurses. (FY95–96)

3. Facilitate Member Board data collection to promote ongoing internal (intraboard) program evaluation and cross program (interboard) comparisons and research (FY94–95)[110]

At its meeting in June 1994, the board of directors reviewed the Report of the Committee on Chemical Dependency Issues, which described its plan for a study of the regulatory management of chemically dependent nurses. After reviewing the 1988 action of the delegate assembly relative to the issue, the board directed that a recommendation should be presented to the delegate assembly in order to provide internal funding for the two year study.[111] The committee included its report in the *NCSBN Book of Reports* for the annual meeting in August. *The Model Guidelines: A Nondisciplinary Alternative Program for Impaired Nurses* was included with the report. The following is a description of the *Model Guidelines*, which was included in the report:

The *Guidelines*...were developed to provide information to Member Boards that are interested in implementing a nondisciplinary alternative program. A survey on regulatory management of chemically dependent nurses was conducted by the committee. Of the forty-four jurisdictions responding, twenty Member Boards reported that they were interested in establishing a nondisciplinary option.

The *Guidelines* provide a core model which is a composite of those alternative programs currently being implemented by Member Boards. According to the survey, fifteen Member Boards have alternative programs as defined by the committee. A nondisciplinary alternative program (i.e., diversion program) is defined by the committee as a "...voluntary confidential alternative to license discipline for nurses with chemical dependence. The nurses may also have accompanying psychiatric and/or physical conditions." The *Guidelines* may be adapted to meet the specific needs of individual Member Boards.[112]

The delegate assembly adopted the *Model Guidelines*.[113] These guidelines were a significant contribution by NCSBN to the member boards at a time when many were looking at alternative-to-discipline programs for impaired nurses. Assistance ranged from suggested legislation through policies to reporting and sample forms. Emphasis on monitoring, record keeping, and reporting was an essential aspect of the work.

The second major activity of the Committee on Chemical Dependency Issues in 1994 was to provide consultation to the staff in relation to the development of a research protocol designed to evaluate the effectiveness and costs of two different regulatory approaches for the management of chemically impaired nurses. Factors to be addressed in the two-year study included: (a) chemical dependence history; (b) physical, psychosocial, psychiatric and family history, and current status; (c) work history and current employment characteristics; (d) therapeutic interventions; and (e) regulatory approach (disciplinary vs. nondisciplinary). Outcome effectiveness was to be measured in terms of: (a) licensure status of the nurse, (b) recidivism rates, and (c) return to employment in nursing. Cost comparisons would be made to address the fiscal implications for member boards and the impaired nurse.[114] The delegate assembly adopted the recommendation that the board of directors provide funding for the study.[115] At its meeting on August 7, 1994, the board established a designated fund of $255,000 and authorized the expenditure of up to $130,000 in FY95 for the study.[116]

The Report of the Task Force on Chemical Dependency Issues, formerly a committee, in the 1995 *NCSBN Book of Reports*, described the task force's role in assisting staff to obtain member board participation in the study, A Comparison of Two Regulatory Approaches to the Management of Chemically Dependent Nurses. The member boards that agreed to take part in the study were the following:

Ohio, South Carolina, and Virginia: those using a disciplinary approach
Florida, Maryland, and Washington: those using a nondisciplinary approach

---

The task force expected data collection to be complete by the end of the year.[117] In 1996 the Chemically Impaired Nurse Issues Task Force reported that it had continued to work with the staff on the research study. In addition, the task force coordinated a conference titled "Alternatives to License Discipline Programs for Chemically Impaired Nurses." The conference, held in late winter, was designed for staff of alternative programs and representatives of member boards interested in establishing alternative programs. An interim report of the research project accompanied the task force report in 1996. The interim report was titled *A Comparison of Two Regulatory Approaches to the Management of Chemically Impaired Nurses*. The authors listed were Carolyn Yocom, director of Research Services for NCSBN, and Mary R. Haack, senior research scientist at the Center for Health Policy Research, George Washington University. The interim report shared selected findings in the areas of socio-demographic, licensure, and drug/alcohol use characteristics of chemically impaired nurses who have had disciplinary actions against their licenses or who are in alternative programs. In addition, the impact of two factors on the regulatory management approach—recidivism rate and retention in or return to the workforce—was discussed. Early information showed that recidivism rates were no higher for alternative program participants than for those in the disciplinary group. The retention in and/or return to employment in nursing was highest in the alternative program group.[118] NCSBN staff indicated that there was no final report of the study.

The Annual Progress Report October 2002–May 2003 found in the 2003 *NCSBN Business Book* included the following tactic: "to develop a plan and research methodology for study to evaluate effectiveness of alternative programs including the impact on member boards that do not have alternative programs."[119] Additional information about this tactic (method to achieve the initiative) appeared in a September 2003 *Council Connector* article. The article stated that a five-member team representing the member boards and supported by the NCSBN staff would conduct a new study on the regulatory oversight of chemically dependent nurses. The research questions listed in the article were as follows:

1. What elements of the process of regulating chemically dependent nurses are most effective in protecting the public?

2. How are alternative-to-discipline programs different than traditional discipline in monitoring practice during intervention/investigation, preparation of the nurse to return to practice and the type of follow-up conducted upon completion of the program/board action?[120]

In 1993 NCSBN developed a funding proposal for a study to evaluate the effectiveness of nurse disciplinary actions. The proposal was submitted to the Division of Quality Assurance, Health Services and Resources Administration of the United States Department of Health and Human Services. NCSBN received a $25,000 award for the study. The purposes of the study were as follows:

• Development of common classification systems and definitions for disciplinary actions.

• Comparison of types of actions taken against licensees in relation to the grounds, case characteristics and the disciplinary process used.

• Evaluation of the effectiveness of disciplinary actions.[121]

The Discipline Modules Task Force, chaired by Nan Twigg of New Mexico, described its activities in the 1997 *NCSBN Book of Reports* for the annual meeting. The members participated in the Second Annual Conference for Alternative Program Directors and revised the *Model Guidelines* on alternative programs included in the *Chemical Dependency Handbook for Boards of Nursing*. In other activity, the task force developed a brochure titled *Something's Not Right*, which addressed chemical dependency in health care professionals. There were two outlines attached to the task force report. The first was for a chemical dependency handbook for boards of nursing and the second was for a chemical dependency handbook with an intended audience of nurses, employers of nurses, and consumers.[122]

An article in a 2001 Council Connector reported that NCSBN had released a video on chemical dependency issues. Entitled *Breaking the Habit: When Your Colleague is Chemically Dependent*, the content focused on nurses working with chemically dependent colleagues. The material for the video was prepared by Vickie Sheets of the NCSBN staff, in consultation with Linda Smith from the Washington Intervention Project for Nurses and Jean Stevens, the former president of the Washington Nursing Commission.[123]

Educational Programs for Investigators

As early as 1965, representatives of boards of nursing recognized the need for educational opportunities for those involved in the discipline program. The following is an announcement of such an offering that year:

The "Legal Responsibility of Boards of Nursing Including Action on Disciplinary Problems" will be studied at the annual educational conference sponsored by the ANA Committee of State Boards of Nursing in San Francisco April 29–30. The Arizona Board of Nursing will present a mock hearing.

Other speakers include Grace C. Barbee, staff attorney of the CA Nurses Association and Kathleen Sward, director of the ANA Program on Nursing Practice.[124]

In 1993 the NCSBN Communications Committee, with Mary Howard of New Jersey as its chair, presented a recommendation that the board of directors determine the methodology to implement educational programs for discipline investigators that best meet the needs of the membership. The delegate assembly adopted the recommendation.[125] In December the board of directors appointed the Disciplinary Investigators Education Task Force. The charge to the task force was to collaborate with CLEAR to develop an educational program for nursing investigators. The program was planned as an add-on component to the CLEAR program for training investigators. On completion of the program, the participant would receive a certificate and continuing education units.[126] The board approved the contract with CLEAR early in 1994 to offer "Nursing/Health Investigators Instructional Module: Add-on to the National Certified Investigator Training (NCID)."[127]

The Task Force to Develop an Educational Program for Disciplinary Investigators, with Florence Stillman of Missouri as chair, reported in August that it had developed and planned the eight-hour instructional program specific to the investigation of health care practitioners. The pilot presentation of the program was scheduled for September 1994.[128] On September 29 and 30 in Boston, 30 participants participated in the "Specialized Health Care Investigators Program" in conjunction with the CLEAR conference. Pat Malloy of Rhode Island and Teresa Mullin of Virginia, members of the task force, were the primary faculty supported by Stillman and Sheets. The program was well received.[129] A second pilot presentation of the module was held in conjunction with the NCSBN Annual Meeting in August 1995.[130]

In 1999 NCSBN sponsored a program session at the annual meeting titled Dialogue on Discipline.[131] The 2001 *NCSBN Business Book* for the annual meeting contained a Report of the Board Investigators Curriculum Advisory Panel. Paula Meyer of Washington was chair of the advisory panel, which stated that its purpose was to identify learning needs and priorities of board investigators; plan an educational summit; and develop a sustainable, long range plan to meet the ongoing needs of the group. The advisory panel conducted a survey of need and developed the curriculum for a summit, which it planned and presented for the board investigators.[132] Held in June, the summit was so successful that the board of directors decided to hold another in 2002, and to develop a long-range plan for the education of investigators.[133] A summit attended by both attorneys and investigators, was held in 2002 and again in 2003.[134]

Sexual Misconduct by Licensees

NCSBN also responded to the needs expressed by the member boards related to sexual misconduct by licensees. In 1994 the delegate assembly adopted a resolution that asked NCSBN to study the issue of sexual misconduct as it related to nurses' practice and that a model be developed to assist member boards in making decisions regarding disciplinary action.[135] The Disciplinary Guidelines for Managing Sexual Misconduct Cases Focus Group was appointed, and Jean Stevens of Washington served as its chair. The first report of the focus group to the board of directors in 1995 resulted in the board authorizing the focus group to carry out its recommendations pertaining to the development of resource material for the member boards in FY96. The board of directors agreed to direct the implementation of the other recommendations from the focus group as stated below:

- Collaborative educational effort with professional organizations.

- Publicizing the availability of Focus Group members as expert resources.

- Offering the topic of disciplinary guidelines for sexual misconduct cases for the 1996 Regulatory Days of Dialogue.

The board also authorized that a prospective study of sexual misconduct cases for recidivism be conducted.[136] The Sexual Misconduct Focus Group reported in 1996 that the following recommendations had been presented to the board of directors:

---

1. That the NCSBN distribute to the Member Boards and promote the use of the educational packets developed to assist in raising awareness regarding professional boundaries and issues regarding professional sexual misconduct.

2. That the NCSBN produce a video addressing professional boundaries for use by Member Boards to orient new board members, staff, investigators, and attorneys and for use to educate students, nurses and the public.

The educational packet developed by the focus group was entitled *Preventing Sexual Misconduct: A Resource Packet for Boards of Nursing.*[137]

Conclusion

A significant number of representatives from the member boards, the staff of NCSBN, and various external consultants and organizations have collaborated to meet the identified needs of the member boards in the area of discipline. Beginning with attention to limited licenses, the efforts have looked beyond punitive actions to identify preventive or alternative actions that member boards may consider consistent with their duty to protect the public health, safety, and welfare. Perhaps one of the most difficult factors one encounters in trying to provide answers to the questions related to discipline is that each member board must comply with its own state laws and regulations. The differences in terminology also inhibit the development of uniform suggestions and recommendations. Although the actions by NCSBN related to discipline have not been dramatic, the efforts of the past 25 years have made a difference in the way boards of nursing protect the public. When viewed in relation to the total number of nursing licensees in the United States, the number of individuals investigated and charged and the cases adjudicated is very small. Nonetheless, for the licensee who is charged and for the board members adjudicating the case the situation may appear overwhelming.

CHAPTER FOURTEEN
RESEARCH AND EVALUATION

Since its inception as an independent organization in 1978, the National Council has steadily increased its involvement in research. Initially, research activities focused on basic psychometric analyses and job analysis studies related to provision of the licensure examinations. Over the ensuing...years, these activities have expanded to address broader issues that relate to the regulation of nursing practice and the needs of boards of nursing.

The Research Agenda of NCSBN, 1991[1]

NCSBN Research Agenda

THE FIRST EDITION of *Issues* in 1991 highlighted the research program of the National Council of State Boards of Nursing, Inc. (NCSBN®). One article discussed the research agenda and stated that it was directed toward strengthening services provided to the member boards. The outcomes of the research were shared with the nursing community and others for consideration in shaping the future of nursing practice and education. Two organization goals that impelled the research agenda were (a) to develop a comprehensive information system for use by members, organizations, and the public; and (b) to advance research that contributes to public health, safety, and welfare. Another major reason for the research was to provide licensure examinations that would be based upon current accepted psychometric and legal considerations. A few of the ongoing research activities included job analysis studies, the Computerized Clinical Simulation Testing (CST) Project, studies related to chemically impaired nurses, information clearinghouse activities, licensing and examination statistics, and the study of licensure requirements. It was also noted that NCSBN was an active member of the Interagency Conference on Nursing Statistics (ICONS). An article described ICONS as an informal group of nine national nursing and health care organizations and federal agencies that routinely performed research that assisted in describing the supply of and demand for nurses.[2]

NCSBN has conducted significant research studies, surveys, and evaluations during its first 25 years. The results of many of these efforts have been included in other chapters of this work. Each year NCSBN sent questionnaires to the member boards for the purpose of obtaining information on a variety of subjects to assist the work of committees, and to fulfill requests for information as directed by the delegate assembly. In addition, the Long Range Planning Committee conducted several trend analyses in preparation for organization planning.

Research Staff and Policies

In 1983 the board of directors adopted the NCSBN Guidelines for Research Requests.[3] The board adopted procedures in 1987 to assure that NCSBN research, including the use of human subjects, was in compliance with the standards of ethical conduct and procedures for reviewing of research protocols to ensure compliance.[4] At its February 1987 meeting the board of directors approved a new staff position, director of Research Services.[5] Carolyn Yocom was named to the position and was listed with other staff present at the October board meeting. Yocom had been a staff member in the Testing Department.[6] When she resigned in 2000, Lynda Crawford was named to the position.[7]

At the March 1994 board of directors meeting a motion was adopted that raw research data could be released to a member board by staff at the direction of the executive director. Release was contingent upon the written description of the specific intended use of the data and analyses to be performed being consistent with conditions under which data were originally collected, and that the study objectives were consistent with the NCSBN mission and goals.[8]

An ad hoc committee of the board of directors that met to consider the NCSBN research approaches made its report to the board in February 1995. After reviewing the report the board took the following three actions:

1. Created a Research Advisory Panel for FY96 with one member who was also a member of the Long Range Planning Task Force.

2. Authorized a subgroup of the board of directors to collaborate with the Research Services staff to assist member boards in framing researchable questions and to make recommendations, where appropriate, to the Resolutions Committee and/or the board of directors relative to the merits and feasibility of proceeding with new projects proposed at the annual meeting.

3. Directed that the following factors be considered by staff in decision making relative to who shall perform NCSBN research:

   A. Urgency of need for information

   B. Narrowness of area to be researched

   C. Specificity of the research question

   D. Expertise required

   E. Costs

   F. Confidentiality of data

   G. NCSBN proprietary interest

   H. Amount of control needed[9]

The Research Advisory Panel, with Mary Pat Curtis of Mississippi as its chair, listed the following responsibilities in its report to the delegate assembly:

- to provide input to the Long Range Planning Task Force and the Research Services staff;

- to assist the member boards in identifying and framing researchable issues; and

- to provide input related to research to the Resolutions Committee, the board of directors and the Research Services staff.

The report also presented the proposed FY97 research agenda and the preliminary FY98 and FY99 research agendas.[10]

At the March 2002 meeting the board of directors approved a policy for distribution of research findings, and asked legal counsel to add language to the policy regarding protection of NCSBN intellectual property and confidentiality agreements with the member boards. The board also approved the research findings communication plan.[11]

Member Board Statistics

In August 1984 the board of directors received a report on the collection and distribution of member board statistics and information. The board approved the concept that NCSBN would be a central source of information on licensure data. The board also approved, in concept, the five-part plan (which included licensure and examination statistics, licensure requirements, board of nursing structure, discipline, and education programs) for collection and dissemination of the information with the first two parts to be completed by FY85.[12] This action by the board of directors initiated a process of data collection and publication of important information about the member boards that continues into the end of the first 25 years of the organization. The most recent publication was issued in 2003 as *Profiles of Member Boards 2002*. The major headings listed in the table of contents were: Board Structure, Educational Programs, Educational Requirements for Entry to Practice, Licensure Requirements/Maintenance, Continued Competence Activities, Assistive Personnel Competency Evaluation, Discipline, Scope of Practice, and Regulation of Advanced Practice. The number of member boards was listed as 61 with 51 jurisdictions licensing both registered nurses (RNs) and licensed practical/vocational nurses (LPN/VNs). In addition, 5 states had separate boards for RNs and those same 5 states had separate boards for LPN/VNs. These states were California, Georgia, Louisiana, Texas, and West Virginia. The collection and compilation of the information in the 2003 edition was done by NCSBN staff members Lynda Crawford, director of Research Services, and Esther White, research project coordinator.[13] These publications have been used extensively within and outside of NCSBN.

Research in Cooperation with Others

NCSBN has cooperated with individuals and organizations on many research projects and studies. In 1982 the board of directors authorized participation and cooperation in a study proposed by James D. Chesney at the University of Michigan regarding possible adverse impact of the licensure examination, subject to conditions that would be established by a special advisory committee for the University of Michigan Study. Joan Nuttall of Wisconsin and Sharon Weisenbeck of Kentucky served on this advisory committee.[14] *The Practical Nurse Role Delineation and Validation Study for the NCLEX® for Practical Nurses*, an important early research project for NCSBN that is discussed in detail in Chapter 9, was completed in cooperation with California Testing Bureau/McGraw-Hill (CTB). In 1983 the board of directors approved a request from Helen Ference, principal investigator for this study, to submit an article to the *American Journal of Nursing (AJN)* with appropriate acknowledgements.[15] That same year the board of directors received a report of the W. K. Kellogg-Pennsylvania State University Continued Professional Education Project.[16] Mary Romelfanger of Kentucky, who represented NCSBN on the Nursing Profession Team, reported to the delegate assembly in the 1984 *NCSBN Book of Reports*. She described a five-year project to develop practice-oriented continuing education programming through the use of collaborative professional relationships. Nursing was one of six professions participating in the study.[17] In 1985, as part of her final report, Romelfanger discussed the Practice Audit Model and its "hallmark" singular approach to identification of learning needs necessary for competent practice. The report continued,

The clear logic of the model is, at once, its most appealing and practical feature. As a result…the end product of the model is continuing education programming expressly designed to address practice oriented deficiencies, be they cognitive, psychomotor or affective spheres.

Romelfanger concluded with public protection as the charge to regulatory agencies. The model has applications for both voluntary and nonvoluntary continuing education jurisdictions.[18]

A major NCSBN research project began in 1984 when the board of directors reviewed bids submitted in response to a request for proposals (RFP) to conduct a job analysis, role delineation, and nursing practice study. The board authorized negotiations with its first choice of the respondents, American College Testing (ACT).[19] The contract with ACT was signed by the end of August.[20] Michael Kane was director of the project, with Carole Kingsbury serving as the assistant director.[21] The research project was called *The Study of Nursing Practice, Role Delineation and Job Analysis of Entry-level Performance of Registered Nurses*, but was usually referred to as the ACT Study. The latter designation will be used in the following paragraphs.

In 1985 a preliminary report of findings to date was available for discussion at the area meetings.[22] The board of directors reviewed a staff summary of the final report of the ACT Study in August 1986 and took actions to recommend that the delegate assembly adopt the following:

- That the report be considered a study document during FY87 and referred to the Examination and the Nursing Practice and Standards (NP&S) Committees to identify implications for the licensure examinations and the regulation of nursing, respectively.

- To schedule time at the Area meetings for sharing and discussion.

In addition, the board of directors supported the recommendation of the Examination Committee that the RN Test Plan be revised to reflect the findings of the job analysis.[23] The delegate assembly adopted the recommendations stated above and asked the Examination Committee and NP&S Committee to also examine the findings of the ACT Study in order to identify the need for secondary analyses of the data to be done by NCSBN. The committees were asked to identify the need for additional follow-up research.[24] The following quote from the ACT Study stated its purposes as follows:

The two general purposes of the study, as specified by the National Council of State Boards of Nursing, were 1) to perform a job analysis of the entry level practice of registered nurses, as a basis for examination of the content validity of the licensure examination for registered nurses and 2) to do a role delineation study comparing the work activities of registered nurses, licensed practical/ vocational nurses, and nurses' aides, as well as administrators, nursing faculty and advanced practitioners. These two purposes are closely related—the first focuses on the entry-level registered nurse in particular while the second compares practice patterns across different categories of nursing personnel. In this study, a common approach was used for both purposes. With a common design, findings related to the two purposes could be integrated.[25]

A succinct review of the ACT Study appeared as an article in a late 1986 *Issues*. It listed the purposes of the study as follows:

1. To determine the commonalities and differences among the roles of registered nurses, licensed practical/vocational nurses, nurses' aides and advanced practitioners;

2. To determine if practice patterns of various categories of nurses vary as a function of practice setting;

3. To identify the point of transition from entry-level practice to beyond entry-level practice for newly licensed registered nurses;

4. To determine if differences in work activities exist among registered nurse graduates of diploma, associate degree, and baccalaureate degree programs; and

5. To identify the implications of data describing the practice of newly licensed registered nurses on the validity of the NCLEX®-RN [National Council Licensure Examination for RNs] test plan.

The article stated further,

The data were collected using a task inventory composed of 222 nursing activities. The sample consisted of newly licensed RNs, all levels of nursing personnel, including advanced practitioners and nursing administrators employed by health care provision agencies and nurse educators.[26]

In the study 17 categories of client needs were identified using factor analysis. These categories suggested three areas of nursing activity: coordination of care and health system management, direct client care and health promotion, and client self-care. The study results showed some major similarities and some major differences across the categories of nursing personnel. But it also found that "one commonality was the close agreement on the criticality ratings for activities." Another finding showed that there was transition in the work settings of newly licensed RNs around the six month time period leading to the conclusion that "it appears that the transition from entry-level practice to beyond entry-level occurs at about six months." The same article in *Issues* noted that, due to the approach to data collection, the results "did not indicate whether or not differences exist in the performance of activities among new graduates of the three types of educational programs."[27] The board of directors approved guides to be used to facilitate discussion of the implications of the ACT Study by the member boards and by the nursing community.[28]

The 1987 delegate assembly adopted the following motion:

That data collection instruments developed for use in future job analysis be redesigned to facilitate identification of qualitative differences in the performance of nursing care activities by nurses with different levels of educational preparation or categories of nursing personnel.[29]

The ACT Study was a major and far-reaching accomplishment of NCSBN. Elements of the study influenced subsequent research related to both the licensure examinations and to nursing practice activities and decisions. The questionnaire used in the study was extensive and provided a substantial amount of information about the practice of nursing. In June 1986 the board of directors authorized the use of this questionnaire by Peggy Primm, the project director for a study sponsored by the Midwest Alliance in Nursing (MAIN). The Virginia Board of Nursing was also authorized to use the questionnaire as it studied the need to revise the definitions of nursing and practical nursing in Virginia. The responses to the questionnaire contributed valuable information to that study.[30]

NCSBN determined that the ACT Study, while including data on LPN/VNs, "was not designed to include a systematic sampling of newly licensed LPN/VNs."[31] Since the data for the newly licensed RNs had been useful in modifying the NCLEX-RN, the board of directors also authorized ACT to conduct a two-year job analysis of entry-level LPN/VNs.[32] This analysis was done using the techniques from the earlier study in order to update the National Council Licensure Examination for LPN/VNs (NCLEX-PN®). The response rate for the two samples of newly licensed LPN/VNs in October 1986 and October 1987 was good, and the quality of the responses indicated that those responding had done so carefully and accurately.[33]

The LPN/VN study described the practice patterns of those sampled in terms of variables such as work settings, shift worked, and client characteristics. Other data obtained included time spent in various functions, hours worked per week, and length of time in the current job.[34] The researchers examined and reported on the implications of the outcomes of the study "for the validity (in the sense of job-relatedness) of the NCLEX-PN® Test Plan" and its three independently weighted dimensions: practical nursing activities, practice settings, and age range for clients. The findings suggested that there was a need to give more emphasis to elderly clients in the test plan and more weight to long-term care settings and less to acute care. Other findings related to frequency and criticality of the nursing activities suggested some changes in the percentage of items for the eight nursing activity categories of the test plan.[35]

The Job Analysis of Newly Licensed Practical/Vocational Nurses 1986-1987 (the ACT PN/VN Study) was completed in 1988 and the board of directors asked the Nursing Practice and Education (NP&E) Committee to review it with a view to its general implications as well as specific nursing practice.[36] The Report of the Examination Committee in 1988 included a summary of the review of the ACT PN/VN Study. As a result of the review, the committee recalculated the percentage of items to be given in each test plan category. The 1988 delegate assembly adopted the report. The Examination Committee continued its review of the study results to devise a test plan framework to be used as a basis for further development of the NCLEX-PN.[37]

NCSBN leaders participated in discussions and meetings related to research in 1994. President Rosa Lee Weinert of Ohio, Executive Director Jennifer Bosma, and Director of Research Services Yocom, met with Nancy Dickerson-Hazard, the executive director of Sigma Theta Tau and Judith Cross, the director of the Virginia Henderson Library. They discussed the research efforts of NCSBN and Sigma Theta Tau. The representatives from Sigma Theta Tau urged nurses affiliated with NCSBN to enter their research into the Sigma Theta Tau Registry of Nursing Research.[38] Bosma and Yocom also participated in the annual meeting of the Nursing Research Roundtable, an informal association of national and regional nursing organizations with significant research interests.[39]

In June 1995 the Research Advisory Panel again reported to the board of directors. The group had reviewed a request from the Division of Nursing, located in the United States Department of Health and Human Services (HHS), that NCSBN apply for a sole source contract for a project titled Curriculum Guidelines and Criteria for the Evaluation of Pharmacology Content to Prepare Family Nurse Practitioners [FNP] for Prescriptive Authority in Managing Pharmacotherapeutics in Primary Care (The FNP Pharmacotherapeutics and Prescriptive Privileges Project). The board of directors decided to submit a proposal and received the contract that year.[40] According to the report on this project included in the 1996 *NCSBN Book of Reports*, NCSBN subcontracted the curriculum development component of the project to the National Organization of Nurse Practitioner Faculties. The project between NCSBN and two agencies located within the Department of HHS, the Division of Nursing and the Agency for Health Care Policy and Research, was funded in the amount of $249,000. Supporting activities in preparation for the annual meeting included the drafting of documents for review, discussion, and critique.[41] In 1996 the delegate assembly authorized the board of directors to give final approval to The FNP Pharmacotherapeutics and Prescriptive Privileges Project and, with prior opportunity for review and comment by the member boards, indicated organizational support for the project as a model that could be used by the member boards.[42] An article in *Issues* early in 1998 announced the completion of the project.[43]

Another article in *Issues* in 1998 entitled "Commitment to Public Protection through Excellence in Nursing Regulation," introduced a project recently undertaken by NCSBN. The article opened with the following statement: "A number of forces have encouraged discussion regarding the outcomes for which a regulatory board should be held accountable and how board effectiveness can be assessed." A recommendation from the Pew Health Professions Commission in 1995 said that "states should develop evaluation tools that assess the objectives, successes and shortcomings of their regulatory systems and bodies in order to best protect and promote the public's health." The Pew report did not address how this effectiveness could be measured. The article continued to discuss the need to define regulatory outcomes and measurable indicators to begin the evaluation and quality improvement process. The board of directors contracted with The Urban Institute to proceed with the Commitment to Public Protection through Excellence in Nursing Regulation Project (Commitment to Excellence Project) to:

1. Determine the expected roles and functions of an effective nursing regulatory board based on the input of multiple stakeholders.

2. Identify exemplar performance outcome indicators that can serve as a baseline/model for use in individual Member Board strategic planning and performance outcome management activities.

3. Facilitate data collection and establishment of a central data base to support bench marking and the identification of best practices.

4. Facilitate strategic planning and performance outcome measurement and enhancement activities within boards of nursing.

The article concluded with the anticipation that the project would assist the member boards to demonstrate effectively their abilities to meet their legislative mandate to protect the public.[44]

When the board of directors decided to contract with The Urban Institute in February 1998, $50,000 was added to the funding for Phase I of the Commitment to Excellence Project. The board asked the Policy Futures Panel to serve as the advisory group to The Urban Institute.[45] In November the board of directors approved proceeding to Part I of Phase II of the Commitment to Excellence Project, allocated $153,681 to the project, and directed staff to seek external funding for the project.[46]

At the end of 1998 an article in the *Newsletter to the Member Boards* reported that the advisory group had reviewed The Urban Institute Phase I Report summarizing the information obtained from the member boards regarding the expected roles and responsibilities of nursing regulatory agencies. The report gave strong support for:

- determining/interpreting the scope of practice for nurses;
- issuing licenses to qualified nurses;
- assuring continued competency for nurses;
- investigating complaints, imposing appropriate discipline, and establishing rehabilitation options for impaired nurses; and
- communicating with or educating constituencies.

There was mixed support for regulatory involvement in the approval of nursing education programs. The Commitment to Excellence Project Advisory Group, hereafter Advisory Group, began planning for Phase II, which would include the identification of a manageable set of indicators and data collection procedures that could be used in the measurement of regulatory performance outcomes. This phase was scheduled for completion in nine months. The activities for Phase III would include pilot testing.[47]

Material for a forum on the Commitment to Excellence Project was included in the 1999 *NCSBN Business Book.* The five-member Advisory Group was chaired by Diana Vander Woude of South Dakota, and a 10-member Technical Working Group was assigned to the project. The description of the project in the report included the fact that the project was planned to span 30 months, beginning in 1998. The ultimate goal was to establish the processes essential for providing the member boards with the necessary, ongoing support and assistance that would permit them to strengthen the quality of the regulatory services they provided in support of their mandate to protect the public's health and safety. The report stated that Phase I was completed, and the objectives for Phase II and III provided for the development of:

- a set of feasible procedures that individual member boards could use regularly to track performance.

- a process for obtaining comparable data on board performance, especially service outcomes that would enable comparisons to be made across states and that could be used to identify best practices that other boards could adopt as appropriate.

- an educational component for member boards that focused on the complementary nature of performance outcome measurement and strategic planning activities.

The report also detailed the roles of both the Advisory Group and the Technical Working Group.[48] In December Executive Director Eloise Cathcart advised the board of directors that the newly appointed senior director for Nursing Practice and Regulation, Donna Nowakowski, would assume staff responsibility for the project.[49]

The following statement of purpose was included in the report of the Advisory Group in the 2000 *NCSBN Business Book*:

The purpose of the Commitment to Public Protection through Excellence in Nursing Regulation Project is the establishment of a performance measurement system that incorporates data collection from internal and external sources and the use of bench marking strategies and identification of best practices…this exciting and ground-breaking project (no other regulatory group has approached performance evaluation in this manner or to this extent) will clarify the important work of boards of nursing, demonstrate value and identify best practices.[50]

At its February 2000 meeting the board of directors received a report on the status of the Commitment to Excellence Project. Representatives from 11 member boards met in February to finalize the templates and questionnaires formulated by The Urban Institute, but a number of questions and concerns remained. The board of directors agreed to schedule a joint meeting of the pilot member boards and the Advisory Group to respond to the changes recommended by the NCSBN staff to realign the study's methodology, scope, and timeline.[51] This second meeting was held in March. Phase II of the project was completed in 2000.[52] The report of the Advisory Group in the 2000 *NCSBN Business Book* included a section on activities for the year. The 12 member boards selected from the volunteers to participate in the pilot test were Kentucky, Louisiana-RN, Maryland, Missouri, Nebraska, New Mexico, North Carolina, North Dakota, Ohio, Tennessee, West Virginia-PN, and Texas-RN. After the two meetings mentioned above, the group agreed on a conceptual framework to guide tool development and data collection, and narrowed the scope of the first pilot test to two regulatory roles. The data collection began in July.[53]

Chair Vander Woude reported to the board of directors in January 2001. The pilot test was proceeding and the committee was reviewing the data and refining data collection tools. Vander Woude said that she anticipated a recommendation to the board of directors that the board support the development of second generation tools and a computerized software package to enable a more efficient collection of data. The committee was also exploring a peer review process and asked legal counsel for advice on data confidentiality.[54] In April Vander Woude met with the board of directors and discussed a proposed agreement that would guarantee the project participants the confidentiality of the data submitted to NCSBN. Categories of information submissions included licensure, complaint, investigation, disciplinary, practice, education, and governance data. The agreement would allow NCSBN to publish aggregate data. Legal counsel Thomas Abram and Donna Nowakowski developed a survey to examine statutory constraints that could prohibit participation.[55] In May the board of directors learned that 42 states would participate in the pilot test for the project. The Advisory Group was conducting conference calls to explore issues hindering data collection.[56] In her report to the delegate assembly in 2001, Vander Woude described the future plans of the Advisory Group to collect data for the second group of member boards and to recommend a plan to the board of directors to "position performance outcomes evaluation as a sustainable, prospective effort of the NCSBN."[57]

At the January 2002 meeting, the board of directors considered recommendations from the Advisory Group that resulted from its work to accomplish the purpose stated above. The board took the following actions:

- Adopted the Performance Measurement System for member boards.

- Approved the *Performance Measurement System Manual* for distribution to member boards.

- Approved a six member committee to oversee the Performance Measurement System.[58]

In 2003, Lynda Crawford, director of Research Services, reported to the board of directors on the Commitment to Ongoing Regulatory Excellence (CORE) Advisory Panel. The activities of the panel included development of new, shorter tools; identification of best practices; and finding similarities in the top outcome listings. The board agreed to continue the CORE Advisory Panel.[59]

NCSBN was a major collaborator in a Robert Wood Johnson funded project in 1999. An article in *Issues* entitled "Strengthening Nursing Education to Improve End of Life Care" described the research aspects of the project. The American Association of Colleges of Nursing (AACN) and the National League for Nursing (NLN) also participated. The project was conducted by nurse researchers at the City of Hope National Medical Center. Staff members Ruth Elliott and Anne Wendt represented NCSBN as consultants for the project. The central purpose of the project was to "strengthen nursing education to improve end of life care" by accomplishing the following goals:

- Improve the content regarding end of life care included in major textbooks used in nursing education;

- Insure the adequacy of content in end of life care as tested by the national nursing examination, the NCLEX® examination; and

- Support the three key nursing organizations in their efforts to promote nursing education and practice in end of life care.[60]

NCSBN staff discussed additional cooperative research in 2002. At its September meeting the board of directors discussed a letter from the AACN President Kathleen Long to NCSBN President Donna Dorsey of Maryland regarding the feasibility of a collaborative project between the two organizations. They decided that the executive directors of the two groups would discuss the matter further, and the NCSBN research staff would develop possible research questions for consideration by the board of directors.[61]

Lynda Crawford and June Smith, Research Services manager, presented a report in December titled "Evaluating the Effectiveness of Continuing Education Mandates." The aim of this study was to examine the connection between continuing education and competence. This NCSBN study was a collaborative effort with the Interprofessional Work Group for Health Professional Regulations, composed of regulatory bodies overseeing medical technologists, occupational therapists, physicians' assistants, physical therapists, and respiratory therapists.[62]

Ongoing NCSBN Research

In August 1988, Carolyn Yocom, director of Research Services, presented to the board of directors plans for implementation of future job analysis studies to be conducted by NCSBN. The board acted to approve the timeline for conducting a pilot test of the proposed revision of the instrument for data collection, and directed that staff report the outcomes at the 1989 pre-convention meeting of the board of directors. The board also directed that an internal advisory committee consisting of two to five individuals, not currently serving on the Examination Committee, be appointed to monitor conduct of the pilot study and that an external advisory committee of two individuals also be appointed.[63]

The board of directors received a report from the Job Analysis Monitoring Committee in 1989. The committee had reviewed the results of a pilot study conducted by the Research Department. The board decided to incorporate a critical incident approach in the FY90 RN job analysis study, and agreed to appoint two people external to NCSBN to serve on an External Job Analysis Monitoring Committee.[64]

In 1990, the board of directors approved the plan to conduct a role delineation study with a focus on the practice of experienced LPN/VNs. This study was a follow up to an earlier survey of LPN/VNs who served on the member boards. Additional information gathered in this study was identified as having potential use to member boards in the following areas:

- The distribution of experienced LPN/VNs across work settings.

- The types of nursing activities engaged in and how these activities compare to those performed by experienced nurse aides, RNs and advanced practice registered nurses (APRNs.)

Further, the study would offer to individual member boards the option to augment the data collection within their jurisdictions. This would allow for local level data analyses of LPN/VN activities.[65]

At the February 1991 board of directors meeting, Yocom reported on the status of several studies. The longitudinal study of entry-level RN practice at six months and 12 months was ready for review by the Examination Committee. The Critical Incident Description Analysis and the LPN/VN Job Analysis Study were in progress.[66] Later in the year, the board of directors adopted two recommendations from the Examination Committee. The first was that the timeframe for job analysis studies remain at six months after graduation, and the second was that a study similar to the *Examination of Differences in the Practice of Newly Licensed RNs Between the First and Second Six Months of Practice* be repeated every six years in connection with a job analysis study.[67]

In 1992, the delegate assembly adopted a resolution that would enable NCSBN to provide services related to a logical job analysis through a contract with the Maine and/or the Alaska boards of nursing.[68]

Executive Director Jennifer Bosma reported on staff activities in support of research in 1993. These activities included support for:

- A major role delineation study that included nurse aides, LPN/VNs, RNs, and APRNs.

- A logical job analysis of the role of baccalaureate-educated nurses under a contract with the Maine Board of Nursing.

- Maintenance of a database of surveys and studies conducted by the member boards or NCSBN.[69]

A preliminary report of the Role Delineation Study, begun after the board of director's action in 1990, was included in the 1993 *NCSBN Book of Reports*. This study was initiated at the direction of the board of directors and involved a random sample of 15,411 individuals. The report stated that the response rate was 49.3 percent. The following summary was included in the report:

A descriptive study of the nursing practice of nurse aides, LPN/VNs, RNs and APRNs in the United States, the District of Columbia and the US territories was undertaken using a newly developed data collection instrument. A major component of the instrument consisted of a list of

238 nursing activities. For each activity, respondents were asked to provide information regarding frequency of performance and delegation and activity criticality. Data were collected using a four-phase mailing process over approximately three months. Screening procedures were implemented to eliminate respondents' data when there was evidence of carelessness or misinterpretation. Based on the outcomes of a series of selected data analysis procedures, there was no evidence of response bias or other problem that would invalidate interpretation of the results.

An initial analysis of data provided by 6,930 respondents provided general information about the similarities and differences relative to their respective demographic characteristics; educational preparation; work setting; functional roles; and, for those providing direct care to clients, client characteristics and practice activities. It is anticipated that further analysis of this rich data set, including information relative to the delegation of tasks by one personnel category to another, will yield more specific descriptions of the practice characteristics of each personnel category within and across a variety of client care settings.[70]

Carolyn Yocom presented the report of the *Validation Study: Functional Abilities Essential for Nursing Practice (Functional Abilities Study)* in the 1996 *NCSBN Book of Reports*. The executive summary began with a discussion of the reliance on graduation from a school of nursing and success on the licensure examination as the means of determining that a licensee possesses necessary knowledge, skills, and abilities to begin practice. Questions had arisen related to the initial and/or continued competence of persons with disabilities and were heightened by the impact of the Americans with Disabilities Act. As a result, questions were raised regarding functional ability activities/attributes and types of competency accommodations. The summary concluded with the following section, headed "Implications":

This study identifies the "core functional ability activities/attributes essential for an individual to perform nursing activities in a safe and effective manner." Boards of nursing may use this information when considering the eligibility of an individual for initial or continuing licensure. However, the presence of a disability that impacts an individual's ability to demonstrate competence in these areas should not be considered in isolation from the accommodations that can be used to compensate for a noted "deficiency." Secondly, this information may be found useful by individuals considering nursing as a career and by nurse educators evaluating both applicants for admission and students enrolled in their programs.

Additionally, identification of both "core" and "non-core" essential functional ability activities/attributes, as delineated by job position and by employment setting, provides guidance to boards of nursing in their consideration to restrict a nurse's authority to practice nursing by limiting scope, setting, or type of nursing role and activities. In both instances, the nature of the specific disability, and the degree of compensation, if any, from use of special accommodations must be considered. The position-specific and employment setting-specific lists of activities/attributes can be a valuable resource during career counseling opportunities—both with prospective licensees and with licensees who acquired a disability following initial licensure. A further implication for boards of nursing imposing limitations, involves policy determination—whether or not such limitations should be imposed by disciplinary or non-disciplinary methods.

Within each jurisdiction, the board of nursing has a legislative mandate to protect the public from incompetent providers of nursing care. When evaluating the competence of licensure applicants and licensees, the board cannot neglect or dismiss this mandate. While several boards have taken various positions on the use of limited licenses, this study does not advocate one position or another on this policy issue. It is hoped that the judicious use of information reported in this report will assist them in their evaluation of nurses with disabilities, many of whom could function safely and effectively in selected employment settings/environments and/or in selected positions.[71]

In the Supplemental Report of the Continued Competence Subcommittee (of the NP&E Committee), Chair Shirley Brekken of Minnesota included the following recommendations:

To disseminate and promote the *Functional Abilities Study*.

To develop guidelines for implications of the *Functional Abilities Study*.

To consider the implications for revision of the *NCSBN Model Nursing Practice Act* and the *NCSBN Model Nursing Administrative Rules*.[72]

Director of Research Services Crawford presented a research proposal to the board of directors in August 2001. The title of the study was "Post-Entry Competencies." The proposal was for:

a cross-sequential and longitudinal study that aimed to perform a comprehensive examination of the characteristics of post-entry practice, identify the chronologic evolution of nursing practice and evaluate the contribution of internal and external factors in the evolution of nursing practice.

The board of directors approved the proposal with changes to encourage incentives and to the title of participants.[73]

At the January 2002 board of directors meeting, Lynda Crawford and June Smith, members of the NCSBN staff, presented results from several surveys and studies. These included: the 2002 Newly Licensed Nurse Practice and Professional Issues Survey, the 2001 NCSBN Employer Survey, and the 2001 RN Practice Analysis Update Survey. The board discussed publication of findings and the necessity of keeping the information as proprietary until the member boards had reviewed the results. The Research Department asked the board for additional funding to expand the collection of data for the job analysis. These funds were needed for the "Job Analysis Think Tank," a two-day meeting of outside panelists and members of the Research and Testing departments, to ensure continuous quality improvement for the RN and LPN/VN job analyses. The board approved the NCSBN Practice Analysis Research Agenda and added an additional $5,000 to the budget.[74]

At a meeting in 2002, the board of directors approved the immediate dissemination of the Practice and Professional Issues Survey, the Employer Survey, and the RN Practice Analysis.[75] Two articles in the 2002 *Council Connector* featured information about the NCSBN Research Department. In March a listing of new research reports that were currently summarized on the NCSBN Web site was highlighted. These included the following:

- July 2001 Newly Licensed Nurse Practice and Professional Issues (PPI) Survey
- 2001 Registered Nurse Practice Analysis Update Survey
- 2001 NCSBN Employer Survey
- The NCLEX Delay Pass Rate Study
- Brief Analysis of NCLEX® Passing Rates
- Performance of Repeat Testers[76]

In April an announcement appeared that Crawford and Smith had two abstracts accepted for the Thirteenth International Nursing Research Congress in Brisbane, Australia in July. They presented the findings from the 2001 Practice and Professional Issues Survey and the Post-Entry Competence Study.[77]

Evaluations of NCSBN and Its Programs and Services

The first reference to organizational evaluation appeared in the minutes of the board of directors in 1983. The board received a report of the Council Review Committee, an ad hoc committee of the board chaired by Kate Fenner of Illinois. Two recommendations were included in the report. The first stated the need to consider amending the bylaws related to the experience needed to serve on the board and to allow officers to complete their terms even if they were no longer members or staff of a board of nursing. The board referred this recommendation to the Bylaws Committee. The second recommendation agreed to by the board asked staff to develop a fact sheet identifying the increased involvement of LPN/VN and public members of the member boards in the current structure of NCSBN.[78] The 1983 *NCSBN Book of Reports* included the position paper of the Council Review Committee. The paper stated the purposes of the committee as follows:

1. To review the objectives of NCSBN in order to determine whether they are consistent with current expectations of Member Boards.

2. To review the required composition of the Board of Directors to determine whether Member Boards (including all categories of board members, nurse staff and non-nurse staff) are ensured adequate representation.

3. To review the structure of NCSBN to determine whether Board members, nurse staff and non-nurse staff are ensured sufficient methods of involvement in deliberations in decision making.

The following recommendations were included in the position paper:

A. No action in regard to objectives or Board composition.

B. Stating objectives as ranked and prefacing the ranking with a statement that the objectives reflect prioritization.

C. Sharing of Review Committee Survey on Board Qualifications and Composition results with members of the Nominating Committee.

D. Examination of a requirement that Board members have a minimum of one year of experience prior to election.

E. Communication of current NSCBN structure to allay concerns and increase involvement of LPN members and others.

F. Amendment of Bylaws to enable a Board member's completion of term of office when they have been a board member or staff employee at time of election.

G. Exploration of establishment of associate membership through appointment of a Study Committee or referral to an appropriate committee of the NCSBN

H. Attention to areas for further study including: disciplinary action, educational program approval, and legal rights and responsibilities of board members.

I. Attention to research on issues related to continuing competency, practice areas, examination, disciplinary actions and National Council.

J. Consideration of alternative organizational mechanisms to facilitate Member Board networking by size, organizational format, and role complexity.

K. Ongoing study of survey data by appropriate body for reference on issues of relevance not mandated in the committee's charge.[79]

In 1984 the board of directors considered a proposal to perform an analysis of membership needs at its meeting in August. The board adopted a motion to accept the recommendation of the Finance Committee to approve the proposal of Touche Ross & Company entitled "Proposal to Perform and Analysis of Membership Needs" at a cost not to exceed $50,000 with the following stipulations:

That the objective of the project is to provide an independent market survey of the services of NCSBN with primary emphasis on cost/benefit analysis of services.

Services to be analyzed are to include current and expanded services to member boards and other appropriate groups.

Approximation of cost/benefit and financial analysis should be more accurate than a ±30% level.[80]

In May 1985 the board of directors received and discussed the Report of the Steering Committee on the Analysis of Membership Needs. H. Jean Bruhn of Pennsylvania, NCSBN Executive Director Eileen McQuaid Dvorak, Ruth Elliott of Tennessee, Lois Johnson of Colorado, Sharon Weisenbeck of Kentucky, and Nancy Wilson of West Virginia-PN were members of the committee, with Phyllis Sheridan of Idaho serving as chair. The board took the following actions in response to the report:

• Directed that the Touche Ross & Company *Analysis of Membership Needs* be copyrighted and sent to the member boards.

• Agreed that an article on the report be included in *Issues*.

• Directed that the survey results were to be copyrighted and filed in the NCSBN office.

• Decided that the raw data would not be available for distribution.

• Decided to distribute the report to the Finance Committee and the Long Range Planning Committee as a resource for planning.[81]

An article in *Issues* provided details about the *Analysis of Membership Needs*. The results of the study by Touché Ross & Company provided NCSBN with a comprehensive examination of the current services and needs of the membership. The needs were placed in relation to financial possibilities of new and expanded services, and to anticipated benefits to NCSBN and the member boards. In addition to the member boards, staff members of the American Nurses Association (ANA), NLN, the American Association of Nurse Anesthetists and their Council on Certification and Accreditation were contacted for responses. Separate surveys were sent to the members and the executive directors of the 60 member boards, and to one non-member, California-VN. Responses were received from 50 executive directors and 126 board members. There was a positive response to maintain current services. The new needs that were identified included a nurse licensee database, a legal information system, member board profiles, and computer testing. There was an extensive listing of NCSBN services to the member boards included in the article. The article stated further,

The National Council can now turn its efforts towards achieving a broader base of service to its membership, to nursing, and to the general public that the regulation of nursing practice serves. It is a new area of challenge for the National Council…with the membership needs survey, and the determination of its Member Boards, the National Council's future is quickly becoming one of broader achievements.[82]

In February 1988 Carolyn Yocom reported to the board of directors regarding another Survey of NCSBN Services. The survey requested responses as to member board satisfaction with NCSBN services.

The response rate was 80 percent. The survey reviewed licensure, nursing practice, communication, and future services. The member boards were satisfied with all services provided with the exception of those of the National Nursing Licensure Data Committee. President Ruth Elliott of Tennessee compared the survey results with those of a similar personal survey that she had conducted. The board of directors referred the information obtained in the survey to respective committees and staff for appropriate actions, and directed that a composite of the survey results be distributed with the *Newsletter to the Member Boards*.[83]

In 1994 the board of directors decided that, in addition to an informal evaluation of the board of director's process, an annual formal evaluation would be implemented. The board members agreed to complete a self-assessment questionnaire for the Center for Non-Profit Board to receive the information to report the result at the June meeting.[84] In June the board reviewed the response to the self-assessment questionnaires and found that most aspects of board performance were rated as satisfactory. The board also identified several strategies for improvement in specific areas.[85]

Also in 1994 the American Society of Association Executives (ASAE) conducted a peer review of NCSBN. Executive Director Bosma reported on the review to the board of directors in March and presented highlights of the draft of the report.[86] The complete report was attached to Bosma's Report of Staff Activities in the 1994 *NCSBN Book of Reports*. The following are excerpts from the report of the ASAE review:

OVERVIEW

The mission of the National Council of State Boards of Nursing is to promote public policy related to the safe and effective practice of nursing in the interest of public welfare.

Because of NCSBN's expanding role in policy development as it relates to public welfare, the expanding role of nursing practice and health care reform, the elected leadership and staff executives undertook steps to evaluate its current operations and future directions. A part of this ongoing evaluation included an audit of current operations (programs and activities), management (governance, organizational structure) and a look at future directions. To accomplish this, NCSBN contacted the American Society of Association Executives (ASAE) to conduct an evaluation to cover ten areas of association management. ASAE assembled a peer review team of three experienced association executives with relevant but diverse backgrounds to review NCSBN documents, publications, manuals, audits, programs and other significant data. The materials supplied to the ASAE Evaluation Team were prepared by NCSBN's leadership, its Executive Director and professional staff.

The survey team met at NCSBN's headquarters and interviewed in person or by phone, two officers and seven senior staff.

Before concluding the site visit, the team members met to reach consensus about their findings, in preparation for their exit interview with the Executive Director and senior staff. This provided an opportunity to share some of the key findings and to clarify any unresolved issues.

It would be inappropriate to conclude this overview without noting the extraordinary commitment to the National Council of State Boards of Nursing, by both its leadership and its staff. The level of mutual respect and trust and their shared belief in the mission and values of NCSBN, bodes well for the future of the organization.

The performance of NCSBN was audited according to 10 criteria:

Criterion 1.   Mission and Objectives

Criterion 2.   Governing Body, Officers and Directors

Criterion 3.   Organizational Structure and Documents

Criterion 4.   Programs, Services and Activities

Criterion 5.   Association Staff

Criterion 6.   Financial Planning and Reporting

Criterion 7.   Membership Development and Retention

Criterion 8.   Communications

Criterion 9.   Government Affairs

Criterion 10.   Office Automation and Information Management

NCSBN met the requirements for Criteria 1 through 8 and 10. Criterion 9 was not ranked because of the nature of the organization membership. However, the comment in the ASAE report suggested that NCSBN might explore legitimate and allowable government affairs activities. Other comments accompanying the ranking of the criteria were the following:

Criterion 1.   Suggested clarification of promotion of public policy, i.e., to insure a minimum level of competency of nurses entering the profession vs. the broader policy "to assure safe and effective nursing care for the public." If the latter was chosen, activities would need to be expanded to embrace the broader policy.

Criterion 2.   Recommended that the bylaws be amended to delineate the respective roles of the delegate assembly and the board of directors.

Criterion 3.   Suggested that a more comprehensive record of members serving on the member boards would allow for more extensive communication.

Criterion 8.   Suggested that NCSBN was missing opportunities to fulfill its public trust and public relations role. There was a need to improve the frequency and reach of communication with the "outside public."[87]

At its October meeting the board of directors reviewed the recommendations from the ASAE Peer Evaluation Team. The following statement appeared in the minutes of that meeting:

Regarding recommendations with respect to organizational structure, the Board made suggestions for more formal and consistent committee chair orientation and directed that a survey of committee chairs be performed in order to ascertain the need for a leadership conference or other orientation type activities. With respect to recommendations addressing programs and services, the Board directed staff to survey Member Boards regarding communication channels to board members and board staff; it was also agreed to request that this item be placed on the agendas of the Executive Officers Network and the Board Members Network at the next annual meeting. With respect to recommendations in all other criterion areas, the Board noted satisfactory progress being made or acknowledged the areas as the responsibility of administration.[88]

The board of directors reviewed and revised a governance survey form at its January 2000 meeting. The survey was designed to assess how well NCSBN was functioning and the ways in which the governance structure might be improved. The board of directors agreed to have the final report ready for discussion at the Executive Officers Forum and area meetings, and for use by the Bylaws Committee.[89] The survey was distributed in January 2000 to the delegates who attended the 1996 through 1999 annual meetings, current members and executive officers of member boards, and past and current members of the board of directors.[90] President Joey Ridenour of Arizona and Executive Director Eloise Cathcart met with Dr. Michela Perrone, a board consultant, to discuss the results of the governance survey. The board received the report of this meeting in March 2000 and considered these findings:

- There was a need for delegates to receive more education about the delegate assembly process and their role within the process.
- There was a need for continuity between the work of the board of directors and NCSBN committee work.
- There was a need for leadership development among the membership.
- There was a need for the Nominations Committee to be more knowledgeable about NCSBN processes.
- There was a need for clear definition between the board of directors and the delegate assembly.[91]

In January 2002 Executive Director Kathy Apple and Alicia Byrd, Member Board Relations manager, recommended to the board of directors that NCSBN enter into a contract with Research USA, Inc., to conduct a thorough and comprehensive survey of member board satisfaction with NCSBN products and services. The board approved the recommendation.[92] In August the board of directors reviewed and discussed the raw data from the Member Board Needs Assessment Survey completed by Research USA.[93] The board received the results of the survey in February 2003, including a secondary analysis that separated responses according to the respondents (board presidents, members, staff, and executive officers). The lowest response rate was from member board presidents. Generally, NCSBN appeared to be on target with providing the services and products needed by the member boards. There was a clear indication of a need for improved communication at all levels to ensure direct relationships of programs and services to the mission and strategic initiatives. The board of directors referred specific recommendations to key staff members.[94]

Conclusion

NCSBN established its research agenda and employed staff with strong research credentials in order to conduct a variety of studies. This staff has been successful in obtaining grants to fund a number of its projects. This chapter has provided an overview of the research function of NCSBN, including several major studies and the ongoing research and compilation of statistics. Many studies were also ongoing, particularly those related to the examinations; a number have not been included and significant research activities have been described in other chapters, particularly Chapters 9 and 13. A number of endeavors have been accomplished in cooperation with other individuals and organizations. The competent efforts of those staff members who have directed and assisted the Research Department, the volunteers from the member boards who have provided advice and oversight, and the representatives from outside groups who have collaborated in NCSBN research all deserve recognition for their dedicated work. The individuals who were the subject of much of the research and who took the time to participate were especially important to the success of the research conducted by NCSBN over the years.

In 1983 the NCSBN Board of Directors began its ongoing effort to assure that the needs of the member boards were being met through research, self-studies, and external evaluations. This effort continues as the organization reaches its 25th year and beyond. All of this research has shown general satisfaction with the services of NCSBN to the member boards. Where the findings have indicated the need for change, the organization has responded to the need.

CHAPTER FIFTEEN
AWARDS, RECOGNITIONS, AND CELEBRATIONS

The pioneer spirit which gave birth to the organization a decade ago must remain alive in each of us as we face the challenges of regulation and licensure tomorrow.

Renatta Loquist, 1988[1]

The Dr. R. Louise McManus Award

WITHIN A SHORT TIME after its organization, the National Council of State Boards of Nursing, Inc. (NCSBN®) recognized the importance of honoring those who continue the dedication and commitment to the organization seen at its inception. At its meeting in March 1982 the NCSBN Board of Directors voted to establish an award "to honor, periodically, an individual or organization that has made contributions to the purpose of NCSBN and further, that the award be named for Dr. R. Louise McManus."[2] R. Louise McManus joined the faculty at Teachers College, Columbia University, New York City, in 1925 and became director of Nursing Education in 1947. She continued as director until her retirement in 1961, and she died at the age of 97 in 1993. During her lengthy tenure at Teachers College, McManus was recognized for many significant achievements, including the following:

- The initiation of the National League for Nursing (NLN) Testing Service.
- The initiation of the Institute for Nursing Research at Columbia University.
- The development of a national licensing examination for nurses—the State Board Test Pool Examination (SBTPE).
- The initiation of the research project directed by Mildred Montag that led to the two-year Associate Degree Nursing Education Program.
- The development of a "hospital-accepted" Patient's Bill of Rights.[3]

The contributions of McManus to the development of the SBTPE are discussed in Chapter 9.

The NCSBN Delegate Assembly had adopted a resolution at the annual meeting in 1980 in recognition of Dr. R. Louise McManus. *(see fig. 15-A)* As speaker at the 1980 meeting, McManus reminisced about her experiences in the development of the licensing examinations in the early 1940s. The resolution read, in part, as follows:

Whereas: The National council of State Boards of Nursing, Inc., is in convention assembled June 4-6 in Minneapolis, Minnesota; and

Whereas: Dr. McManus has participated actively in professional organizations and associations related to nursing having served in many roles; and

Whereas: The profession of nursing has benefited greatly by her pioneer efforts in establishing a national licensing examination; and

Whereas: Dr. McManus has volunteered her talent freely in promoting the progress of nursing service and nursing education; now

Therefore Be It Resolved That: The National Council of State Boards of Nursing, Inc. express its deepest gratitude to R. Louise McManus for her outstanding service and leadership.[4]

At the March 1982 board meeting the board authorized the president to appoint an Awards Committee to propose the criteria and procedures related to the award. The committee was also asked to review the nominations submitted and to recommend those qualified to the board of directors who would select the recipient. This practice continued until 2003. The board also decided that the first award would be presented at the 1983 annual meeting, concurrent with the fifth anniversary of the establishment of NCSBN.[5] The first members of the Awards Committee were Marianna Bacigalupo of New Jersey, Kathleen Dwyer of Rhode Island, and Merlyn Maillian of Louisiana-RN.[6] H. Jean Bruhn of Pennsylvania, another member of the board of directors, was added in January 1983.[7]

After reviewing the report of the Awards Committee, the board adopted the procedure for selection and presentation of the R. Louise McManus Award.[8] In May the board learned that McManus had agreed to have the award named for her. The Awards Committee reported that four individuals and three organizations were nominated. The item to be presented to the recipient had been designed and was being produced by a jeweler in Chicago.[9]

The board of directors selected Mildred S. Schmidt, executive secretary of the New York State Board of Nurse Examiners to be the first recipient.[10] This was the only time the recipient was identified in the minutes of a meeting of the board of directors. The fact of all subsequent selections was reported, but the name was not included so that the name of the recipient could be announced publicly at the time the award was presented. Schmidt accepted the award at a banquet at the 1983 annual meeting. Schmidt had long supported the establishment of NCSBN as a free-standing organization and served on the Special Task Force—State Boards of Nursing that developed the organizational structure in 1977 and 1978. She also served as the first treasurer, the third president of NCSBN, and had a long and distinguished career with the New York State Board of Nurse Examiners.

The McManus Award continues to be presented as the most prestigious award of NCSBN to individuals who have made sustained and significant contributions through the highest commitment and dedication to the purposes of NCSBN. The original symbol for the award was a flame with NCSBN logo superimposed on it. Suggest insert picture of award. Appears in *Issues*, Fall/Winter 1983 In 1986 the award was a large crystal bowl etched with the original NCSBN logo. Since 1989 the symbol has been a 12-inch tall engraved crystal obelisk etched with the second NCSBN logo.

In 1985 the board of directors decided to present the McManus Award every three years. When the board changed the award program in 1993, nominations for this award were accepted at any time. The 14 recipients through 2003 are as follows:

DR. R. LOUISE MCMANUS AWARD

1983	Mildred Schmidt, New York
1986	Joyce Schowalter, Minnesota
1989	Marianna Bacigalupo, New Jersey
1992	Renatta Loquist, South Carolina
1995	Corinne Dorsey, Virginia
1996	Joan Bouchard, Oregon
1997	Jean Caron, Maine
1998	Elaine Ellibee, Wisconsin; Marcia Rachel, Mississippi; Jennifer Bosma, Executive Director, NCSBN
1999	Donna Dorsey, Maryland
2001	Charlie Dickson, Alabama
2002	Katherine Thomas, Texas
2003	Sharon Weisenbeck, Kentucky

Member Board Award/Regulatory Achievement Award

The Awards Committee continued as a committee of the board of directors in 1984 and considered the criteria for the selection of award recipients, the frequency of the presentation of the McManus Award, and the possibility of additional awards. The committee, comprising Dorothy Davy of Oregon, Marilyn Meinert of Missouri, and Lois O'Shea of Delaware, was asked to make recommendations as to the type and cost of award symbols.[11] With the report of the Awards Committee in May 1985, the board of directors agreed to the recommendations for two new awards, the Member Board Award and the Meritorious Service Award.[12]

The first of these awards, the Member Board Award, was to be presented every two years to a member board for identifiable, significant contributions to the purposes of NCSBN. However, in 1986 the board of directors accepted a recommendation from the Public Relations Committee that both the Member Board Award and the Meritorious Service Award could be given in the years the McManus Award was not presented.[13] The Member Board Award continued to be given through 2003. The name of the award was changed to the Regulatory Achievement Award in 2001. Since 1987 the award has taken the form of a wall-sized plaque. The Kentucky Board was the first recipient and is shown with subsequent recipients below:

MEMBER BOARD AWARD

1987	Kentucky Board of Nursing
1988	Minnesota Board of Nursing
1990	Texas Board of Nurse Examiners-RN
1991	Wisconsin Board of Nursing
1993	Virginia Board of Nursing
1994	Alaska Board of Nursing
1997	Nebraska Board of Nursing
1998	Utah State Board of Nursing
2000	Arkansas Board of Nursing

REGULATORY ACHIEVEMENT AWARD

2001   Alabama Board of Nursing

2002   West Virginia State Board of Examiners for Licensed Practical Nurses

2002   North Carolina Board of Nursing

Meritorious Service Award

The second new award agreed to by the board of directors in 1984 was the Meritorious Service Award. This award was for an individual who had made significant contributions to the purpose and growth of NCSBN, and had a significant impact on the promotion of matters of common interest and concern affecting public health, safety, and welfare. Originally it was given annually, except when the McManus Award was presented. The award took the form of a framed certificate. President Ruth Elliot of Oklahoma presented the first Meritorious Service Award in 1987 to Eileen McQuaid Dvorak, the original executive director of NCSBN. In addition to her dedicated work in developing the organization, McQuaid Dvorak was recognized for her work as a staff member with the New York State Board of Nurse Examiners, as the first chair of the NCSBN Examination Committee, and as chair of the corresponding committee for the American Nurses Association (ANA) Council of State Boards of Nursing.[14] *(see fig. 15-B)*

MERITORIOUS SERVICE AWARD

1987   Eileen McQuaid Dvorak, Executive Director, NCSBN

1988   Merlyn Maillian, Louisiana-RN

1990   Sister Lucie Leonard, Louisiana-RN

1991   Sharon Weisenbeck, Kentucky

1993   Charlie Dickson, Alabama

1994   Billie Haynes, California-VN

1995   Gail McGuill, Alaska

1996   Thomas O'Brien, Legal Counsel for NCSBN,

1997   Sister Teresa Harris, New Jersey; Helen Kelley, Massachusetts

1998   Helen (Pat) Keefe, Florida; Gertrude (Trudy) Malone, Montana

1999   Katherine Thomas, Texas-RN

2000   Margaret Howard, New Jersey

2001   Shirley Brekken, Minnesota

Silver Achievement Award

A new award category was added in 1998 by the board of directors. It was the Silver Achievement Award, presented for 25 years of service to a member board and NCSBN.[15] Joyce Schowalter was the first recipient of this award. It was presented in recognition of her 25 years of service to the Minnesota Board of Nursing and to NCSBN since its inception.[16] Nancy Wilson was the recipient of this award in 2000 after 25 years of service to the West Virginia State Board of Examiners for Licensed Practical Nurses. The Silver Achievement Award was eliminated with the creation of the Service Recognition Award acknowledging from 10 to 30 years of cumulative service to regulation and to a member board. Because of this change, Sharon Weisenbeck of Kentucky received the Service Recognition Award in 2001 rather than the Silver Achievement Award previously presented.

Other Awards

The Awards Committee of the board of directors continued until 1986 when the board referred activities related to awards to the Public Relations Committee, also a committee of the board.[17]

At its meeting in April 1991, the board of directors reviewed the report of the Communications Committee and discussed issues identified at the fall planning retreat related to the NCSBN Awards Program. The committee planned to present suggestions to enhance the effectiveness of the Awards Program in recognizing the efforts of volunteer leaders.[18]

The board of directors substantially changed the Awards Program in 1993 when it decided to accept nominations for all of the awards at any time. The revised process called for the board to review all nominations and present the award or awards "for which a deserving recipient has been identified."[19] At a later meeting in 1993 the board of directors adopted a policy related to board member participation in the selection of award recipients. The policy stated that board members should not nominate or support any award candidate, but if they did, then they could not participate in discussion or debate regarding that candidate.[20]

In 2000 the board of directors discussed the existing Awards Program and explored the possibility of a peer review process conducted by senior representatives from the member boards. Myra Broadway of Maine and Deborah Burton of Oregon, both directors-at-large, were charged with the development of recommendations for enhancements to the current awards process.[21] In 2001 an Awards Panel comprising Sharon Weisenbeck of Kentucky as chair, Donna Dorsey of Maryland, and Nancy Wilson of West Virginia-PN, presented a report in the *NCSBN Business Book* for the annual meeting. The purpose of the panel was to promote the consistency, fairness, and value of the Awards Program. The board of directors charged the three "senior leaders" to refine the nomination and selection process and establish clear, concise award objectives and criteria. The panel members explored the history of the Awards Program, expanded the categories of the awards, standardized the nomination forms and process, and established an objective selection process. In addition, the panel recommended that NCSBN explore the concept of a hall of fame. Finally, the panel suggested that its charge be expanded to play a role in the awards selection by screening, with a blind review of the candidates, and then making recommendations for consideration and final selection by the board of directors. The panel recommended that NCSBN continue the McManus Award, the Meritorious Service Award, and the Member Board Award, with the name of the latter changed to the Regulatory Achievement Award. The panel also recommended several new awards as follows:

- Exceptional Leadership Award—to be granted to a member board president for significant contributions to NCSBN.

- Outstanding Contribution Award—to be granted to a board of nursing member or staff member other than the president or the executive officer for significant contributions to NCSBN.

- Service Recognition—to recognize the contributions of the executive officers after 10 to 30 years of service.[22]

The board of directors agreed to the recommendations of the Awards Panel.[23] At the awards luncheon during the 2001 annual meeting, several awards were presented for the first time. These included the following:

EXCEPTIONAL LEADERSHIP AWARD

2001	June Bell, Kentucky
2002	Richard Sheehan, Maine
2003	Cookie Bible, Nevada

OUTSTANDING CONTRIBUTION AWARD

2001   **Julia Gould**, Georgia-RN; Lori Scheidt, Missouri; Ruth Lindgren, Wisconsin

2002   **Cora Clay**, Texas-VN

2003   **Sandra MacKenzie**, Minnesota

SERVICE RECOGNITION AWARDS FOR 2002

10-Year Service Recognition Awards—Dorothy Fulton, Alaska; Sandra Evans, Idaho; Joey Ridenour, Arizona; Elizabeth Tores Untalen, Northern Marianas Islands; Kathy Yokouchi, Hawaii; Charlene Kelley, Nebraska; Diana Vander Woude, South Dakota; Faith Fields, Arkansas; Polly Johnson, North Carolina; Barbara Morvant, Louisiana-RN; Katherine Thomas, Texas-RN; Iva Boardman, Delaware; Theresa Bonanno, Massachusetts; Winifred Garfield, Virgin Islands; Anita Ristau, Vermont

15-Year Service Recognition Awards—Teresa Bello-Jones, California-VN; Debra Brady, New Mexico; Ruth Ann Terry, California-RN; Shirley Brekken, Minnesota; Lorinda Inman, Iowa; Nancy Durrett, Virginia; Clair Glaviano, Louisiana-PN; Libby Lund, Tennessee; Marcia Rachel, Mississippi; Miriam Limo, Pennsylvania

20-Year Service Recognition Awards—Joan Bouchard, Oregon; Donna Dorsey, Maryland

25-Year Service Recognition Award—Sharon Weisenbeck, Kentucky

In 2002 the board of directors referred the concept of an NCSBN Hall of Fame to the Awards Recognition Panel for discussion and recommendations.[24] In May the board approved the recommendation from the Awards Recognition Panel for ceremonies at the opening and closing of the annual meeting, and asked former President Weisenbeck to preside at the awards ceremony that year.[25] In June the board decided to present a special recognition to Dr. Patricia Benner, a consultant to NCSBN, for her multiple contributions to and involvement with the NCSBN practice breakdown research and development of a curriculum for post-graduate degrees.[26] Some details of the accomplishments of the Awards Recognition Panel appeared in a report in the 2002 *NCSBN Business Book*. The report listed some of the activities of the panel as follows:

- Collaboration in the design of the Awards Program brochure.

- Development of an installation ceremony and for recognition of outgoing officers at the closing of the delegate assembly meeting.

- Recommendation that the outgoing president should receive a special resolution and a crystal gavel at the end of the term of office.

- Worked with the Twenty-fifth Anniversary Planning Advisory Panel to host the NCSBN birthday party at the 2003 awards luncheon.[27]

In June 2002 the board of directors decided to consider candidates for NCSBN awards regardless of their connections to the board of directors, and to seek information from the area meetings during the annual meeting regarding current awards policy and process and the continuation of the Awards Recognition Panel.[28] At its September 2002 meeting the board of directors decided that the awards nomination and selection process should not be a board function but rather the function of an independent group. The board of directors had been making the selections since 1983. The board appointed the four-person Awards Recognition Panel to include a representative from each area and, if possible, members who were former award recipients.[29] For the first time the Awards Recognition Panel, consisting of Louise Bailey of California-RN (Area I), Richard Sheehan of Maine (Area IV), Katherine Thomas of Texas-RN (Area III), and Susan Wambach of Michigan (Area II), conducted a blind review of all nominees for all awards, and selected the 2003 award recipients.[30]

Recognitions

Over the years, in addition to the on-going awards described above, NCSBN provided special recognition to individuals through resolutions, certificates, or plaques. On occasion the assembly would pause to acknowledge the death of an individual who had been active in the organization, commend executive officers on the occasion of their retirements, or to recognize other special events in the lives of individuals with connections to NCSBN. Throughout the first 25 years of NCSBN, the membership has acknowledged special people at appropriate occasions. Each year NCSBN continues to recognize the extensive volunteer service of those who serve on committees. Names are included in the awards luncheon programs, and certificates of appreciation are presented. Outgoing members of the board of directors receive special recognition as they complete their terms. Lapel pins consisting of the original NCSBN logo were presented to the past presidents and the incoming president beginning in 1983, a practice which continues today.[31] Since 2003 a crystal gavel has been presented to the outgoing president.

At the annual meeting in 1979 the delegate assembly began this process of recognition for commitment to the organization with the following actions:

- Expression of appreciation to Dr. Eileen McQuaid of New York for her significant contributions as a member and chair of the Examination Committee (formerly the Blueprint Committee) for the past seven years.

- Recognition of Martha Chesser, a delegate from the Georgia State Board of Licensed Practical Nurses, for her historic presence as the first LPN to serve as a voting member in the delegate assembly.

- Adoption of a resolution for Jessie Scott on her retirement as assistant surgeon general and director of the Division of Nursing at the US Department of Health, Education and Welfare.

- Adoption of a resolution expressing deep gratitude to Elaine Ellibee for her service as chair of the Special Task Force—State Boards of Nursing and first president of NCSBN.[32]

Some examples of resolutions and other acknowledgements follow. At the 1982 annual meeting, the delegate assembly adopted resolutions of appreciation for the NLN Test Service after almost 40 years of providing national licensing examinations for nurses in the United States.[33] In 1984 Executive Director McQuaid Dvorak presented a tribute in the form of a resolution commemorating the service to NCSBN and to nursing by Ray Showalter. Showalter was assistant executive director of NCSBN at the time of his death earlier in the year.[34] Later in the meeting the delegate assembly adopted a resolution of appreciation that recognized the contributions of Henrietta Marjan, who served as parliamentarian for the Special Task Force—State Boards of Nursing and NCSBN from 1977 through 1984.[35] The 1989 delegate assembly adopted a resolution to express appreciation to Eileen McQuaid Dvorak, the first executive director of NCSBN who served from 1979 to 1989.[36] In 1993 the membership recognized Ann Watkins, executive secretary at the NCSBN office. Watkins was honored as the longest serving member of the staff.[37] In 1994 the board of directors voted to contribute $1,000 to the Eileen Dvorak Memorial Fund at Loyola University School of Nursing following her death earlier in the year.[38] At the annual meeting that year, the delegate assembly adopted a resolution that called attention to the invaluable service rendered to both the profession and to the public by the California Testing Bureau/McGraw-Hill (CTB) in its 14-year involvement with the development of the National Council Licensure Examination (NCLEX®).[39]

At a meeting in February 1987 the board of directors approved a recommendation for the Communications Committee to initiate a program to recognize the efforts required of the volunteers on the NCSBN committees and task forces, the item writers, and the subject matter experts.[40] In 1988 the board of directors decided to present recognition plaques to past and current members of the board of directors who were completing their terms. The presentations were made for the first time at the 10th anniversary luncheon.[41] At the awards luncheon in 1989 NCSBN recognized 62 members completing terms on committees with appropriate certificates of appreciation.[42]

As a part of the 25th anniversary celebration in 2003, President Donna Dorsey of Maryland, on behalf of NCSBN, presented a special recognition in the category of individual service and another in the category of organizational service. Barbara Nichols, the executive director of the Commission on Graduates of Foreign Nursing Schools (CGFNS), accepted her recognition for individual service. Nichols, from 1977 to 1978, represented the ANA Board of Directors at the meetings of the Special Task Force—State Boards of Nursing that developed the process that led to the action to establish NCSBN. She became president of the ANA in 1978 and worked with the NCSBN leaders during its early years. Later Nichols' career took her into the regulation of health care providers in Wisconsin where she also interacted with NCSBN. In 2003 Nichols continues her long association with NCSBN.

The second special recognition was presented to the ANA. President Barbara Blakeney was present to accept the recognition. The dedication of the ANA, from its inception, to establishing legislation for the regulation of nursing was acknowledged, and both President Blakeney and President Dorsey commented on the continuing support for the regulatory process of the ANA Council of State Boards of Nursing until 1978, and a continuing liaison relationship between the ANA and NCSBN since that time.

The member boards from North Carolina, New Jersey, New York, and Virginia were recognized at the 2003 awards luncheon as they celebrated the centennial of their nursing practice acts—the first four in the United States—enacted in 1903. All four member boards were represented by a number of current and former members and staff and others from the states. *(see fig. 15-C)* A painting, commissioned by NCSBN, was unveiled to celebrate the anniversary of NCSBN and the guests enjoyed a birthday cake celebrating both 25 years and 100 years.

Awards Received

NCSBN received several awards in its first 25 years. In 1982 Vice President Schowalter accepted an honorary award of recognition of NCSBN from the Midwest Alliance in Nursing (MAIN) for the advancement of regulation and the support of research.[43] In 1990 the Clearinghouse on Licensure, Enforcement and Regulation (CLEAR), at its national annual conference, presented its 1990 Program Award to NCSBN. The award honored NCSBN for its quality program and the presentation cited three examples of innovative projects: the Computerized Adaptive Testing Project, the computerized Clinical Simulation Testing Project, and the Disciplinary Date Bank for Nursing. The award made reference to the "continuing leadership in the improvement of professional and occupational regulation," and was accepted by Vice President Joan Bouchard and Executive Director Jennifer Bosma.[44]

The Center for Telemedicine Law, in October 1999, presented its Health Innovators Award to NCSBN for the development of the Interstate Nurse Licensure Compact. The award recognized the leadership of NCSBN in "exploring regulatory solutions that would facilitate telehealth practice while permitting enforcement and ensuring the safety of health care consumers."[45]

Sigma Theta Tau International recognized NCSBN twice. Vickie Sheets accepted, on behalf of NCSBN, the 1998–1999 Region 4 Media Award for a video project entitled *Crossing the Line: When Professional Boundaries Are Violated.*[46] Another video, *Breaking the Habit: When Your Colleague Is Chemically Dependent*, received the 2002 Nursing Electronic Award from Sigma Theta Tau.[47]

Celebrations

Beginning in 1983 NCSBN has taken time out at the annual meeting every five years to celebrate its founding and to recognize those who have dedicated so much to building a strong and independent organization that serves the member boards in their responsibility to protect the public's health, safety, and welfare. In September 1982 the board of directors began to plan for the fifth anniversary observance. The board decided to invite all previous presidents who were no longer employed by a member board to the 1983 annual meeting and to pay their expenses. Gertrude (Trudy) Malone of Montana, former president, was employed as a consultant for a fee of $1,000, plus expenses, to prepare a publication for the anniversary.[48] This publication was completed with the assistance of Shirley Fondiller, a consultant to NCSBN and an internationally known journalist, educator, and nurse historian, and David Heidorn, a member of the NCSBN staff. Titled *From an Idea to an Organization*, the publication presented a history of the activities leading up to the organization of NCSBN in 1978, and its achievements during the first five years.[49] A fifth anniversary banquet was held in June at the annual meeting in Boston. A highlight of the program was an address on the history of NCSBN by one of the "founding architects," Trudy Malone. Of the first five presidents, four were at the dinner; only Elaine Ellibee of Wisconsin was unable to attend.[50]

In February 1988 the board of directors approved the plans for the 10th anniversary celebration luncheon, and authorized payment of all past presidents' expenses to attend the celebration.[51] NCSBN again published an anniversary booklet entitled *The Promise Continues: A Decade of Progress*. Shirley Fondiller, executive director of the Mid-Atlantic Regional Nursing Association and adjunct professor at Columbia University, was the author of this comprehensive history of NCSBN.[52] Of the six past presidents, five attended the luncheon in Des Moines: Elaine Ellibee, Trudy Malone, Mildred Schmidt, Joyce Schowalter, and Sharon Weisenbeck, as well as Ruth Elliott, the current president. Pat Keefe of Florida was unable to attend. In her first President's Message in *Issues*, Renatta Loquist of South Carolina reflected on the 10th anniversary celebration in August, saying,

> Nostalgia characterized the awards luncheon as Elaine Ellibee, first president of the organization, captured the pioneer spirits of those nurses who invested numerous hours and their personal financial resources to begin the organization. Ten years later, with 61 licensing jurisdictions as members and a 4.8 million dollar annual budget, the promise continues.

Loquist continued citing accomplishments in testing, the NCSBN Model Nursing Practice Act, position papers, and research, in addition to the response to the Nursing Home Reform Act and new services in response to the needs of the member boards. She concluded with the quotation that appears at the beginning of this chapter.[53]

In July 1992 the board of directors appointed Jean Caron of Maine to chair a committee to coordinate the 15th anniversary celebration at the 1993 annual meeting.[54] The celebration took place at an awards luncheon with Caron presiding. The decorations and costumes of the planners had an outer space theme, keeping with the location of the meeting at Disney World and the proximity to the Kennedy Space Center at Cape Canaveral. NCSBN did not publish an updated history for this anniversary. There was a pamphlet/program distributed at the luncheon that listed information about the awards, past presidents, area designations, and the NCSBN Mission Statement.

The board of directors began to plan for the 20th anniversary celebration in February 1998. The board decided to invite the original founders and to fund their travel. Other special invitees included past members of the board of directors, past awards recipients, and executive officers of the member boards, at their own expense.[55] President Thomas Neumann of Wisconsin presided at the 20th anniversary celebration program at the annual meeting in Albuquerque that preceded the awards luncheon. Former President Joyce Schowalter presented the framed, cancelled $50 check that was her donation in 1977 to start the work to create NCSBN. Elaine Ellibee, first president of NCSBN, spoke to the group. Other past presidents who were present included Pat Keefe, Sharon Weisenbeck, Ruth Elliott, Carolyn Hutcherson, and Renatta Loquist, as well as current President Rosa Lee Weinert. Mildred Schmidt was unable to attend and Trudy Malone's son was present to receive the Meritorious Service Award presented to her posthumously. A gala evening event with a theme related to historic Route 66, which passes through Albuquerque, was also part of the celebration.[56] Once again a booklet describing the preceding years of NCSBN was published and distributed at the 1998 annual meeting. The title of the publication was *The Road Traveled for Twenty Years—1998*. No specific author was cited as it was assembled by the staff of NCSBN with contributions from many who had actively participated in creating the history of "the road traveled."[57]

1978–2003: 25 Years of the National Council of State Boards of Nursing
Honoring Our Past to Create Our Future *(see fig. 15-D)*

The year 2003 had special significance for NCSBN and its member boards. The first four laws to regulate nursing in the United States were adopted in 1903. Therefore the 25th anniversary of NCSBN coincided with the centennial of the enactment of these laws. This was indeed an occasion for celebration and planning began early. The board of directors first discussed the commemoration in August of 2000 and decided to establish a committee to explore items related to the anniversaries.[58] Libby Lund of Tennessee served as chair of this committee. At a meeting in 2001 the board approved the plan to hold the 25th anniversary gala celebration at the Women in the Military Museum at Arlington National Cemetery. At the same meeting, at the suggestion of President Joey Ridenour of Arizona, the board of directors agreed to commission a painting to reflect NCSBN on its anniversary in 2003.[59] In 2002 the board approved a budget of $150,000 for the celebration.[60] Further, the board accepted the following recommendations from the Twenty-Fifth Anniversary Planning Advisory Panel:

- That the gala cost be contained in the registration fee for the annual meeting and that for those individuals who wish to attend only the gala, separate registration be offered on a first-come, first-serve basis after delegate assembly registration is closed, up to a maximum number of 450 attendees.

- That each member board be responsible for inviting their significant and former members who may wish to attend the gala.

- That only past NCSBN presidents be invited to attend the gala at a waived fee.

- That there would be no speaker at the gala, but NCSBN past presidents could make a few remarks and/or other luminaries and dignitaries could give introductions or toasts.

- That the preliminary revenue target budget for external sponsorships be set at $50,000 and that a letter be sent to Pearson/Vue requesting that they be the "Platinum Sponsor"[61]

In February 2003 the board of directors learned that fundraising for the celebration had exceeded expectations.[62] The Report of the Twenty-fifth Anniversary Planning Advisory Panel listed numerous activities that had been accomplished. These included the following:

- Planned for the gala dinner.

- Assisted in the selection of the logo.

- Assisted with fundraising and development activities.

- Planned the historical booklet to include data on all member boards and other NCSBN facts.

- Collaborated with the Awards Panel to plan the awards and birthday luncheon where special recognition would be extended to the ANA, to Barbara Nichols, and to the four member boards celebrating the centennial of their nursing practice acts.[63]

The booklet, *1978–2003: 25 Years of the National Council of State Boards of Nursing: Honoring Our Past to Create Our Future*, was distributed at the gala. It is a valuable resource on the history of the regulation of nursing in the Untied States as well as the 25 years of activity of NCSBN. Each past president and the current president, Donna Dorsey of Maryland, is highlighted, with direct quotes from most.[64] At the gala special recognition was given to the past presidents. Of the 14 presidents who had served NCSBN, 8 were present. They were Joyce Schowalter, Sharon Weisenbeck, Renatta Loquist, Carolyn Hutcherson, Rosa Lee Weinert, Marcia Rachel, Joey Ridenour, and Donna Dorsey. However, none of the four original members of the Special Task Force—State Boards of Nursing, who were the first officers of NCSBN, were present.

Conclusion

Since its inception NCSBN has recognized the importance of rewarding outstanding contributions. Perhaps the most difficult part of the process has been found in the problem of discriminating among so many committed, talented leaders. It is noteworthy that NCSBN has gone outside its member boards and the board of directors to recognize excellence, leadership, and service. The celebration continues in anticipation of the 30th anniversary of NCSBN in 2008.

This history of NCSBN appropriately closes with the chapter that describes the awards and celebrations that have occurred in the first 25 years of the organization. The early chapters describe efforts that span more than 100 years beginning with the first licensing laws in the early 20th century, and culminate with the plans for international administration of the licensing examination at the beginning of a new century. The members and staff of the boards of nursing, the staff of NCSBN, the staff of the test services, and the representatives from many other organizations collaborated to achieve phenomenal accomplishments in the relatively short time between 1978 and 2003. The description of these accomplishments has been difficult because of the vastness and depth of them. Additional recognition should be given to each representative of a member board who, acting collectively as the NCSBN Delegate Assembly, made decisions that allowed the dreams, ideas and efforts of their predecessors to become reality.

APPENDIX A
EVOLUTION OF GOALS AND OBJECTIVES
1986-2001

GOALS AND OBJECTIVES (1986)

Goals

I.   Develop, promote, and provide relevant and innovative services.

Objectives

    A.   Develop licensure examinations that are based upon current accepted psychometric principles and legal considerations.

    B.   Establish policies for the licensing examinations in nursing.

    C.   Provide consultative services for council members, groups, agencies, and individuals regarding the safe and effective practice of nursing.

    D.   Maintain and enhance communication about NCSBN, its members, and issues concerning safe and effective nursing practice.

    E.   Promote consistency in the licensing process among the respective jurisdictions.

II. Utilize human and fiscal resources efficiently to allow growth and creativity

    A.   Implement a planning model to be used as a guide for the development of NCSBN.

    B.   Strengthen the organizational structure in the complex environment of high technology, transforming health care delivery systems, global communications and international interaction.

III. Expand collaborative relationships with relevant organizations to facilitate the development of health related public policy.

    A.   Provide specific opportunity for direct dialogues, interactions, and mutual decision-making among national health groups.

B.   Promote and facilitate effective communications with related organizations, groups, and individuals.

C.   Increase consumer involvement in NCSBN.

IV.   Develop a comprehensive information system for use by members, organizations, and the public.

A.   Implement a five year plan for an information system.

B.   Collect, analyze, and disseminate data and statistics in such areas as licensure, educational programs, and regulatory functions.

V.   Advance research that contributes to the public health, safety and welfare.

A.   Conduct and disseminate research pertinent to the mission of the NCSBN.

B.   Promote research proposals annually which merit funding.

C.   Involve member boards in research at the jurisdictional level for use and distribution by the NCSBN.

Adopted 1986
Amended 1992

STRATEGIC INITIATIVES AND OUTCOMES (2001)

Strategic Initiatives

I.   Nursing Competence. National Council will assist Member Boards in their role in the evaluation of nurse and nurse aide competence.

Outcomes

A.   NCLEX® is state-of-the-art entry-level nurse licensure assessment.

B.   NCLEX® is administered at international sites for purposes of domestic licensure.

C.   International testing examinations are explored for foreign nurse licensure.

D.   Nurse aide competence is assessed.

E.   Inform stakeholders about the NCLEX® examination program and related products/services.

F.   Research demonstrates relationships of various regulatory approaches to validate continued competence.

II.   Regulatory effectiveness. The National Council will assist Member Boards to implement strategies to promote regulatory effectiveness to fulfill their public protection role.

A.   Advanced regulatory strategies promote public protection and effective nursing practices.

B.   Models for system and individual accountability address practice issues.

C.   Strategies assist Member Boards to respond effectively to critical issues and trends impacting nursing education and practice.

D.   Approaches and resources assist Member Boards in the regulation of advanced practice registered nurses.

E.   Approaches and resources address issues related to assistive nursing personnel.

F.   New knowledge and research support regulatory approaches to discipline, remediation and alternative processes.

G. National Council supports, monitors and evaluates the implementation of the Mutual Recognition Model.

H. Resources and tools assist Member Boards to measure performance.

III. Public Policy. The National Council will analyze the changing health care environment to develop state and national strategies to impact public policy and regulations affecting public protection.

A. National Council and Member Board leadership impact national and state health care and regulatory policy.

B. Effective collaboration exists among practice, education and regulation.

C. National Council analysis of national and international trends impacting public protection is current and disseminated to Member Boards.

IV. Information Technology. The National Council will develop information technology solutions valued and utilized by Member Boards to enhance regulatory efficiency.

A. Information technology infrastructure is enhanced among Member Boards, National Council and service providers.

B. Information technology provided improves Member Boards efficiency and productivity.

C. Nur*sys*™ [now a registered trademark] is the preferred national data base among Member Boards, employers and nurses for licensure information.

D. The collection, storage and use of data by Member Boards are standardized, accurate.

E. The Web site maximizes access to regulatory education and information by Member Boards and the public.

V. Governance and Leadership Development. The National Council will support the education and development of Member Board Staff Members and the Board of Directors.

A. Member Board staffs and members access multiple levels of educational programs to develop core competencies in regulation.

B. Member Boards understand the services of National Council.

C. A sound organizational governance advances the NCSBN mission and vision.

D. The planning process promotes Member Board satisfaction with National Council products and services.

Adopted 1998
Amended 2001

APPENDIX B
BOARDS OF DIRECTORS
1978–2003

1978–1979

Elaine Ellibee, WI, President (resigned 5/79)
S. Gertrude Malone, MT, Vice-President (succeeded to Presidency 5/79)
Helen P. Keefe, FL, Secretary
Mildred S. Schmidt, NY, Treasurer
Elaine Laeger, AZ, Area I Director
Joyce Schowalter, MN, Area II Director
Margaret Rowland, TX-RN, Area III Director
Marianna Bacigalupo, NJ, Area IV Director
Ruth Seigler, SC, Director-at-Large

1979–1980

Mildred Schmidt, NY, President
Elaine Laeger, AZ, Vice-President
Merlyn Maillian, LA-RN, Treasurer
Helen Keefe, FL, Secretary
Ann Petersen, UT, Area I Director
Joyce Schowalter, MN, Area II Director
Margaret Rowland, TX-RN, Area III Director
Marianna Bacigalupo, NJ, Area IV Director
Ruth Seigler, SN, Director-at-Large

1980–1981

Mildred Schmidt, NY, President
Joyce Schowalter, MN, Vice-President
Merlyn Maillian, LA-RN, Treasurer
Marianna Bacigalupo, NJ, Secretary
Ann Petersen, UT, Area I Director
Jo Franklin, IL, Area II Director
Margaret Rowland, TX-RN, Area III Director
Kathleen Dwyer, RI, Area IV Director
Margaret Sullivan, WA-RN, Director-at-Large

1981–1982

Helen Keefe, FL, President
Joyce Schowalter, MN, Vice-President
Nancy Dean, GA-RN, Treasurer
Marianna Bacigalupo, NJ, Secretary
Phyllis Sheridan, ID, Area I Director
Jo Franklin, IL, Area II Director (resigned 1982)
Joan Nuttall, WI, Area II Director (appointed 1982 to replace Jo Franklin)
Merlyn Maillian, LA-RN, Area III Director
Kathleen Dwyer, RI, Area IV Director
Margaret Sullivan, WA-RN, Director-at-Large

1982–1983

Joyce Schowalter, MN, President
Kathleen Dwyer, RI, Vice-President (resigned 9/82)
Ann Petersen, UT, Vice-President (appointed 9/82 to replace Kathleen Dwyer)
Nancy Dean, GA-RN, Treasurer (resigned 12/82)
Gertrude Hodges, MD, Treasurer (appointed 12/82 to replace Nancy Dean)
Sharon Weisenbeck, KY, Secretary
Phyllis Sheridan, ID, Area I Director
Joan Nuttall, WI, Area II Director
Merlyn Maillian, LA-RN, Area III Director
Lois O'Shea, DE, Area IV Director
Ann Petersen, UT, Director-at-Large (until 9/82 when appointed vice president)
H. Jean Bruhn, PA, Director-at-Large (appointed 9/82 to replace Ann Petersen)

1983–1984

Joyce Schowalter, MN, President
Ann Petersen, UT, Vice-President
Nancy Wilson, WV-PN, Treasurer
Sharon Weisenbeck, KY, Secretary
Phyllis Sheridan, ID, Area I Director
Vivien Deback, WI, Area II Director
Anna Kuba, SC, Area III Director (resigned 2/84)
Mary Schilling, NC, Area III Director (appointed 2/84 to replace Anna Kuba)
Lois O'Shea, DE, Area IV Director
H. Jean Bruhn, PA, Director-at-Large

1984–1985

Sharon Weisenbeck, KY, President
Phyllis Sheridan, ID, Vice-President
Nancy Wilson, WV-PN, Treasurer
Constance Roth, WA-RN, Secretary
Dorothy Davy, OR, Area I Director
Marilyn Meinert, MO, Area II Director
Ruth Elliott, OK, Area III Director
Lois O'Shea, DE, Area IV Director (resigned 12/84)
H. Jean Bruhn, PA, Area IV Director (appointed 12/84 to replace Lois O'Shea)
Renatta Loquist, SC, Director-at-Large

1985–1986

Sharon Weisenbeck, KY, President
Phyllis Sheridan, ID, Vice-President
Nancy Wilson, WV-PN, Treasurer
Constance Roth, WA-RN, Secretary
Dorothy Davy, OR, Area I Director
Marilyn Meinert, MO, Area II Director (resigned 12/85)
Elizabeth Kinney, IA, Area II Director (appointed 12/85 to replace Marilyn Meinert)
Ruth Elliott, OK, Area III Director
Jean Caron, ME, Area IV Director
Renatta Loquist, SC, Director-at-Large

1986–1987

Ruth Elliott, OK, President
Joan Bouchard, WY, Vice-President
Donna Dorsey, MD, Treasurer
Constance Roth, WA-RN, Secretary
Dorothy Davy, OR, Area I Director
Leota Rolls, NE, Area II Director
Sandra Brown, AR, Area III Director
Jean Caron, ME, Area IV Director
H. Jean Bruhn, PA, Director-at-Large

1987–1988

Ruth Elliott, OK, President
Joan Bouchard, OR, Vice-President
Donna Dorsey, MD, Treasurer
Renatta Loquist, SC, Secretary
Nancy Twigg, NM, Area I Director
Leota Rolls, NE, Area II Director
Carolyn Hutcherson, GA-RN, Area III Director
Jean Caron, ME, Area IV Director
H. Jean Bruhn, PA, Director-at-Large

1988–1989

Renatta Loquist, SC, President
Joan Bouchard, OR, Vice-President
Donna Dorsey, MD, Treasurer
Helen Kelley, MA, Secretary
Nancy Twigg, NM, Area I Director
Judy Jondahl, IL, Area II Director
Carolyn Hutcherson, GA-RN, Area III Director
Jean Caron, ME, Area IV Director
Lonna Burress, NV, Director-at-Large (resigned 4/89)
Carol Stuart, SD, Director-at-Large (appointed 5/89 to replace Lonna Burress)

1989–1990

Renatta Loquist, SC, President
Joan Bouchard, OR, Vice-President
Donna Dorsey, MD, Treasurer
Helen Kelley, MA, Secretary
Gail McGuill, AK, Area I Director
Judy Jondahl, IL, Area II Director
Carolyn Hutcherson, GA-RN, Area III Director
Jean Caron, ME, Area IV Director
Carol Stuart, SD, Director-at-Large

1990–1991

Carolyn Hutcherson, GA-RN, President
Joan Bouchard, OR, Vice-President
Donna Dorsey, MD, Treasurer
Helen Kelley, MA, Secretary
Gail McGuill, AK, Area I Director
Shirley Brekken, MN, Area II Director
Charlie Dickson, AL, Area III Director
Jean Caron, ME, Area IV Director
Carol Stuart, SD, Director-at-Large (resigned 12/90)
Susan Boots, WA-PN, Director-at-Large (appointed 1/91 to replace Carol Stuart)

1991–1992

Carolyn Hutcherson, GA-RN, President
Joan Bouchard, OR, Vice-President
Carol Osman, NC, Treasurer
Judie Ritter, FL, Secretary (resigned 8/92)
Helen Kelley, MA, Secretary (appointed 8/92 to replace Judie Ritter)
Gail McGuill, AK, Area I Director
Shirley Brekken, MN, Area II Director
Marcella McKay, MS, Area III Director
Jean Caron, ME, Area IV Director
Susan Boots, WA-PN, Director-at-Large

1992–1993

Rosa Lee Weinert, OH, President
Gail McGuill, AK, Vice-President
Carol Osman, NC, Treasurer
Helen Kelley, MA, Secretary
Fran Roberts, AZ, Area I Director
Thomas Neumann, WI, Area II Director
Marcella McKay, MS, Area III Director
Sr. Teresa Harris, NJ, Area IV Director
Judi Crume, AL, Director-at-Large

1993–1994

Rosa Lee Weinert, OH, President
Gail McGuill, AK, Vice-President
Charlene Kelly, NE, Treasurer
Cynthia VanWingerden, VI, Secretary
Fran Roberts, AZ, Area I Director
Thomas Neumann, WI, Area II Director
Nancy Durrett, VA, Area III Director
Sr. Teresa Harris, NJ, Area IV Director
Judi Crume, AL, Director-at-Large

1994–1995

Marcia Rachel, MS, President
Thomas Neumann, WI, Vice-President
Charlene Kelly, NE, Treasurer
Cynthia VanWingerden, VI, Secretary
Fran Roberts, AZ, Area I Director
Linda Seppanen, MN, Area II Director
Nancy Durrett, VA, Area III Director
Marie Hilliard, CT, Area IV Director
Roselyn Holloway, TX-RN, Director-at-Large

1995–1996

Marcia Rachel, MS, President
Thomas Neumann, WI, Vice-President
Charlene Kelly, NE, Treasurer
Jo Elizabeth Ridenour, AZ, Area I Director
Linda Seppanen, MN, Area II Director
Nancy Durrett, VA, Area III Director
Marie Hilliard, CT, Area IV Director
Roselyn Holloway, TX-RN, Director-at-Large
Janet Wood-Yanez, TX-VN, Director-at-Large

1996–1997

Thomas Neumann, WI, President
Margaret Howard, NJ, Vice-President
Charlene Kelly, NE, Treasurer
Jo Elizabeth Ridenour, AZ, Area I Director
Linda Seppanen, MN, Area II Director
Nancy Durrett, VA, Area III Director
Marie Hilliard, CT, Area IV Director (resigned 1/96)
Anna Yoder, MA, Director-at-Large (resigned 1/96)
Anna Yoder, MA, Area IV Director (appointed 1/96 to replace Marie Hilliard)
Gregory Howard, AL, Director-at-Large (appointed 1/96 to replace Anna Yoder)
Laura Poe, UT, Director-at-Large

1997–1998

Thomas Neumann, WI, President
Margaret Howard, NJ, Vice-President
Charlene Kelly, NE, Treasurer
Jo Elizabeth Ridenour, AZ, Area I Director
Lorinda Inman, IA, Area II Director
Julia Gould, GA-RN, Area III Director
Anna Yoder, MA, Area IV Director
Gregory Howard, AL, Director-at-Large
Laura Poe, UT, Director-at-Large

1998–1999

Jo Elizabeth Ridenour, AZ, President
Margaret Howard, NJ, Vice-President
Barbara Morvant, LA-RN, Treasurer
Dorothy Fulton, AK, Area I Director
Lorinda Inman, IA, Area II Director
Julia Gould, GA-RN, Area III Director
Anna Yoder, MA, Area IV Director
Kathy Apple, NV, Director-at-Large
Cindy VanWingerden, VI, Director-at-Large

1999–2000

Jo Elizabeth Ridenour, AZ, President
Margaret Howard, NJ, Vice-President
Barbara Morvant, LA-RN, Treasurer
Dorothy Fulton, AK, Area I Director
Lorinda Inman, IA, Area II Director
Julia Gould, GA-RN, Area III Director
Iva Boardman, DE, Area IV Director
Kathy Apple, NV, Director-at-Large
Faith Fields, AR, Director-at-Large

2000–2001

Jo Elizabeth Ridenour, AZ, President
Kathy Apple, NV, Vice President (resigned 5/01 when appointed executive director)
Lorinda Inman, IA, Vice-President (appointed 5/01 to replace Kathy Apple)
Barbara Morvant, LA-RN, Treasurer
Dorothy Fulton, AK, Area I Director
Lorinda Inman, IA, Area II Director (until 5/01 when appointed vice president)
Charlene Kelly, NE, Area II Director (appointed 5/01 to replace Lorinda Inman)
Julia Gould, GA-RN, Area III Director
Iva Boardman, DE, Area IV Director
Deborah Burton, OR, Director-at-Large
Myra Broadway, ME, Director-at-Large

2001–2002

Jo Elizabeth Ridenour, AZ, President
Marcia Hobbs, KY, Vice-President
Barbara Morvant, LA-RN, Treasurer
Paula Meyer, WA, Area I Director
Deborah Johnson, ND, Area II Director
Mark Majek, TX-RN, Area III Director
Iva Boardman, DE, Area IV Director
Deborah Burton, OR, Director-at-Large
Myra Broadway, ME, Director-at-Large

2002–2003

Donna Dorsey, MD, President
Marcia Hobbs, KY, Vice-President
Sandra Evans, ID, Treasurer
Paula Meyer, WA, Area I Director
Deborah Johnson, ND, Area II Director
Mark Majek, TX-RN, Area III Director
Iva Boardman, DE, Area IV Director
Polly Johnson, NC, Director-at-Large
Gregory Harris, AZ, Director-at-Large

2003–2004

Donna Dorsey, MD, President
Marcia Hobbs, KY, Vice-President
Sandra Evans, ID, Treasurer
Gregory Harris, AZ, Area I Director
Mary Blubaugh, KS, Area II Director
Mark Majek, TX-RN, Area III Director
Myra Broadway, ME, Area IV Director
Polly Johnson, NC, Director-at-Large
Marjesta Jones, AL, Director-at-Large

APPENDIX C
STAFF MEMBERS
1978–2003

This listing is as complete as possible following a search of available resources.
The authors and the current staff of NCSBN regret any possible omissions from the listing.

Richard Albert, Jr.

Deirdre L. Ambrose

Talinda M. Anderson

Wanda Anderson

Burleigh P. Angle

Kathy L. Apple

Renee L. Aye

Sean M. Barden

Christian R. Barden

Richard E. Bentel

Cynthia M. Bentel

Ruth Bernstein Spiro

Anna K. Bersky

Amanda A. Bird

Amy S. Bloom

Brian D. Bontempo

Jodi L. Borger

Jennifer L. Bosma

Tamara D. Bowles

Casey R. Braun

Sandra O. Brooks

Patricia A. Brown

Valerie D. Brown

Yvonne Brown

Ladon A. Brumfield

William E. Burd

Eric W. Burnley

Alicia E. Byrd

Delores A. Caruso

Huan D. Cassioppi Tran

Eloise Cathcart

Kathryn D. Cavittt

Beth A. Cayia

Wayne Chamberlain

Andrea L. Change

Nancy L. Chornick

Lisa A. Clare

Robert Clayborne

Leslee R. Clements

Robert M. Coffman

Darcy R. Colby

Andrea D. Coleman

Sister Mary Carol Conroy

Anita R. Cooper

Lynda H. Crawford

Diane M. Creal

Victor M. Crown

Caroliah Cullins

Amy C. Dancisak

Deborah S. Danielson

Susan M. Davids

Audrey L. Davis

Patricia E. Deeb

Beth D. DeMars

Frankie R. Desmangles

Angela Diaz-Kay

Cheryl Dillon

John E. Ditzel

Dennis Dixon Jr.

Patrick J. Donahue

Joseph R. Dudzik

Sharon T. Dust

Eileen McQuaid Dvorak

Larry A. Early

Michelle L. Eich

Ruth L. Elliott

Gloria M. Evans

Dawn Elizabeth Farwell

Charisse L. Franklin

Magdalene J. Frazier

Heather J. Freise

Rosemary E. Gahl

Abigail R. Gahol

Jennifer E. Gallagher

Kristin D. Garcia

Susan H. Gawel

Mary Gerace

Irene M. Geschke

Karen M. Ginsberg

Ellen M. Gleason

Thomas H. Glover

Amy P. Gray

Dorothy Fay Green

Marie L. Halverson

Maria Hambesis-Martino

Laila H. Hameed

Haiba A. Hamilton

Christopher T. Handzlik

Lenore L. Harris

Mattie A. Harris

Debbie C. Hart

Carol A. Hartigan

Kathleen J. Hayden

Steve Yi He

Linda F. Heffernan

David L. Heidorn

Kristin A. Hellquist

Gracellen Heneghan

David V. Henley

Judith E. Hertz

Jacquelin E. Hill

Ellyn M. Hirsch

Laura Hoeckner

Thomas Hoffman

James Dean Hope

Beverly J. Howard

Marco A. Huerta

Kathy K. Hughes

Carolyn M. Hutcherson

Kristin L. Hutcherson

Vera Barbara Hynes

Peggy E. Iverson

Jerrold W. Jacobson

Clayton M. Johnson

Carolyn M. Johnson

Kimberly A. Jones

Ellen R. Julian

Steven A. Kaiser

Dmitri A. Karasik

Julie A. Kayman

Christine M. Keller

Marsha D. Kelly

Lorraine E. Kenny

Heather M. Keys

Jin H. Kim

Rita R. Kirkendall

Deborah A. Knoner

June Krawczak

Michael P. Kreusch

Dmitri Kucherina

David G. Kuester

Tara D. Kumar

Danni M. Kuzyk

Philip J. LaForge

Catherine Latturner

William J. Lauf

Stephen J. Lawler

Shari Lawler

Marci B. Leon

David P. Lloyd

Daoxin Lu

Lisa M. Luke

Amy C. Lund-Langen

Sharon R. Lunn

Naseeruddin Mahmood

Michelle S. Maloney

Casey Marks

Donna M. Masiulewicz

Wendy E. Mathews

Jenny McClain

Margaret C. McGrath

Nancy J. Miller

Craig S. Moore

Danyetta E. Murray

Doris E. Nay

Melanie L. Neal

Bryan M. Newson

Lea R. Newson

Valerie Nichols

Virginia M. Noga

Donna M. Nowakowski

Kerry L. Nowicki

Lamika M. Obichere

Maria G. Ojeda

Thomas R. O'Neill

Harlene L. Pearlman

Helene S. Pensinger

Louise W. Peter

Nancy A. Peterson

Barbara A. Pieta

Kathleen M. Potvin

Arleen Putlak

Sandra L. Rhodes

Marian L. Rippy-Hogins

Carol J. Ritchell

Lori A. Robbins

Jennifer O. Roberts

Anne M. Rocco

Pamela A. Rogalski

Brenda J. Ross

Bruce C. Rowe

Toni A. Rucker

Faisal N. Saiyed

Maureen L. Sanders

Larry A. Sankey

Maribel Santigo

Renee M. Scaletta

Barbara J. Schimke

Anthony W. Schmidt

Amanda L. Schreiner

Barbara Schroeder-Halsey

Matthew E. Schulz

Vickie R. Sheets

Michael D. Sheets

Amanda M. Sheets

Susan K. Shepherd

Raymond Showalter

Kathleen A. Siggeman

Susan A. Siwinski-Hebel

Jill A. Slaski

Richard A. Smiley

June E. Smith

Tammy K. Spangler

Nancy M. Spector

Kevin J. Stock

Wade A. Strawbridge

Cathy Y. Streeter

Annaliese A. Studer

Marcy Sylvester

Patrick J. Terry

Denetrice M. Theard

Jennifer M. Tiffen

Cynthia D. Titus

Valerie Tolson

Michael J. Tomaselli

Debra A. Tomsky

Mary C. Trucksa

Leslie A. Uriss

Bexaida Vargas

Sara S. Venkus

Thomas C. Vicek

Frances R. Vlasses

Ruth I. Volpert

Christine M. Ward

Ernestine Ware

Ann B. Watkins

Ernestine Welch

Anne L. Wendt

Tracey J. Whitaker

Esther L. White

Andrea Wilburn

Keith A. Williams

Susan H. Williamson

Holly L. Wilson

Jennifer L. Wilson

Susan K. Woodward

Deborah L. Woolley

Fleurette J. Workman

Deborah S. Wright

Carolyn J. Yocom

Mildred L. Yopst

Rayda D. Young

Anthony R. Zara

Mary L. Zayas

Xiaoqiong (Cindy) Zhang

Carin L. Zuger

APPENDIX D
EVOLUTION OF DEFINITIONS OF NURSING

From the *NCSBN Model Nursing Practice Act* as adopted in 1982:

ARTICLE II. DEFINITIONS

Section 1. Practice of Nursing. The "Practice of Nursing" means assisting individuals or groups to maintain or attain optimal health throughout the life process by assessing their health status, establishing a diagnosis, planning and implementing a strategy of care to accomplish defined goals, and evaluating responses to care and treatment.

Section 2. Registered Nurse. "Registered Nurse" means a person who practices professional nursing by:

A. Assessing the health status of individuals and groups;

B. Establishing a nursing diagnosis;

C. Establishing goals to meet identified health care needs;

D. Planning strategies of care;

E. Prescribing nursing interventions to implement the strategy of care;

F. Implementing the strategy of care;

G. Authorizing nursing interventions that may be performed by others and that do not conflict with this Act;

H. Maintaining safe and effective nursing care rendered directly or indirectly;

I. Evaluating responses to interventions;

J. Teaching the theory and practice of nursing;

K. Managing the practice of nursing, and;

L. Collaborating with other health professionals in the management of health care.

Section 3. Licensed Practical Nurse. "Licensed Practical Nurse" means a person who practices nursing by:

    A.   Contributing to the assessment of the health status of individuals and groups;

    B.   Participating in the development and modification of the strategy of care;

    C.   Implementing the appropriate aspects of the strategy of care as defined by the Board;

    D.   Maintaining safe and effective nursing care rendered directly or indirectly;

    E.   Participating in the evaluation of responses to interventions, and;

    F.   Delegating nursing interventions that may be performed by others and that do not conflict with this Act.

The Licensed Practical Nurse functions at the direction of the Registered Nurse, licensed physician, or licensed dentist in the performance of activities delegated by that health care professional.

From the *NCSBN Model Nursing Practice Act* as adopted in 2004:

ARTICLE II. SCOPE OF NURSING PRACTICE

Section 1. Practice of Nursing. Nursing is a scientific process founded on a professional body of knowledge; it is a learned profession based on an understanding of the human condition across the lifespan and the relationship of a client with others and within the environment; and it is an art dedicated to caring for others. The practice of nursing means assisting clients to attain or maintain optimal health, implementing a strategy of care to accomplish defined goals within the context of a client centered health care plan, and evaluating responses to nursing care and treatment. Nursing is a dynamic discipline that is continually evolving to include more sophisticated knowledge, technologies and client care activities.

Section 2. Registered Nurse. Practice as a registered nurse means the full scope of nursing, with or without compensation or personal profit, that incorporates caring for all clients in all settings; is guided by the scope of practice authorized in this section through nursing standards established or recognized by the board and includes, but is not limited to:

    A.   Providing comprehensive nursing assessment of the health status of clients

    B.   Collaborating with health care team to develop an integrated client-centered health care plan.

    C.   Developing a strategy of nursing care to be integrated within the client-centered health care plan that establishes nursing diagnoses; setting goals to meet identified health care needs; determining nursing interventions; and implementing nursing care through the execution of independent nursing strategies and regimens requested, ordered or prescribed by authorized health care providers.

    D.   Delegating and assigning nursing intervention to implement the plan of care.

    E.   Providing for the maintenance of safe and effective nursing care rendered directly or indirectly.

    F.   Promoting a safe and therapeutic environment.

    G.   Advocating for clients by attaining and maintaining what is in the best interest of clients.

    H.   Evaluating responses to interventions and the effectiveness of the plan of care.

    I.   Communicating and collaborating with other health care providers in the management of health care and the implementation of the total health care regimen within and across care settings.

    J.   Acquiring and applying critical new knowledge and technologies to the practice domain.

    K.   Managing, supervising and evaluating the practice of nursing.

L. Teaching the theory and practice of nursing.

M. Participating in development of policies, procedures and systems to support the client.

N. Other acts that require education and training as delineated by the board commensurate with the registered nurse's continuing education, demonstrated competencies and experience. Each nurse is accountable for complying with the requirements of this act and for the quality of nursing care rendered; and for recognizing limits of knowledge, experience and planning of situations beyond the nurse's expertise.

Section 3. Licensed Practical/Vocational Nurse. Practice as a licensed practical/vocational nurse means a directed scope of nursing practice, with or without compensation or personal profit, under the direction of the registered nurse, advanced practice registered nurse, licensed physician or other health care provider authorized by the state; is guided by nursing standards established or recognized by the board; and includes, but is not limited to:

A. Collecting data and conducting focused nursing assessments of the health status of individuals.

B. Planning nursing care episode for individuals with stable conditions.

C. Participating in the development and modification of the comprehensive plan of care for all types of clients.

D. Implementing appropriate aspects of the strategy of care within client centered health care plan.

E. Participating in nursing care management through delegating to assistive personnel and assigning to other LPN/VNs nursing interventions that may be performed by others and do not conflict with this act.

F. Maintaining safe and effective nursing care rendered directly or indirectly.

G. Promoting a safe and therapeutic environment.

H. Participating in health teaching and counseling to promote, attain and maintain the optimum health level of clients.

I. Serving as an advocate for the client by communicating and collaborating with other health service personnel.

J. Participating in the evaluation of client responses to interventions.

K. Communicating and collaborating with other health care professionals.

L. Providing input into the development of policies and procedures.

M. Other acts that require education and training as delineated by the board, commensurate with the licensed practical nurse's experience, continuing education and demonstrated licensed practical/vocational nurse competencies. Each nurse is accountable for complying with the requirements of this Act; and for the quality of nursing care rendered; and for recognizing limits of knowledge and experience and planning for management of situations beyond the nurse's expertise.

Section 4. Advanced Practice Registered Nurse. Advanced practice registered nursing by nurse practitioners, nurse anesthetists, nurse midwives or clinical nurse specialists is based on knowledge and skills acquired in basic nursing education; licensure as a registered nurse, graduation from or completion of a graduate level APRN program accredited by a national accrediting body and current certification by a national certifying body acceptable to the board in the specified APRN role and specialty.

Practice as an advanced practice registered nurse means a scope of nursing in a category approved by the board, with or without compensation or personal profit, and includes the registered nurse scope of practice. The scope of an advanced practice registered nurse includes but is not limited to performing acts of advanced assessment, diagnosing, prescribing, selecting, administering and dispensing therapeutic measures, including over-the-counter drugs, legend drugs and controlled substances, within the advance practice registered nurse's role and specialty, appropriate education and certification. The advanced practice registered nurse scope of practice supersedes the registered nurse scope of practice.

Advanced practice registered nurses are expected to practice within standards established or recognized by the board. Each advanced practice registered nurse is accountable to clients, the nursing profession and the board for complying with the requirements of this Act and the quality of advanced nursing care rendered; for recognizing limits of knowledge and experience, planning for the management of situations beyond the APRN's expertise; and for consulting with or referring clients to other health care providers as appropriate.

APPENDIX E
IMAGES AND SUPPORTING DOCUMENTS

Images and documents placed in this section are referenced throughout the work with "see Fig." followed by the corresponding reference number. Each image or document is followed by a caption. To enjoy the full impact of this section, images and documents should be referred to when read about in the context of their given chapter.

Chapter One

Fig. 1-A

Mary Lewis Wyche   Sophia French Palmer   Sadie Heath Cabaniss

fig. 1-B

◆

States Having Laws Providing for Training and Licensing of Practical Nurses or Other Nursing Groups with Similar Preparation
July, 1953

State	Separate Law	Length of Course	Separate Board of Examiners	Titles and Abbreviations Protected in Law
Alaska	No		No	Practical Nurse
Alabama	Yes	9-12 months	No	Licensed Practical Nurse, LPN
Arizona	No		No	Licensed Practical Nurse
Arkansas*	No		Yes	Licensed Practical Nurse, LPN
California	Yes	12 months	Yes	Licensed Vocational Nurse, LVN
Connecticut	No	12 months	No	Trained Attendant, TA
Florida	No	12 months	No	Licensed Practical Nurse, LPN
Georgia	Yes		Yes	Licensed Practical Nurse, LPN
Hawaii	No		No	Practical Nurse
Idaho*	No		No	Licensed Practical Nurse, LPN
Illinois	No	9 months	No	Licensed Practical Nurse, LPN
Indiana	No	12 months	No	Licensed Practical Nurse, LPN
Iowa	No	12 months	No	Licensed Practical Nurse, LPN
Kansas	No	9-12 months	No	Licensed, Trained, or Certified Practical Nurse, LPN
Kentucky	Yes		No	Licensed Practical Nurse, LPN
Louisiana*	Yes		Yes	Licensed Practical Nurse, LPN
Maine	Yes	9-12 months	No	Licensed Nursing Attendant, LNA
Maryland	No		No	Licensed Practical Nurse, LPN
Massachusetts	No		No	Licensed Attendant, LA
Michigan	No	9 months	No	Trained Attendant, TA Licensed Practical Nurse, LPN
Minnesota	Yes	9 months	No	Licensed Practical Nurse, LPN
Missouri	No		No	Licensed Practical Nurse, LPN
Montana	No		No	Certified or Licensed Practical Nurse, LPN
Nevada*	Yes		No	Practical Nurse
New Hampshire	Yes		No	Licensed Practical Nurse, LPN
New Jersey	No		No	Licensed Practical Nurse, LPN
New Mexico	No		No	Licensed Practical Nurse, LPN
New York*	No	9 months	No	Licensed Practical Nurse
North Carolina	No	12 months	No	Licensed Practical Nurse, LPN
North Dakota	Yes	9-12 months	No	Licensed Practical Nurse, LPN
Oklahoma	No	12 months	No	Licensed Practical Nurse, LPN
Oregon	Yes	9 months	No	Licensed Practical Nurse, LPN
Pennsylvania	No	12 months	No	Licensed Attendant
Puerto Rico	Yes	12 months	No	Nurses Aide
Rhode Island*	No		No	Licensed Practical Nurse, LPN
South Carolina	No	9-12 months	No	Licensed Practical Nurse, LPN
South Dakota	Yes	12 months	Yes	Licensed Practical Nurse, LPN
Tennessee	No		No	Licensed Practical Nurse, LPN
Texas	Yes	12 months	Yes	Licensed Vocational Nurse, LVN
Utah	No		No	Licensed Practical Nurse, LPN
Vermont	Yes		No	Licensed Practical Nurse, LPN
Virginia	No	9 months	No	Registered Practical Nurse
Virgin Islands	No		No	Licensed Practical Nurse
Washington	Yes		Yes	Licensed Practical Nurse, LPN
Wisconsin	No	9-12 months	No	Trained Practical Nurse, TPN Licensed Practical Nurse, LPN Trained Attendant, TA

*Mandatory law   Compiled by American Nurses' Association

July, 1953: Table with information about LPNs, compiled by the ANA, published in the AJN.

Chapter Two

Fig. 2-A

Elizabeth Burgess – New York

Fig. 2-B

June 1954: New members of the ANA's Special Committee on State Boards of Nursing.
Left to right: Sara Gibson – DE; Gertrude Gould – WY; Adele Stahl – WI; Clara Lewis – ND.

Fig. 2-C

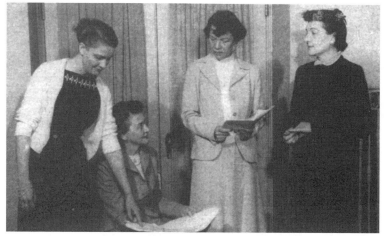

July 1956: New members of the ANA's Special Committee
on State Boards of Nursing ponder their responsibilities.
Left to right: Emma Bowen – ID; Vivian Culver – NC;
Dorothy Spears – HI; Freda Treptow – IL.

Fig. 2-D

1960: At the meeting of the ANA's Special Committee
on State Boards of Nursing reports are considered.
Left to right: Donna Monkman – OR; Ilva Benjamin – Virgin Islands; Faye McGuffry – TX.

Chapter Three

Fig. 3-A

Special Task Force.
Left to right: Albert Kelm; Barbara Nichols; Wade Boardman,
Council; Helen Keefe; Sharon Weisenbeck.
Seated: Elaine Ellibee; Trudy Malone; Mildred Schmidt.

Albany, NY, October 1977: Special Task Force meeting with NLN Representatives.
Left to right: Lorraine Sachs, NLN; Margaret Walsh, NLN;
David Grams, TF Council; Trudy Malone, TF; Edward Spencer, NLN Council.
Seated: Mildred Schmidt, TF; Barbara Nichols, ANA; Helen Keefe, TF; Elaine Ellibee, TF.

Fig. 3-A (cont.)

Oak Brook, IL, December 1977: Special Task Force funding meeting with W.K. Kellogg Foundation.
Left to right: Trudy Malone, TF; Barbara Lee, Kellogg Foundation; David Gram, TF Council;
Elaine Ellibee, TF; Mildred Schmidt, TF; Helen Keefe, TF.

Kansas City, MO, March 1978: Special Task Force meeting with
ANA Council of State Boards of Nursing Executive Committee.
Left to right: Elaine Ellibee, TF; Helen Keefe, TF;
Margaret Rowland, ANA CSBN; Lynne Isles, ANA CSBN.
Seated: Marilyn Maillian, ANA CSBN; Elaine Laeger, ANA CSBN Council;
Trudy Malone, TF; Mildred Schmidt, TF.

Chapter Four

Fig. 4-A

First NCSBN logo

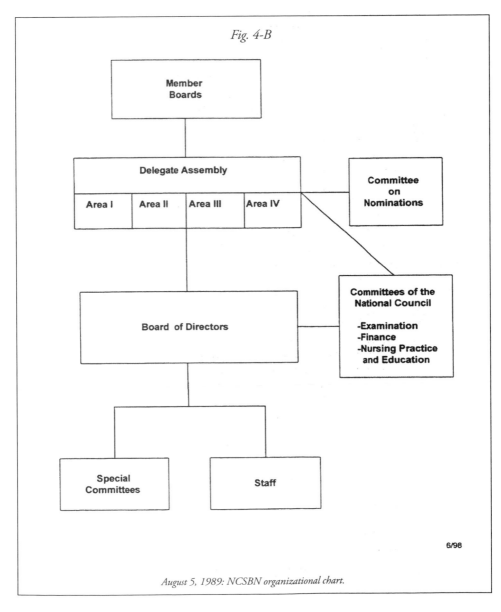

Fig. 4-B

August 5, 1989: NCSBN organizational chart.

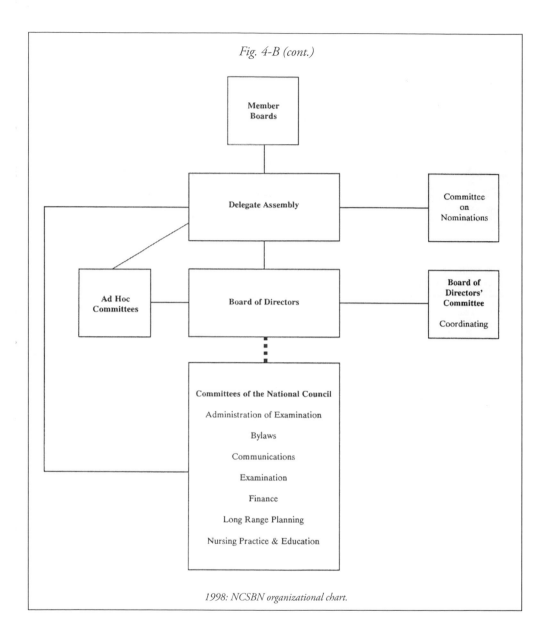

Fig. 4-B (cont.)

Member Boards

Delegate Assembly

Committee on Nominations

Ad Hoc Committees

Board of Directors

Board of Directors' Committee

Coordinating

Committees of the National Council

Administration of Examination

Bylaws

Communications

Examination

Finance

Long Range Planning

Nursing Practice & Education

1998: NCSBN organizational chart.

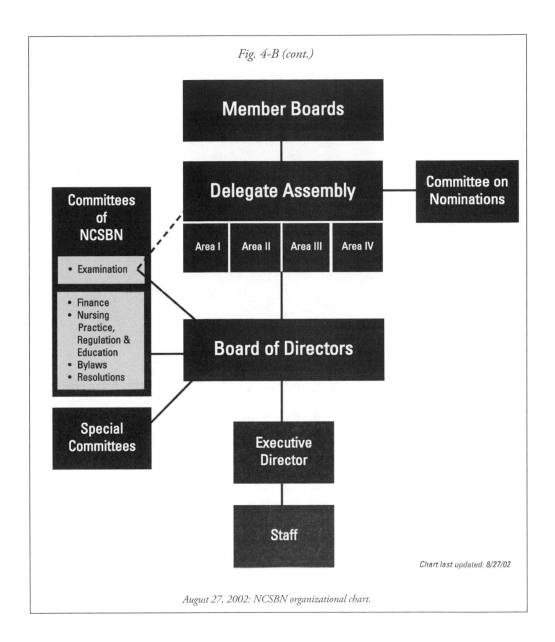

Fig. 4-B (cont.)

August 27, 2002: NCSBN organizational chart.

Fig. 4-C

Elaine Ellibee

Fig. 4-D

Gertrude (Trudy) Malone

Fig. 4-E

Mildred Schmidt

Fig. 4-F

Helen (Pat) Keefe

Fig. 4-G

Joyce Schowalter

Fig. 4-H

Sharon Weisenbeck

Fig. 4-I

Ruth Elliot

Fig. 4-J

Renatta Loquist

Fig. 4-K

Carolyn Hutcherson

Fig. 4-L

Rosa Lee Weinert

Fig. 4-M

Marcia Rachel

Fig. 4-N

Thomas Neumann

Fig. 4-O

Jo Elizabeth Ridenour

Fig. 4-P

Donna Dorsey

Fig. 4-Q

**National Council
of State Boards of Nursing, Inc.**

Second NCSBN logo

Fig. 4-R

Third (present) NCSBN logo

Fig. 4-S

Eileen McQuaid Dvorak

Fig. 4-T

Jennifer Bosma

Fig. 4-U

Eloise Cathcart

Fig. 4-V

Kathy Apple

Chapter Five

Fig. 5-A

ISSUES

**NATIONAL COUNCIL
OF STATE BOARDS OF NURSING, INC.**

VOLUME I, NUMBER 1   SPRING 1980

To Whom is the NCSBN Accountable?

The action taken by the boards of nursing in June 1978, to organize as the National Council of State Boards of Nursing, Inc., a nonprofit corporation, was a dramatic move capturing the interest of members of the profession. Article II of the Articles of Incorporation sets forth the purposes of the corporation as follows:

The purposes for which the Corporation is organized are educational and charitable purposes, including the lessening of the burdens of government by providing an organization through which Boards of Nursing act on matters of common interest and concern affecting the public health, safety, and welfare including the development of licensing examinations in nursing.

The Articles of Incorporation provide for members. In the corporation bylaws, it is stated that members of the Council shall be boards of nursing that use licensing examinations developed by the Council.

During the past year and a half, one of the questions asked of boards of nursing is—"To whom is the Council responsible?" That is an interesting question, probably arising because, historically, the representatives of boards of nursing have been appointed by the Board of Directors of the American Nurses' Association to serve on its Council of State Boards of Nursing. The accountability of the Council is spelled out in the ANA bylaws: "The Council of State Boards of Nursing shall be accountable to the Board and shall report to the Board and the House of Delegates." (Article X, Section 5). The NCSBN, however, is free standing and therefore not accountable to the ANA.

If the NCSBN is not accountable to the ANA, then to *whom* is it accountable? NCSBN's member boards are administrative agencies responsible for implementing the nurse practice acts in their respective states. Each board of nursing is accountable to the people of the state for protecting the public health, safety and welfare with respect to the practice of nursing. When the member boards of the NCSBN meet together in convention, they act collectively through their voting body, the Delegate Assembly.

As delegates vote on matters before the Delegate Assembly, they are cognizant of the provision of the statute in their respective states as well as board rules and/or regulations. For example, each board of nursing is responsible for administer-

ing a licensing examination for the titles stipulated in its nurse practice act. When a delegate votes on a matter affecting the licensing examination, such as a revision of the test plan, that delegate is casting a vote for the respective member board which, in turn, has responsibility to the people of the state for the licensing examination. On the other hand, when a break occurs in the security of the examination in a jurisdiction, the board of nursing is responsible to the NCSBN and its test

Continued on back page

Issues...

The National Council of State Boards of Nursing, Inc. launches this new periodical, a quarterly, as one form of communication designed to share ideas, questions and developments. Our purpose is to present timely issues of concern to the Council as discussed by experts in the field.

In this first issue, the theme is accountability to the public. Mildred Schmidt discusses the accountability of the National Council itself. Her commentary is in response to inquiries concerning the change in status of the Council—from being a part of the American Nurses' Association to becoming an independent organization.

In her article differentiating between professional and legal definitions of nursing practice, Thelma Cleveland emphasizes that legal definitions aim to protect the public's health, welfare and safety.

Phyllis Sheridan addresses an important question about the new test plan for the registered nurse licensure examination. She reminds the reader that the purpose of the licensure process, including the licensure examination, is protection of the public.

We can conclude, therefore, that the National Council of State Boards of Nursing, Inc., through its Member Boards, is accountable to the public for the performance of safe and effective nursing practice. By its very existence, it speaks to the question, "What does the public have a right to expect of those who are titled 'nurse'?"

We invite reader response to the presentations in this issue. Also encouraged are requests for additional information on the topics.

Eileen A. McQuaid, Ph.D., R.N.
Executive Director
National Council of State Boards of Nursing, Inc.

First edition of Issues

Fig. 5-B

**National
Council of
State Boards of Nursing, Inc.**

303 East Ohio Street · Suite 2010 · Chicago, IL 60611

NEWSLETTER

TO THE

MEMBER BOARDS   4 February 1983

Plan Ahead for the Delegate Assembly
————————————————————————————

The 1983 Convention of the NCSBN
Delegate Assembly will be held at the
Westin Hotel in Chicago, Illinois,
August 23-26.
    Registration forms for the Conven-
ɔn will be mailed to Member Boards
May 27, and Delegate Assembly Books
will be mailed on July 8.
    Boards may wish to schedule, or
reschedule, a Board meeting date to
discuss items placed on the agenda
of the Delegate Assembly Business
Meetings, which will be published in
the Delegate Assembly Books.
    Would Member Boards please notify
Marian Rippy at the National Council
office of the approximate number of
people who will be attending the
convention from your jurisdiction.
Estimated attendance will help us in
planning activities.

Accompanying the Newsletter:
————————————————————————————

1. The Disciplinary Report
2. Minutes, September 20-21, 1982
   Board of Directors' Meeting
3. Minutes, October 15, 1982 Board
   of Directors' Conference Call
4. Minutes, November 15, 1982 Board
   of Directors' Conference Call
5. Summary of Major Action, January
   24-26, 1983 Board of Directors'
   Meeting

A Reminder to Submit Nominations
and Bylaw, Standing Rule Changes
————————————————————————————

Nominations for Vice President,
Secretary, Treasurer, Area I Director and Director-at-Large must be
postmarked by March 7, 1983 and be
submitted to the National Council
office. Nominations from the Area
Directors must originate from the
Member Boards within the respective
area.
    Any suggested changes in the
Bylaws or Standing Rules of the
National Council should be forwarded
to the National Council office by
April 22, 1983.

Please Respond to the Council Review
Committee's Survey
————————————————————————————

The Council Review Committee of
the National Council requested
Member Boards to respond to a survey
on the objectives and structure of
the National Council by February 1.
    The Council Review Committee
requests that those Member Boards
who have not yet returned the
completed survey please do so as
soon as they can complete it.

First Newsletter to the Member Boards

Fig. 5-C

National Council
of State Boards of Nursing, Inc.

INSIGHT

NACEP News & Issues

| Volume 1 | Number 1 | Summer, 1992 |

OBRA '87: Implications for Home Health and Nurse Aides

Inside Insight

On December 22, 1987, President Ronald Reagan signed legislation that made a dramatic impact on care for the elderly across the United States. Known as Public Law 100-203, or the Omnibus Budget Reconciliation Act of 1987 (OBRA '87), this piece of legislation contained a section—Title IV—dealing with Medicare, Medicaid and other home-related programs. Subtitle A of this section mandated requirements for care offered in the home; Subtitle C mandated nursing home reform. The Health Care Financing Administration (HCFA) was given the responsibility for implementing the reform specified in OBRA '87.

Home Health Requirements

Home health agencies provide valuable services to the homebound elderly and the disabled. Prior to OBRA '87, these services were not regulated. OBRA '87 specified requirements for protecting and promoting patient rights as well as for the training and evaluation of home health aides. Requirements for clinical recordkeeping, operation of home health care services and licensing or certification of home health aides were also specified in the rule. The final rule, which was issued on July 18, 1991, became effective on August 19, 1991.

Final regulations specify the requirements for training and evaluation of nurse aides. Home health aides must participate in a minimum of 75 hours of training, 16 of which must be

simulated clinical training. This simulated clinical training must be completed before actual clinical training commences. Training may be conducted by any organization except a home health agency that is determined to be out of compliance with any of the requirements for Medicare-participating agencies within a 24-month period before training begins.

Home health aide training must be conducted by qualified instructors. Instructors must be registered nurses with two years' experience as a registered nurse and at least one year of experience in home health care. Instruction consists of training in: communication skills; personal hygiene and grooming; reading and recording temperature, pulse and respiration; range of motion exercises; basic infection control; nutrition; maintenance of a clean, safe and healthy environment; and basic elements in body functioning.

Following training, a home health aide must successfully complete a competency evaluation program before he or she may provide home health aide

services. The content of the evaluation program must address each area of required instruction. Any organization, except a home health agency determined to be out of compliance with Medicare regulations, may conduct evaluations. An evaluation must be conducted by a registered nurse who has two years of experience as a registered nurse, with at least one year working in home health care. Each specified area must be evaluated by the registered nurse after observing the home health aide perform all required tasks for a patient. Other areas may be evaluated through a written or oral examination. A home health aide may not perform the duties of a home health aide if he or she has received an unsatisfactory rating in more than one area of the evaluation.

Home health agencies must keep documentation of the satisfactory completion of a training and evaluation program for each home health aide it employs. There is no national registry for home health aides,

Continued ...*on page 3*

Figure 1

Grade 12
71%

Grade 11 or
under
19%

College
(undergraduate or beyond)
10%

Level of education attained by nurse aide candidates who took the NACEP ™ between 9/1/91 and 2/29/92.

First edition of Insight

Chapter Eight

Fig. 8-A

THE PROBLEM: AREAS OF INCONGRUENCE AMONG PRACTICE, EDUCATION, REGULATION

- Differing requirements, standards, processes, expectations.
- Staff/faculty shortages and increased nursing complexity.
- Limited collaboration among nursing leadership groups.
- Blurring of nursing scopes of practice and roles of assistive personnel.
- Increased reports of negative outcomes for patients/clients.
- Duplication of efforts in spite of resource limitations.
- Insufficient evidenced based outcomes for practice, education, regulation and nurse competency.

Pathway to Congruence of Practice, Education and Regulation

NCSBN: PROMOTE EDUCATION, COLLABORATION, INFORMATION

- Foster open, honest communication among members, Board of Directors, NCSBN staff and enhance communication with nursing stakeholders and public (I).
- Create a professional culture based on mutual respect and trust where opinions of practice, education, regulation representatives and members and staff are valued (I).
- Enhance educational and informational resources regarding the purpose of NCSBN and State Boards of Nursing (I).
- Commit to ongoing evaluation and improvement as an NCSBN core competency (I).
- Assess the health care and nursing environments and analyze the impact of change and innovation on regulation (I).
- Create a comprehensive, unduplicated database of nursing and regulatory information for member and public use (II).
- Collaborate with accrediting agencies and nursing education programs for an effective approval and accreditation process (III).
- Enhance model rules to reflect standards and indicators of quality nursing education (III).
- Clarify current foreign nurse regulatory issues and identify potential solutions (III).
- Develop model rules for licensing foreign-educated nurses (III).
- Design ways to build flexible and consistent Nurse Practice Acts and regulations that allow for changes in practice across jurisdictions (IV).
- Promote equivalency in essential elements of licensing and scope of practice for all nurses (IV).
- Develop tested measures and methods to ensure continued competence of all nurses and promote patient safety (IV).
- Assume a leadership role in designing processes to ensure patient safety, collaborating with health care systems (IV).
- Identify and promote effective models to facilitate a successful transition by new nurses from education to practice (IV).

PRACTICE: ENSURE QUALITY OF PRACTICE BY NURSES AND ASSISTIVE PERSONNEL

- Assess the health care and nursing environments and analyze the impact of change and innovation on regulation (I).
- Develop and implement a performance measurement model and indicators of excellence in regulation (II).
- Create a comprehensive, unduplicated database of nursing and regulatory information for member and public use (II).
- Design ways to build flexible and consistent NPAs and regulations that allow for changes in practice across jurisdictions (IV).
- NCSBN and member boards take a leadership role in designing processes to ensure patient safety, collaborating with health care systems (IV).
- Identify parameters of practice and competencies for nursing assistive personnel (IV).
- Participate in strategies for retention of the new graduate (IV).

EDUCATION: ENSURE QUALITY NURSING EDUCATION & FACULTY

- Enhance educational and informational resources regarding the purpose of NCSBN and State Boards of Nursing (I).
- Develop and utilize evidence-based indicators of quality nursing education for the roles of all nurses and ensure quality nursing education programs (III).
- Collaborate with accrediting agencies and nursing education programs for an effective approval and accreditation process (III).
- Enhance model rules to reflect standards and indicators of quality nursing education (III).
- Participate in strategies for retention of the new graduate (IV).

"Pathway to Congruence of Practice, Education and Regulation," NCSBN Business Book (Chicago: NCSBN, 2002): 226.

Fig. 8-A (cont.)

PERC CHARGE

The committee will develop and recommend an action plan to the 2002 Delegate Assembly to clearly delineate and establish congruence among education, practice, and regulation for nursing. The committee will develop the plan in collaboration with members and a broad base of health care stakeholders for presentation no later than the 2002 Delegate Assembly for a decision regarding implementation of the plan.

PRACTICE, EDUCATION, REGULATION CONGRUENCE

- Strengthen communication among practice, education and regulation (I).
- Create a professional culture based on mutual respect and trust where opinions of practice, education, regulation representatives and members and staff are valued (I).
- Develop and implement a performance measurement model and indicators of excellence in regulation (II).
- Identify and promote effective models to facilitate a successful transition by the foreign educated nurse into US practice roles and environment (III).
- Identify and promote effective models to facilitate a successful transition by new nurses from education to practice (IV).
- Develop tested measures and methods to ensure continued competence of all nurses and promote patient safety (IV).
- Build collaboration to promote innovative strategies to address issues pertinent to education, practice and regulation.
- Ensure that US educated graduates are prepared for safe practice.
- Promote equivalency in essential elements of licensing and scope of practice for all nurses (IV).

REGULATION: ENSURE QUALITY REGULATORY PRACTICE & PUBLIC PROTECTION

- Foster open, honest communication among member boards, Board of Directors, NCSBN staff, and strengthen communication with nursing stakeholders and the public (I).
- Enhance educational and informational resources regarding the purpose of NCSBN and State Boards of Nursing (I).
- Assess the health care and nursing environments and analyze the impact of change and innovation on regulation (I).
- Develop and implement a performance measurement model and indicators of excellence in regulation (II).
- Create a comprehensive, unduplicated database of nursing and regulatory information for member and public use (II).
- Develop and utilize evidence-based indicators of quality nursing education for the roles of all nurses and ensure quality nursing education programs (III).
- Enhance model rules to reflect standards and indicators of quality nursing education (III).
- Collaborate with accrediting agencies and nursing education programs for an effective approval and accreditation process (III).
- Clarify current foreign nurse regulatory issues and identify potential solutions (III).
- Develop model rules for licensing foreign-educated nurses (III).
- Design ways to build flexible and consistent NPAs and regulations that allow for changes in practice across jurisdictions (IV).
- NCSBN and member boards take a leadership role in designing processes to ensure patient safety, collaborating with health care systems (IV).

Chapter Nine

Fig. 9-A

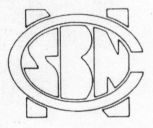

Diagnostic
Assessment
Program
for the

NCLEX

**Sponsored
by the
National
Council
of
State
Boards
of
Nursing**

Cover of Diagnostic Assessment Program for NCLEX®

Fig. 9-B

Resolution
of Appreciation

WHEREAS,   CTB/McGraw-Hill, a leader in testing development, was selected by the National Council of State Boards of Nursing, Inc., as its test service in 1981 to assist with the development of the nursing licensure examinations; and

WHEREAS,   CTB/McGraw-Hill has provided assistance in the area of test development, including three test plan revisions, creation of the panel of content experts, and revision of the diagnostic profiles; and

WHEREAS,   CTB/McGraw-Hill has conducted research on behalf of the National Council that has led to improved criterion-referenced standard setting procedures, the development of bias sensitivity review and psychometric support for the initiation of computerized adaptive testing; and

WHEREAS,   CTB/McGraw-Hill has enhanced NCLEX™ security, has assisted with the development of a crisis management plan and has provided candidates with more information about NCLEX than ever before to assist them to be well-prepared for their examinations; and

WHEREAS,   CTB/McGraw-Hill has assisted the National Council with development of procedures that have allowed for openness and accessibility regarding NCLEX for all qualified candidates, including modifications for disabled candidates, failure candidate reviews and handscoring; and

WHEREAS,   CTB/McGraw-Hill has provided services to the nursing community at large, including development of summary profiles, *NCLEX News and Notes*, and nine invitational conferences; be it therefore

RESOLVED,   That the National Council of State Boards of Nursing, Inc., calls the attention of the profession to the invaluable service rendered both to the profession and to the public by CTB/McGraw-Hill in its fourteen-year involvement with the development of the National Council Licensure Examinations; and be it further

RESOLVED,   That a copy of this resolution be retained in the archives of the National Council as a lasting tribute to CTB/McGraw-Hill for its role in the development of licensing examinations in nursing; and be it further

RESOLVED,   That a copy of this resolution be forwarded to CTB/McGraw-Hill.

President

Resolution for NLN, adopted at 1982 Delegate Assembly.

Fig. 9-C

"Therefore, be it Resolved, That the National Council of State Boards of Nursing, Inc., call the attention of the profession to the invaluable service rendered both to the profession and to the public by the National League for Nursing, Inc., and its predecessor, the National League for Nursing Education in the development of the State Board Test Pool Examination, and be it further

'Resolved, That a copy of this resolution be retained in the Archives of the Council as a lasting tribute to the National League for Nursing, Inc., for its role in the development of licensing examinations in nursing; and be it further

'Resolved, That a copy of this resolution be forwarded to the National League for Nursing, Inc."

PRESIDENT KEEFE: Question is on the adoption of the resolution of appreciation to the National League for Nursing, Inc. All in favor of the resolution, please say Aye. Thank you. Next resolution?

MS. SCHMIDT: Madam Chairman, I now present a resolution by the Resolutions Committee that

Resolution for CTB

Fig. 9-C (cont.)

'Whereas, The National League for Nursing
Education, the predecessor of the National League for
Nursing, responded during World War II to the needs of
state boards of nursing for assistance in preparing
standardized licensing examinations which could be
administered and scored rapidly; and

'Whereas, The Board of Directors of the
National League for Nursing Education authorized the
operation of a 'pool' of licensure tests in 1943 to be
funded through the Committee as Nursing Tests; and

'Whereas, The first series of the State
Board Test Pool Examination for Registered Nurse Licens-
ure was released by the National League for Nursing
Education in January, 1944, and the first form of the
Practical Nurse Licensure Examination was released in
1947; and

'Whereas, The National League for Nursing
Education and its successor, the National League for
Nursing, Inc., have produced the State Board Test Pool
Examination for Registered Nurse Licensure and Practical
Nurse Licensure for a total of 38 years:

Resolution for CTB (p.2)

Fig. 9-C (cont.)

of licensure; and

"Whereas, Difference in state regulations
regarding licensure of graduates of foreign schools of
nursing creates problems with endorsement by individual
states:

"Be It Resolved that the National Council
of State Boards of Nursing assume a leadership role in
the development of a resource center to facilitate
access to and exchange of information regarding regulations governing licensure of graduates of foreign schools
of nursing in each state."

PRESIDENT KEEFE: You have heard the
resolution. The question is on the adoption of the
resolution to facilitate information exchange regarding
graduates of foreign school of nursing licensure.

Are you ready for the question? All in
favor of the resolution, please say Aye. Opposed, No.
The Ayes have it. The motion is carried.

MS. SCHMIDT: The second resolution,
Madam President, is on the topic of Resolution of
Appreciation to the National League for Nursing, Inc.

Resolution for CTB (p.3)

Chapter Ten

Fig. 10-A

Name of Member Board
Street
City, State Zip

DRAFT NATIONAL LICENSURE VERIFICATION FORM

PART I: To be completed by the applicant and forwarded to all appropriate licensing boards, including original state of licensure.

A P P L I C A N T

Name (Last, First, Middle/Maiden)	Previous Name(s)		
Current Street Address	City, State, Zip		
Date of Birth (mo/day/yr) — Social Security Number	Current License Number	Type ☐ RN ☐ LP/VN	State
Name as it appears on original license (Last, First, Middle/Maiden)	Original State of Licensure		
Original License Number — Type ☐ RN ☐ LP/VN	Date Issued		
Nursing Education Program Completed	Location (city/state)	Graduation Date	

LIST ALL OTHER STATES OF LICENSURE
State: _____ License Number: _____ Date Issued: _____
State: _____ License Number: _____ Date Issued: _____
State: _____ License Number: _____ Date Issued: _____
State: _____ License Number: _____ Date Issued: _____

I hereby authorize all identified Boards of Nursing to release my licensure data to the _____ Board of Nursing.
(state)
Signature _____
Date _____

PART II: To be completed by licensing board and forwarded to Board of Nursing listed at the top of this form.

L I C E N S I N G   B O A R D   O N L Y

This is to certify that the above named individual was issued license number _____ Date Issued _____
to practice ☐ registered nursing.
☐ practical/vocational nursing.

Licensed by: ☐ Examination ☐ Endorsement ☐ Waiver
Current Licensure Status: ☐ Active ☐ Inactive ☐ Lapsed
Expiration Date: _____

Has this license ever been encumbered (denied, revoked, suspended, surrendered, limited, placed on probation)? ☐ Yes ☐ No
Disciplinary Action Pending? ☐ Yes ☐ No   Explain yes responses on the reverse side.

Nursing Education Program Completed
Approved by State? ☐ Yes ☐ No   Graduated from: ☐ H.S. ☐ H.S. Equivalency ☐ Completion of 10th Grade
Location (city/state)   Graduation Date

	STATE BOARD TEST POOL EXAMINATION Registered Nurse						NCLEX		
	Medical Nursing	Psychiatric Nursing	Obstetric Nursing	Surgical Nursing	Nursing of Children	LP/VN	RN		LP/VN
Score									
Series/Form #									

	Score	Number of times applicant wrote exam: _____ Dates: _____
☐ State/Provincial Constructed Exam	_____	
☐ CNATS Exam	_____	Exam in English? ☐ Yes ☐ No
☐ Other (please explain)	_____	

SEAL

Signature _____
Title _____
State _____ Date _____

1991 Sample: Draft National Licensure Verification Form

Chapter Thirteen

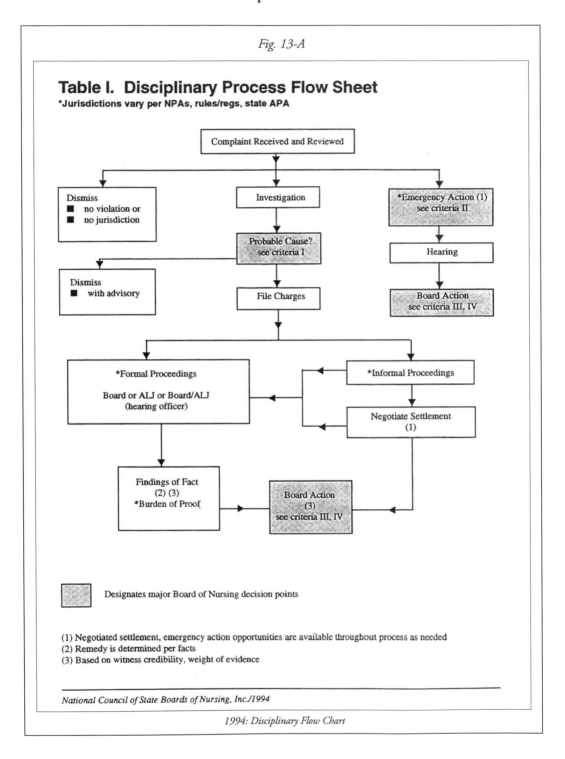

Fig. 13-A

Table I. Disciplinary Process Flow Sheet
*Jurisdictions vary per NPAs, rules/regs, state APA

Complaint Received and Reviewed

Dismiss
- no violation or
- no jurisdiction

Investigation

*Emergency Action (1)
see criteria II

Probable Cause?
see criteria I

Hearing

Dismiss
- with advisory

File Charges

Board Action
see criteria III, IV

*Formal Proceedings

Board or ALJ or Board/ALJ
(hearing officer)

*Informal Proceedings

Negotiate Settlement
(1)

Findings of Fact
(2) (3)
*Burden of Proof

Board Action
(3)
see criteria III, IV

Designates major Board of Nursing decision points

(1) Negotiated settlement, emergency action opportunities are available throughout process as needed
(2) Remedy is determined per facts
(3) Based on witness credibility, weight of evidence

National Council of State Boards of Nursing, Inc./1994

1994: Disciplinary Flow Chart

Chapter Fifteen

Fig. 15-A

R. Louise McManus

Fig. 15-B (cont.)

Eileen Dvorak: The first
recipient of the Meritorious
Service Award.

Fig. 15-B

The original McManus Award

Fig. 15-C

2003 Awards Luncheon:
Elizabeth Lund – TN; Barbara Zittel – NY

2003 Awards Luncheon:
Elizabeth Lund – TN; George Hebert – NJ

2003 Awards Luncheon:
Elizabeth Lund – TN; Jay Douglas – VA

2003 Awards Luncheon:
Elizabeth Lund – TN; Polly Johnson – NC

Fig. 15-D

Logo for the 25th Anniversary celebration

ENDNOTES

Chapter One

1. Sophia Palmer, "International Unity on State Registration," *American Journal of Nursing* 2 (1901): 233.

2. Minnie Goodnow, *Outlines of Nursing History*, 4th ed. (Philadelphia: W.B. Saunders, 1928), 113–15.

3. Ibid., 301.

4. Ibid.

5. Milton J. Lesnik and Bernice E. Anderson, *Nursing Practice and the Law* (Westport, Connecticut: Greenwood Press, 1976), 77.

6. Sophia Palmer, "The Editor," *American Journal of Nursing* 1 (1901): 941.

7. Goodnow, *Outlines*, 300.

8. "Third Annual Convention of the Associated Alumnae of Trained Nurses of the United States Held in The Academy of Medicine, 17 West 43rd Street, New York City, May 3, 4, and 5," *American Journal of Nursing* 1 (1900): 88.

9. Isabel H. Robb, "Address of the President," *American Journal of Nursing* 1 (1900): 100–02.

10. Sophia Palmer, "State Organization in New York," *American Journal of Nursing* 1 (1900): 59–60.

11. Goodnow, *Outlines*, 446–47.

12. Ibid., 300–01.

13. Lavinia Dock, "What We May Expect From the Law," *American Journal of Nursing* 1 (1900): 8–9.

14. Sophia Palmer, "The Editor," *American Journal of Nursing* 1 (1900): 167.

15. Ethel Fenwick, "International Unity on State Registration," *American Journal of Nursing* 2 (1901): 233–34.

16. Patricia T.   VanBetten and Melissa Moriarity, *Nursing Illuminations: A Book of Days* (St. Louis, MO: Mosby, 2004): 293.

17. Lesnik and Anderson, *Nursing Practice*, 57–59.

18. Sophia Palmer, "The New York State Meeting in Rochester," *American Journal of Nursing* 3 (1902): 158–59.

19. Sophia Palmer, "Editorial Comment," *American Journal of Nursing* 3 (1903): 670–71.

20. Sharon M.   Weisenbeck and Patricia A.   Calico, "Licensure and Related Issues in Nursing," in *Issues and Trends in Nursing*, edited by Grace Deloughery (St. Louis, MO: Mosby, 1991): 244–45.

21. Emily J. Hicks, "A Crusade for Safer Nursing," *American Journal of Nursing* 38 (1938): 563–66.

22. Sophia Palmer, "Important Meetings of the Month," *American Journal of Nursing*, 4 (1903): 156.

23. Louis C. Boyd, *State Registration for Nurses* (Philadelphia: W. B. Saunders Company, 1915): 1–2.

24. Sophia Palmer, "Progress of State Registration" *American Journal of Nursing* 4–20 (1903–1920).

25. National Council of State Boards of Nursing, *1978–2003: 25 Years of the National Council of State Boards of Nursing: Honoring Our Past to Create Our Future*, (Chicago: NCSBN, 2003): 4–5.

26. Sophia Palmer, "State Registration," *American Journal of Nursing* 2 (1901): 238–40.

27. Sophia Palmer, "Registration of Nurses," *American Journal of Nursing* 4 (1903): 71–72.

28. Sophia Palmer, "Legislative Procedure," *American Journal of Nursing* 2 (1902): 562.

29. Sophia Palmer, "Editorial Comment," *American Journal of Nursing* 3 (1903): 749–52.

30. "Seventh Annual Convention of the Nurses' Associated Alumnae of the United States Held in Drexel Institute, Philadelphia, Pennsylvania, May 12, 13 and 14, 1904, Minutes of the Proceedings," *American Journal of Nursing* 4 (1904): 786–91.

31. Sophia Palmer, "Progress of Registration," *American Journal of Nursing* 4 (1904): 493–94.

32. Sophia Palmer, "Progress of State Registration," *American Journal of Nursing* 4 (1904): 583.

33. Sophia Palmer, "Progress of State Registration," *American Journal of Nursing* 5 (1905): 352–53.

34. Sophia Palmer, "Progress of State Registration," *American Journal of Nursing* 6 (1906): 285.

35. Sophia Palmer, "Progress of State Registration," *American Journal of Nursing* 8 (1908): 750–51.

36. Sophia Palmer, "Progress of State Registration," *American Journal of Nursing* 9 (1909): 387–89.

37. Sophia Palmer, "Progress of State Registration," *American Journal of Nursing* 10 (1910): 633.

38. M. M. Riddle, "Why We Should Have State Registration for Nurses," *American Journal of Nursing* 7 (1907): 240–42.

39. Sophia Palmer, "Important Meetings of the Month: Pennsylvania State," *American Journal of Nursing* 4 (1903): 156.

40. Sophia Palmer, "Progress of State Registration," *American Journal of Nursing* 5 (1905): 488.

41. Sophia Palmer, "Affairs in Pennsylvania," *American Journal of Nursing* 8 (1908): 750–51.

42. Sophia Palmer, "Organized Opposition to Nursing Progress," *American Journal of Nursing* 10 (1909): 4–6.

43. Sophia Palmer, "Progress of State Registration," *American Journal of Nursing* 13 (1913): 491–96.

44. Sophia Palmer, "After Ten Years," *American Journal of Nursing* 13 (1913): 410–11.

45. "Ninth Annual Convention of the Nurses' Associated Alumnae of the United States Held in the Young Women's Christian Association Building, Detroit, Michigan, June 5, 6 and 7, 1906, Minutes of the Proceedings," *American Journal of Nursing* 6 (1906): 731–828.

46. Sophia Palmer, "The St. Louis Meetings," *American Journal of Nursing* 14 (1914): 497–99.

47. "Proceedings of the Eighteenth Annual Convention of the American Nurses' Association Held at the First Congregational Church, San Francisco, California, June 20–25, 1915," *American Journal of Nursing* 15 (1915): 1037–56.

48. Sophia Palmer, "Progress of State Registration," *American Journal of Nursing* 16 (1916): 173.

49. Minutes, Meeting of Virginia State Board of Nurse Examiners: May 25, 1904, Library of Virginia, Richmond, VA, 2.

50. Sophia Palmer, "Progress of State Registration," *American Journal of Nursing* 6 (1906): 354–58.

51. Boyd, State Registration, 11.

52. Sophia Palmer, "Editorial Comment," *American Journal of Nursing* 14 (1913): 160.

53. "Proceedings of the Eighteenth Annual Convention of the American Nurses' Association Held at the First Congregational Church, San Francisco, California, June 20–25, 1915," *American Journal of Nursing* 15 (1915): 934–38.

54. Marietta B. Squire, "Is Compulsory Registration Desirable and How May it be Obtained?" *American Journal of Nursing* 13 (1913): 956.

55. G. E. Allison, "Shall Attendants be Trained and Registered?" *American Journal of Nursing* 13 (1913): 928–34.

56. Sophia Palmer, "Virginia Leads in the Training and Licensing of Attendants," *American Journal of Nursing* 18 (1918): 857–58.

57. "State News," *American Journal of Nursing* 26 (1926): 159–63.

58. "Resolutions on the General Staff Nurse and Employment Conditions on Which Good Nursing Service Depends," *American Journal of Nursing* 36 (1936): 817.

59. "The Subsidiary Worker," *American Journal of Nursing* 37 (1937): 283–85.

60. "The Biennial," *American Journal of Nursing* 38 (1938): 673–700.

61. Dorothy Deming, "Practical Nursing and the Changing Professional Attitude," *American Journal of Nursing* 46 (1946): 366–70.

62. "News Here and There: Practical Nursing Defined," *American Journal of Nursing* 46 (1946): 267.

63. "Practical Nursing Schools Form NLN Council," *American Journal of Nursing* 62 (1962): 32.

64. "Trained Attendants and Practical Nurses," *American Journal of Nursing* 44 (1944): 7.

65. "The State Board Conference in Chicago," *American Journal of Nursing* 44 (1944): 67–69.

66. "States Having Laws Providing for Training and Licensing of Practical Nurses or Other Nursing Groups With Similar Preparation, July 1953" (table), *American Journal of Nursing* 53 (1953): 1368.

67. "Practical Nurses Licensed in District of Columbia," *American Journal of Nursing* 60 (1960): 1654.

68. "Types of Clinical Courses for Graduate Nurses," *American Journal of Nursing* 44 (1944): 1163.

69. Barbara J. Seifert, "Health Care Dollars and Regulatory Sense: The Role of Advanced Practice Nursing," *Yale Journal on Regulation* 9 (1992): 445.

70. "Amendment to Arizona *Nursing Practice* Law Broadens Definition of Professional Nursing," *American Journal of Nursing* 72 (1972): 1203.

71. Mary Roberts, "State Registration," *American Journal of Nursing* 23 (1923): 562–64.

72. Lizzie M. Cox, "Editor's Miscellany," *American Journal of Nursing* 7 (1906): 50.

Chapter Two

1. Mary M. Riddle, "Address of the President," *American Journal of Nursing* 5 (1905): 733.

2. Ibid.

3. "Eighth Annual Convention of the Nurses' Associated Alumnse of the United States Held in George Washington University, Washington, D.C. May 4–5, 1905," *American Journal of Nursing* 5 (1905): 800.

4. Bowen (first name unknown), "History of Registration," *American Journal of Nursing* 4 (1904): 771–72.

5. Sophia Palmer, "The Effects of Registration Upon the Educational Standards of Training Schools as Shown by Results in New York State," *American Journal of Nursing* 4 (1904): 773–75.

6. Sadie Heath Cabaniss, "The Justice of an Examining Board Composed of Nurses," *American Journal of Nursing* 4 (1904): 775–76.

7. M. Adelaide Nutting, "State Reciprocity," *American Journal of Nursing* 4 (1904): 779–85

8. Ibid.

9. M. E. Cameron, "Examining Boards of Nurses and Their Powers," *American Journal of Nursing* 5 (1905): 820–23.

10. Sophia Palmer, "The Actions of the National Societies on the Three Years' Course," *American Journal of Nursing* 7 (1907): 679–80.

11. "Proceedings of the Tenth Annual Convention of the Nurses' Associated Alumnae of the United States Held in Richmond, Virginia, May 14, 15 and 16, 1907, Minutes of the Proceedings," *American Journal of Nursing* 7 (1907): 815–57.

12. Sophia Palmer, "Progress of State Registration," *American Journal of Nursing* 8 (1907): 4.

13. Anna L. Alline, "State Supervision of Nursing Schools in New York," *American Journal of Nursing* 9 (1909): 911–23.

14. Sophia Palmer, "The Newer Obligation of State Registration," *American Journal of Nursing* 11 (1911): 418–20.

15. Sophia Palmer, "Meetings of the Two National Societies in Boston," *American Journal of Nursing* 11 (1911): 771–74.

16. I. F. Giles, "Report of the Special Conference on State Registration," *American Journal of Nursing* 12 (1912): 978.

17. Sophia Palmer, "State Boards of Examiners," *American Journal of Nursing* 14 (1914): 255–56.

18. "Proceedings of the Eighteenth Annual Convention of the American Nurses' Association Held at the First Congregational Church, San Francisco, California, June 20–25, 1915," *American Journal of Nursing* 15 (1915): 899–1066.

19. Ibid.

20. Anna C. Jamme, Sutherland Lauder, and Mary B. Eyre, "Report of Sub-committee on Legislation," *American Journal of Nursing* 16 (1916): 926–43.

21. Sophia Palmer, "A National Board of Medical Examiners," *American Journal of Nursing* 16 (1916): 1067–68.

22. Anna C. Jamme, "Report of Committee on Legislation," *American Journal of Nursing* 17 (1917): 918–25.

23. Ibid.

24. Anna C. Jamme, "Report of Round Table on Legislation," *American Journal of Nursing* 17 (1917): 1013.

25. "Proceedings of the Twenty-second Convention of the American Nurses' Association," *American Journal of Nursing* 20 (1920): 761–868.

26. "Proceedings of the Twenty-first Annual Convention of the American Nurses' Association Held at the Hotel Hollenden, Cleveland, Ohio, May 7–11, 1918," *American Journal of Nursing* 18 (1918): 999–1094.

27. Ibid.

28. "An Institute for State Inspectors and for Nurse Examiners," *American Journal of Nursing* 21 (1921): 653–54.

29. H. Gillette, "Institute for Inspectors and State Boards of Nurse Examiners, at Teachers College," *American Journal of Nursing* 21 (1921): 883–85.

30. "Proceedings of the Twenty-third Convention of the American Nurses' Association Held at Plymouth Congregational Church, Seattle, Washington, June 26–July 1, 1922," *American Journal of Nursing* 22 (1922): 969–1100.

31. "Grading Schools of Nursing," *American Journal of Nursing* 26 (1926): 401–02.

32. Gerald J. Griffin and Joanne K. Griffin, *Jensen's History and Trends of Professional Nursing* (St. Louis, MO: Mosby, 1969): 151–52.

33. Everett S. Elwood, "The National Board of Medical Examiners and Medical Licensure," *American Journal of Nursing* 26 (1926): 769–73.

34. Mary Roberts, "A National Board of Nurse Examiners," *American Journal of Nursing* 26 (1926): 791.

35. Elizabeth C. Burgess, "Advancement of Education Through Legislation," *American Journal of Nursing* 29 (1929): 765–69.

36. "Highlights of the Biennial," *American Journal of Nursing* 30 (1930): 915–39.

37. Ibid.

38. Adda Eldredge, "Effect of Standardization Programs," *American Journal of Nursing* 31 (1931): 471–80.

39. Mary Roberts, "Editorials," *American Journal of Nursing* 31 (1931): 721.

40. "Professional Nursing as Defined by the Committee to Outline a Definition of Nursing," *American Journal of Nursing* 32 (1932): 551.

41. Shirley H. Fondiller, *The Entry Dilemma: The NLN and the Higher Education Movement 1952–1972* (New York: National League for Nursing, 1983): 10.

42. "Highlights of the Biennial," *American Journal of Nursing* 32 (1932): 585–602.

43. "Notes From Headquarters American Nurses' Association," *American Journal of Nursing* 32 (1932): 795–96.

44. "Special Conference, State Boards of Nurse Examiners," *American Journal of Nursing* 33 (1933): 809–12.

45. Adda Eldredge, "Legislation and the Future of Nursing," *American Journal of Nursing* 34 (1934): 542–49.

46. The Biennial," *American Journal of Nursing* 34 (1934): 605–27.

47. Ibid.

48. "Excerpts From the Minutes of the ANA Board of Directors' Meeting Held in New York January 1936," *American Journal of Nursing* 36 (1936): 525–28.

49. "The Convention," *American Journal of Nursing* 36 (1936): 790–97.

50. "Conference of State Boards of Nurse Examiners," *American Journal of Nursing* 37 (1937): 678–83.

51. "The Biennial," *American Journal of Nursing* 38 (1938): 365.

52. Mary Roberts, "A National Board of Examiners," *American Journal of Nursing* 41 (1941): 440.

53. "NLNE Conducts State Board Conference," *American Journal of Nursing* 41 (1941): 858.

54. "State Board Conference," *American Journal of Nursing* 42 (1942): 952–53.

55. Ibid.

56. "State Board Recommendations," *American Journal of Nursing* 43 (1943): 282–84.

57. "The State Board Conference," *American Journal of Nursing* 43 (1943): 764–65.

58. "ANA Clearing Bureau on State Board Problems," *American Journal of Nursing* 43 (1943): 1048.

59. "Meetings of the Board of Directors: American Nurses Association [ANA}: Digest of Minutes, June 1944," *American Journal of Nursing* 44 (1944): 908–13.

60. "About People You Know," *American Journal of Nursing* 44 (1944): 1092.

61. "The Bureau of State Boards of Nurse Examiners," *American Journal of Nursing* 45 (1945): 458–59.

62. "State Board Conference Makes Recommendations," *American Journal of Nursing* 46 (1946): 266.

63. "Recent Meetings," *American Journal of Nursing* 46 (1946): 887–88.

64. "News From National Headquarters," *American Journal of Nursing* 47 (1947): 128.

65. Ibid., 836.

66. "Recommendations Made by Boards of Nurse Examiners," *American Journal of Nursing* 48 (1948): 26–27 adv.

67. Mary Roberts, "State Boards Consider the Future," *American Journal of Nursing* 49 (1949): 327–28.

68. "State Boards," *American Journal of Nursing* 50 (1950): 402–03.

69. Eula M. Benton, "History of the Council of State Boards of Nursing" (paper presented at the Twenty-fifth Anniversary Luncheon, ANA Council of State Boards of Nursing, Detroit, 1972).

70. "Education for Nursing Service," *American Journal of Nursing* 51 (1951): 433–35.

71. "The Six Nursing Organizations to be Studied," *American Journal of Nursing* 46 (1946): 279.

72. "Biennial," *American Journal of Nursing* 52 (1952): 824–27.

73. "ANA's Committee of State Board of Nursing Education and Nurse Registration," *American Journal of Nursing* 53 (1953): 960–62.

74. "State Boards of Nursing," *American Journal of Nursing* 54 (1954): 746–54.

75. "Midwest State Boards Confer," *American Journal of Nursing* 55 (1955): 90.

76. "Report of the Southern Regional Conference of State Boards of Nursing," Minutes, Meeting of the Virginia State Board of Nurse Examiners: March 24, 1958, Library of Virginia, Richmond, VA, Attachment.

77. "The State Board Meetings," *American Journal of Nursing* 55 (1955): 847–50.

78. "Qualifications for State Board Members," *American Journal of Nursing* 56 (1956): 293.

79. "News From National Headquarters," *American Journal of Nursing* 57 (1957): 913.

80. "The State Boards of Nursing," *American Journal of Nursing* 58 (1958): 1112–14.

81. "State Board Guide," *American Journal of Nursing* 59 (1959): 322.

82. "Officials of State Boards of Nursing Convene," *American Journal of Nursing* 59 (1959): 1137–38.

83. "ANA Decries NLN Action on State Board Relationships," *American Journal of Nursing* 64, no. 7 (1964): 11, 14, and 16.

84. Barbara G. Schutt, "Cause for Concern," *American Journal of Nursing* 64, no. 6 (1964): 71.

85. "News," *American Journal of Nursing* 64, no. 6 (1964): 30.

86. "ANA and NLN Sign Agreement," *American Journal of Nursing* 65, no. 5 (1965): 20–21.

87. "Proposed Amendments to the ANA Bylaws," *American Journal of Nursing* 66 (1966): 936.

88. "State Board Council Ponders Separate Incorporation," *American Journal of Nursing* 70 (1970): 1416–17.

89. Ibid.

90. "Council of State Boards of Nursing to Stay With ANA," *American Journal of Nursing* 71 (1971): 1499.

91. "State Board Changes," *American Journal of Nursing* 70 (1970): 2436.

92. Benton, "History of the Council."

93. "State Board Members Hear Explanations of Immigration Laws," *American Journal of Nursing* 73 (1973): 1152.

94. "Section Meeting Boards of Nurse Examiners," *American Journal of Nursing* 14 (1914): 850–55.

95. Benton, "History of the Council."

96. Ibid.

97. R. Louise McManus, "State Boards Test Pool: A Retrospective View," *Issues* 1, no. 3 (1980): 6–7.

98. "Digest of Meetings of the ANA Board of Directors," *American Journal of Nursing* 28 (1928): 289–90.

99. "Special Conference, State Boards of Nurse Examiners," *American Journal of Nursing* 33 (1933): 809–12.

100. "State Board Conference," *American Journal of Nursing* 42 (1942): 952–53.

101. McManus, "State Boards," 6–7.

102. "The State Board Test Pool," *American Journal of Nursing* 44 (1944): 73.

103. Fondiller, *The Entry Dilemma*, 12.

104. R. Louise McManus, "The State Board Test Pool," *American Journal of Nursing* 44 (1944): 380–84.

105. "The State Board Conference Recommends: Recommendations From the Conference of Representatives of State Boards of Nurse Examiners, St. Louis, Missouri," *American Journal of Nursing* 45 (1945): 573–74.

106. "State Board Conference Makes Recommendations," *American Journal of Nursing* 46 (1946): 266.

107. "The New State Board Test Pool Series," *American Journal of Nursing* 49 (1949): 668.

108. Staff of the Department of Measurement and Guidance, National League of Nursing Education, "The State Board Test Pool Examination," *American Journal of Nursing* 52 (1953): 613–15.

109. Thelma M. Schorr, "Securing Licensure," *American Journal of Nursing* 75 (1975): 1131.

110. Eleanor A. Lynch, *An Historical Survey of the Test Services of the National League for Nursing* (New York: National League for Nursing, 1980): iii, 35, 46.

Chapter Three

1. Gertrude Malone, Shirley Fondiller, and David Heidorn *From an Idea to an Organization* (Chicago: National Council of State Boards of Nursing, Inc. [NCSBN], 1983): 4.

2. Malone, Fondiller, and Heidorn, *From an Idea*, 13.

3. Mildred Schmidt, "Background Paper on the Council of State Boards of Nursing—Its Roots, Present Status and Future," 10 November, 1977, NCSBN Archives, Chicago, IL, 2.

4. Minutes, Meeting of the Executive Committee, American Nurses Association Council of State Boards of Nursing: March 1–2, 1977, NCSBN Archives, Chicago, IL, 3.

5. Mildred Schmidt, "Monies Received in Support of the Re-organization of the Council of State Boards of Nursing," (Madison: Special Task Force—State Boards of Nursing Revised October 6, 1977), NCSBN Archives, Chicago, IL, 2.

6. Minutes, Meeting of the American Nurses Association Council of State Boards of Nursing: June 7–9, 1977, NCSBN Archives, Chicago, IL, 18.

7. Ibid., 19–20.

8. Ibid., 18.

9. Ibid., 19.

10. Ibid.

11. Ibid., 20.

12. Minutes, Meeting of the Task Force on the Reorganization of the Council of State Boards of Nursing: August 25–27, 1977, NCSBN Archives, Chicago, IL, 1.

13. Ibid., 1–3.

14. "Report of the Special Task Force—State Boards of Nursing," 1978, NCSBN Archives, Chicago, IL, 2–5.

15. Malone, Fondiller, and Heidorn, *From an Idea*, 3.

16. Memorandum by Elaine Ellibee to the members of the ANA Council of State Boards of Nursing regarding contracts for the State Board Test Pool Examination, 13 February, 1978, NCSBN Archives, Chicago, IL, 1–2.

17. Malone, Fondiller, and Heidorn, *From an Idea*, 26.

18. "Format for Final Annual Financial Report to W. K. Kellogg Foundation," 31 August, 1978, Special Task Force—State Boards of Nursing, NCSBN Archives, Chicago, IL.

19. Memorandum by Barbara Nichols to Anne Zimmerman, president of the American Nurses Association, regarding attendance at the meeting of the Special Task Force—State Boards of Nursing, NCSBN Archives, Chicago, IL, 2.

20. Memorandum by Helen P. Keefe, to the members of area III of the American Nurses Association Council of State Boards of Nursing regarding completion of task force assignment, 12 May, 1978, NCSBN Archives, Chicago, IL, 2.

21. Minutes, Meeting of the American Nurses Association Council of State Boards of Nursing: June 5, 1978, NCSBN Archives, Chicago, IL, 17–18.

22. Summary report by Anna Kuba of the meeting of the American Nurses Association Council of State Boards of Nursing, 12 June, 1978, NCSBN Archives, Chicago, IL, 1.

23. Malone, Fondiller, and Heidorn, *From an Idea*, 28.

24. *The National Council of State Boards of Nursing Articles of Incorporation* (Madison, WI: NCSBN, 1978): 1.

25. Minutes, Meeting of the National Council of State Boards of Nursing: June 6–7, 1978, NCSBN Archives, Chicago, IL, 1–5.

26. Marianna Bacigalupo to Anne Zimmerman, 8 June, 1978, NCSBN Archives, Chicago, IL.

27. Myrtle K. Aydelotte to Elaine Ellibee, 28 June, 1978 NCSBN Archives, Chicago, IL.

28. Record of telephone message from Barbara Nichols to Elaine Ellibee, 7 July, 1978, NCSBN Archives, Chicago, IL.

29. "State Boards Establish Special Council," *The American Nurse* 10, no. 7 (1978): 3.

30. Memorandum by Elaine Ellibee to National Council of State Boards of Nursing members, 31 July, 1978, NCSBN Archives, Chicago, IL.

31. Financial statement of the NCSBN, Madison, WI, 7 July, 1978, NCSBN Archives, Chicago, IL.

32. Elaine Ellibee, "Report of President—National Council of State Boards of Nursing," 7 June, 1978–May 2, 1979, NCSBN Archives, Chicago, IL, 3.

33. Ibid., 1.

34. Elaine Ellibee to Nancy Dean, 21 June, 1978, NCSBN Archives, Chicago, IL.

Chapter Four

1. Henry M. Robert, *Robert's Rules of Order Newly Revised*, 10th ed. (Cambridge, MA: DeCapo, 2000), v.

2. Ibid., 10–11.

3. "Report of the Board of Directors," *NCSBN Book of Reports* (Chicago: National Council of State Boards of Nursing, Inc. [NCSBN], 1985): 54–55.

4. Minutes, Meeting of the NCSBN Delegate Assembly: August 27, 1984, NCSBN Archives, Chicago, IL, 5–6.

5. "Memorandum on Council Reincorporation," *NCSBN Book of Reports* (Chicago: NCSBN, 1985): 5–34.

6.   Minutes, Meeting of the NCSBN-Wisconsin Delegate Assembly: August 21, 1985, NCSBN Archives, Chicago, IL, 4.

7.   Minutes, Meeting of the NCSBN-Pennsylvania Delegate Assembly: August 21, 1985, NCSBN Archives, Chicago, IL, 3.

8.   Robert, *Robert's Rules*, 12–14.

9.   "National Council of State Boards of Nursing, Inc. Bylaws: Adopted 1978," (Madison, WI: NCSBN), NCSBN Archives, Chicago, IL.

10.   "Report of the Bylaws Committee," Minutes, Meeting of the NCSBN Delegate Assembly: June 6–8, 1979, NCSBN Archives, Chicago, IL, Attachment, 1–19.

11.   Minutes, Meeting of the NCSBN Delegate Assembly: August 5-9, 1986, NCSBN Archives, Chicago, IL, 17.

12.   "Report of the Bylaws Special Committee," *NCSBN Book of Reports* (Chicago: NCSBN, 1987): 129–60.

13.   "Report of the Bylaws Special Committee," *NCSBN Book of Reports* (Chicago: NCSBN, 1988): 133–54.

14.   Minutes, Meeting of the NCSBN Delegate Assembly: August 6-11, 1990, NCSBN Archives, Chicago, IL, 9.

15.   Minutes, Meeting of the NCSBN Delegate Assembly: July 31–August 2, 1991, NCSBN Archives, Chicago, IL, 10–11.

16.   Minutes, Meeting of the NCSBN Delegate Assembly: August 18–22, 1992, NCSBN Archives, Chicago, IL, 17–18.

17.   Minutes, Meeting of the NCSBN Delegate Assembly: August 5–6, 1994, NCSBN Archives, Chicago, IL, 5–6.

18.   "Report of the Bylaws Committee," *NCSBN Book of Reports* (Chicago: NCSBN, 1994): 1–10.

19.   Ibid.

20.   "Report of the Bylaws Task Force," *NCSBN Book of Reports* (Chicago: NCSBN, 1997): Tab 10A, 1–10.

21.   Minutes, Meeting of the NCSBN Delegate Assembly: August 20–23, 1997, NCSBN Archives, Chicago, IL, 3–5.

22.   "Report of the Board of Directors," *NCSBN Business Book* (Chicago: NCSBN, 1998): Tab 9, 1–2.

23.   Minutes, Meeting of the NCSBN Delegate Assembly: August 4–8, 1998, NCSBN Archives, Chicago, IL, 5

24.   "Report of the Bylaws Audit Group," *NCSBN Business Book* (Chicago: NCSBN, 2000): 121.

25.   Minutes, Meeting of the NCSBN Delegate Assembly: August 8–12, 2000, NCSBN Archives, Chicago, IL, 5.

26.   Minutes, Meeting of the NCSBN Board of Directors: March 4, 2001, NCSBN Archives, Chicago, IL, 2–3.

27.   "Report of the Bylaws Committee," *NCSBN Business Book* (Chicago: NCSBN, 2001): 67–109.

28.   "Report of the Bylaws Committee," *NCSBN Business Book* (Chicago: NCSBN, 2002): 230.

29.   "Report of the Bylaws Committee," *NCSBN Business Book* (Chicago: NCSBN, 2003): 83–93.

30.   Minutes, Meeting of the NCSBN Board of Directors: April 30–May 1, 2003, NCSBN Archives, Chicago, IL, 4.

31. Minutes, Meeting of the NCSBN Board of Directors: December 2–4, 2003, NCSBN Archives, Chicago, IL, 5.

32. Robert, *Robert's Rules*, 18.

33. "NCSBN Standing Rules: Adopted in 1978," (Madison, WI: NCSBN, 1978), NCSBN Archives, Chicago, IL, 1–6.

34. "NCSBN Standing Rules: Amended in 1979," (Madison, WI: NCSBN, 1979), NCSBN Archives, Chicago, IL, 1–9.

35. *National Council of State Boards of Nursing Policy and Procedures* (Chicago: NCSBN, 2006), CD-ROM.

36. Robert, *Robert's Rules*, 599–602.

37. Minutes, Meeting of the NCSBN Board of Directors: January 24–26, 1983, NCSBN Archives, Chicago, IL, 8.

38. Minutes, Meeting of the NCSBN Board of Directors: May 23–25, 1983, NCSBN Archives, Chicago, IL, 12–13.

39. Minutes, Meeting of the NCSBN Delegate Assembly: August 27–29, 1984, NCSBN Archives, Chicago, IL, 7–8.

40. Minutes, Meeting of the NCSBN Delegate Assembly: August 21–23, 1985, NCSBN Archives, Chicago, IL, 12.

41. Minutes, Meeting of the NCSBN Delegate Assembly: August 5–9, 1986, NCSBN Archives, Chicago, IL, 7.

42. "Report of the Long Range Planning Committee," *NCSBN Book of Reports* (Chicago: NCSBN, 1986): 68–73.

43. Minutes, Meeting of the NCSBN Board of Directors: February 8–10, 1988, NCSBN Archives, Chicago, IL, 8.

44. "Report of the Board of Directors," *NCSBN Book of Reports* (Chicago: NCSBN, 1988): 49.

45. Minutes, Meeting of the NCSBN Board of Directors: August 15, 1989, NCSBN Archives, Chicago, IL, 2.

46. Minutes, Meeting of the NCSBN Board of Directors: April 30–May 11, 1990, NCSBN Archives, Chicago, IL, 7.

47. "Report of the Long Range Planning Committee," *NCSBN Book of Reports* (Chicago: NCSBN, 1990): Tab 13, 1–5.

48. Minutes, Meeting of the NCSBN Delegate Assembly: August 18–22, 1992, NCSBN Archives, Chicago, IL, 10.

49. Minutes, Meeting of the NCSBN Delegate Assembly: August 6–10, 1996, NCSBN Archives, Chicago, IL, 7.

50. "Report of the Long Range Planning Task Force," *NCSBN Book of Reports* (Chicago: NCSBN, 1997): Tab 10B, 1–7.

51. Minutes, Meeting of the NCSBN Board of Directors: February 12–14, 1997, NCSBN Archives, Chicago, IL, 6.

52. Minutes, Meeting of the NCSBN Board of Directors: May 14–16, 1997, NCSBN Archives, Chicago, IL, 2–3.

53. Minutes, Meeting of the NCSBN Board of Directors: June 25–26, 1997, NCSBN Archives, Chicago, IL, 4–5.

54. Minutes, Meeting of the NCSBN Delegate Assembly: August 20–23, 1997, NCSBN Archives, Chicago, IL, 8.

55. Minutes, Meeting of the NCSBN Delegate Assembly: August 4–8, 1998, NCSBN Archives, Chicago, IL, 5–6.

56. Minutes, Meeting of the NCSBN Delegate Assembly: August 5–8, 2003, NCSBN Archives, Chicago, IL, 4–5.

57. Carolyn Hutcherson, "Report of the President," *NCSBN Book of Reports* (Chicago: NCSBN, 1992): Tab 4, 3.

58. "Report of the Board of Directors," *NCSBN Book of Reports* (Chicago: NCSBN, 1992): Tab 8, 1.

59. Rosa Lee Weinert, "Report of the President," *NCSBN Book of Reports* (Chicago: NCSBN, 1993): Tab 4, 1.

60. Minutes, Meeting of the NCSBN Board of Directors: February 1–3, 1995, NCSBN Archives, Chicago, IL, 3.

61. "Report of the Board of Directors," *NCSBN Book of Reports* (Chicago: NCSBN, 1995): Tab 10, 4.

62. Minutes, Meeting of the NCSBN Board of Directors: May 14–16, 1997, NCSBN Archives, Chicago, IL, 2–3.

63. "Report of the Board of Directors," *NCSBN Business Book* (Chicago: NCSBN, 2002): 40–74.

64. Minutes, Meeting of the NCSBN Board of Directors: September 4–5, 2003, NCSBN Archives, Chicago, IL, 2.

65. Robert, *Robert's Rules*, 3.

66. Mildred S. Schmidt, "To Whom is the NCSBN Accountable?" *Issues* (Spring 1980): 1, 4

67. Robert, *Robert's Rules*, 6.

68. "NCSBN Bylaws: Amended and Revised 2003," (Chicago: NCSBN, 2003): NCSBN Archives, Chicago, IL.

69. "NCSBN Bylaws: Adopted 1978," (Madison, WI: NCSBN, 1978): NCSBN Archives, Chicago, IL.

70. Minutes, Meeting of the NCSBN Delegate Assembly: December 14–15, 1997, NCSBN Archives, Chicago, IL, 4.

71. Minutes, Meeting of the NCSBN Delegate Assembly: June 6–8, 1979, NCSBN Archives, Chicago, IL, 10-11.

72. Robert, *Robert's Rules*, 9.

73. "NCSBN Bylaws, 1978."

74. "NCSBN Bylaws, 2003."

75. Vedder, Price, Kaufman and Kammholz to the NCSBN Board of Directors, November 5, 1985, NCSBN Archives, Chicago, IL.

76. William C. Walsh for Vedder, Price, Kaufman and Kammholz to Eileen Dvorak, Executive Director, NCSBN, February 19, 1988, NCSBN Archives, Chicago, IL.

77. Robert, *Robert's Rules*, 471–74.

78. "NCSBN Organizational Chart," *NCSBN Book of Reports* (Chicago: NCSBN, 1989): Tab 22, Appendix A.

79. "NCSBN Organizational Chart," *NCSBN Business Book* (Chicago: NCSBN, 1998): Tab 11, 8.

80.   "NCSBN Organizational Chart," *NCSBN Business Book* (Chicago: NCSBN, 2003): 253.

81.   National Council of State Boards of Nursing, *1978–2003: 25 Years of the National Council of State Boards of Nursing: Honoring Our Past to Create Our Future*, (Chicago: NCSBN, 2003): 17.

82.   Gertrude Malone, Shirley Fondiller, and David Heidorn, From An Idea To An Organization (Chicago: NCSBN, 1983): 2, 26–27.

83.   Ibid., 4 and 28.

84.   Ibid., 26-27.

85.   *Honoring Our Past*, 17.

86.   Sharon Weisenbeck, "Report of the President," *NCSBN Book of Reports* (Chicago: NCSBN, 1985): 41.

87.   Shirley Fondiller, The Promise Continues: A Decade of Progress (Chicago: NCSBN, 1988): 28.

88.   Renatta Loquist, "President's Message," *Issues* 9, no. 2 (1988): 3.

89.   Carolyn Hutcherson, "Report of the President," *NCSBN Book of Reports* (Chicago: NCSBN, 1992): Tab 4, 2.

90.   Rosa Lee Weinert, "Report of the President," *NCSBN Book of Reports* (Chicago: NCSBN, 1994): Tab 4, 1.

91.   Marcia Rachel, "Report of the President," *NCSBN Book of Reports* (Chicago: NCSBN, 1995): Tab 4, 1.

92.   Thomas Neumann, "Report of the President," *NCSBN Business Book* (Chicago: NCSBN, 1998): Tab 5, 1.

93.   Honoring Our Past, 32.

94.   Ibid., 38–39.

95.   Ibid., 26.

96.   Minutes, Meeting of the NCSBN Board of Directors: November 28–December 1, 1978, NCSBN Archives, Chicago, IL, 5.

97.   "Report of the Finance Committee," *NCSBN Business Book* (Chicago: NCSBN, 2003): 153.

98.   Minutes, Meeting of the NCSBN Board of Directors: June 7–9, 1993, NCSBN Archives, Chicago, IL, 4.

99.   Minutes, Meeting of the NCSBN Board of Directors: August 3–4, 1993, NCSBN Archives, Chicago, IL, 4.

100. Minutes, Meeting of the NCSBN Board of Directors: October 5–6, 1993, NCSBN Archives, Chicago, IL, 3–4.

101. Minutes, Meeting of the NCSBN Board of Directors: December 1–3, 1993, NCSBN Archives, Chicago, IL, 3–5.

102. William C. Walsh, Vedder, Price, Kaufman and Kammholz, to Jennifer Bosma, Executive Director, NCSBN, November 23, 1993, NCSBN Archives, Chicago, IL.

103. Minutes, Meeting of the NCSBN Board of Directors: January 24, 1994, NCSBN Archives, Chicago, IL, 1–2.

104. Minutes, Meeting of the NCSBN Board of Directors: March 7–9, 1994, NCSBN Archives, Chicago, IL, 3–4.

105. Minutes, Meeting of the NCSBN Board of Directors: May 2, 1994, NCSBN Archives, Chicago, IL, 1.

106. "Report of the Board of Directors," *NCSBN Book of Reports* (Chicago: NCSBN, 1994): Tab 20, 1–46.

107. Minutes, Meeting of the NCSBN Delegate Assembly: August 5–6, 1994, NCSBN Archives, Chicago, IL, 10.

108. Minutes, Meeting of the NCSBN Board of Directors: August 7, 1994, NCSBN Archives, Chicago, IL, 3.

109. Minutes, Meeting of the NCSBN Board of Directors: June 21–23, 1995, NCSBN Archives, Chicago, IL, 8.

110. "Report of the Special Services Division," *NCSBN Book of Reports* (Chicago: NCSBN, 1995): Tab 10O, 1–2.

111. Minutes, Meeting of the NCSBN Board of Directors: October 19–20, 1995, NCSBN Archives, Chicago, IL, 7.

112. Minutes, Meeting of the NCSBN Board of Directors: January 17–18, 1996, NCSBN Archives, Chicago, IL, 8.

113. Minutes, Meeting of the NCSBN Board of Directors: May 8–10, 1996, NCSBN Archives, Chicago, IL, 8.

114. Minutes, Meeting of the NCSBN Board of Directors: June 26–28, 1996, NCSBN Archives, Chicago, IL, 5.

115. "Report of the Special Services Division," *NCSBN Book of Reports* (Chicago: NCSBN, 1996): Tab 10T, 1–3.

116. Minutes, Meeting of the NCSBN Delegate Assembly: August 9–10, 1996, NCSBN Archives, Chicago, IL, 8

117. Minutes, Meeting of the NCSBN Board of Directors: May 14–16, 1997, NCSBN Archives, Chicago, IL, 5.

118. Ibid., 8.

119. Minutes, Meeting of the NCSBN Board of Directors: August 17–18, 1997, NCSBN Archives, Chicago, IL, 3.

120. "Report of the Special Services Division," *NCSBN Book of Reports* (Chicago: NCSBN, 1997): Tab 10D, 1–2.

121. Minutes, Meeting of the NCSBN Board of Directors: August 1 and 8, 1998, NCSBN Archives, Chicago, IL, 2.

122. Minutes, Meeting of the NCSBN Board of Directors: November 4–5, 1998, NCSBN Archives, Chicago, IL, 7.

123. Minutes, Meeting of the NCSBN Board of Directors: February 3–5, 1999, NCSBN Archives, Chicago, IL, 7.

124. Minutes, Meeting of the NCSBN Board of Directors: May 5–7, 1999, NCSBN Archives, Chicago, IL, 6–7.

125. Minutes, Meeting of the NCSBN Board of Directors: December 1–3, 1999, NCSBN Archives, Chicago, IL, 3.

126. Minutes, Meeting of the NCSBN Board of Directors: February 23 and 24, 2000, NCSBN Archives, Chicago, IL, 6.

127. "Summary of Recommendations to the 2000 Delegate Assembly with Rationale," *NCSBN Business Book* (Chicago: NCSBN, 2000): 27.

128. Minutes, Meeting of the NCSBN Delegate Assembly: August 8–12, 2000, NCSBN Archives, Chicago, IL, 5

129. "Report of the Board of Directors," *NCSBN Business Book* (Chicago: NCSBN, 2001): 20.

130. Marcia Rachel, "Report of the President," *NCSBN Book of Reports* (Chicago: NCSBN, 1995): Tab 4, 1.

131. "Policy 6.5: Liaison Relationships With External Organizations," National *Council of State Boards of Nursing Policy and Procedure* (Chicago: NCSBN, 2002) CD-ROM.

132. Minutes, Meeting of the NCSBN Delegate Assembly: August 7–11, 1990, NCSBN Archives, Chicago, IL, 6–7.

133. "Policy 6.6: Requests for Endorsement of External Organization Position Statements," *National Council of State Boards of Nursing Policy and Procedure* (Chicago: NCSBN, 2002): CD-ROM.

134. Minutes, Meetings of the NCSBN Board of Directors: 1978–1979, NCSBN Archives, Chicago, IL.

135. Minutes, Meeting of the NCSBN Board of Directors: July 16–17, 1990, NCSBN Archives, Chicago, IL, 3.

136. Minutes, Meeting of the NCSBN Board of Directors: February 10–12, 1987, NCSBN Archives, Chicago, IL, 4.

137. "Liaison Organizations," Minutes, Meeting of the NCSBN Board of Directors: January 14–15, 1996, NCSBN Archives, Chicago, IL, Attachment.

138. "Report of the Board of Directors," *NCSBN Book of Reports* (Chicago: NCSBN, 2003): 45–50.

139. Minutes, Meetings of the NCSBN Delegate Assembly: 1978–2003, NCSBN Archives, Chicago, IL.

Chapter Five

1. Renatta Loquist, "Report of the President," *National Council of State Boards of Nursing, Inc. (NCSBN) Book of Reports* (Chicago: NCSBN, 1990): Tab 3, 2.

2. Minutes, Meeting of the NCSBN Board of Directors: June 6, 1980, NCSBN Archives, Chicago, IL, 4.

3. Minutes, Meeting of the NCSBN Board of Directors: September 22–24, 1980, NCSBN Archives, Chicago, IL, 3.

4. Minutes, Meeting of the NCSBN Board of Directors: April 9–11, 1980, NCSBN Archives, Chicago, IL, 7.

5. Eileen McQuaid, "Report of the Executive Director to the Delegate Assembly," *NCSBN Book of Reports* (Chicago: NCSBN, 1980).

6. Eileen McQuaid, ed., *Issues* 1, no. 1 (1980).

7. Eileen McQuaid, "Report of the Executive Director," *NCSBN Book of Reports* (Chicago: NCSBN, 1981).

8. Eileen Dvorak, "Report of the Executive Director," *NCSBN Book of Reports* (Chicago: NCSBN, 1982): 57.

9. Minutes, Meeting of the NCSBN Board of Directors: September 20–21, 1982, NCSBN Archives, Chicago, IL, 6

10.   "Publications List, NCSBN," *Newsletter to the Member Boards*, 1, no. 10 (1983): Attachment.

11.   Eileen Dvorak, "Report of the Executive Director," *NCSBN Book of Reports* (Chicago: NCSBN, 1984): 93.

12.   Eileen Dvorak, "Report of the Executive Director," *NCSBN Book of Reports* (Chicago: NCSBN, 1983): 105.

13.   Minutes, Meeting of the NCSBN Board of Directors: December 12–14, 1983, NCSBN Archives, Chicago, IL, 8.

14.   Minutes, Meeting of the NCSBN Board of Directors, January 24–26, 1983, NCSBN Archives, Chicago, IL, 7.

15.   Minutes, Meeting of the NCSBN Board of Directors: May 6–8, 1985, NCSBN Archives, Chicago, IL, 7.

16.   Minutes, Meeting of the NCSBN Board of Directors: February 10–12, 1987, NCSBN Archives, Chicago, IL, 8–9.

17.   Minutes, Meeting of the NCSBN Board of Directors: February 8–10, 1988, NCSBN Archives, Chicago, IL, 6–7.

18.   "Report of Communications Committee," *NCSBN Book of Reports* (Chicago: NCSBN, 1990): Tab 14, 3.

19.   Minutes, Meeting of the NCSBN Board of Directors: December 2–4, 1992, NCSBN Archives, Chicago, IL, 4.

20.   "Report of Communications Evaluation Task Force," *NCSBN Book of Reports* (Chicago: NCSBN, 1996): Tab 10O, 1–3.

21.   "Report of Communications Evaluation Task Force," *NCSBN Book of Reports* (Chicago: NCSBN, 1997): Tab 10E, 1–6.

22.   Minutes, Meeting of the NCSBN Board of Directors: June 12, 1981, NCSBN Archives, Chicago, IL, 1.

23.   Minutes, June 12, 1981, 3.

24.   "NCSBN Brochure," *Newsletter to the Member Boards* 2, no. 7 (1984): 1.

25.   Eileen Dvorak, "Report of the Executive Director," *NCSBN Book of Reports* (Chicago: NCSBN, 1985): 87.

26.   Minutes, Meeting of the NCSBN Board of Directors: May 5–7, 1987, NCSBN Archives, Chicago, IL, 7.

27.   Eileen Dvorak, "Report of the Executive Director," *NCSBN Book of Reports* (Chicago: NCSBN, 1987): 119–20.

28.   Minutes, Meeting of the NCSNB Delegate Assembly: August 26–29, 1987, NCSBN Archives, Chicago, IL, 20.

29.   "*State Nursing Legislative Quarterly* Published," *Newsletter to the Member Boards* 7, no. 2 (1988): 2.

30.   "Washington News," *Issues* 8, no. 3 (1987): 5–7.

31.   Minutes, Meeting of the NCSBN Board of Directors: October 26, 1987, NCSBN Archives, Chicago, IL, 6.

32.   "New Registered Nurse Study Guide Published," *Newsletter to the Member Boards* 8, no. 7 (1988): 4.

33.   Minutes, Meeting of the NCSBN Delegate Assembly: August 16–20, 1988, NCSBN Archives, Chicago, IL, 7

34. Minutes, Meeting of the NCSBN Board of Directors: January 29–February 1, 1989, NCSBN Archives, Chicago, IL, 14–15.

35. Minutes, Meeting of the NCSBN Board of Directors: April 26–28, 1989, NCSBN Archives, Chicago, IL, 4.

36. Minutes, Meeting of the NCSBN Delegate Assembly: August 1–5, 1989, NCSBN Archives, Chicago, IL, 14.

37. Minutes, Meeting of the NCSBN Board of Directors: January 29–31, 1990, NCSBN Archives, Chicago, IL, 6–7.

38. Minutes, Meeting of the NCSBN Board of Directors: April 30–May 2, 1990, NCSBN Archives, Chicago, IL, 2.

39. Minutes, Meeting of the NCSBN Board of Directors: July 16–17, 1990, NCSBN Archives, Chicago, IL, 4–5

40. Minutes, Meeting of the NCSBN Delegate Assembly: August 7–11, 1990, NCSBN Archives, Chicago, IL, 11.

41. "Report of the Board of Directors," *NCSBN Book of Reports* (Chicago: NCSBN, 1990): Tab 4, 5.

42. "Communication Corner," *Issues* 1, no. 1 (1991): 2.

43. Minutes, Meeting of the NCSBN Delegate Assembly: July 30–August 2, 1991, NCSBN Archives, Chicago, IL, 7.

44. "Report of the Board of Directors," *NCSBN Book of Reports* (Chicago: NCSBN, 1991): Tab 4, 1–5.

45. "Report of the Communications Committee," *NCSBN Book of Reports* (Chicago: NCSBN, 1991): Tab 17, 1–3.

46. "The NCLEX Process," *Newsletter to the Member Boards* 11, no. 24 (1991): Attachment.

47. Minutes, Meeting of the NCSBN Board of Directors: January 16, 1992, NCSBN Archives, Chicago, IL, 2.

48. Minutes, Meeting of the NCSBN Board of Directors: February 20–23, 1992, NCSBN Archives, Chicago, IL, 3–4.

49. Christopher T. Handzlik, ed., *Insight* 1, no. 1 (1992).

50. Minutes, Meeting of the NCSBN Board of Directors: June 7–9, 1993, NCSBN Archives, Chicago, IL, 4.

51. Minutes, Meeting of the NCSBN Board of Directors: January 24, 1994, NCSBN Archives, Chicago, IL, 1.

52. Minutes, Meeting of the NCSBN Board of Directors: May 27, 1994, NCSBN Archives, Chicago, IL, 2.

53. Minutes, Meeting of the NCSBN Board of Directors: June 6–8, 1994, NCSBN Archives, Chicago, IL, 5–6

54. Minutes, Meeting of the NCSBN Board of Directors: June 21–23, 1995, NCSBN Archives, Chicago, IL, 7.

55. "National Council Publishes Nurse Aide Job Analysis," *Insight* 4, no. 2 (1995): 6.

56. "Introducing Policy Currents," *Newsletter to the Member Boards* 16, no. 5 (1996): 1.

57. Minutes, Meeting of the NCSBN Board of Directors: August 8–10, 1996, NCSBN Archives, Chicago, IL, 4.

58. Minutes, Meeting of the NCSBN Board of Directors: June 26–28, 1996, NCSBN Archives, Chicago, IL, 5

59. Jennifer Bosma, "Report of Staff Activities," *NCSBN Book of Reports* (Chicago: NCSBN, 1996): Tab 5, 3–7.

60. Jennifer Bosma, "Report of Staff Activities," *NCSBN Book of Reports* (Chicago: NCSBN, 1997): Tab 5, 7.

61. "Video on Chemical Dependency Issues Is Released," *The Council Connector* (July 2001): 1.

62. "Committee Reports Go Online," *Newsletter to the Member Boards* 18, no. 1 (1998): 3.

63. "Curriculum Guide and Regulatory Criteria for FNP Seeking Prescriptive Authority to Manage Pharmacotherapeutics in Primary Care Now Available," *Issues* 20, no. 2 (1999): 15.

64. Minutes, Meeting of the NCSBN Board of Directors: March 9, 2000, NCSBN Archives, Chicago, IL, 3.

65. "Office Relocation and 25th Anniversary Support NCSBN Logo Change," *The Council Connector* (November 2002): 1.

Chapter Six

1. Lizzie M. Cox, Editor's miscellany. *American Journal of Nursing* 7 (1906): 50.

2. Gertrude Malone, Shirley Fondiller and David Heidorn, *From An Idea to an Organization*, (Chicago: National Council of State Boards of Nursing, Inc. [NCSBN] 1983): 5.

3. Helen Keefe, "Report of the Secretary," *NCSBN Book of Reports* (Chicago: NCSBN, 1980).

4. Minutes, Meeting of the NCSBN Board of Directors: December 2–4, 2002, NCSBN Archives, Chicago, IL, 6.

5. Minutes, Meeting of the NCSBN Board of Directors: January 24–26, 1983, NCSBN Archives, Chicago, IL, 9.

6. Eileen Dvorak, "Report of the Executive Director," *NCSBN Book of Reports* (Chicago: NCSBN, 1988): 121.

7. Eileen Dvorak, "Report of the Executive Director," *NCSBN Book of Reports* (Chicago: NCSBN, 1989): Tab 9, 4.

8. "Report of Subcommittee on Nurse Shortage," *NCSBN Book of Reports* (Chicago: NCSBN, 1989): Tab 16, 1–7.

9. "Guidelines for Responding to Requests for Endorsement of Position Statements," *NCSBN Book of Reports* (Chicago: NCSBN, 1990): Tab 4, 38.

10. Minutes, Meeting of the NCSBN Board of Directors: February 20–22, 1992, NCSBN Archives, Chicago, IL, 5.

11. Jennifer Bosma, "Report of Staff Activities," *NCSBN Book of Reports* (Chicago: NCSBN, 1995): 3.

12. "Board of Directors Corner," *Newsletter to the Member Boards* 15, no. 3 (1995): 1.

13. Minutes, Meeting of the NCSBN Board of Directors: October 11–12, 2000, NCSBN Archives, Chicago, IL, 5–6.

14. Minutes, Meeting of the NCSBN Board of Directors: November 14, 2000, NCSBN Archives, Chicago, IL, 1.

15. Minutes, Meeting of the NCSBN Board of Directors: January 10–12, 2001, NCSBN Archives, Chicago, IL, 4.

16. Minutes, January 10–12, 2001, 10.

17. Minutes, Meeting of the NCSBN Board of Directors: November 14, 2000, NCSBN Archives, Chicago, IL, 1.

18. Minutes, Meeting of the NCSBN Board of Directors: January 10–12, 2001, NCSBN Archives, Chicago, IL, 10.

19. Minutes, Meeting of the NCSBN Board of Directors: May 6–8, 2001, NCSBN Archives, Chicago, IL, 4.

20. Minutes, Meeting of the NCSBN Board of Directors: August 5, 2001, NCSBN Archives, Chicago, IL, 2.

21. Minutes, Meeting of the NCSBN Board of Directors: October 2–3, 2001, NCSBN Archives, Chicago, IL, 5.

22. Minutes, Meeting of the NCSBN Delegate Assembly: August 7–11, 2001, NCSBN Archives, Chicago, IL, 6.

23. "AHCA Study Shows Impact of Nursing Shortage on Elderly," *Council Connector* 1, no. 10 (2001): 8–9.

24. "Hospital CEOs Concerned about Nursing Workforce," *Council Connector* 1, no. 10 (2001): 9.

25. "NCSBN Participating in the Call to the Nursing Profession," *The Council Connector* 2, no. 4 (2002): 1–2.

26. "Nursing Shortage Will Get Worse," *Council Connector* 2, no. 6 (2002): 1.

27. Minutes, Meeting of the NCSBN Board of Directors: March 24, 2003, NCSBN Archives, Chicago, IL, 2.

28. "Regulatory Response to Acquired Immune Deficiency Syndrome," *Issues* 9, no. 1 (1988): 1–2 and 4–6.

29. Eileen Dvorak, "From the Executive Director," *Issues* 9, no. 1 (1988): 2.

30. Minutes, Meeting of the NCSBN Board of Directors: April 14, 1992, NCSBN Archives, Chicago, IL, 12.

31. Minutes, Meeting of the NCSBN Board of Directors: April 30–May 1, 1990, NCSBN Archives, Chicago, IL, 11.

32. "The Proposed NAFTA Agreement," *Emerging Issues, Newsletter to the Member Boards* 12, no. 23 (1992): attachment.

33. "North American Free Trade Agreement," *Newsletter to the Member Boards* 13, no. 22 (1993): 2.

34. Minutes, Meeting of the NCSBN Board of Directors: June 6–8, 1994, NCSBN Archives, Chicago, IL, 3.

35. "Meeting Report: Canada, Mexico, US Nursing Education," *Newsletter to the Member Boards* 14, no. 9 (1994): 2–4.

36. "North American Free Trade Agreement (NAFTA)," *Newsletter to the Member Boards* 15, no. 1 (1995): 1–2.

37. Minutes, Meeting of the NCSBN Board of Directors: June 26–28, 1996, NCSBN Archives, Chicago, IL, 2.

38. "North American Free Trade Agreement," *Newsletter to the Member Boards* 16, no. 2 (1996): 3.

39. "Comprehensive Assessment of North American Nursing Available in December," *Newsletter to the Member Boards* 16, no. 22 (1996): 3.

40. Minutes, Meeting of the NCSBN Board of Directors: August 4, 2003, NCSBN Archives, Chicago, IL, 2.

41. Minutes, Meeting of the NCSBN Board of Directors: July 28–29, 1991, NCSBN Archives, Chicago, IL, 3.

42. Minutes, Meeting of the NCSBN Board of Directors: October 20–22, 1991, NCSBN Archives, Chicago, IL, 9.

43. Minutes, Meeting of the NCSBN Board of Directors: May 6–8, 1992, NCSBN Archives, Chicago, IL, 5.

44. Minutes, Meeting of the NCSBN Delegate Assembly: August 18–22, 1992, NCSBN Archives, Chicago, IL, 14.

45. Minutes, Meeting of the NCSBN Board of Directors: September 1, 1993, NCSBN Archives, Chicago, IL, 1–2.

46. Minutes, Meeting of the NCSBN Board of Directors: September 17, 1993, NCSBN Archives, Chicago, IL, 1–2.

47. Ibid.

48. Minutes, Meeting of the NCSBN Board of Directors: October 5–6, 1993, NCSBN Archives, Chicago, IL, 5.

49. Minutes, Meeting of the NCSBN Board of Directors: December 1–3, 1993, NCSBN Archives, Chicago, IL, 4–5.

50. Minutes, Meeting of the NCSBN Board of Directors: March 7–9, 1994, NCSBN Archives, Chicago, IL, 5.

51. Minutes, Meeting of the NCSBN Board of Directors: July 30–31, 1995, NCSBN Archives, Chicago, IL, 2.

52. "National Council Collaborates on Medication Error Reporting," *Newsletter to the Member Boards* 17, no. 16 (1997): 2.

53. Minutes, Meeting of the NCSBN Board of Directors: August 12, 2000, NCSBN Archives, Chicago, IL, 2.

54. Minutes, Meeting of the NCSBN Board of Directors: January 10–12, 2001, NCSBN Archives, Chicago, IL, 4.

55. Minutes, Meeting of the NCSBN Board of Directors: August 31, 2001, NCSBN Archives, Chicago, IL, 3.

56. Minutes, Meeting of the NCSBN Board of Directors: August 12, 2002, NCSBN Archives, Chicago, IL, 3.

57. Minutes, Meeting of the NCSBN Board of Directors: March 24, 2003, NCSBN Archives, Chicago, IL, 2.

58. Minutes, Meeting of the NCSBN Board of Directors: June 21–23, 1995, NCSBN Archives, Chicago, IL, 7.

59. Minutes, Meeting of the NCSBN Board of Directors: August 6, 1995, NCSBN Archives, Chicago, IL, 2.

60. Minutes, Meeting of the NCSBN Board of Directors: October 19–20, 1995, NCSBN Archives, Chicago, IL, 7.

61. Minutes, Meeting of the NCSBN Board of Directors: January 17–18, 1996, NCSBN Archives, Chicago, IL, 7.

62. Minutes, Meeting of the NCSBN Board of Directors: May 28, 1996, NCSBN Archives, Chicago, IL, 2.

63. "National Council of State Boards of Nursing's Response to the Pew Task Force on Health Care Workforce Regulations, *Reforming Health Care Workforce Regulation: Policy Considerations for the 21st Century*," (Chicago: NCSBN, 1996): NCSBN Archives, Chicago, IL, Tab 10K, 5–18.

64. Ibid.

65. "Report of Nursing Regulation Task Force," *NCSBN Book of Reports* (Chicago: NCSBN, 1996): Tab 10K, 1–18.

66. Minutes, Meeting of the NCSBN Delegate Assembly: August 9–10, 1996, NCSBN Archives, Chicago, IL, 7.

67. Minutes, Meeting of the NCSBN Board of Directors: September 18, 1996, NCSBN Archives, Chicago, IL, 1.

68. "National Council Adds to its World Wide Web Site," *Issues*, 18, no. 1 (1977): 15.

69. "Pew Health Professions Commission Revived," *Newsletter to the Member Boards* 1997, May: 1.

70. Minutes, Meeting of the NCSBN Board of Directors: February 11–13, 1998, NCSBN Archives, Chicago, IL, 7.

71. "New Pew Report," *Newsletter to the Member Boards* 18, no. 23 (1998): 3.

72. Minutes, Meeting of the NCSBN Board of Directors: February 3–5, 1999, NCSBN Archives, Chicago, IL, 4.

73. Ibid., 8.

74. "Pew Health Professions Commission Report," *Newsletter to the Member Boards* 19, no. 6 (1999): 1.

75. Minutes, Meeting of the NCSBN Board of Directors: May 5–7, 1999, NCSBN Archives, Chicago, IL, 8.

76. "US Supreme Court Decision Triggers Calls," *Newsletter to the Member Boards* 14, no. 11 (1994): 2–4.

77. "Report of the Board of Directors," *NCSBN Book of Reports* (Chicago: NCSBN, 1995): Tab 10, 2.

78. "Institute of Medicine (IOM), Nursing Staff in Hospitals and Nursing Homes: Is It Adequate?" *Newsletter to the Member Boards* 16, no. 3 (1996): 2.

79. Minutes, Meeting of the NCSBN Board of Directors: February 23–24, 2000, NCSBN Archives, Chicago, IL, 5.

80. Minutes, Meeting of the NCSBN Board of Directors: June 1, 2000, NCSBN Archives, Chicago, IL, 4.

81. Ibid., 4–5.

82. Minutes, Meeting of the NCSBN Board of Directors: June 16, 2000, NCSBN Archives, Chicago, IL, 2.

83. "Report of the NP&E Committee," *NCSBN Business Book* (Chicago: NCSBN, 2000): 91–97.

84. Minutes, Meeting of the NCSBN Board of Directors: August 12, 2000, NCSBN Archives, Chicago, IL, 2.

85. Minutes, Meeting of the NCSBN Board of Directors: May 6–8, 2001, NCSBN Archives, Chicago, IL, 3.

86.   "Health Professions Education: A Bridge to Quality," *Council Connector* 3, no. 4 (2003): 2.

87.   Parable of the UPs and DOWNs excerpted from speech by Katherine Thomas at the NCSBN Annual Meeting, August 13–17, 2002, also published in *Council Connector* 2, no. 8 (2002): 8.

Chapter Seven

1.   Elizabeth C. Burgess, "The Nurse Practice Act—A Protective Device for the Community," *Bits of News* 5, no. 2 (1936): 14–18.

2.   "Proceedings of the Fifteenth Annual Convention of the American Nurses Association [ANA] held at Orchestra Hall, Chicago, Illinois, June 5–7, 1912," *American Journal of Nursing* 12 (1912): 971–72.

3.   Anna Jamme, "Report of the Committee on Legislation," *American Journal of Nursing* 17 (1917): 918–25.

4.   "Excerpts of Minutes of ANA Board of Directors' Meeting held in New York January 1936," *American Journal of Nursing* 36 (1936): 525–28.

5.   George V. Fleckstein, "Nurse Practice Acts," *American Journal of Nursing* 36 (1936): 231–34.

6.   "Professional Nursing as Defined by the Committee to Outline a Definition of Nursing," *American Journal of Nursing* 32 (1932): 552.

7.   "Professional Nursing Defined," *American Journal of Nursing* 37 (1937): 518.

8.   Sophia Palmer, "Progress of State Registration," *American Journal of Nursing* 14 (1913): 160.

9.   "Meeting of the ANA Board of Directors," *American Journal of Nursing* 37 (1937): 913.

10.   "ANA-NLNE Conference for State Boards of Nurse Examiners," *American Journal of Nursing* 47 (1947): 836.

11.   "ANA Issues Revisions of Nurse Practice Act Suggestions," *American Journal of Nursing* 48 (1948): 541.

12.   Elaine F. Ellibee, "The Philosophy and Purpose of Licensure" (paper presented at the meeting of the ANA Council of State Boards of Nursing, Minnesota, 1973).

13.   Virginia C. Hall, "The Legal Scope of Nursing Practice" (paper presented at the meeting of the ANA Council of State Boards of Nursing, New Orleans, 1975).

14.   Ibid.

15.   Ibid.

16.   Sharon M. Weisenbeck and Patricia A Calico, "Licensure and Related Issues in Nursing," Grace L. Deloughery, ed. *Issues and Trends in Nursing* (St. Louis: Mosby, 1991): 247.

17.   Minutes, Meeting of ANA Council of State Boards of Nursing: March 25–26, 1976, NCSBN Archives, Chicago, IL, 7.

18.   Ibid.

19.   *The Nursing Practice Act: Suggested State Legislation* (Washington DC: ANA, 1980).

20.   *American Nurses Association Model Practice Act* (Washington, DC: ANA, 1996).

21.   Ibid.

22.   Minutes, Meeting of the National Council of State Boards of Nursing, Inc. (NCSBN) Board of Directors: June 25–26, 1997, NCSBN Archives, Chicago, IL, 4.

23. Minutes, Meeting of the NCSBN Board of Directors: August 17–18, 1997, NCSBN Archives, Chicago, IL, 2.

24. Minutes, Meeting of the NCSBN Board of Directors: November 4–5, 1997, NCSBN Archives, Chicago, IL, 4.

25. Minutes, Meeting of the NCSBN Board of Directors: November 4–5, 1998, NCSBN Archives, Chicago, IL, 9.

26. Inez Hinsvark, "Report of the Study of Credentialing in Nursing," Minutes, Meeting of the ANA Council of State Boards of Nursing: June 7–9, 1977, 23–32.

27. Ibid.

28. "National Council of State Boards of Nursing, Inc. Bylaws Adopted 1978," (Madison, WI: NCSBN, 1978), NCSBN Archives, Chicago, IL.

29. Ibid.

30. "ANA House of Delegates Resolution," received by NCSBN from Barbara Nichols, President, ANA, July 7, 1978, NCSBN Archives, Chicago, IL.

31. "State Boards Establish Separate Council," *The American Nurse* 10, no. 7 (1978): 3.

32. Minutes, Meeting of the NCSBN Board of Directors: July 6–8, 1978, NCSBN Archives, Chicago, IL, 7.

33. Minutes, Meeting of the NCSBN Board of Directors: September 11–13, 1978, NCSBN Archives, Chicago, IL, 5.

34. Minutes, Meeting of the NCSBN Board of Directors: January 22–24, 1979, NCSBN Archives, Chicago, IL, 5.

35. Minutes, Meeting of the NCSBN Board of Directors: November 28–December 1, 1978, NCSBN Archives, Chicago, IL, 1–2.

36. Minutes, Meeting of the NCSBN Board of Directors: June 4–5, 1979, NCSBN Archives, Chicago, IL, 8.

37. Minutes, Meeting of the NCSBN Delegate Assembly: June 6–8, 1979, NCSBN Archives, Chicago, IL, 8–9.

38. Ibid., 9–10.

39. "Report of the Nursing Practice and Standards (NP&S) Committee," *NCSBN Book of Reports* (Chicago: NCSBN, 1980).

40. "Difference Between Statutory and Professional Definitions of Nursing Practice, Working Draft # 5," NCSBN NP&S Committee, March 4, 1980, 1, NCSBN Archives, Chicago, IL.

41. "Report of the NP&S Committee," *NCSBN Book of Reports* (Chicago: NCSBN, 1980).

42. Ruth Seigler, "Report of Director-at-Large," NCSBN, Book of Reports (Chicago: NCSBN,1980).

43. Weisenbeck and Calico, 248–49.

44. Hildegard E. Peplau, "Internal vs. External Regulation," *New Jersey Nurse* 1984, January/February, 12–23.

45. Frances I. Waddle, "Legal Regulation of Nursing Practice," Report Prepared for ANA, September 1986, NCSBN Archives, Chicago, IL, 1–36.

46. Ibid.

47. Ibid.

48. "Introduction," *NCSBN Model Nursing Practice Act* (Chicago: NCSBN, 1982): i–iii.

49. "Report of NP&S Committee," *NCSBN Book of Reports* (Chicago: NCSBN, 1981).

50. Minutes, Meeting of the NCSBN Delegate Assembly: June 9–12, 1981, NCSBN Archives, Chicago, IL, 6–7.

51. Minutes, Meeting of the NCSBN Board of Directors: March 8–10, 1982, NCSBN Archives, Chicago, IL, 6.

52. "Report of NCSBN-ANA Liaison Committee, *NCSBN Book of Reports* (Chicago: NCSBN, 1982): 43.

53. "Report of NP&S Committee, *NCSBN Book of Reports* (Chicago: NCSBN, 1982): 127–218.

54. Minutes, Meeting of the NCSBN Delegate Assembly: June 22–25, 1982, NCSBN Archives, Chicago, IL, 7–9.

55. Minutes, Meeting of the NCSBN Board of Directors: June 20–22, 1982, NCSBN Archives, Chicago, IL, 6.

56. Joan Bouchard, "Planning and Cooperation: Wyoming Adopts a Practice Act Based on NCSBN Model," *Issues* 4, no. 2 (1983): 4.

57. Minutes, Meeting of the NCSBN Board of Directors: May 23–25, 1983, NCSBN Archives, Chicago, IL, 3.

58. Minutes, Meeting of the NCSBN Delegate Assembly: August 27–29, 1984, NCSBN Archives, Chicago, IL, 14.

59. "Statement on Model Legal Standards," *NCSBN Book of Reports* (Chicago: NCSBN, 1984): 163–64.

60. "Report of NP&S Committee," *NCSBN Book of Reports* (Chicago: NCSBN, 1983): 173–74.

61. Minutes, Meeting of the NCSBN Delegate Assembly: August 24–26, 1983, NCSBN Archives, Chicago, IL, 15–17.

62. Ibid.

63. Minutes, Meeting of the NCSBN Board of Directors: May 14, 1986, NCSBN Archives, Chicago, IL, 3.

64. Minutes, Meeting of the NCSBN Board of Directors, June 16, 1986, NCSBN Archives, Chicago, IL, 4.

65. "Report of NP&S Committee," *NCSBN Book of Reports* (Chicago: NCSBN, 1986): 123–31.

66. Minutes, Meeting of the NCSBN Delegate Assembly: August 5–9, 1986, NCSBN Archives, Chicago, IL, 19.

67. "Report of NP&S Committee," *NCSBN Book of Reports* (Chicago: NCSBN, 1986): 152–78,

68. Minutes, August 5–9, 1986, 19–20.

69. Ibid., 6.

70. "Report of NP&E Committee, *NCSBN Book of Reports* (Chicago: NCSBN, 1991): Tab 18, 55–61.

71. "Report of NP&E Committee, *NCSBN Book of Reports* (Chicago; NCSBN, 1992): Tab 18, 15–18.

72. Minutes, Meeting of the NCSBN Delegate Assembly, August 18–22, 1992, NCSBN Archives, Chicago, IL, 18.

73. Minutes, Meeting of the NCSBN Delegate Assembly: August 20–23, 1997, NCSBN Archives, Chicago, IL, 7.

74. Minutes, Meeting of the NCSBN Delegate Assembly: August 5–8, 1998, NCSBN Archives, Chicago, IL, 5.

75. "Report of the NP&S Committee," *NCSBN Book of Reports* (Chicago: NCSBN, 1985): 120–22.

76. Minutes, Meeting of the NCSBN Delegate Assembly: August 21–23, 1985, NCSBN Archives, Chicago, IL, 15–16.

77. Minutes, Meeting of the NCSBN Delegate Assembly: August 26–29, 1987, NCSBN Archives, Chicago, IL, 10.

78. Minutes, Meeting of the NCSBN Board of Directors: April 26–28, 1989, NCSBN Archives, Chicago, IL, 8–9.

79. Minutes, Meeting of the NCSBN Delegate Assembly: August 9–10, 1996, NCSBN Archives, Chicago, IL, 5.

80. "Report of NP&E Committee," *NCSBN Book of Reports* (Chicago: NCSBN, 1991): Tab 18, 7–14.

81. Minutes, Meeting of the NCSBN Delegate Assembly: July 31–August 2, 1991, NCSBN Archives, Chicago, IL, 15.

82. "Report of the NP&E Committee," *NCSBN Book of Reports* (Chicago: NCSBN, 1991): Tab 18, 17–20.

83. "Report of the NP&S Committee," *NCSBN Book of Reports* (Chicago: NCSBN, 1988): 189–97.

84. Minutes, Meeting of the NCSBN Delegate Assembly: August 16–20, 1988, NCSBN Archives, Chicago, IL, 21–22.

85. "Report of Task Force on Examinations of the Future," *NCSBN Book of Reports* (Chicago: NCSBN, 1988): 198–204.

86. Minutes, Meeting of the NCSBN Delegate Assembly: August 1–5, 1989, NCSBN Archives, Chicago, IL, 4.

87. Minutes, August 1–5, 1989, 16.

88. Sister Lucie Leonard, "Nursing Practice and Education Committee Contributions to the Nursing Regulatory Community," *Issues* 10, no. 3 (1989): 1–2 and 4–5.

89. "Texas Board of Nursing and Sister Lucie Leonard Honored During 1990 Annual Convention," *Issues* 11, no. 3 (1990): 4.

90. "Report of the NP&E Committee," *NCSBN Book of Reports* (Chicago: NCSBN, 1993): Tab 20, 1–41.

91. Minutes, Meeting of the NCSBN Delegate Assembly: August 5–7, 1993, NCSBN Archives, Chicago, IL, 13.

92. "Report of the NP&E Committee," *NCSBN Book of Reports* (Chicago: NCSBN, 1994): Tab 13, 1–4.

93. Minutes, Meeting of the NCSBN Delegate Assembly: August 5–6, 1994, NCSBN Archives, Chicago, IL, 6.

94. "Report of the NP&E Committee," *NCSBN Book of Reports* (Chicago: NCSBN, 1995): Tab 9, 21–23.

95. "Nursing Regulation Task Force," *Newsletter to the Member Boards* 15, no. 24 (1995): 4.

96.   Minutes, Meeting of the NCSBN Board of Directors: January 10–12, 2001, NCSBN Archives, Chicago, IL, 3 4.

97.   Minutes, Meeting of the NCSBN Board of Directors: June 23–25, 2001, NCSBN Archives, Chicago, IL, 5.

98.   "NCSBN to Explore the Value of Mandatory Continuing Education," *Council Connector* 1, no. 9 (2001): 4–5.

99.   Minutes, Meeting of the NCSBN Delegate Assembly: August 14–17, 2002, NCSBN Archives, Chicago, IL, 5.

100. Minutes, Meeting of the NCSBN Board of Directors: February 19–21, 2003, NCSBN Archives, Chicago, IL, 5.

101. Minutes, Meeting of the NCSBN Delegate Assembly: August 5–8, 2003, NCSBN Archives, Chicago, IL, 6.

102. Minutes, Meeting of the NCSBN Delegate Assembly: August 3–6, 2004, NCSBN Archives, Chicago, IL, 4–5.

103. Minutes, Meeting of the NCSBN Board of Directors: January 29–February 1, 1989, NCSBN Archives, Chicago, IL, 11.

104. Minutes, Meeting of the NCSBN Delegate Assembly: August 1–5, 1989, NCSBN Archives, Chicago, IL, 14.

105. Minutes, Meeting of the NCSBN Board of Directors: November 6–8, 1989, NCSBN Archives, Chicago, IL, 5.

106. Minutes, Meeting of the NCSBN Delegate Assembly: August 7–11, 1990, NCSBN Archives, Chicago, IL, 12.

107. Minutes, Meeting of NCSBN Delegate Assembly: August 26–29, 1987, NCSBN Archives, Chicago, IL, 19.

108. Minutes, Meeting of the NCSBN Board of Directors: January 29–31, 1990, NCSBN Archives, Chicago, IL, 8.

109. Minutes, Meeting of the NCSBN Board of Directors: November 5–7, 1990, NCSBN Archives, Chicago, IL, 10.

110. "Report of the NP&E Committee," *NCSBN Book of Reports* (Chicago: NCSBN, 1990): Tab 18, 1–11.

111. Minutes, Meeting of the NCSBN Board of Directors: April 8, 1996, NCSBN Archives, Chicago, IL, 2.

112. Minutes, Meeting of the NCSBN Board of Directors: June 26–28, 1996, NCSBN Archives, Chicago, IL, 5.

113. Minutes, Meeting of the NCSBN Delegate Assembly: August 9–10, 1996, NCSBN Archives, Chicago, IL, 5.

114. "Report of the Board of Directors," *NCSBN Book of Reports* (Chicago: NCSBN, 1997): Tab 10, 23–26.

115. Minutes, Meeting of the NCSBN Delegate Assembly: August 20–23, 1997, NCSBN Archives, Chicago, IL, 12.

116. Ibid., 11.

117. Minutes, Special Meeting of the NCSBN Delegate Assembly, December 14–15, 1997, 3.

118. "Report of the NP&E Committee," *NCSBN Business Book* (Chicago: NCSBN, 1999): Tab 11, 5.

119. "Report of the NP&E Committee," 1999, Tab 11, 1–23.

120. Minutes, Meeting of the NCSBN Delegate Assembly: July 28–31, 1999, NCSBN Archives, Chicago, IL, 6.

121. Minutes, Meeting of the NCSBN Board of Directors: June 1–2, 1990, NCSBN Archives, Chicago, IL, 4.

122. "Report of he NP&E Committee," *NCSBN Business Book* (Chicago: NCSBN, 2000): 91–97.

123. Minutes, Meeting of the NCSBN Delegate Assembly: August 8–12, 2000, NCSBN Archives, Chicago, IL, 4.

124. Lavinia L. Dock, "What We May Expect from the Law," *American Journal of Nursing* 1 (1900): 9.

Chapter Eight

1. Sophia Palmer, "1901 International unity on state registration," *American Journal of Nursing* 1 (1901): 233–34.

2. "Report of the Nursing Practice and Standards (NP&S) Committee," *NCSBN Book of Reports* (Chicago: National Council of State Boards of Nursing, Inc. [NCSBN], 1980).

3. Minutes, Meeting of the National Council of State Boards of Nursing (NCSBN) Delegate Assembly: June 22–25, 1982, NCSBN Archives, Chicago, IL, 9.

4. Minutes, Meeting of the NCSBN Board of Directors: June 25, 1982, NCSBN Archives, Chicago, IL, 1.

5. Ruth L. Elliot, "Should State Boards of Nursing Accredit Nursing Education Programs," *Issues* 3, no. 3 (1982): 3–4.

6. Minutes, Meeting of the NCSBN Delegate Assembly: August 23–26, 1983, NCSBN Archives, Chicago, IL, 15–17.

7. "Seventh Annual Delegate Assembly Convention Held in Chicago," *Issues* 6, no. 3. (1985): 1–2.

8. Minutes, Meeting of the NCSBN Delegate Assembly: August 5–9, 1986, NCSBN Archives, Chicago, IL, 19.

9. Ibid., 20.

10. Karen MacDonald, "North Dakota Rule Changes Require Associate, Baccalaureate Education," *Issues* 7, no. 2 (1986): 1–3.

11. "Challenges of Boards of Nursing Authority to Accredit Schools," *Newsletter to the Member Boards* 4, no. 18 (1986): 2–3

12. "Report of the Board of Directors," *NCSBN Book of Reports* (Chicago: NCSBN, 1987): 48–63.

13. "An Analysis of Trends in the Legislation and Regulations of Nursing Practice: 1984–1994," *Issues* 6, no. 4 (1985): 7–10.

14. "An Analysis of Trends in Nursing Education: 1984–1994," *Issues* 7, no.1 (1986): 6–8.

15. Minutes, Meeting of the NCSBN Board of Directors: February 5–7, 1987, NCSBN Archives, Chicago, IL, 2.

16. "Survey on School Approval/Accreditation," *Newsletter to the Member Boards* 7, no. 6 (1988): 3.

17. Minutes, Meeting of the NCSBN Delegate Assembly: August 16–20, 1988, NCSBN Archives, Chicago, IL, 22.

18. Minutes, Meeting of the NCSBN Board of Directors: June 21–23, 1995, NCSBN Archives, Chicago, IL, 5.

19. "Supplemental Report of the Nursing Practice and Education (NP&E) Committee," *NCSBN Book of Reports* (Chicago: NCSBN, 1995): Tab 9, 29–30.

20. "Report of NP&E Committee," *NCSBN Book of Reports* (Chicago: NCSBN, 1996): Tab 9, 1–2.

21. "Report of Subcommittee to Analyze Clinical Experience," *NCSBN Book of Reports* (Chicago: NCSBN, 1996): Tab 9, 57–65.

22. Minutes, Meeting of the NCSBN Board of Directors: May 14–16, 1997, NCSBN Archives, Chicago, IL, 5.

23. Minutes, Meeting of the NCSBN Delegate Assembly: August 20–23, 1997, NCSBN Archives, Chicago, IL, 7.

24. "Report of Nursing Program Accreditation/Approval Subcommittee," NCSBN Book of Reports (Chicago: NCSBN, 1997): 15–29.

25. Ibid.

26. "Report of NP&E Committee," *NCSBN Book of Reports* (Chicago: NCSBN, 1998): Tab 7, 1–27.

27. Minutes, Meeting of the NCSBN Delegate Assembly: August 5–8, 1998, NCSBN Archives, Chicago, IL, 5

28. "About NLNAC," National League for Nursing Accrediting Commission, http://www.nlnac. org/about%20NLNAC/whatsnew.htm (accessed March 15, 2007).

29. Minutes, Meeting of the NCSBN Board of Directors: October 14–15, 1999, NCSBN Archives, Chicago, IL, 2–3.

30. Minutes, Meeting of the NCSBN Board of Directors: October 11–12, 2000, NCSBN Archives, Chicago, IL, 3

31. Minutes, Meeting of the NCSBN Board of Directors: February 23–24, 2000, NCSBN Archives, Chicago, IL, 4

32. Minutes, Meeting of the NCSBN Delegate Assembly: August 8–12, 2000, NCSBN Archives, Chicago, IL, 6.

33. "Congruence to be Examined," *Council Connector* 1, no. 5 (2000): 1–2.

34. Minutes, Meeting of the NCSBN Board of Directors: January 10–12, 2001, NCSBN Archives, Chicago, IL, 9

35. Minutes, Meeting of the NCSBN Board of Directors: April 4, 2001, NCSBN Archives, Chicago, IL, 3.

36. Minutes, Meeting of the NCSBN Board of Directors: May 6–8, 2001, NCSBN Archives, Chicago, IL, 4.

37. Minutes, Meeting of the NCSBN Board of Directors: August 5, 2001, NCSBN Archives, Chicago, IL, 4

38. "Report of the Practice, Education and Regulation Congruence (PERC) Task Force," *NCSBN Book of Reports* (Chicago: NCSBN, 2001): 227–32.

39. Minutes, Meeting of the NCSBN Board of Directors: April 4, 2001, NCSBN Archives, Chicago, IL, 4.

40. Minutes, Meeting of the NCSBN Board of Directors: January 23–25, 2002, NCSBN Archives, Chicago, IL, 7.

41. Minutes, Meeting of the NCSBN Board of Directors: May 1–3, 2002, NCSBN Archives, Chicago, IL, 4–5.

42. "Report of the Practice, Regulation and Education Committee," *NCSBN Business Book* (Chicago: NCSBN, 2002): 138–41.

43. "Report of the Practice, Education and Regulation Congruence Task Force," *NCSBN Business Book* (Chicago: NCSBN, 2002): 196–227.

44. Corinne F. Dorsey, *A History of the Virginia State Board of Nursing 1903—2003* (Quinton, VA: Self-published, 2003): 16.

45. "Mission and History," Commission on Graduates of Foreign Nursing Schools, http://www.cgfns.org/sections/about/hist.shtml (accessed March 15, 2007).

46. Minutes, Meeting of the NCSBN Board of Directors: November 28–December 1, 1978, NCSBN Archives, Chicago, IL, 11.

47. Ibid., 4–5.

48. Minutes, Meeting of the NCSBN Board of Directors: June 4–5, 1979, NCSBN Archives, Chicago, IL, 8.

49. Minutes, Meeting of the NCSBN Delegate Assembly: June 6–8, 1979, NCSBN Archives, Chicago, IL, 10.

50. Minutes, Meeting of the NCSBN Board of Directors: March 8–10, 1982, NCSBN Archives, Chicago, IL, 3.

51. Minutes, Meeting of the NCSBN Board of Directors: April 2–4, 1991, NCSBN Archives, Chicago, IL, 6–7.

52. Minutes, Meeting of the NCSBN Board of Directors, March 8–10, 1993, NCSBN Archives, Chicago, IL, 9.

53. Minutes, Meeting of the NCSBN Board of Directors, July 20, 1993, NCSBN Archives, Chicago, IL, 1.

54. "Report of the Foreign Educated Nurse Credentialing Committee," *NCSBN Book of Reports* (Chicago: NCSBN, 1993): Tab 10, 1–2.

55. Minutes, Meeting of the NCSBN Delegate Assembly: August 5–7, 1993, NCSBN Archives, Chicago, IL, 16.

56. Minutes, Meeting of the NCSBN Board of Directors: December 1–3, 1993, NCSBN Archives, Chicago, IL, 6.

57. Minutes, Meeting of the NCSBN Delegate Assembly, August 5–6, 1994, NCSBN Archives, Chicago, IL, 7.

58. Minutes, Meeting of the NCSBN Board of Directors: June 24–25, 2001, NCSBN Archives, Chicago, IL, 4.

59. Minutes, Meeting of the NCSBN Board of Directors: October 31, 2002, NCSBN Archives, Chicago, IL, 2.

60. "Report of the Practice, Regulation and Education Committee," *NCSBN Business Book* (Chicago: NCSBN, 2002): 76–79.

61. Minutes, Meeting of the NCSBN Board of Directors: December 2–4, 2003, NCSBN Archives, Chicago, IL, 7.

62. Ibid., 4.

63.   "An Institute for State Inspectors and Nurse Examiners," *American Journal of Nursing* 21 (1921): 653–54.

64.   Eileen McQuaid, "Report of the Executive Director," *NCSBN Book of Reports* (Chicago: NCSBN, 1980).

65.   Eileen McQuaid, "Report of the Executive Director," *NCSBN Book of Reports* (Chicago: NCSBN, 1981).

66.   Eileen McQuaid, "Report of the Executive Director," *NCSBN Book of Reports* (Chicago: NCSBN, 1982): 62–63.

67.   Minutes, Meeting of the NCSBN Board of Directors: August 26, 1983, NCSBN Archives, Chicago, IL, 2.

68.   "Four Interest Groups Attract NCSBN Delegates," *Issues* 5, no. 3 (1984): 4–5.

69.   "1985 Convention Schedule," *NCSBN Book of Reports* (Chicago: NCSBN, 1985): 1–2.

70.   "1986 Convention Schedule," *NCSBN Book of Reports* (Chicago: NCSBN, 1986): 1–4.

71.   Minutes, Meeting of the NCSBN Board of Directors: May 5–7, 1987, NCSBN Archives, Chicago, IL, 6

72.   Minutes, Meeting of the NCSBN Board of Directors: October 26, 1987, NCSBN Archives, Chicago, IL, 2.

73.   "1987 Convention Schedule," *NCSBN Book of Reports* (Chicago: NCSBN, 1987): 1–5.

74.   "National Council Holds Orientation/Planning Session," *Newsletter to the Member Boards* 7, no. 23 (1988): 1–2.

75.   Jennifer Bosma, "Report of the Executive Director," *NCSBN Book of Reports* (Chicago: NCSBN, 1989): Tab 9, 1–17.

76.   Minutes, Meeting of the NCSBN Board of Directors: April 26–28, 1989, NCSBN Archives, Chicago, IL, 4.

77.   "Commission on Nursing Reports Recommendations at Educational Sessions," *Issues* 10, no. 4 (1989): 4 and 6.

78.   Minutes, Meeting of the NCSBN Board of Directors: July 16–17, 1990, NCSBN Archives, Chicago, IL, 4.

79.   Minutes, Meeting of the NCSBN Board of Directors: November 5–7, 1990, NCSBN Archives, Chicago, IL, 6.

80.   "Attend 1991's Premier Conference on Nursing Regulation," *Issues* 1, no. 3 (1990): 12.

81.   Minutes, Meeting of the NCSBN Board of Directors: January 16, 1992, NCSBN Archives, Chicago, IL, 2.

82.   Minutes, Meeting of the NCSBN Delegate Assembly: August 18–22, 1992, NCSBN Archives, Chicago, IL, 16.

83.   "Surveys Performed by Member Boards," *Newsletter to the Member Boards* 12, no. 3 (1992): 1–2.

84.   Minutes, Meeting of the NCSBN Delegate Assembly: August 5–7, 1993, NCSBN Archives, Chicago, IL, 10.

85.   Ibid.

86.   "Annual Meeting of National Council's Delegate Assembly Held in Orlando, Florida," *Issues* 14, no. 3 (1993): 1 and 5.

87.   Minutes, Meeting of the NCSBN Board of Directors: March 7–9, 1994, NCSBN Archives, Chicago, IL, 4–5.

88. Minutes, Meeting of the NCSBN Board of Directors: October 27–28, 1994, NCSBN Archives, Chicago, IL, 2 and 5.

89. "Report of Task Force to Develop Educational Programs for Nursing Education Program Surveyors," *NCSBN Book of Reports* (Chicago: NCSBN, 1994): Tab 19, 43–48.

90. "National Council Holds Annual Meeting in Chicago," *Issues* 15, no. 3 (1994): 1 and 5.

91. "The National Council Will be Cosponsor of a National consumer Summit," *Newsletter to the Member Boards* 14, no. 2 (1994): 3.

92. Minutes, Meeting of the NCSBN Board of Directors: February 1–3, 1995, NCSBN Archives, Chicago, IL, 4.

93. Minutes, Meeting of the NCSBN Board of Directors: May 3–5, 1995, NCSBN Archives, Chicago, IL, 4.

94. Minutes, Meeting of the NCSBN Board of Directors: August 6, 1995, NCSBN Archives, Chicago, IL, 2–3.

95. "Report of the Board of Directors," *NCSBN Book of Reports* (Chicago: NCSBN, 1995): Tab 10, 1–4.

96. Minutes, Meeting of the NCSBN Board of Directors: October 19–20, 1995, NCSBN Archives, Chicago, IL, 5–6.

97. "Report of the Task Force to Implement Educational Programs for Nursing Education Program Surveyors," *NCSBN Book of Reports* (Chicago: NCSBN, 1995): Tab 10I, 1.

98. Milene Naegle and Gail Rosetti, "New York's Regent's College," *Issues* 15, no. 3 (1994): 3 and 6.

99. "Florida Board Takes Action Regarding Regent's Program," *Newsletter to the Member Boards* 14, no. 17 (1994): 3.

100. "Update on Regent's Program Acceptance," *Newsletter to the Member Boards* 15, no. 11 (1995): 1–2.

101. "Speaker Added for 1995 Annual Meeting," *Newsletter to the Member Boards* 15, no. 13 (1995): 2.

102. "Joint Conference with Citizens Advocacy Center Planned in December 4, 1995," *Newsletter to the Member Boards* 15, no. 16 (1995): 1.

103. "Symposium on the Future of Nursing Regulation," *Newsletter to the Member Boards* 15. no. 23 (1995): 2–3.

104: Jennifer Bosma, "Report of Staff Activities," *NCSBN Book of Reports* (Chicago: NCSBN, 1996): Tab 5, 1–8.

105. Minutes, Meeting of the NCSBN Board of Directors: May 8–10, 1996, NCSBN Archives, Chicago, IL, 6.

106. "Report of the Institute for Promotion of Regulatory Excellence," *NCSBN Book of Reports*, (Chicago: NCSBN, 1996): Tab 10, 47.

107. "Ruth Elliott Named Director for Education and Practice," *Issues* 17, no. 4 (1996): 10.

108. "New Executive Officer Orientation," *Newsletter to the Member Boards* 16, no. 2 (1996): 2.

109. "Nursing Educator Workshops—Assessment Strategies for Nursing Educators," *Newsletter to the Member Boards* 16, no. 6 (1996): 1–2.

110. Minutes, Meeting of the NCSBN Board of Directors: May 14–16, 1997, NCSBN Archives, Chicago, IL, 5.

111. "Report of Institute for the Promotion of Regulatory Excellence," *NCSBN Book of Reports* (Chicago: NCSBN, 1997): Tab 8, 15–29.

112. Nursing education articles, *Issues* 18, no. 2 (1997): 3–5.

113. Minutes, Meeting of the NCSBN Board of Directors: May 13–15, 1998, NCSBN Archives, Chicago, IL, 5–6.

114. Ibid., 8.

115. "Annual Meeting Schedule," *NCSBN Business Book* (Chicago: NCSBN, 1998): 1–3.

116. "Executive Officer Orientation Group Meets," *Newsletter to the Member Boards* 18, no. 2 (1998): 3.

117. Minutes, Meeting of the NCSBN Board of Directors: June 24–25, 1999, NCSBN Archives, Chicago, IL, 6.

118. "Nursing Educator Workshop Transition to Online Environment a Success," *Issues* 20, no.4 (1999): 10.

119: "Board Staff Education Network Plans Dialogue on Education Programs," *Newsletter to the Member Boards* 19, no. 2 (1999): 1–2.

120. "New Executive Officer Orientation," *Newsletter to the Member Boards*, 19, no. 10 (1999): 1.

121. Minutes, Meeting of the NCSBN Board of Directors: February 23–24, 2000, NCSBN Archives, Chicago, IL, 7.

122. Minutes, Meeting of the NCSBN Board of Directors: August 12, 2000, NCSBN Archives, Chicago, IL, 2.

123. Minutes, Meeting of the NCSBN Board of Directors: October 11–12, 2000, NCSBN Archives, Chicago, IL, 2.

124. Minutes, Meeting of the NCSBN Delegate Assembly: August 8–12, 2000, NCSBN Archives, Chicago, IL, 5.

125. "Report of Executive Officer Fellowship Program Advisory Group," *NCSBN Business Book* (Chicago: NCSBN, 2000): 129.

126. "Annual Meeting Schedule," *NCSBN Business Book* (Chicago: NCSBN, 2001): 9–11.

127. "Report of the Member Board Leadership Development Task Force," *NCSBN Business Book* (Chicago: NCSBN, 2001): 209–13.

128. Minutes, Meeting of the NCSBN Board of Directors: January 23–25, 2002, NCSBN Archives, Chicago, IL, 8.

129. Minutes, Meeting of the NCSBN Board of Directors: May 1–3, 2002, NCSBN Archives, Chicago, IL, 2.

130. Ibid., 4–5.

131. Minutes, Meeting of the NCSBN Board of Directors: December 2–4, 2002, NCSBN Archives, Chicago, IL, 5.

132. Minutes, Meeting of the NCSBN Board of Directors: August 12, 2002, NCSBN Archives, Chicago, IL, 2.

133. "Report of Member Board Leadership Development Task Force," *NCSBN Business Book* (Chicago: NCSBN, 2002): 284.

134. "Report of Regulatory Credentialing Program Development Task Force," *NCSBN Business Book* (Chicago: NCSBN, 2002): 334–38.

135. Minutes, Meeting of the NCSBN Board of Directors: February 19–21, 2003, NCSBN Archives, Chicago, IL, 4

136. Minutes, Meeting of the NCSBN Board of Directors: April 30–May 1, 2003, NCSBN Archives, Chicago, IL, 8.

137. Minutes, Meeting of the NCSBN Board of Directors: July 10, 2003, NCSBN Archives, Chicago, IL, 3.

138. "Report of the Member Board Leadership Development Advisory Group," NCSBN Business Book (Chicago: NCSBN, 2003): 161–63.

139. "Events at NCSBN for 2003," *Council Connector* 3, no. 2 (2003): 6.

140. "Opportunities to Educate About Nursing," *Council Connector* 3, no. 3 (2003): 2.

141. "Joint Irish Board of Nursing and National Council Presentation," *Newsletter to the Member Boards* 7, no. 2 (1988): 1.

142. "Regulatory Workshop and Computers in Nursing Symposium in Dublin, Ireland," *Newsletter to the Member Boards* 7, no. 14 (1988): 1–2.

143. "Resources," NCSBN, http://www.ncsbn.org/resources.htm (accessed March 15, 2007).

Chapter Nine

1. Sophia Palmer, "State Boards of Examiners," *American Journal of Nursing* 14 (1914): 255–56.

2. R. Louise McManus, "State Board Test Pool: A Retrospective View," *Issues* 1, no. 3 (1980): 6–7.

3. Sandra MacKenzie, "Licensure Examination: Subjects and Passing Score History." Unpublished paper, Minnesota Board of Nursing, 1994.

4. Eleanor A Lynch, *An Historical Survey of the Test Services of the National League for Nursing* (New York: National League for Nursing, 1980): 20.

5. McManus, "State Board Test Pool," 6–7.

6. Minutes, Meeting of the National Council of State Boards of Nursing, Inc. (NCSBN) Delegate Assembly: June 6–7, 1978, NCSBN Archives, Chicago, IL, 4–5.

7. Minutes, Meeting of the NCSBN Board of Directors: June 7, 1978, NCSBN Archives, Chicago, IL, 1 and 7.

8. Minutes, Meeting of the NCSBN Board of Directors: September 11–13, 1978, NCSBN Archives, Chicago, IL, 9–13.

9. Minutes, Meeting of the NCSBN Board of Directors: November 28–December 1, 1978, NCSBN Archives, Chicago, IL, 8 and 11.

10. Minutes, Meeting of the NCSBN Board of Directors: June 8, 1979, NCSBN Archives, Chicago, IL, 4.

11. "Report of Test Specifications Committee," *NCSBN Book of Reports* (Chicago: NCSBN, 1981).

12. Minutes, Meeting of the NCSBN Board of Directors: November 28–December 1, 1978, NCSBN Archives, Chicago, IL, 3–5.

13. Angeline M. Jacobs, Grace Fivars, Dorothy S. Edwards and Robert Fitzpatrick, *Critical Requirements for Safe/Effective Nursing Practice* (New York: American Nurses Association [ANA], 1978): ix, 1, 11 and 40.

14. Minutes, Meeting of the NCSBN Board of Directors: June 4–5, 1979, NCSBN Archives, Chicago, IL, 5.

15. Minutes, Meeting of the NCSBN Board of Directors: January 22–24, 1979, NCSBN Archives, Chicago, IL, 10–11.

16. Minutes, Meeting of the NCSBN Delegate Assembly: June 6–8, 1979, NCSBN Archives, Chicago, IL, 8.

17. "A New Licensing Exam for Nurses," *American Journal of Nursing* 80 (1980): 723.

18. Minutes, January 22–24, 1979, 11–12.

19. Minutes, Meeting of the NCSBN Board of Directors: November 26–28, 1979, NCSBN Archives, Chicago, IL, 6.

20. Minutes, Meeting of the NCSBN Board of Directors: June 6, 1980, NCSBN Archives, Chicago, IL, 3.

21. Minutes, Meeting of the NCSBN Board of Directors: September 22–24, 1980, NCSBN Archives, Chicago, IL, 2–3.

22. Minutes, Meeting of the NCSBN Board of Directors: December 23, 1980, NCSBN Archives, Chicago, IL, 1.

23. Minutes, Meeting of the NCSBN Board of Directors: March 8–11, 1981, NCSBN Archives, Chicago, IL, 3.

24. Minutes, March 8–11, 1981, 1–2.

25. Minutes, Meeting of the NCSBN Board of Directors, April 23, 1981, NCSBN Archives, Chicago, IL, 1–2.

26. Mildred Schmidt, "Report of the President to the Delegate Assembly," *NCSBN Book of Reports* (Chicago: NCSBN, 1981).

27. Minutes, Meeting of the NCSBN Delegate Assembly: June 9–12, 1981, NCSBN Archives, Chicago, IL, 5.

28. Minutes, Meeting of the NCSBN Delegate Assembly: June 4–6, 1980, NCSBN Archives, Chicago, IL, 9.

29. Minutes, Meeting of the NCSBN Board of Directors: June 12, 1981, NCSBN Archives, Chicago, IL, 1.

30. Phyllis Sheridan, "The Single Score: A Controversial Issue," *Issues* 1, no. 1 (1980): 2.

31. "Report of Board of Directors," *NCSBN Book of Reports* (Chicago: NCSBN, 1982): 41–42.

32. Eileen Dvorak, "Report of Executive Director," *NCSBN Book of Reports* (Chicago: NCSBN, 1982): 57.

33. "Clinical Simulation Examination Underway," *Issues* 3, no. 3 (1982): 1.

34. Minutes, Meeting of the NCSBN Delegate Assembly: June 22–25, 1982, NCSBN Archives, Chicago, IL, 12.

35. Minutes, Meeting of the NCSBN Board of Directors: January 24–26, 1983, NCSBN Archives, Chicago, IL, 11.

36. Minutes, Meeting of the NCSBN Board of Directors: May 23–25, 1983, NCSBN Archives, Chicago, IL, 5.

37. Minutes, Meeting of the NCSBN Delegate Assembly: August 24–26, 1983, NCSBN Archives, Chicago, IL, 8–10.

38. Minutes, Meeting of the NCSBN Delegate Assembly: August 6–7, 1979, NCSBN Archives, Chicago, IL, 8.

39. Minutes, June 4–5, 1979, 4.

40. Minutes, Meeting of the NCSBN Board of Directors: March 8, 1982, NCSBN Archives, Chicago, IL, 3.

41. Minutes, Meeting of the NCSBN Board of Directors: May 23–25, 1983, NCSBN Archives, Chicago, IL, 9.

42. Minutes, Meeting of the NCSBN Delegate Assembly: August 24–26, 1983, NCSBN Archives, Chicago, IL, 13–14.

43. Minutes, Meeting of the NCSBN Delegate Assembly: August 26–29, 1984, NCSBN Archives, Chicago, IL, 14.

44. Minutes, January 22–24, 1979, 3–4.

45. Minutes, June 4–5, 1979, 6–7.

46. Minutes, June 6–8, 1979, 3.

47. Minutes, Meeting of the NCSBN Board of Directors: June 2–3, 1980, NCSBN Archives, Chicago, IL, 2.

48. Minutes, September 22–24, 1980, 1–2.

49. Minutes, Meeting of the NCSBN Board of Directors: November 6–8, 1989, NCSBN Archives, Chicago, IL, 6–7.

50. "Report of Administration of Examination Committee," *NCSBN Book of Reports* (Chicago: NCSBN, 1989): Tab 13, 1–2.

51. "Initiation of a Bias Sensitivity Review Panel," *Issues* 10, no. 5 (1989): 10.

52. Minutes, Meeting of the NCSBN Board of Directors: February 20–23, 1992, NCSBN Archives, Chicago, IL, 7.

53. Minutes, Meeting of the NCSBN Delegate Assembly: August 18–22, 1992, NCSBN Archives, Chicago, IL, 12–13.

54. Minutes, Meeting of the NCSBN Board of Directors: April 26, 1993, NCSBN Archives, Chicago, IL, 3.

55. Minutes, Meeting of the NCSBN Board of Directors: June 20–22, 1982, NCSBN Archives, Chicago, IL, 3.

56. "Interactive Program Launched on Web for NCLEX Examination Diagnostic Profiles," *Newsletter to the Member Boards* 17, no. 8 (1997): 1.

57. "Report of Administration of Examination Committee," *NCSBN Book of Reports* (Chicago: NCSBN, 1980).

58. "State is Rejecting Tests Given Nurses Throughout Nation," *New York Times*, September 16, 1979.

59. Minutes, Meeting of the NCSBN Board of Directors: July 25, 1979, NCSBN Archives, Chicago, IL, 1–4.

60. Minutes, Meeting of the NCSBN Board of Directors: July 30, 1979, NCSBN Archives, Chicago, IL, 1–3.

61. Minutes, Meeting of the NCSBN Board of Directors: May 18, 1979, NCSBN Archives, Chicago, IL, 1–2.

62. Minutes, Meeting of the NCSBN Board of Directors: September 11, 1979, NCSBN Archives, Chicago, IL, 6–8.

63. Minutes, Meeting of the NCSBN Board of Directors: September 24–26, 1979, NCSBN Archives, Chicago, IL, 1–9.

64. Minutes, Meeting of the NCSBN Board of Directors: November 26–28, 1979, NCSBN Archives, Chicago, IL, 5 and attachments.

65. Ibid.

66. "Report of Treasurer," *NCSBN Book of Reports* (Chicago: NCSBN, 1980).

67. Minutes, Meeting of the NCSBN Board of Directors: March 8–10, 1982, NCSBN Archives, Chicago, IL, 3.

68. Minutes, March 8–10, 1982, 5.

69. Minutes, Meeting of the NCSBN Board of Directors: June 20–22, 1982, NCSBN Archives, Chicago, IL, 5.

70. Minutes, Meeting of the NCSBN Board of Directors: January 24–26, 1983, NCSBN Archives, Chicago, IL, 4–5.

71. Minutes, Meeting of the NCSBN Board of Directors: August 21–22, 1983, NCSBN Archives, Chicago, IL, 2.

72. Minutes, meeting of the NCSBN Delegate Assembly: August 24–26, 1983, NCSBN Archives, Chicago, IL, 14.

73. Minutes, Meeting of the NCSBN Board of Directors: December 12–14, 1982, NCSBN Archives, Chicago, IL, 5.

74. Minutes, Meeting of the NCSBN Board of Directors: August 24–25, 1984, NCSBN Archives, Chicago, IL, 9.

75. Minutes, Meeting of the NCSBN Board of Directors: February 10–12, 1987, NCSBN Archives, Chicago, IL, 4.

76. "Report of Board of Directors," *NCSBN Book of Reports* (Chicago: NCSBN, 1988): 49–53.

77. Ibid.

78. "Security Break Update," *Newsletter to the Member Boards* 7, no. 4 (1988): 2.

79. "Update on Anomaly Analysis and Retesting," *Newsletter to the Member Boards* 8, no. 6 (1988): 4.

80. "Update on NCLEX-RN 288 Security Break," *Newsletter to the Member Boards* 8, no. 26 (1988): 5.

81. Minutes, Meeting of the NCSBN Board of Directors: December 14, 1988, NCSBN Archives, Chicago, IL, 1–3.

82. Minutes, Meeting of the NCSBN Board of Directors: January 23–February 1, 1989, NCSBN Archives, Chicago, IL, 9.

83. Minutes, Meeting of the NCSBN Board of Directors: August 5–6, 1990, NCSBN Archives, Chicago, IL, 1–2.

84. Minutes, Meeting of the NCSBN Board of Directors: August 23, 1990, NCSBN Archives, Chicago, IL, 1–2.

85. Minutes, Meeting of the NCSBN Board of Directors: January 28, 1991, NCSBN Archives, Chicago, IL, 1–2.

86. "Update on the NCLEX-RN 793 Security Break and Statistical Analyses," *Newsletter to the Member Boards* 12, no. 20 (1992): 1.

87. "July 1992 NCLEX Candidate Results," *Newsletter to the Member Boards* 12, no. 26 (1992): 1–2.

88. Minutes, Meeting of the NCSBN Board of Directors: October 7–8, 1992, NCSBN Archives, Chicago, IL, 5.

89. Minutes, Meeting of the NCSBN Board of Directors: December 21, 1992, NCSBN Archives, Chicago, IL, 1–2.

90. Minutes, Meeting of the NCSBN Board of Directors: April 26, 1993, NCSBN Archives, Chicago, IL, 1.

91. Minutes, Meeting of the NCSBN Board of Directors: October 25, 1993, NCSBN Archives, Chicago, IL, 1.

92. Minutes, Meeting of the NCSBN Board of Directors: March 7–9, 1994, NCSBN Archives, Chicago, IL, 3–4.

93. "Security Break at 294 Exam," *Newsletter to the Member Boards* 14, no. 3 (1994): 5.

94. "NCLEX Candidate Arrested for Bribery," *Newsletter to the Member Boards* 15, no. 8 (1995): 3.

95. Minutes, June 6–8, 1979, 1–2.

96. Ibid., 6.

97. "Report of Examination Committee," *NCSBN Book of Reports* (Chicago: NCSBN, 1980).

98. "Report of Administration of Examination Committee," *NCSBN Book of Reports* (Chicago: NCSBN, 1980).

99. Minutes, March 8–11, 1981, 9.

100. Minutes, June 9–12, 1981, 5.

101. "Report of Examination Committee," *NCSBN Book of Reports* (Chicago: NCSBN, 1981).

102. Minutes, Meeting of the NCSBN Delegate Assembly: June 9–12, 1981, NCSBN Archives, Chicago, IL, 6.

103. Minutes, June 9–12, 1981, 6.

104. Ibid., 7.

105. Minutes, Meeting of the NCSBN Board of Directors: October 15, 1982, NCSBN Archives, Chicago, IL, 1–2.

106. Minutes, Meeting of the NCSBN Board of Directors: March 8–10, 1982, NCSBN Archives, Chicago, IL, 7.

107. Minutes, Meeting of the NCSBN Board of Directors: June 20–22, 1982, NCSBN Archives, Chicago, IL, 7.

108. Minutes, Meeting of the NCSBN Board of Directors: September 20–21, 1982, NCSBN Archives, Chicago, IL, 3.

109. Minutes, Meeting of the NCSBN Delegate Assembly: June 22–25, 1982, NCSBN Archives, Chicago, IL, 4–11.

110. Minutes, Meeting of the NCSBN Delegate Assembly: August 23–26, 1983, NCSBN Archives, Chicago, IL, 5, 14 and 18.

111. "Report of Examination Committee," *NCSBN Book of Reports* (Chicago: NCSBN, 1983): 157–59.

112. Minutes, Meeting of the NCSBN Board of Directors: December 12–14, 1983, NCSBN Archives, Chicago, IL, 12.

113. "Developing, Constructing and Scoring the National Council Licensure Examination Part I," *Issues* 4, no. 1 (1983): 1 and 3–4; "Developing, Constructing and Scoring the National Council Licensure Examination Part II," *Issues* 4, no. 2 (1983): 1 and 6–7.

114. "Diagnostic Profile for Failure Candidates," *Issues* 4, no. 1 (1983): 6.

115. Minutes, Meeting of the NCSBN Board of Directors: May 24–25, 1984, NCSBN Archives, Chicago, IL, 3–6.

116. "Annual Report of Test Service for National Council Licensure Examination," *NCSBN Book of Reports* (Chicago: NCSBN, 1984): 81–83.

117. Minutes, May 24–25, 1984, 9.

118. Ibid.

119. "Report of Administration of Examination Committee" *NCSBN Book of Reports* (Chicago: NCSBN, 1984): 151–57.

120. Minutes, Meeting of the NCSBN Board of Directors: August 29, 1984, NCSBN Archives, Chicago, IL, 6.

121. "Report of Nursing Practice and Standards (NP&S) Committee," *NCSBN Book of Reports* (Chicago: NCSBN, 1984): 160–62.

122. "Report of Board of Directors," *NCSBN Book of Reports* (Chicago: NCSBN, 1985): 58.

123. Minutes, Meeting of the NCSBN Board of Directors: February 11–13, 1985, NCSBN Archives, Chicago, IL, 4.

124. "Report of Examination Committee," *NCSBN Book of Reports* (Chicago: NCSBN, 1985): 110.

125. Minutes, Meeting of the NCSBN Board of Directors: February 18, 1986, NCSBN Archives, Chicago, IL, 1–2.

126. Minutes, Meeting of the NCSBN Board of Directors: February 27, March 3, April 22–24, 1986, NCSBN Archives, Chicago, IL, 1–2.

127. Minutes, Meeting of the NCSBN Board of Directors: April 22–24, 1986, NCSBN Archives, Chicago, IL, 2.

128. Minutes, Meeting of the NCSBN Board of Directors: July 7, 1986, NCSBN Archives, Chicago, IL, 1–2.

129. "Report of Examination Committee," *NCSBN Book of Reports* (Chicago: NCSBN, 1986): 105–09.

130. Minutes, Meeting of the NCSBN Delegate Assembly: August 5–9, 1986, NCSBN Archives, Chicago, IL, 6.

131. Minutes, Meeting of the NCSBN Board of Directors: August 3–4, 1986, NCSBN Archives, Chicago, IL, 5.

132. "1986 Delegate Assembly Actions," *Issues* 7.4 (1986): 4–5 and 12.

133. Minutes, Meeting of the NCSBN Board of Directors: February 10–12, 1987, NCSBN Archives, Chicago, IL, 4.

134. Minutes, Meeting of the NCSBN Delegate Assembly: August 26–29, 1987, NCSBN Archives, Chicago, IL, 20.

135. Minutes, Meeting of the NCSBN Board of Directors: May 5–7, 1987, NCSBN Archives, Chicago, IL, 5.

136. Minutes, August 26–29, 1987, 19.

137. "Report of the Test Service," *NCSBN Book of Reports* (Chicago: NCSBN, 1987): 64–70.

138. "Report of the Examination Committee—Team I," *NCSBN Book of Reports* (Chicago: NCSBN, 1987): 163–78.

139. "Report of Examination Committee—Team II," *NCSBN Book of Reports* (Chicago: NCSBN, 1987): 179–208.

140. Minutes, August 26–29, 1987, 17.

141. "Memo to Member Boards Pass/fail Score Reporting," *Newsletter to the Member Boards* 5, no. 5 (1987): attachments.

142. Minutes, Meeting of the NCSBN Delegate Assembly: August 16–20, 1988, NCSBN Archives, Chicago, IL, 20–21.

143. Minutes, August 16–20, 1988, 19.

144. "Report of Task Force on Examinations for the Future," *NCSBN Book of Reports* (Chicago: NCSBN, 1988): 198.

145. Minutes, Meeting of the NCSBN Board of Directors: January 29–February 1, 1989, NCSBN Archives, Chicago, IL, 8.

146. Minutes, Meeting of the NCSBN Board of Directors: May 8, 1989, NCSBN Archives, Chicago, IL, 3.

147. Minutes, Meeting of the NCSBN Delegate Assembly: August 1–5, 1989, NCSBN Archives, Chicago, IL, 12.

148. Minutes, Meeting of the NCSBN Board of Directors: April 26–28, 1989, NCSBN Archives, Chicago, IL, 4–5.

149. Minutes, August 1–5, 1989, 8–9.

150. "New Name for CTB," *Newsletter to the Member Boards* 9, no. 17 (1989): 2, NCSBN Archives, Chicago, IL.

151. Minutes, Meeting of the NCSBN Board of Directors: July 6–7, 1989, NCSBN Archives, Chicago, IL, 5.

152. Minutes, Meeting of the NCSBN Board of Directors: August 1–5, 1989, NCSBN Archives, Chicago, IL, 3.

153. Minutes, Meeting of the NCSBN Board of Directors: January 29–February 1, 1989, NCSBN Archives, Chicago, IL, 8.

154. Minutes, August 1–5, 1989, 7.

155. Minutes, Meeting of the NCSBN Board of Directors: January 29–31, 1990, NCSBN Archives, Chicago, IL, 9.

156. "Comparison of CNATS to NCLEX-RN," *Newsletter to the Member Boards* 10, no. 8 (1990): attachment.

157. Minutes, Meeting of the NCSBN Board of Directors: April 30–May 2, 1990, NCSBN Archives, Chicago, IL, 8.

158. Minutes, Meeting of the NCSBN Board of Directors: July 16–17, 1990, NCSBN Archives, Chicago, IL, 2–3.

159. Minutes, Meeting of the NCSBN Delegate Assembly: August 7–11, 1990, NCSBN Archives, Chicago, IL, 4.

160. Minutes, Meeting of the NCSBN Board of Directors: February 11–13, 1991, NCSBN Archives, Chicago, IL, 3.

161. "NCLEX Repeater Tracking Service," *Newsletter to the Member Boards* 11, no. 20 (1991): attachment.

162. Minutes, February 11–13, 1991, 9.

163. Minutes, Meeting of the NCSBN Board of Directors: August 2, 1991, NCSBN Archives, Chicago, IL, 1; Minutes, Meeting of the NCSBN Board of Directors: August 19, 1991, NCSBN Archives, Chicago, IL, 1.

164. Minutes, Meeting of the NCSBN Board of Directors: August 19, 1991, NCSBN Archives, Chicago, IL, 1–2.

165. Minutes, Meeting of the NCSBN Delegate Assembly: July 30 August 2, 1991, NCSBN Archives, Chicago, IL, 12–15.

166. "Report of Job Analysis Monitoring Committee," *NCSBN Book of Reports* (Chicago: NCSBN, 1991): Tab 8, 1–3.

167. "Report of Resolutions Committee," *NCSBN Book of Reports* (Chicago: NCSBN, 1991): Tab 21, 1–9.

168. "Puerto Rico Plans to Administer July 1991 NCLEX," *Newsletter to the Member Boards* 11, no. 4 (1991): 1.

169. Minutes, Meeting of the NCSBN Board of Directors: February 20–23, 1992, NCSBN Archives, Chicago, IL, 8.

170. Minutes, Meeting of the NCSBN Board of Directors: August 17–21, 1992, NCSBN Archives, Chicago, IL, 2.

171. Minutes, Meeting of the NCSBN Delegate Assembly: August 18–22, 1992, NCSBN Archives, Chicago, IL, 8–9.

172. Minutes, August 18–22, 1992, 11.

173. "Report of Administration of Examination Committee, *NCSBN Book of Reports* (Chicago: NCSBN, 1992): Tab 15, 1–7.

174. Minutes, Meeting of the NCSBN Board of Directors: September 20–21, 1982, NCSBN Archives, Chicago, IL, 4.

175. "Report of Board of Directors," *NCSBN Book of Reports* (Chicago: NCSBN, 1983): 46–47.

176. "Annual Report of the Test Service," *NCSBN Book of Reports* (Chicago: NCSBN, 1983): 99–100.

177. Minutes, Meeting of the NCSBN Board of Directors: January 24–26, 1983, NCSBN Archives, Chicago, IL, 12.

178. Bruce Kramer, "An Appointment for NCLEX," *Issues* 5, no. 2 (1984): 3–4, NCSBN Archives, Chicago, IL.

179. Minutes, Meeting of the NCSBN Board of Directors: May 16–18, 1985, NCSBN Archives, Chicago, IL, 10.

180. Minutes, Meeting of the NCSBN Board of Directors: August 18–20, 1985, NCSBN Archives, Chicago, IL, 5.

181. Minutes, Meeting of the NCSBN Board of Directors: November 7–8, 1985, NCSBN Archives, Chicago, IL, 3.

182. Minutes, Meeting of the NCSBN Board of Directors: August 3–4, 1986, NCSBN Archives, Chicago, IL, 6–7.

183. Minutes, Meeting of the NCSBN Board of Directors: November 6–7, 1986, NCSBN Archives, Chicago, IL, 4–5.

184. Minutes, Meeting of the NCSBN Board of Directors: February 10–12, 1987, NCSBN Archives, Chicago, IL, 7.

185. Minutes, Meeting of the NCSBN Board of Directors: October 26, 1987, NCSBN Archives, Chicago, IL, 5–7.

186. "Report Task Force on Examinations for Future," *NCSBN Book of Reports* (Chicago: NCSBN, 1987): 295–310.

187. Minutes, Meeting of the NCSBN Delegate Assembly: August 2–9, 1987, NCSBN Archives, Chicago, IL, 18.

188. "CAT Software Pilot Testing Underway," *Newsletter to the Member Boards* 5, no. 23 (1987): 2.

189. "CAT Project," *Issues* 9, no. 2 (1988): 4–5 and 7–8.

190. Ibid.

191. Minutes, Meeting of the NCSBN Board of Directors: February 8–10, 1988, NCSBN Archives, Chicago, IL, 9–10.

192. Minutes, Meeting of the NCSNB Delegate Assembly: August 16–20, 1988, NCSBN Archives, Chicago, IL, 11.

193. Minutes, August 16–20, 1988, 7.

194. Minutes, Meeting of the NCSBN Board of Directors: April 26–28, 1989, NCSBN Archives, Chicago, IL, 10.

195. Minutes, Meeting of the NCSBN Board of Directors: July 6–7, 1989, NCSBN Archives, Chicago, IL, 5–6.

196. Minutes, Meeting of the NCSBN Delegate Assembly: August 1–5, 1989, NCSBN Archives, Chicago, IL, 8.

197. "Report, Committee on Special Projects," *NCSBN Book of Reports* (Chicago: NCSBN, 1988): 103–08.

198. Minutes, Meeting of the NCSBN Board of Directors: October 8, 1990, NCSBN Archives, Chicago, IL, 2.

199. Minutes, Meeting of the NCSBN Board of Directors: November 30–December 1, 1990, NCSBN Archives, Chicago, IL, 2–3.

200. "Report of President," *NCSBN Book of Reports* (Chicago: NCSBN, 1990): Tab 3, 1–2.

201. Susan Woodward, ed., *Issues* 11, no. 4 (1990).

202. Minutes, Meeting of the NCSBN Board of Directors: February 11–13, 1991, NCSBN Archives, Chicago, IL, 2.

203. Minutes, Meeting of the NCSBN Board of Directors: June 17–19, 1991, NCSBN Archives, Chicago, IL, 2–4.

204. "Report of Board of Directors," *NCSBN Book of Reports* (Chicago: NCSBN, 1991): Tab 4, 1–6.

205. "Report of Committee for Special Projects," *NCSBN Book of Reports* (Chicago: NCSBN, 1991): Tab 7, 1–26.

206. Minutes, Meeting of the NCSBN Delegate Assembly: July 30–August 2, 1991, NCSBN Archives, Chicago, IL, 6–7.

207. Minutes, July 30–August 2, 1991, 7.

208. Carolyn Hutcherson, "President's Message," *Issues* 12, no. 3 (1991): 2.

209. "Report of Board of Directors," *NCSBN Book of Reports* (Chicago: NCSBN, 1992): Tab 8, 1–6.

210. "Report of Board of Directors," 1992, Tab 8, 7–10.

211. Minutes, Meeting of the NCSBN Board of Directors: December 2–4, 1992, NCSBN Archives, Chicago, IL, 8.

212. "Report of Board of Directors," 1992, Tab 8, 11–16.

213. Ibid., Tab 8, 17–18.

214. Minutes, Meeting of the NCSBN Board of Directors: June 24, 1992, NCSBN Archives, Chicago, IL, 1.

215. Minutes, Meeting of the NCSBN Board of Directors: July 13–15, 1992, NCSBN Archives, Chicago, IL, 6 and 8.

216. Minutes, Meeting of the NCSBN Board of Directors: December 9–10, 1991, NCSBN Archives, Chicago, IL, 1–3.

217. Minutes, Meeting of the NCSBN Delegate Assembly: August 18–22, 1992, NCSBN Archives, Chicago, IL, 9.

218. Minutes, December 2–4, 1992, 5.

219. "Staff Changes," *Newsletter to the Member Boards* 12, no. 3 (1992): 1.

220. "Beta Testing," *Issues* 13, no. 4 (1992): 3.

221. Minutes, Meeting of the NCSBN Board of Directors: March 8–10, 1993, NCSBN Archives, Chicago, IL, 9–12.

222. Minutes, Meeting of the NCSBN Board of Directors: May 10, 1993, NCSBN Archives, Chicago, IL, 2.

223. Minutes, Meeting of the NCSBN Board of Directors: August 3–4, 1993, NCSBN Archives, Chicago, IL, 2.

224. Minutes, Meeting of the NCSBN Delegate Assembly: August 5–7, 1993, NCSBN Archives, Chicago, IL, Tab 6, 1–5.

225. "Report of Board of Directors," *NCSBN Book of Reports* (Chicago: NCSBN, 1993): Tab 6, 1–5.

226. Minutes, Meeting of the NCSBN Board of Directors: October 25, 1993, NCSBN Archives, Chicago, IL, 2.

227. Minutes, August 5–7, 1993, 10–11.

228. Ibid., 14.

229. Ibid., 15.

230. "CAT Corner," *Newsletter to the Member Boards* 13, no. 7 (1993): 3.

231. "For Immediate Release, NCLEX® Beta Test Completed" *Newsletter to the Member Boards* 13, no. 14 (1993): attachment.

232. "National Council Updates," *Issues* 15, no. 1 (1994): 6–7.

233. Minutes, Meeting of the NCSBN Board of Directors: March 7–9, 1994, NCSBN Archives, Chicago, IL, 7.

234. Minutes, Meeting of the NCSBN Delegate Assembly: August 5–6, 1994, NCSBN Archives, Chicago, IL, 6.

235. "Report of Administration of Examination Committee," *NCSBN Book of Reports* (Chicago: NCSBN, 1994): Tab 10, 1–2.

236. Jennifer Bosma, "Report of Staff Activities," *NCSBN Book of Reports* (Chicago: NCSBN, 1994): Tab 5, 1.

237. Minutes, August 5–6, 1994, 14.

238. "National Council Updates," *Issues* 15, no. 4 (1994): 10.

239. Minutes, Meeting of the NCSBN Board of Directors: February 1–3, 1995, NCSBN Archives, Chicago, IL, 5.

240. Minutes, Meeting of the NCSBN Board of Directors: August 16, 1995, NCSBN Archives, Chicago, IL, 3.

241. Minutes, Meeting of the NCSBN Board of Directors: February 28, 1995, NCSBN Archives, Chicago, IL, 5.

242. Minutes, Meeting of the NCSBN Board of Directors: May 3–5, 1995, NCSBN Archives, Chicago, IL, 5.

243. Minutes, Meeting of the NCSBN Board of Directors: November 21, 1995, NCSBN Archives, Chicago, IL, 2.

244. Minutes, Meeting of the NCSBN Delegate Assembly: August 4–5, 1995, NCSBN Archives, Chicago, IL, 5.

245. "Report of Staff Activities," *NCSBN Book of Reports* (Chicago: NCSBN, 1995): Tab 5, 1.

246. Minutes, Meeting of the NCSBN Board of Directors: November 21, 1995, NCSBN Archives, Chicago, IL, 2.

247. "Test Service Report, CGI," *NCSBN Book of Reports* (Chicago: NCSBN, 1996): Tab 7, 1–16.

248. Minutes, Meeting of the NCSBN Board of Directors: May 8–10, 1996, NCSBN Archives, Chicago, IL, 5.

249. Minutes, Meeting of the NCSBN Board of Directors: August 4–5, 1996, NCSBN Archives, Chicago, IL, 2.

250. Minutes, Meeting of the NCSBN Board of Directors: August 11, 1996, NCSBN Archives, Chicago, IL, 2.

251. Minutes, May 8–10, 1996, 4.

252. Minutes, Meeting of the NCSBN Delegate Assembly: August 6–10, 1996, NCSBN Archives, Chicago, IL, 4.

253. "Report Examination Committee," *NCSBN Book of Reports* (Chicago: NCSBN, 1996): Tab 6, 1–5.

254. Minutes, Meeting of the NCSBN Delegate Assembly: August 20–23, 1997, NCSBN Archives, Chicago, IL, 7.

255. "Report Examination Committee," *NCSBN Book of Reports* (Chicago: NCSBN, 1997): Tab 6, 1–5.

256. Minutes, August 20–23, 1997, 9.

257. "Examination Committee Implements Bylaws Change," *Issues* 18, no. 3 (1997): 14.

258. "National Council Completes 1997 Job Analysis of Newly Licensed Practical/Vocational Nurses," *Issues* 18, no. 4 (1997): 8.

259. Minutes, Meeting of the NCSBN Board of Directors: February 12–13, 1998, NCSBN Archives, Chicago, IL, 3.

260. Minutes, Meeting of the NCSBN Board of Directors: May 22, 1998, NCSBN Archives, Chicago, IL, 1.

261. Minutes, Meeting of the NCSBN Delegate Assembly: August 5–8, 1998, NCSBN Archives, Chicago, IL, 4.

262. "NCLEX Examination Results-by-Phone Pilot Project Begins," *Newsletter to the Member Boards* 18, no. 16 (1998): 2.

263. Minutes, Meeting of the NCSBN Board of Directors: February 3–5, 1999, NCSBN Archives, Chicago, IL, 7.

264. Minutes, Meeting of the NCSBN Board of Directors: June 2, 1999, NCSBN Archives, Chicago, IL, 1.

265. Minutes, Meeting of the NCSBN Board of Directors: October 14–15, 1999, NCSBN Archives, Chicago, IL, 2.

266. Minutes, Meeting of the NCSBN Board of Directors: July 28–31, 1999, NCSBN Archives, Chicago, IL, 5.

267. Minutes, Meeting of the NCSBN Board of Directors: August 1, 1999, NCSBN Archives, Chicago, IL, 2.

268. Minutes, Meeting of the NCSBN Delegate Assembly: July 28–31, 1999, NCSBN Archives, Chicago, IL, 7.

269. Minutes, Meeting of the NCSBN Board of Directors: June 1–2, 2000, NCSBN Archives, Chicago, IL, 2 and 6.

270. Minutes, Meeting of the NCSBN Board of Directors: July 11, 2000, NCSBN Archives, Chicago, IL, 2.

271. Minutes, Meeting of the NCSBN Delegate Assembly: August 8–12, 2000, NCSBN Archives, Chicago, IL, 4.

272. "Report of Examination Committee," *NCSBN Business Book* (Chicago: NCSBN, 2000): 47.

273. Minutes, Meeting of the NCSBN Board of Directors: October 11–12, 2000, NCSBN Archives, Chicago, IL, 5.

274. Minutes, Meeting of the NCSBN Board of Directors: November 11, 2000, NCSBN Archives, Chicago, IL, 2–3.

275. "Test Service Transition Newsletter Introduced," *Council Connector* 1, no. 4 (2000): 4.

276. "Who Owns NCLEX® Exam Data?" *Council Connector* 1, no. 4 (2000): 5.

277. Minutes, Meeting of the NCSBN Delegate Assembly: August 7–11, 2001, NCSBN Archives, Chicago, IL, 5.

278. Minutes, Meeting of the NCSBN Board of Directors: November 10–12, 2001, NCSBN Archives, Chicago, IL, 9–10.

279. Minutes, Meeting of the NCSBN Board of Directors: May 6–8, 2001, NCSBN Archives, Chicago, IL, 4.

280. Minutes, Meeting of the NCSBN Board of Directors: June 24–25, 2001, NCSBN Archives, Chicago, IL, 4–5.

281. Minutes, Meeting of the NCSBN Board of Directors: August 5, 2001, NCSBN Archives, Chicago, IL, 3.

282. "Report of Examination Committee," *NCSBN Business Book* (Chicago: NCSBN, 2001): 111.

283. "Annual Report of VUE, an NCS Pearson Business," *NCSBN Business Book* (Chicago: NCSBN, 2001): 132.

284. "Pilot Study for Next Generation NCLEX Completed." *Council Connector* 1, no. 10 (2001): 4.

285. "Alpha Testing Begins on Preparation for the Transition to VUE," *Council Connector* 1, no. 6 (2001): 1–2.

286. "Study Shows Repeat Testers' Passing Rate," *Council Connector* 1, no. 6 (2001): 5.

287. Minutes, Meeting of the NCSBN Board of Directors: January 23–25, 2002, NCSBN Archives, Chicago, IL, 2.

288. Minutes, Meeting of the NCSBN Board of Directors: May 1–3, 2002, NCSBN Archives, Chicago, IL, 3.

289. Minutes, Meeting of the NCSBN Delegate Assembly: August 14–17, 2002, NCSBN Archives, Chicago, IL, 3.

290. Minutes, August 14–17, 2002, 5.

291. Minutes, Meeting of the NCSBN Board of Directors: March 24, 2003, NCSBN Archives, Chicago, IL, 2–3.

292. "Innovative Items Added to NCSBN's NCLEX-RN Review Course," *Council Connector* 3, no. 6 (2003): 1.

293. Minutes, Meeting of the NCSBN Delegate Assembly: August 5–8, 2003, NCSBN Archives, Chicago, IL.

294. Minutes, Meeting of the NCSBN Board of Directors: July 10, 2003, NCSBN Archives, Chicago, IL, 3.

295. Minutes, Meeting of the NCSBN Board of Directors: August 4, 2003, NCSBN Archives, Chicago, IL, 2.

296. "Wait Period Between Same-Type NCLEX Exam Reduced to 45 Days," *Council Connector* 3, no. 8 (2003): 3.

297. Minutes, Meeting of the NCSBN Board of Directors: February 8–10, 1988, NCSBN Archives, Chicago, IL, 4.

298. "Public Law 100-203: Nursing Home Reform Act," *Newsletter to the Member Boards* 7, no. 4 (1988): 2.

299. Minutes, Meeting of the NCSBN Board of Directors: June 6, 1988, NCSBN Archives, Chicago, IL, 2.

300. Minutes, Meeting of the NCSBN Delegate Assembly: August 16–20, 1988, NCSBN Archives, Chicago, IL, 12.

301. Minutes, Meeting of the NCSBN Board of Directors: November 2–3, 1988, NCSBN Archives, Chicago, IL, 4.

302. Minutes, December 14, 1988, 3.

303. Minutes, January 29–February 1, 1989, 10.

304. Minutes, Meeting of the NCSBN Board of Directors: November 6–8, 1989, NCSBN Archives, Chicago, IL, 8.

305. "Nurse Aide Competency Evaluation Program," *Newsletter to the Member Boards* 9, no. 8 (1989): attachment.

306. "Nurse Aide Competency Evaluation Program," *Newsletter to the Member Boards* 9, no. 22 (1989): attachment.

307. Minutes, April 30–May 2, 1990, 3–4.

308. "Report of the NACEP Test Service," *NCSBN Book of Reports* (Chicago: NCSBN, 1990): Tab 10, 15–26.

309. "NACEP Update," *Issues* 11, no. 2 (1990): 11.

310. Minutes, February 11–13, 1991, 4–5.

311. Minutes, Meeting of the NCSBN Board of Directors: October 20–21, 1991, NCSBN Archives, Chicago, IL, 4.

312. Minutes, Meeting of the NCSBN Delegate Assembly: July 30–August 2, 1992, NCSBN Archives, Chicago, IL, 4.

313. Minutes, Meeting of the NCSBN Board of Directors: May 6–8, 1992, NCSBN Archives, Chicago, IL, 4.

314. Minutes, Meeting of the NCSBN Board of Directors: October 7–8, 1992, NCSBN Archives, Chicago, IL, 6.

315. Minutes, Meeting of the NCSBN Board of Directors: April 21–23, 1995, NCSBN Archives, Chicago, IL, 6.

316. "Report of Nurse Aide Competency Evaluation Program (NACEP) Task Force," *NCSBN Book of Reports* (Chicago: NCSBN, 1995): Tab 10E, 1–6.

317. "National Council Publishes Nurse Aide Job Analysis," *Insight* 4, no. 2 (1995): 6.

318. Minutes, Meeting of the NCSBN Board of Directors: April 8, 1996, NCSBN Archives, Chicago, IL, 1.

319. "Annual Report of the NACEP Test Service," *NCSBN Book of Reports* (Chicago: NCSBN, 1996): Tab 7, 17.

320. "Report of NACEP Task Force," *NCSBN Book of Reports* (Chicago: NCSBN, 1996): Tab 10F, 1.

321. "Report of National Nurse Aide Assessment Program," *NCSBN Business Book* (Chicago: NCSBN, 2002): 285.

322. "Report of the National Nurse Aide Assessment Program," *NCSBN Business Book* (Chicago: NCSBN, 2003): 134.

323. Minutes, Meeting of the NCSBN Board of Directors: March 24, 2003, NCSBN Archives, Chicago, IL, 3.

324. Minutes, Meeting of the NCSBN Board of Directors: May 8, 1986, NCSBN Archives, Chicago, IL, 1.

325. Eileen Dvorak, "Report of Executive Director," *NCSBN Book of Reports* (Chicago: NCSBN, 1987): 118.

326. Minutes, February 8–10, 1988, 10–11.

327. Minutes, Meeting of the NCSBN Delegate Assembly: August 16–20, 1988, NCSBN Archives, Chicago, IL, 1.

328. Ruth Elliott, "Report of President," *NCSBN Book of Reports* (Chicago: NCSBN, 1988): 25–27.

329. Minutes, January 29–February 1, 1989, 5.

330. Minutes, April 26–28, 1989, 5.

331. Renatta Loquist, "Report of President," *NCSBN Book of Reports* (Chicago: NCSBN, 1990): Tab 3, 1–2.

332. Minutes, February 11–13, 1991, 7.

333. Minutes, Meeting of the NCSBN Board of Directors: October 20–22, 1991, NCSBN Archives, Chicago, IL, 2.

334. Minutes, July 30–August 2, 1991.

335. "Report of Steering Committee for the Computerized Clinical Simulated Testing (CST) Project," *NCSBN Book of Reports* (Chicago: NCSBN, 1991): Tab 9, 1–59.

336. Minutes, December 2–4, 1992, 5–6.

337. "Report of Steering Committee for CST Project," *NCSBN Book of Reports* (Chicago: NCSBN, 1992): Tab 10, 1–3.

338. Debra Brady, "A New Generation in Competence Assessment in Nursing," *Issues* 14, no. 1 (1993): 1, 4–5, and 8.

339. Minutes, Meeting of the NCSBN Board of Directors: April 26, 1993, NCSBN Archives, Chicago, IL, 2.

340. "Report of Steering Committee for the CST Project," *NCSBN Book of Reports* (Chicago: NCSBN, 1993, Tab 9 1–3.

341. "Report of Steering Committee of CST Project," *NCSBN Book of Reports* (Chicago: NCSBN, 1994): Tab 17, 1–2.

342. Minutes, Meeting of the NCSBN Board of Directors: June 26–28, 1996, NCSBN Archives, Chicago, IL, 4.

343. "Report of CST Task Force, *NCSBN Book of Reports* (Chicago: NCSBN, 1996): Tab 10B, 1–2.

344. Minutes, Meeting of the NCSBN Board of Directors: February 12–14, 1997, NCSBN Archives, Chicago, IL, 4.

345. Minutes, Meeting of the NCSBN Board of Directors: May 14–16, 1997, NCSBN Archives, Chicago, IL, 4.

346. "Report of CST Task Force," *NCSBN Book of Reports* (Chicago: NCSBN, 1997): Tab 10K, 1–3.

347. Minutes, Meeting of the NCSBN Board of Directors: May 13–15, 1998, NCSBN Archives, Chicago, IL, 4.

348. Minutes, Meeting of the NCSBN Board of Directors: June 22, 1998, NCSBN Archives, Chicago, IL, 2.

349. Minutes, August 5–8, 1998, 6.

350. Minutes, Meeting of the NCSBN Board of Directors: November 4–5, 1998, NCSBN Archives, Chicago, IL, 5.

351. "Summary of Recommendations to the 1999 Delegate Assembly with Rationale," *NCSBN Business Book* (Chicago: NCSBN, 1999): Tab 3, 1–2.

352. Minutes, July 28–31, 1999, 7.

Chapter Ten

1. M. Adelaide Nutting, "State Reciprocity," *American Journal of Nursing* 4 (1904): 779–85.

2. "Official Reports of Societies," *American Journal of Nursing* 4 (1904): 976–77.

3. "Session on Legislation," *American Journal of Nursing* 15 (1915): 1037–56.

4. Anna Jamme, "Report of Committee on Legislation," *American Journal of Nursing* 17 (1917): 918–24.

5. Victoria Neufeldt, ed., *Webster's New World Dictionary*, 3rd ed. (Simon and Schuster: New York, 1988), 1121.

6. Mary M Roberts, "The Effects of Grading Schools Upon Accrediting Schools," *American Journal of Nursing* 30 (1930): 919.

7.   Webster's, 449.

8.   Minutes, Meeting of the National Council of State Boards of Nursing, Inc. (NCSBN) Board of Directors: June 4–5, 1979, NCSBN Archives, Chicago, IL, 7.

9.   Minutes, Meeting of the NCSBN Delegate Assembly: June 9–12, 1981, NCSBN Archives, Chicago, IL, 7.

10.   Minutes, Meeting of the NCSBN Board of Directors: September 20–21, 1982, NCSBN Archives, Chicago, IL, 5.

11.   "Report of the Area Directors," *NCSBN Book of Reports* (Chicago: NCSBN, 1983): 39–41.

12.   Minutes, Meeting of the NCSBN Board of Directors: May 23–25, 1983, NCSBN Archives, Chicago, IL, 11.

13.   Minutes, Meeting of the NCSBN Board of Directors: August 26, 1983, NCSBN Archives, Chicago, IL, 2.

14.   Lois O'Shea, "Report of Area IV Director," *NCSBN Book of Reports* (Chicago: NCSBN, 1984): 47.

15.   "Commonalities of Licensure Requirements Collected," *Newsletter to the Member Boards* 3, no. 9 (1985): 2–3.

16.   Minutes, Meeting of the NCSBN Board of Directors: May 6–8, 1985, NCSBN Archives, Chicago, IL, 5.

17.   Minutes, Meeting of the NCSBN Board of Directors: January 28–30, 1986, NCSBN Archives, Chicago, IL, 3–4.

18.   Sharon Weisenbeck, "Report of the President," *NCSBN Book of Reports* (Chicago: NCSBN, 1986): 16–17.

19.   Minutes, Meeting of the NCSBN Delegate Assembly: August 26–29, 1987, NCSBN Archives, Chicago, IL, 11.

20.   "Report of Nurse Licensee Data Base Committee," *NCSBN Book of Reports* (Chicago: NCSBN, 1987): 110–113.

21.   "National Nursing Licensee Data Base (NNLDB) Committee," *Newsletter to the Member Boards* 5, no. 21 (1987): 6.

22.   "Report of the National Nursing Licensee Data Base Committee," *NCSBN Book of Reports* (Chicago: NCSBN, 1988): 99–102.

23.   "National Nursing Licensee Data Base Committee," *Newsletter to the Member Boards* 7, no. 24 (1988): 2.

24.   Minutes, Meeting of the NCSBN Board of Directors: January 29–February 1, 1989, NCSBN Archives, Chicago, IL, 13.

25.   "Report of Nursing Practice and Standards Committee," *NCSBN Book of Reports* (Chicago: NCSBN, 1988): 190.

26.   Minutes, August 26–29, 1987, 19.

27.   Minutes, Meeting of the NCSBN Delegate Assembly: August 1–5, 1989, NCSBN Archives, Chicago, IL, 14.

28.   "Report of Nursing Practice and Education (NP&E) Committee," *NCSBN Book of Reports* (Chicago: NCSBN, 1989): Tab 14, 1–11.

29.   "Report of Nurse Information System (NIS) Committee," *NCSBN Book of Reports* (Chicago: NCSBN, 1989): Tab 5, 1–4.

30. Minutes, Meeting of the NCSBN Board of Directors: November 6–8, 1989, NCSBN Archives, Chicago, IL, 6.

31. Minutes, Meeting of the NCSBN Board of Directors: January 29–31, 1990, NCSBN Archives, Chicago, IL, 7.

32. "Report of NIS Committee," *NCSBN Book of Reports* (Chicago: NCSBN, 1990): Tab 6, 1–3.

33. "Report of NP&E Committee," *NCSBN Book of Reports* (Chicago: NCSBN, 1990): Tab 18, 1–2.

34. Minutes, Meeting of the NCSBN Delegate Assembly: August 7–11, 1990, NCSBN Archives, Chicago, IL, 12.

35. "National NIS," *Issues* 11, no. 4 (1990): 13.

36. Minutes, Meeting of the NCSBN Board of Directors: November 5–7, 1990, NCSBN Archives, Chicago, IL, 2–3.

37. Minutes, Meeting of the NCSBN Board of Directors: February 11–13, 1991, NCSBN Archives, Chicago, IL, 11–12.

38. "Report of Nurse Information System Committee," *NCSBN Book of Reports* (Chicago: NCSBN, 1991): Tab 6, 1–4.

39. Minutes, Meeting of the NCSBN Board of Directors: August 2, 1991, NCSBN Archives, Chicago, IL, 3.

40. Minutes, Meeting of the NCSBN Board of Directors: December 9–10, 1991, NCSBN Archives, Chicago, IL, 3.

41. "NIS Update," *Newsletter to the Member Boards* 11, no 23(1991): 1 and attachments.

42. Minutes, Meeting of the NCSBN Board of Directors: May 6–8, 1992, NCSBN Archives, Chicago, IL, 6–7.

43. Minutes, Meeting of the NCSBN Board of Directors: July 13–15, 1992, NCSBN Archives, Chicago, IL, 6.

44. Minutes, Meeting of the NCSBN Delegate Assembly: August 18–22, 1992, NCSBN Archives, Chicago, IL, 11.

45. "Report of NIS Committee," *NCSBN Book of Reports* (Chicago: NCSBN, 1992): Tab 11, 1–10.

46. "Report of NP&E Committee," *NCSBN Book of Reports* (Chicago: NCSBN, 1992): Tab 18, 2.

47. Minutes, Meeting of the NCSBN Board of Directors: December 2–4, 1992, NCSBN Archives, Chicago, IL, 6.

48. Minutes, Meeting of the NCSBN Board of Directors: March 8–10, 1993, NCSBN Archives, Chicago, IL, 6.

49. "NC Awarded Grant for Nurse Information System," *Issues* 14, no. 1 (1993): 5.

50. "Nurse Information System Update," Newsletter to the Member Board 13, no. 19 (1993): 2.

51. "Report of Nurse Information System Committee," *NCSBN Book of Reports* (Chicago: NCSBN, 1994): Tab 16, 1–2.

52. "Nurse Information System News," *Newsletter to the Member Boards* 14, no. 20 (1994): 3.

53. Jennifer Bosma, "Report of Staff Activities," *NCSBN Book of Reports* (Chicago: NCSBN, 1995): Tab 5, 5.

54. "Report of NIS Task Force, *NCSBN Book of Reports* (Chicago: NCSBN, 1995): Tab 10M, 1–2.

55. Minutes, Meeting of the NCSBN Board of Directors: October 19–20, 1995, NCSBN Archives, Chicago, IL, 5.

56. "NIS Update," *Newsletter to the Member Boards* 15, no. 11 (1995): 2.

57. Minutes, Meeting of the NCSBN Board of Directors: June 26–28, 1996, NCSBN Archives, Chicago, IL, 4.

58. "Report of Licensure Verification Task Force," *NCSBN Book of Reports* (Chicago: NCSBN, 1996): Tab 10D, 1–7.

59. Minutes, Meeting of the NCSBN Delegate Assembly: August 9–10, 1996, NCSBN Archives, Chicago, IL, 8.

60. Minutes, Meeting of the NCSBN Board of Directors: August 11, 1996, NCSBN Archives, Chicago, IL, 3.

61. Minutes, Meeting of the NCSBN Board of Directors: January 7, 1997, NCSBN Archives, Chicago, IL, 3.

62. Ibid.

63. Minutes, Meeting of the NCSBN Board of Directors: August 17–18, 1997, NCSBN Archives, Chicago, IL, 3.

64. "Report of License Verification Task Force, *NCSBN Book of Reports* (Chicago: NCSBN, 1997): Tab 10M 1–4.

65. Minutes, Meeting of the NCSBN Delegate Assembly: August 20–23, 1997, NCSBN Archives, Chicago, IL, 9–10.

66. Minutes, Meeting of the NCSBN Board of Directors: April 1, 1998, NCSBN Archives, Chicago, IL, 1–2.

67. "Licensure Verification Pilot Project Completed," *Newsletter to the Member Boards* 12, no. 5 (1992): 3 and attachment.

68. Ibid.

69. Minutes, Meeting of the NCSBN Board of Directors: March 7–9, 1994, NCSBN Archives, Chicago, IL, 8.

70. Minutes, Meeting of the NCSBN Delegate Assembly: August 5–6, 1994, NCSBN Archives, Chicago, IL, 13.

71. Minutes, Meeting of the NCSBN Board of Directors: October 27–28, 1994, NCSBN Archives, Chicago, IL, 6.

72. "Advanced Practice Registered Nurse Mobility Survey," *Newsletter to the Member Boards* 15, no. 6 (1995): 3.

73. Minutes, Meeting of the NCSBN Board of Directors: August 1–8, 1998, NCSBN Archives, Chicago, IL, 3.

74. "Nursys™ Development and Implementation," *Issues* 19, no. 2 (1998): 11.

75. Minutes, Meeting of the NCSBN Board of Directors: March 9, 1999, NCSBN Archives, Chicago, IL, 1.

76. Minutes, Meeting of the NCSBN Board of Directors: March 17, 1999, NCSBN Archives, Chicago, IL, 1.

77. Minutes, Meeting of the NCSBN Board of Directors: May 5–7, 1999, NCSBN Archives, Chicago, IL, 5.

78. Minutes, Meeting of the NCSBN Board of Directors: December 1–3, 1999, NCSBN Archives, Chicago, IL, 3.

79. Minutes, Meeting of the NCSBN Board of Directors: February 23–24, 2000, NCSBN Archives, Chicago, IL, 6–7.

80. Minutes, Meeting of the NCSBN Board of Directors: June 1–2, 2000, NCSBN Archives, Chicago, IL, 7.

81. Minutes, Meeting of the NCSBN Board of Directors: August 12, 2000, NCSBN Archives, Chicago, IL, 2.

82. "Nur*sys*™ Update," *Council Connector* 1, no. 5 (2000): 4–5.

83. "Nur*sys*™ – What Have You Done for Me Lately?" *Council Connector* 1, no. 8 (2001): 8–9.

84. "Nur*sys*™ is Enhanced for Interstate Compact States," *Council Connector* 1, no. 10 (2001): 6.

85. Minutes, Meeting of the NCSBN Board of Directors, June 24–25, 2001, NCSBN Archives, Chicago, IL, 6.

86. Nursys™ Panel Increases Member Participation, Plans Conference," *Council Connector* 2, no. 1 (2002): 5.

87. Minutes, Meeting of the NCSBN Board of Directors: January 23–25, 2002, NCSBN Archives, Chicago, IL, 4.

88. Minutes, Meeting of the NCSBN Board of Directors: March 7, 2002, NCSBN Archives, Chicago, IL, 3.

89. Minutes, Meeting of the NCSBN Board of Directors: May 1–3, 2002, NCSBN Archives, Chicago, IL, 2.

90. Minutes, Meeting of the NCSBN Board of Directors: April 30–May 1, 2003, NCSBN Archives, Chicago, IL, 3.

91. "Report of Nur*sys*™ Advisory Panel," *NCSBN Business Book* (Chicago: NCSBN, 2003): 167.

92. "Online Public Access to Nursys™ Now Available," *Council Connector* 3, no. 1 (2003): 3.

93. Minutes, Meeting of the NCSBN Delegate Assembly: August 4–5, 1995, NCSBN Archives, Chicago, IL, 8.

94. Minutes, Meeting of the NCSBN Board of Directors: February 17–18, 1996, NCSBN Archives, Chicago, IL, 6–7.

95. Minutes, Meeting of the NCSBN Board of Directors: March 5, 1996, NCSBN Archives, Chicago, IL, 3.

96. Minutes, Meeting of the NCSBN Board of Directors: April 8, 1996, NCSBN Archives, Chicago, IL, 2.

97. Minutes, Meeting of the NCSBN Board of Directors: June 26–28, 1996, NCSBN Archives, Chicago, IL, 5.

98. "Report of the Nursing Regulation Task Force," *NCSBN Book of Reports* (Chicago: NCSBN, 1996): Tab 10K, 1–4.

99. "Report of the Telecommunications Issues Task Force," *NCSBN Book of Reports* (Chicago: NCSBN, 1996): Tab 10N, 1–10.

100. Minutes, Meeting of the NCSBN Delegate Assembly: August 20–23, 1997, NCSBN Archives, Chicago, IL, 12.

101. Minutes, Meeting of the NCSBN Delegate Assembly: August 9–10, 1996, NCSBN Archives, Chicago, IL, 7.

102. "National Council Task Force Studies Concept of Multistate Regulation," *Issues* 17, no. 4 (1996): 8–9.

103. Ibid.

104. Minutes, Meeting of the NCSBN Board of Directors: February 12–14, 1997, NCSBN Archives, Chicago, IL, 9.

105. Minutes, Meeting of the NCSBN Board of Directors: June 25–26, 1997, NCSBN Archives, Chicago, IL, 5.

106. Minutes, Meeting of the NCSBN Board of Directors: July 14, 1997, NCSBN Archives, Chicago, IL, 1–2.

107. Minutes Meeting of the NCSBN Delegate Assembly: August 20–23, 1997, NCSBN Archives, Chicago, IL, 9–10.

108. Thomas Neumann "President's Message," *Issues* 18, no. 3 (1997): 2.

109. Minutes, Meeting of the NCSBN Board of Directors: September 19, 1997, NCSBN Archives, Chicago, IL, 2.

110. Minutes, Meeting of the NCSBN Board of Directors: November 21, 1997, NCSBN Archives, Chicago, IL, 2.

111. Minutes, Meeting of the NCSBN Board of Directors: November 26, 1997, NCSBN Archives, Chicago, IL, 2.

112. Minutes, Meeting of the NCSBN Delegate Assembly: December 14–15, 1997, NCSBN Archives, Chicago, IL, 3–4.

113. Ibid., 4–5.

114. Ibid., 5.

115. "North Carolina Legislation Empowers Board of Nursing to Enter into Interstate Compacts," *Newsletter to the Member Boards* 17, no. 18 (1997): 1.

116. "American Nurses Association," *Newsletter to the Member Boards* 18, no. 3 (1998): 2–3.

117. Minutes, Meeting of the NCSBN Board of Directors: February 11–13, 1998, NCSBN Archives, Chicago, IL, 8.

118. Minutes, Meeting of the NCSBN Board of Directors: April 13, 1998, NCSBN Archives, Chicago, IL, 1–2.

119. Minutes, Meeting of the NCSBN Board of Directors: May 13–15, 1998, NCSBN Archives, Chicago, IL, 9.

120. Minutes, Meeting of the NCSBN Board of Directors: May 22, 1998, NCSBN Archives, Chicago, IL, 2.

121. Minutes, Meeting of the NCSBN Board of Directors: June 25–26, 1998, NCSBN Archives, Chicago, IL, 3–4.

122. Ibid., 6.

123. Minutes, Meeting of the NCSBN Board of Directors: August 1–8, 1998, NCSBN Archives, Chicago, IL, 3–4.

124. Minutes, Meeting of the NCSBN Delegate Assembly: August 5–8, 1998, NCSBN Archives, Chicago, IL, 7.

125. Thomas Neumann, "Report of the President," *NCSBN Business Book* (Chicago: NCSBN, 1998): Tab 5, 1–2.

126. "Report of the Mutual Recognition Master Plan Coordinating Group," *NCSBN Business Book* (Chicago: NCSBN, 1998): Tab 9, 29–80.

127. Ibid.

128. Ibid.

129. Thomas Neumann, "President's Message," *Issues* 19, no. 1 (1998): 2.

130. "Meetings at National and State Level Result in States Moving Forward to Implement Mutual Recognition," *Issues* 19, no. 4 (1998): 3.

131. Ibid.

132. Minutes, Meeting of the NCSBN Board of Directors: November 4–5, 1998, NCSBN Archives, Chicago, IL, 3 and 6.

133. Minutes, Meeting of the NCSBN Board of Directors: May 5–7, 1999, NCSBN Archives, Chicago, IL, 8.

134. Minutes, Meeting of the NCSBN Board of Directors: June 12, 1999, NCSBN Archives, Chicago, IL, 1.

135. Minutes, Meeting of the NCSBN Board of Directors: June 24–25, 1999, NCSBN Archives, Chicago, IL, 4.

136. Minutes, Meeting of the NCSBN Board of Directors: July 25, 1999, NCSBN Archives, Chicago, IL, 2.

137. Minutes, Meeting of the NCSBN Board of Directors: August 1, 1999, NCSBN Archives, Chicago, IL, 2.

138. "Report of Mutual Recognition Master Plan coordinating Group," *NCSBN Business Book* (Chicago: NCSBN, 1999): Tab 15, 1–9.

139. Minutes, Meeting of the NCSBN Board of Directors: February 23–24, 2000, NCSBN Archives, Chicago, IL, 6–7.

140. Minutes, Meeting of the NCSBN Board of Directors: March 9, 2000, NCSBN Archives, Chicago, IL, 2.

141. Minutes, Meeting of the NCSBN Board of Directors: June 1–2, 2000, NCSBN Archives, Chicago, IL, 3.

142. Minutes, Meeting of the NCSBN Board of Directors: June 16, 2000, NCSBN Archives, Chicago, IL, 2.

143. Minutes, Meeting of the NCSBN Board of Directors: October 2–3, 2001, NCSBN Archives, Chicago, IL, 4.

144. Minutes, Meeting of the NCSBN Board of Directors: January 23–25, 2002, NCSBN Archives, Chicago, IL, 7.

145. Minutes, Meeting of the NCSBN Board of Directors: June 25–27, 2002, NCSBN Archives, Chicago, IL, 4.

146. Minutes, Meeting of the NCSBN Delegate Assembly: August 13–17, NCSBN Archives, Chicago, IL, 14.

147. "Summary of Recommendations to the 2002 Delegate Assembly," *NCSBN Business Book* (Chicago, NCSBN, 2002): 14.

148. "Compact Information Available to Public," *Council Connector* 2, no. 2 (2003): 1.

149. Minutes, Meeting of the NCSBN Board of Directors: December 2–4, 2003, NCSBN Archives, Chicago, IL, 6.

150. Lavinia L. Dock, "What May We Expect from the Law?" *American Journal of Nursing* 1 (1900): 11.

Chapter Eleven

1.   "The Standing of the Nurse Anesthetist," *American Journal of Nursing* 17 (1917): 1152.

2.   Minutes, Meeting of the National Council of State Boards of Nursing, Inc. (NCSBN) Delegate Assembly: June 22–25, 1982, NCSBN Archives, Chicago, IL, 12.

3.   Minutes, Meeting of the NCSBN Board of Directors: September 20–21, 1982, NCSBN Archives, Chicago, IL, 6.

4.   "Report of the Nursing Practice and Standards (NP&S) Committee," *NCSBN Book of Reports* (Chicago: NCSBN, 1984): 159.

5.   "Report of NP&S Committee," *NCSBN Book of Reports* (Chicago: NCSBN, 1985): 120.

6.   Corinne F. Dorsey, "Boards of Nursing and the Regulation of Nurses in Advanced Practice" (paper presented at the Virginia Commonwealth University School of Nursing Centennial Conference, Richmond, VA, 1993): 1–19.

7.   Minutes, Meeting of the NCSBN Delegate Assembly: August 5–9, 1986, NCSBN Archives, Chicago, IL, 19.

8.   "Report of NP&S Committee," *NCSBN Book of Reports* (Chicago: NCSBN, 1986): 122–26.

9.   Dorsey, "Boards of Nursing," 14.

10. Minutes, Meeting of the NCSBN Board of Directors: November 5–7, 1990, NCSBN Archives, Chicago, IL, 9–10.

11. "Report of the Subcommittee to Study the Regulation of Advanced Nursing Practice," *NCSBN Book of Reports* Chicago: NCSBN, 1991): 53–54.

12. "Advanced Practice Survey Results, *Issues* 12, no. 2 (1991): 1, 13–14.

13. Minutes, Meeting of the NCSBN Board of Directors: December 9–10, 1991, NCSBN Archives, Chicago, IL, 3.

14. "Report of the Subcommittee," 1991, Tab 18, 53.

15. Minutes, Meeting of the NCSBN Board of Directors: February 20–23, 1992, NCSBN Archives, Chicago, IL, 6.

16. "Draft NCSBN Position Paper on the Licensure of Advanced Nursing Practice," February 5, 1992, 1–8, NCSBN Archives.

17. Minutes, Meeting of the NCSBN Board of Directors: May 6–8, 1992, NCSBN Archives, Chicago, IL, 6.

18. "Advanced Nursing Practice Leadership Roundtables," *Newsletter to the Member Boards* 12, no. 13 (1992): 1–2.

19. Minutes, Meeting of the NCSBN Delegate Assembly: August 18–22, 1992, NCSBN Archives, Chicago, IL, 18.

20. Leah L. Curtin, Editorial Opinion: "Advanced Licensure: Personal Plum or Public Shield," Nursing Management 23, no. 8 (1992): 7–8.

21. Nancy Sharp, "Second License for the Advanced Practice Nurse?" Nursing Management 23, no. 9 (1992): 28–29.

22. "Advanced Nursing Practice Discipline Survey Results," *Issues* 14.2 (1993): 1, 4–5 and 10.

23. "Report of the Subcommittee to study the regulation of advanced nursing practice," *Newsletter to the Member Boards* 13, no. 5 (1993): 3.

24. Minutes, Meeting of the NCSBN Board of Directors: March 8–10, 1993, NCSBN Archives, Chicago, IL, 7.

25. Vickie R. Sheets, "Second Licensure? ANA and NCSBN Debate the issue." *The American Nurse*, September 1993, 8.

26. Beverly Malone, "Second Licensure? ANA and NCSBN Debate the issue." *The American Nurse*, September 1993, 9.

27. Minutes, Meeting of the NCSBN Delegate Assembly: August 5–7, 1993, NCSBN Archives, Chicago, IL, 13.

28. "Report of the Subcommittee to Study the Regulation of Advanced Nursing Practice," *NCSBN Book of Reports* (Chicago: NCSBN, 1993): Tab 20, 9–22.

29. "Clearinghouse on Advanced Practice," *Newsletter to the Member Boards* 13, no. 24 (1993): 2.

30. "Clearinghouse on Advanced Practice," *Newsletter to the Member Boards* 14, no. 4 (1994): 4.

31. "American Nurses Association Ad Hoc Committee on Credentialing in Advanced Practice," *Newsletter to the Member Boards* 14, no. 7 (1994): 5.

32. Minutes, Meeting of the NCSBN Delegate Assembly: August 5–6, 1994, NCSBN Archives, Chicago, IL, 13.

33. "Task Force to Identify Core Competencies for Nurse Practitioners," *Newsletter to the Member Boards* 14, no. 25 (1994): 4.

34. Minutes, Meeting of the NCSBN Board of Directors: May 3–5, 1995, NCSBN Archives, Chicago, IL, 9.

35. "Report of Advanced Practice Registered Nurse (APRN) Task Force," *NCSBN Book of Reports* (Chicago: NCSBN, 1996): Tab 10A, 5–8.

36. "Report of Task Force to Identify Core Competencies for Nurse Practitioners," *NCSBN Book of Reports* (Chicago: NCSBN, 1995): Tab 10A, 3–11.

37. "Report of the Task Force to Study the Feasibility of a Core Competency Examination for Nurse Practitioners," *NCSBN Book of Reports* (Chicago: NCSBN, 1995): Tab. 10B, 1–5.

38. Minutes, Meeting of the NCSBN Delegate Assembly: August 4–5, 1995, NCSBN Archives, Chicago, IL, 5–6.

39. Ibid., 8.

40. Minutes, Meeting of the NCSBN Board of Directors: January 17–18, 1996, NCSBN Archives, Chicago, IL, 4.

41. "Report of APRN Task Force," *NCSBN Book of Reports* (Chicago: NCSBN, 1996): Tab 10A, 5–8.

42. Minutes, Meeting of the NCSBN Board of Directors: March 5, 1996, NCSBN Archives, Chicago, IL, 2.

43. *NCSBN Book of Reports*, 1996, Tab 10A, 5–8.

44. Ibid.

45. Ibid.

46. Minutes, Meeting of the NCSBN Board of Directors: April 8, 1996, NCSBN Archives, Chicago, IL, 2.

47. Minutes, Meeting of the NCSBN Board of Directors: May 8–10, 1996, NCSBN Archives, Chicago, IL, 4–5 and 8.

48. "APRN Coordinating Task Force," *Newsletter to the Member Boards* 16, no. 9 (1996): 4–5.

49. Virginia Trotter Betts to Marcia M. Rachel, 25 April 1996, NCSBN Archives, Chicago, IL.

50. Marcia M. Rachel to Virginia Trotter Betts, 1 May 1996, NCSBN Archives, Chicago, IL.

51. "APRN Coordinating Task Force," *Newsletter to the Member Boards* 16, no. 11 (1996): 5.

52. "Nurse Practitioner Certification Organizations Meeting," *Newsletter to the Member Boards* 16, no. 111 (1996): 2.

53. "Review of Nurse Practitioner Certification Exams," *Newsletter to the Member Boards* 16, no. 12 (1996): 2.

54. "Board Meeting Highlights," *Newsletter to the Member Boards* 16, no. 14 (1996): 1.

55. Minutes, Meeting of the NCSBN Board of Directors: August 4–10, 1996, NCSBN Archives, Chicago, IL, 2–3.

56. "Annual Meeting Schedule," *NCSBN Book of Reports* (Chicago: NCSBN, 1996): 1–3.

57. Minutes, Meeting of the NCSBN Delegate Assembly: August 9–10, 1996, NCSBN Archives, Chicago, IL, 7.

58. Minutes, Meeting of the NCSBN Board of Directors: August 11, 1996, NCSBN Archives, Chicago, IL, 1.

59. "Using Nurse Practitioner Certification for State Nursing Regulation: An Update," *Issues* 18, no. 1 (1997): 3, 10–11.

60. Minutes, Meeting of the NCSBN Board of Directors: May 14–16, 1997, NCSBN Archives, Chicago, IL, 9.

61. Minutes, Meeting of the NCSBN Board of Directors: June 25–26, 1997, NCSBN Archives, Chicago, IL, 3–4.

62. "Using NP Certification for State Nursing Regulation: An Update," NCSBN News Release, July 11, 1997, NCSBN Archives.

63. Minutes, Meeting of the NCSBN Board of Directors: February 11–13, 1998, NCSBN Archives, Chicago, IL, 3.

64. "Report of the Board of Directors," *NCSBN Business Book* (Chicago: NCSBN, 1998): Tab 9, 3.

65. "APRN Task Force News," *Newsletter to the Member Boards* 19, no. 1 (1999): 3.

66. Minutes, Meeting of the NCSBN Board of Directors: May 5–7, 1999, NCSBN Archives, Chicago, IL, 3.

67. "Report of APRN Task Force," *NCSBN Business Book* (Chicago: NCSBN, 1999): Tab 12, 1–12.

68. Minutes, Meeting of the NCSBN Board of Directors: June 24–25, 1999, NCSBN Archives, Chicago, IL, 3.

69. Minutes, Meeting of the NCSBN Board of Directors: October 14–15, 1999, NCSBN Archives, Chicago, IL, 4.

70. Minutes, Meeting of the NCSBN Board of Directors: December 1–3, 1999, NCSBN Archives, Chicago, IL, 2.

71. Minutes, Meeting of the NCSBN Board of Directors: April 10, 2000, NCSBN Archives, Chicago, IL, 1–2.

72. "Report of the Special Advanced Practice Task Force," *NCSBN Business Book* (Chicago: NCSBN, 2000): 131–32.

73. "APRN Task Force Develops Criteria," *Council Connector* 1, no. 5 (2000): 3.

74. Minutes, Meeting of the NCSBN Board of Directors: June 1–2, 2000, 4, NCSBN Archives, Chicago, IL.

75. Minutes, Meeting of the NCSBN Delegate Assembly: August 8–12, 2000, NCSBN Archives, Chicago, IL, 4.

76. "Report of the Nursing Practice and Education Committee," *NCSBN Book of Reports*, (Chicago: NCSBN 2000): 91–94.

77. "Advanced Practice Task Force Update," *Council Connector* 1, no. 2 (2001): 2–3.

78. "Waivers and Scope of Practice Discussed with American Nurses Credentialing Center," *Council Connector* 1, no. 16 (2001): 15–16.

79. "Report of the Advanced Practice Task Force," *NCSBN Business Book* (Chicago: NCSBN, 2001): 175–83.

80. Minutes, Meeting of the NCSBN Board of Directors: August 21, 2001, NCSBN Archives, Chicago, IL, 2.

81. Minutes, Meeting of the NCSBN Board of Directors: January 23–25, 2002, NCSBN Archives, Chicago, IL, 6.

82. Minutes, Meeting of the NCSBN Board of Directors: May 1–2, 2002, NCSBN Archives, Chicago, IL, 5.

83. Minutes, Meeting of the NCSBN Delegate Assembly: August 14–17, 2002, NCSBN Archives, Chicago, IL, 4.

84. "Position Paper on the Regulation of Advanced Practice Nursing," *NCSBN Business Book* (Chicago: NCSBN, 2002): 7.

85. Minutes, Meeting of the NCSBN Board of Directors: February 19–21, 2003, NCSBN Archives, Chicago, IL, 4.

86. Minutes, Meeting of the NCSBN Board of Directors: April 30–May 1, 2003, NCSBN Archives, Chicago, IL, 7–8.

87. Minutes, Meeting of the NCSBN Board of Directors: July 10, 2003, NCSBN Archives, Chicago, IL, 4.

88. "Regulatory Credentialing Barriers for Clinical Nurse Specialists (CNS)," testimony by Brenda L. Lyons, DNS, on behalf of National Association of Clinical Nurse Specialists, before the Federal Trade Commission, June 11, 2003, NCSBN Archives, Chicago, IL.

89. Donna M. Dorsey to David Hyman, July 31, 2003, NCSBN Archives, Chicago, IL.

90. "Report of the Advanced Practice Task Force," *NCSBN Business Book* (Chicago: NCSBN, 2003): 139.

91. Minutes, Meeting of the NCSBN Board of Directors: September 4–5, 2003, NCSBN Archives, Chicago, IL, 4.

Chapter Twelve

1. Annie Goodrich, "Address of the president of the American Nurses Association" *American Journal of Nursing* 17 (1917): 876–81.

2. Frances Stone, "Is There a Need for Another Class of Sick Attendants Besides Nurses?" *American Journal of Nursing* 17 (1917): 991–93.

3. Edith M. Ambrose, "How and Where Should Attendants be Trained?" *American Journal of Nursing* 17 (1917): 993–1002.

4. Sophia Palmer, "Virginia Leads in the Training and Licensing of Attendants," *American Journal of Nursing* 18 (1918): 857–58.

5. Minutes, Meeting of the National Council of State Boards of Nursing, Inc. (NCSBN) Board of Directors: July 6–8, 1978, NCSBN Archives, Chicago, IL, 7.

6. Kathleen Dwyer, "Report of the Area IV Director," *NCSBN Book of Reports* (Chicago: NCSBN, 1981).

7. Merlyn Maillian, "Report of Area III Director," *NCSBN Book of Reports* (Chicago: NCSBN, 1983): 39–40.

8. Lois O'Shea, "Report of Area IV Director," (NCSBN book of Reports: Chicago, 1983): 41–42.

9. Roger C. Nauert, "How DRG's Will Shape the Profession of Nursing," *Issues* 5, no. 2 (1984) 4–5.

10. Minutes, Meeting of the NCSBN Delegate Assembly: August 21–23, 1985, NCSBN Archives, Chicago, IL, 16.

11. "Questionnaire on Activity of Unlicensed Personnel," *Newsletter to the Member Boards* 3, no. 26 (1985): attachment.

12. "Report of the Nursing Practice and Standards (NP&S) Committee," *NCSBN Book of Reports* (Chicago: NCSBN, 1986): 122.

13. "Report on the Survey of Activities of Unlicensed Personnel," *NCSBN Book of Reports* (Chicago: NCSBN, 1986): 132–51.

14. Ibid.

15. Minutes, Meeting of the NCSBN Delegate Assembly: August 5–9, 1986, NCSBN Archives, Chicago, IL, 18.

16. "Report of NP&S Committee," *NCSBN Book of Reports* (Chicago: NCSBN, 1987): 221–29.

17. Minutes, Meeting of the NCSBN Delegate Assembly: August 26–29, 1987, NCSBN Archives, Chicago, IL, 18.

18. Minutes, Meeting of the NCSBN Board of Directors: February 2, 1990, NCSBN Archives, Chicago, IL, 1–2.

19. Minutes, Meeting of the NCSBN Board of Directors: April 30–May 2, 1990, NCSBN Archives, Chicago, IL, 3.

20. Minutes, Meeting of the NCSBN Delegate Assembly: August 7–11, 1990, NCSBN Archives, Chicago, IL, 7.

21. "Statement on Assistive Personnel to the Registered Nurse," Tri Council for Nursing, January 15, 1990, "Report of the Board of Directors," *NCSBN Book of Reports* (Chicago: NCSBN, 1990): Tab 4, 36.

22. Minutes, August 7–11, 1990, 12.

23. "Report of the Nursing Practice and Education (NP&E) Committee," *NCSBN Book of Reports* (Chicago: NCSBN, 1990): Tab 18, 1–11.

24. Minutes, Meeting of the NCSBN Delegate Assembly: July 30–August 2, 1991, NCSBN Archives, Chicago, IL, 15.

25. "Report of the NP&E Committee," *NCSBN Book of Reports* (Chicago: NCSBN, 1991): Tab 18, 15–16.

26. Minutes, Meeting of the NCSBN Delegate Assembly: August 18–22, 1992, NCSBN Archives, Chicago, IL, 18.

27. "Report of NP&E Committee," *NCSBN Book of Reports* (Chicago: NCSBN, 1994): Tab 13, 1–4.

28. Minutes, Meeting of the NCSBN Delegate Assembly: August 5–6, 1994, NCSBN Archives, Chicago, IL, 13.

29. Vicky Burbach, "Delegation in Nursing," *Issues* 15, no. 3. (1994): 7–8.

30. Minutes, Meeting of the NCSBN Delegate Assembly: August 4–5, 1995, NCSBN Archives, Chicago, IL, 2.

31. Minutes, Meeting of the NCSBN Board of Directors: November 21, 1995, NCSBN Archives, Chicago, IL, 2.

32. "Delegation: Concepts and Decision Making Process" *NCSBN Book of Reports* (Chicago: NCSBN, 1995): 1.

33. Ibid., 1–4.

34. Minutes, Meeting of the NCSBN Board of Directors: March 5, 1996, NCSBN Archives, Chicago, IL, 3.

35. Minutes, Meeting of the NCSBN Board of Directors: October 27–28, 1994, NCSBN Archives, Chicago, IL, 2.

36. "Report of Unlicensed Personnel Subcommittee," *NCSBN Book of Reports* (Chicago: NCSBN, 1995): Tab 9, 23–24.

37. "Report of the Unlicensed Assistive Personnel (UAP) Task Force," *NCSBN Book of Reports* (Chicago: NCSBN, 1996): Tab 10H, 1–18.

38. Minutes, meeting of the NCSBN Board of Directors: November 14–15, 1996, NCSBN Archives, Chicago, IL, 4.

39. Jennifer Bosma, "Report of Staff Activities," *NCSBN Book of Reports* (Chicago: NCSBN, 1997): Tab 5, 1–21.

40. "Report of the UAP Task Force," *NCSBN Book of Reports* (Chicago: NCSBN, 1997): Tab 10O, 1.

41. Heather Freise, ed., *Issues* 6, no.1 (1997).

42. Minutes, Meeting of the NCSBN Board of Directors: May 13–15, 1998, NCSBN Archives, Chicago, IL, 4.

43. Minutes, Meeting of the NCSBN Delegate Assembly: August 5–8, 1998, NCSBN Archives, Chicago, IL, 7.

44. "National Council Conducts Three Studies Examining aspects of Nursing Practice," *Issues* 19, no. 1 (1998): 4–6.

45. "Unlicensed Assistive Personnel Study," *Issues* 19, no. 4 (1998): 11.

46. "Communications," *Issues* 19, no. 1 (1998): 15.

47. "UAP Task Force Meets," *Newsletter to the Member Boards* 18, no. 1 (1998): 4.

48. "UAP Task Force Continuum of Care Paper on Web," *Newsletter to the Member Boards* 18, no. 14 (1998): 3.

49. Minutes, Meeting of the NCSBN Board of Directors: May 5–7, 1999, NCSBN Archives, Chicago, IL, 4.

50. Minutes, Meeting of the NCSBN Board of Directors: June 24–25, 1999, NCSBN Archives, Chicago, IL, 4–5.

51. "Supreme Court Decision May Impact UAP Use in School Nursing," *Insight* 8, no. 1 (1999): 1 and 7.

52. Minutes, Meeting of the NCSBN Board of Directors: October 2–3, 2001, NCSBN Archives, Chicago, IL, 2.

53. Minutes, Meeting of the NCSBN Board of Directors: April 30–May 1, 2003, NCSBN Archives, Chicago, IL, 3.

54. Minutes, Meeting of the NCSBN Board of Directors: September 4–5, 2003, NCSBN Archives, Chicago, IL, 3.

55. Ibid., 4.

56. Minutes, Meeting of the NCSBN Board of Directors: December 2–4, 2003, NCSBN Archives, Chicago, IL, 5–6.

57. Renatta Loquist, "President's Message," *Issues* 9, no. 2. (1988): 3.

58. Minutes, Meeting of the NCSBN Board of Directors: February 8–10, 1988, NCSBN Archives, Chicago, IL, 4.

59. "Nurse Aide Competency Evaluation Program Fact Sheet," *Newsletter to the Member Boards* 11, no. 8 (1991): attachment.

60. "Fact Sheet" 2.

61. "Task Force Appointed to Oversee Feasibility Study of Producing Nursing Assistants Competency Evaluation," *Newsletter to the Member Boards* 7, no. 10 (1988): 2.

62. "Report of NP&S Committee," *NCSBN Book of Reports* (Chicago: NCSBN, 1988): 189.

63. "Nurse Aide Competency Evaluation Program Update," *Newsletter to the Member Boards* 17, no. 23 (1988): 9.

64. Minutes, Meeting of the NCSBN Board of Directors: January 29–February 1, 1989, NCSBN Archives, Chicago, IL, 10.

65. Minutes, Meeting of the NCSBN Board of Directors: November 6–8, 1989, NCSBN Archives, Chicago, IL, 7–9.

66. Minutes, Meeting of the NCSBN Delegate Assembly: August 1–5, 1989, NCSBN Archives, Chicago, IL, 12.

67. "Report of Ad Hoc Nurse Aide Competency Evaluation Program (NACEP) Committee, *NCSBN Book of Reports* (Chicago: NCSBN, 1989): Tab 14, 1–3.

68. "Report of Subcommittee on Model Language for Nurse Aides," *NCSBN Book of Reports* (Chicago: NCSBN, 1990): Tab 20, 1–53.

69. Minutes, Meeting of the NCSBN Delegate Assembly: August 7–11, 1990, NCSBN Archives, Chicago, IL, 12.

70. Minutes, Meeting of the NCSBN Board of Directors: April 3, 1990, NCSBN Archives, Chicago, IL, 2.

71. "Report of Ad Hoc NACEP Committee," *NCSBN Book of Reports* (Chicago: NCSBN, 1990): 1–25.

72. "Conference on Nurse Aides/Assistants II a Success," *Newsletter to the Member Boards* 10, no. 19 (1990): 1–2.

73. "Directory of Nurse Aide Registries," *Newsletter to the Member Boards* 10, no. 3 (1990): attachment.

74. "Nurse Aide Competency Evaluation Program Committee Report," *Newsletter to the Member Boards* 10, no. 16 (1990): 1.

75. Minutes, Meeting of the NCSBN Board of Directors: April 2–4, 1991, NCSBN Archives, Chicago, IL, 9.

76. "Report of Ad Hoc NACEP Committee," *NCSBN Book of Reports* (Chicago: NCSBN, 1991): Tab 19, 1–8.

77. "Report of NACEP Committee," *NCSBN Book of Reports* (Chicago: NCSBN, 1992): Tab 13, 1–2.

78. Sharon Weisenbeck, "Chair's Forum," *Insight* 1, no. 1 (1992): 1–3.

79. Minutes, Meeting of the NCSBN Delegate Assembly: August 18–22, 1992, NCSBN Archives, Chicago, IL, 17.

80. Minutes, Meeting of the NCSBN Delegate Assembly: August 5–7, 1993, NCSBN Archives, Chicago, IL, 8.

81. "Report of NACEP Committee," *NCSBN Book of Reports* (Chicago: NCSBN, 1993): Tab 12, 1–2.

82. Minutes, Meeting of the NCSBN Board of Directors: June 6–8, 1994, NCSBN Archives, Chicago, IL, 5.

83. "National Council Holds 5th Annual Nurse Aide Conference," *Insight* 3, no. 1 (1994): 3.

84. "Report of the Nurse Aide Competency Evaluation Task Force," *NCSBN Book of Reports* (Chicago: NCSBN, 1995): Tab 10E, 1–2.

85. "School Nurse Delegatory Issues Inspire Numerous Questions," *Insight* 4, no. 1 (1995): 3 and 8.

86. Minutes, Meeting of the NCSBN Board of Directors: January 17–18, 1996, NCSBN Archives, Chicago, IL, 7.

87. "NACEP Staff Changes" *Newsletter to the Member Boards* 16, no. 23 (1996): 2.

88. Minutes, Meeting of the NCSBN Board of Directors: March 24, 2003, NCSBN Archives, Chicago, IL, 3.

89. "AMA Proposed Implementation Plan for Nursing Education and the Supply of Nursing Personnel in the United States," *Newsletter to the Member Boards* 8, no. 7 (1988): attachment.

90. Minutes, Meeting of the NCSBN Board of Directors: June 30, 1988, NCSBN Archives, Chicago, IL, 2.

91. Minutes, Meeting of the NCSBN Board of Directors: August 14–16, 1988, NCSBN Archives, Chicago, IL, 2.

92. Ibid., 10.

93. "Response to the American Medical Association's Proposal on Development of the Registered Care Technologist Role (RCT)," Minutes, Meeting of the NCSBN Board of Directors: August 14–16, 1988, attachment.

94. Minutes, Meeting of the NCSBN Delegate Assembly: August 16–22, 1988, NCSBN Archives, Chicago, IL, 22.

95. "Update on RCT Proposal," *Newsletter to the Member Boards* 9, no. 16 (1989): 3–4.

96. "RCT Program Discontinued," *Issues* 11, no. 3 (1990): 8.

Chapter Thirteen

1. Mary M. Riddle, "Why We Should Have State Registration for Nurses," *American Journal of Nursing* 7 (1907): 240–44.

2. Georgia Manning, "Surviving Disciplinary Hearings: A New Board Member's Primer," *Issues* 16, no. 2 (1995): 12–13 and 15.

3. Minutes, Meeting of the National Council of State Boards of Nursing, Inc. (NCSBN) Delegate Assembly: June 6–8, 1979, NCSBN Archives, Chicago, IL, 10.

4. Minutes, Meeting of the NCSBN Board of Directors: March 8–11, 1981, NCSBN Archives, Chicago, IL, 8.

5. "Report of Ad Hoc Committee to Research Limited License Provisions," *NCSBN Book of Reports* (Chicago: NCSBN, 1981).

6. Ibid.

7. Minutes, Meeting of the NCSBN Delegate Assembly: June 9–12, 1981, NCSBN Archives, Chicago, IL, 7.

8. Report of the Nursing Practice & Standards (NP&S) Committee, *NCSBN Book of Reports* (Chicago: NCSBN, 1982).

9. Kathleen Bellinger and Sharon Weisenbeck, "Limited License," *Issues* 5, no. 4 (1984): 4–7.

10. Minutes, Meeting of the NCSBN Board of Directors: April 9–11, 1980, NCSBN Archives, Chicago, IL, 7.

11. Minutes, Meeting of the NCSBN Board of Directors: June 2–3, 1980, NCSBN Archives, Chicago, IL, 3.

12. Eileen McQuaid, "Report of Executive Director," *NCSBN Book of Reports* (Chicago: NCSBN, 1981).

13. Minutes, Meeting of the NCSBN Board of Directors: December 12, 1983, NCSBN Archives, Chicago, IL, 10.

14. Minutes, Meeting of the NCSBN Board of Directors: May 23, 1983, NCSBN Archives, Chicago, IL, 8.

15. "First Computerized Disciplinary Data Report," *Newsletter to the Member Boards* 2, no. 26 (1984): 1.

16. Minutes, Meeting of the NCSBN Board of Directors: July 18, 1988, NCSBN Archives, Chicago, IL, 2.

17. Minutes, Meeting of the NCSBN Board of Directors: August 14–16, 1988, NCSBN Archives, Chicago, IL, 8–9.

18. Minutes, Meeting of the NCSBN Delegate Assembly: August 16–20, 1988, NCSBN Archives, Chicago, IL, 8.

19. "National data banks: the Health Care Quality Improvement Act," *Newsletter to the Member Boards* 7, no. 2 (1988): 2–3.

20. "National Practitioner Data Bank," *Newsletter to the Member Boards* 7, no. 25 (1988): 3–4 and attachment.

21. Minutes, Meeting of the NCSBN Board of Directors: January 29–February 1, 1989, NCSBN Archives, Chicago, IL, 4.

22. Minutes, Meeting of the NCSBN Board of Directors: February 12, 1990, NCSBN Archives, Chicago, IL, 1.

23. Minutes, Meeting of the NCSBN Board of Directors: April 30–May 2, 1990, NCSBN Archives, Chicago, IL, 3.

24. Minutes, Meeting of the NCSBN Delegate Assembly: August 7–11, 1990, NCSBN Archives, Chicago, IL, 7.

25. Minutes, Meeting of the NCSBN Board of Directors: April 2–4, 1991, NCSBN Archives, Chicago, IL, 5.

26. Minutes, Meeting of the NCSBN Delegate Assembly: July 30–August 2, 1991, NCSBN Archives, Chicago, IL, 7.

27. "NPDB Update," *Newsletter to the Member Boards* 11, no. 4 (1991): 3–4.

28. "National Council Disciplinary Data Bank Fact Sheet," *Newsletter to the Member Boards* 11, no. 8 (1991): attachment.

29. Minutes, Meeting of the NCSBN Delegate Assembly: August 18–22, 1992, NCSBN Archives, Chicago, IL, 17.

30. Minutes, Meeting of the NCSBN Board of Directors: April 26, 1993, NCSBN Archives, Chicago, IL, 2.

31. Minutes, Meeting of the NCSBN Delegate Assembly: August 5–7, 1993, NCSBN Archives, Chicago, IL, 8.

32. "NPDB Survey Results," Newsletters to the Member Boards 12, no. 11 (1992): 1–2.

33. Minutes, Meeting of the NCSBN Board of Directors: August 1–2 1994, NCSBN Archives, Chicago, IL, 3.

34. "DDB Update," *Newsletter to the Member Boards* 14, no. 1 (1994): 2.

35. Minutes, Meeting of the NCSBN Board of Directors: July 30–31, 1995, NCSBN Archives, Chicago, IL, 3.

36. "NPDE Section Five Implementation is Coming Soon!" Newsletter to the Member Board 16, no. 24 (1996): 2–3.

37. Minutes, Meeting of the NCSBN Board of Directors: March 11, 1997, NCSBN Archives, Chicago, IL, 2.

38. Minutes, Meeting of the NCSBN Board of Directors: June 25–26, 1997, NCSBN Archives, Chicago, IL, 4.

39. Minutes, Meeting of the NCSBN Board of Directors: August 17–18, 1997, NCSBN Archives, Chicago, IL, 2.

40. Minutes, Meeting of the NCSBN Delegate Assembly: August 20–23, 1997, NCSBN Archives, Chicago, IL, 14.

41. "Report of Disciplinary Data Bank Task Force," *NCSBN Book of Reports* (Chicago: NCSBN, 1997): Tab 10H, 1–2.

42. "Section 5 Rules Under Development," *Newsletter to the Member Boards* 17, no. 6 (1997): 3.

43. "Update on Review and Analysis of Proposed HIPDB Rules," *Newsletter to the Member Boards* 18, no. 24 (1998): 2.

44. Minutes, Meeting of the NCSBN Board of Directors: June 2, 1999, NCSBN Archives, Chicago, IL, 1.

45. Minutes, Meeting of the NCSBN Board of Directors: June 24–28, 1999, NCSBN Archives, Chicago, IL, 5.

46. Minutes, Meeting of the NCSBN Board of Directors: July 25, 1999, NCSBN Archives, Chicago, IL, 2.

47. Minutes, Meeting of the NCSBN Board of Directors: October 14–15, 1999, NCSBN Archives, Chicago, IL, 3.

48. Ibid., 4.

49. Minutes, Meeting of the NCSBN Board of Directors: December 1–3, 1999, NCSBN Archives, Chicago, IL, 4.

50. Minutes, Meeting of the NCSBN Board of Directors: March 9, 2000, NCSBN Archives, Chicago, IL, 1.

51. "Report on Agent Role–Health Integrity and Protection Data Bank (HIPDB) Reporting," *NCSBN Business Book* (Chicago: NCSBN, 2001): 201–08.

52. Minutes, Meeting of the NCSBN Board of Directors: September 4–5, 2003, NCSBN Archives, Chicago, IL, 4.

53. Kathleen Dwyer, "Report of Area IV Director," *NCSBN Book of Reports* (Chicago: NCSBN, 1981).

54. "Nurse Fined $100 for Violation of Registration Act," *American Journal of Nursing* 30 (1930): 584.

55. "Nursing Imposter, Drug Use Discussed by Discipline Resources Task Force," *Council Connector* 3, no. 1 (2003): 4.

56. Minutes, Meeting of the NCSBN Board of Directors: December 12–14, 1983, NCSBN Archives, Chicago, IL, 9.

57. "Convention Program," *NCSBN Book of Reports* (Chicago: NCSBN, 1983): 1.

58. "Position Paper of the Council Review Committee on NCSBN's Objectives and Structure," *NCSBN Book of Reports* (Chicago: NCSBN, 1983): 61–83.

59. Minutes, Meeting of the NCSBN Board of Directors: April 29–May 2, 1984, NCSBN Archives, Chicago, IL, 9–10.

60. "Report of Disciplinary Task Force," *NCSBN Book of Reports* (Chicago: NCSBN, 1984): 67.

61. Minutes, Meeting of the NCSBN Delegate Assembly: August 27–29, 1984, NCSBN Archives, Chicago, IL, 17.

62. "Report of the Disciplinary Task Force," *NCSBN Book of Reports* (Chicago: NCSBN, 1985): 83.

63. Minutes, Meeting of the NCSBN Board of Directors: April 22–24, 1986, NCSBN Archives, Chicago, IL, 8.

64. "Report of Disciplinary Task Force, *NCSBN Book of Reports* (Chicago: NCSBN, 1986): 54–60.

65. "1986 Convention Schedule," *NCSBN Book of Reports* (Chicago: NCSBN, 1986): 3.

66. Minutes, Meeting of the NCSBN Delegate Assembly: August 5–7, 1993, NCSBN Archives, Chicago, IL, 12.

67. Minutes, Meeting of the NCSBN Delegate Assembly: August 5–6, 1994, NCSBN Archives, Chicago, IL, 12.

68. "Health Resources and Services Administration (HRSA) Project Begins," *Newsletter to the Member Boards* 14, no. 19 (1994): 1–2.

69. "External Funding Obtained to Study the Effectiveness of Nurse Disciplinary Actions," *Issues* 16, no. 1 (1995): 13.

70. Minutes, Meeting of the NCSBN Delegate Assembly: August 9–10, 1996, NCSBN Archives, Chicago, IL, 8.

71. "Report of the Nursing Practice and Education (NP&E) Committee," *NCSBN Book of Reports* (Chicago: NCSBN, 1996): Tab 9, 1–3.

72. "Report of the Complex Discipline Cases Subcommittee," *NCSBN Book of Reports* (Chicago: NCSBN, 1996): Tab 9, 23–24.

73. "Complex Discipline Topic Chosen for Educational Program," *Newsletter to the Member Boards* 16, no. 2 (1996): 3.

74. "Report of Disciplinary Modules Task Force," *NCSBN Book of Reports* (Chicago: NCSBN, 1997): Tab 10I, 1–9.

75. Minutes, Meeting of the NCSBN Delegate Assembly: August 5–8, 1998, NCSBN Archives, Chicago, IL, 5.

76. Ibid., 7.

77. "Annual Meeting Schedule," *NCSBN Book of Reports* (Chicago: NCSBN, 1998): Tab 1, 1–2.

78. "Report of Discipline Resources Subcommittee," *NCSBN Book of Reports* (Chicago: NCSBN, 1998): Tab 7, 29–45.

79. "Boards of Nursing Releases Report of Study of Effectiveness of Disciplinary Actions of Nursing," *Newsletter to the Member Boards* 19, no. 26 (1999): attachment.

80. "Report of Disciplinary Issues Task Force," *NCSBN Business Book* (Chicago: NCSBN, 2000): 127.

81. "Report of the Practice Breakdown Research Advisory Task Force," *NCSBN Business Book* (Chicago: NCSBN, 2001): 223–35.

82. Minutes, Meeting of the NCSBN Board of Directors: May 1–3, 2002, NCSBN Archives, Chicago, IL, 5.

83. "Strategic Initiatives and Annual Progress Report," *NCSBN Business Book* (Chicago, NCSBN, 2002): 58.

84. "Report of Discipline Curriculum Advisory Panel," *NCSBN Business Book* (Chicago, NCSBN, 2002): 233–34.

85. Minutes, Meeting of the NCSBN Board of Directors: April 30–May 1, 2003, NCSBN Archives, Chicago, IL, 7.

86. Minutes, Meeting of the NCSBN Board of Directors: December 2–4, 2003, NCSBN Archives, Chicago, IL, 6–7.

87. "Report of Disciplinary Resources Task Force," *NCSBN Business Book* (Chicago: NCSBN, 2003, 147–48.

88. "Report of Practice Breakdown Research Group," *NCSBN Business Book* (Chicago, NCSBN, 2003): 169.

89. Minutes, Meeting of the NCSBN Board of Directors: June 22–25, 1982, NCSBN Archives, Chicago, IL, 11.

90. NCSBN Model Nursing Practice Act as adopted in 1982.

91. "Report of Committee on Disciplinary Case Reporting by Federal Agencies," *NCSBN Book of Reports* (Chicago: NCSBN, 1983): 93.

92. Minutes, Meeting of the NCSBN Delegate Assembly: August 23–26, 1983, NCSBN Archives, Chicago, IL, 17.

93. "Report of Committee on the Disciplinary Case Reporting by Federal Agencies," *NCSBN Book of Reports* (Chicago: NCSBN, 1984): 77.

94. "Chemical Dependency Seminar," *Newsletter to the Member Boards* 1, no. 16 (1983): 3.

95. "Four Interest Groups Attract NCSBN Delegates," *Issues* 5, no. 3 (1984) 4–5.

96. Minutes, Meeting of the NCSBN Board of Directors: August 24–25, 1984, NCSBN Archives, Chicago, IL, 7.

97. Minutes, Meeting of the NCSBN Board of Directors: August 18–20, 1985, NCSBN Archives, Chicago, IL, 6.

98. "Schedule for Annual Meeting," *NCSBN Book of Reports* (Chicago: NCSBN, 1985): 2.

99. "Report of Nursing Practice and Standards (NP&S) Committee," *NCSBN Book of Reports* (Chicago: NCSBN, 1985): 120.

100. Sister Lucie Leonard, "Regulating the Nursing Practice of Chemically Addicted Nurses," *Issues* 7, no. 3 (1986): 1–3.

101. Minutes, Meeting of the NCSBN Delegate Assembly: August 26–29, 1987, NCSBN Archives, Chicago, IL, 18.

102. "Report of NP&S Committee, *NCSBN Book of Reports* (Chicago: NCSBN, 1987): 230–94.

103. Minutes, Meeting of the NCSBN Delegate Assembly: August 16–20, 1988, NCSBN Archives, Chicago, IL, 21.

104. "Report of Subcommittee to Study Regulatory Models for Chemically Dependent Nurses," *NCSBN Book of Reports* (Chicago: NCSBN, 1989): Tab 15, 1–3.

105. Minutes, Meeting of the NCSBN Board of Directors: November 6–8, 1989, NCSBN Archives, Chicago, IL, 5.

106. Minutes, Meeting of the NCSBN Board of Directors: December 20, 1989, NCSBN Archives, Chicago, IL, 4.

107. Minutes, Meeting of the NCSBN Delegate Assembly: August 1–5, 1989, NCSBN Archives, Chicago, IL, 13.

108. Minutes, Meeting of the NCSBN Delegate Assembly: August 7–11, 1990, NCSBN Archives, Chicago, IL, 12.

109. "Report of Subcommittee to Study Regulatory Models for Chemically Dependent Nurses," *NCSBN Book of Reports* (Chicago: NCSBN, 1993): 23–24.

110. Minutes, Meeting of the NCSBN Board of Directors: August 8, 1993, NCSBN Archives, Chicago, IL, 2.

111. Minutes, Meeting of the NCSBN Board of Directors: June 6–8, 1994, NCSBN Archives, Chicago, IL, 7.

112. "Report of Committee on Chemical Dependency Issues," *NCSBN Book of Reports* (Chicago: NCSBN, 1994): Tab 18, 1–92.

113. Minutes, Meeting of the NCSBN Delegate Assembly: August 5–6, 1994, NCSBN Archives, Chicago, IL, 10.

114. "Report of Committee," Tab 18: 1–92.

115. Minutes, Meeting of the NCSBN Delegate Assembly: August 5–6, 1994, NCSBN Archives, Chicago, IL, 10.

116. Minutes, Meeting of the NCSBN Board of Directors: August 7, 1994, NCSBN Archives, Chicago, IL, 3.

117. "Report of Task Force on Chemical Dependency Issues," *NCSBN Book of Reports* (Chicago: NCSBN, 1995): Tab 10F, 1.

118. "Report of the Chemically Impaired Nurse Issues Task Force," *NCSBN Book of Reports* (Chicago: NCSBN, 1996): Tab 10I, 1–22.

119. "Annual Progress Report," *NCSBN Business Book* (Chicago: NCSBN, 2003): 51–64.

120. "New Study Planned on Regulatory Oversight of Chemically Dependent Nurses," *Council Connector* 3, no. 6 (2003): 1.

121. "Effectiveness of Nurse Disciplinary Action by Boards of Nursing," *Newsletter to the Member Boards* 14, no. 4 (1994): 3.

122. "Report of Discipline Modules Task Force," *NCSBN Book of Reports* (Chicago: NCSNB, 1997): Tab 10H, 1–2.

123. "Video on Chemical Dependency Issues is Released," *Council Connector* 1, no. 12 (2001): 1.

124. State Board Representatives to Discuss Discipline," *American Journal of Nursing* 65 (1965): 56.

125. Minutes, Meeting of the NCSBN Delegate Assembly: August 5–7, 1993, NCSBN Archives, Chicago, IL, 10.

126. Minutes, Meeting of the NCSBN Board of Directors: December 1–2, 1993, NCSBN Archives, Chicago, IL, 5.

127. Minutes, Meeting of the NCSBN Board of Directors: March 7–9, 1994, NCSBN Archives, Chicago, IL, 4.

128. "Report of Task Force to Develop an Educational Program for Disciplinary Investigators," *NCSBN Book of Reports* (Chicago: NCSBN, 1994): Tab 19, 37–38.

129. "Specialized Health Care Investigators Program Held," *Newsletter to the Member Boards* 14, no. 22 (1994): 2–3.

130. "1995 Annual Meeting Schedule" *NCSBN Book of Reports* (Chicago: NCSBN, 1995): 1–4.

131. "Annual Meeting Schedule," *NCSBN Business Book* (Chicago: NCSBN, 1999): Tab 1, 1–5.

132. "Report of the Board Investigators Curriculum Advisory Panel," *NCSBN Business Book* (Chicago: NCSBN, 2001): 191–93.

133. Minutes, Meeting of the NCSBN Board of Directors: August 5, 2001, NCSBN Archives, Chicago, IL, 2.

134. "Report of Discipline Curriculum Advisory Panel," *NCSBN Business Book* (Chicago: NCSBN, 2002): 233–35.

135. Minutes, Meeting of the NCSBN Delegate Assembly: August 5–6, 1994, NCSBN Archives, Chicago, IL, 12.

136. Minutes, Meeting of the NCSBN Board of Directors: May 3–5, 1995, NCSBN Archives, Chicago, IL, 4–5.

137. "Report of the Sexual Misconduct Focus Group," *NCSBN Book of Reports* (Chicago: NCSBN, 1996): Tab 10L, 1–3.

Chapter Fourteen

1. "The Research Agenda of the National Council of State Boards of Nursing [NCSBN]", *Issues* 12, no. 11 (1991): 10.

2. Ibid.

3. "Report of the Board of Directors," *NCSBN Book of Reports* (Chicago: NCSBN, 1983): 46.

4. Minutes, Meeting of the NCSBN Board of Directors: October 26, 1987, NCSBN Archives, Chicago, IL, 8.

5. Minutes, Meeting of the NCSBN Board of Directors: February 10–12, 1987, NCSBN Archives, Chicago, IL, 12.

6. Minutes, Meeting of the NCSBN Board of Directors: October 26, 1987, NCSBN Archives, Chicago, IL, 1.

7. "The National Council Welcomes New Director of Research Services," *Newsletter to the Member Boards* 20, no. 3 (2000): 1.

8. Minutes, Meeting of the NCSBN Board of Directors: March 7–9, 1994, NCSBN Archives, Chicago, IL, 3.

9. Minutes, Meeting of the NCSBN Board of Directors: February 1–3, 1995, NCSBN Archives, Chicago, IL, 3.

10. "Report of Research Advisory Panel," *NCSBN Book of Reports* (Chicago: NCSBN, 1996): Tab 10G, 1–10.

11. Minutes, Meeting of the NCSBN Board of Directors: March 7, 2002, NCSBN Archives, Chicago, IL, 2.

12. Minutes, Meeting of the NCSBN Board of Directors: August 24–25, 1984, NCSBN Archives, Chicago, IL, 12.

13. "Profiles of Member Boards 2002," *NCSBN Book of Reports* (Chicago: NCSBN, 2003).

14. Minutes, Meeting of the NCSBN Board of Directors: June 20–22, 1982, NCSBN Archives, Chicago, IL, 4.

15. Minutes, Meeting of the NCSBN Board of Directors: August 21–22 and 25, 1983, NCSBN Archives, Chicago, IL, 8.

16. Minutes, Meeting of the NCSBN Board of Directors: January 24–26, 1983, NCSBN Archives, Chicago, IL, 13.

17. "Continuing Professional Education Development (CPED) Project," *NCSBN Book of Reports* (Chicago: NCSBN, 1984): 79–80.

18. "CPED Project," *NCSBN Book of Reports* (Chicago: NCSBN, 1985): 80–82.

19. Minutes, Meeting of the NCSBN Board of Directors: April 29–May 2, 1984, NCSBN Archives, Chicago, IL, 5.

20. Minutes, Meeting of the NCSBN Board of Directors: August 24–25, 1984, NCSBN Archives, Chicago, IL, 2.

21. Ibid., 14.

22. Minutes, Meeting of the NCSBN Board of Directors: February 11–13, 1985, NCSBN Archives, Chicago, IL, 2.

23. Minutes, Meeting of the NCSBN Board of Directors: August 3–4, 1986, NCSBN Archives, Chicago, IL, 5–6.

24. Minutes, Meeting of the NCSBN Delegate Assembly: August 5–9, 1986, NCSBN Archives, Chicago, IL, 6.

25. Michael Kane, PhD, et al., *A Study of Nursing Practice and Role Delineation and Job Analysis of Entry–Level Performance of Registered Nurses*, (Chicago: NCSBN, 1986): 1.1.

26. "ACT Study Reviewed," *Issues* 7, no. 4 (1986): 10–11.

27. Ibid.

28. "Report of Board of Directors," *NCSBN Book of Reports* (Chicago: NCSBN, 1987): 50.

29. Minutes, Meeting of the NCSBN Delegate Assembly: August 26–29, 1987, NCSBN Archives, Chicago, IL, 11–12.

30. Minutes, Meeting of the NCSBN Board of Directors: June 16, 1986, NCSBN Archives, Chicago, IL, 2.

31. Michael T. Kane and Dean A. Colton, *Job Analysis of Newly Licensed Practical/Vocational Nurses*, 1986–1987 (Chicago: NCSBN, 1988): 1.1.

32. Minutes, Meeting of the NCSBN Board of Directors: August 3–4, 1986, NCSBN Archives, Chicago, IL, 5–6.

33. Kane, *A Study of Nursing*, 1.2.

34. Ibid.

35. Ibid., 1.4–1.5.

36. Minutes, Meeting of the NCSBN Board of Directors: February 8–10, 1988, NCSBN Archives, Chicago, IL, 12–13.

37. "Report of the Examination Committee," *NCSBN Book of Reports* (Chicago: NCSBN, 1988): 175–83.

38. "Liaison Meeting with Sigma Theta Tau," *Newsletter to the Member Boards* 14, no. 6 (1994): 4.

39. "Meeting of National Nursing Research Roundtable," *Newsletter to the Member Boards* 14, no. 7 (1994): 6.

40. Minutes, Meeting of the NCSBN Board of Directors: June 21–23, 1995, NCSBN Archives, Chicago, IL, 8.

41. Jennifer Bosma, Report of staff activities. *NCSBN Book of Reports* (Chicago: NCSBN, 1996): Tab 5, 5.

42. Minutes, Meeting of the NCSBN Delegate Assembly: August 9–10, 1996, NCSBN Archives, Chicago, IL, 7.

43. "FNP Project Completed," *Issues* 19, no.1 (1998): 10.

44. "Commitment to Public Protection Through Excellence in Nursing Regulation," *Issues* 19, no. 1 (1998): 1.

45.   Minutes, Meeting of the NCSBN Board of Directors: February 11–13, 1998, NCSBN Archives, Chicago, IL, 7.

46.   Minutes, Meeting of the NCSBN Board of Directors: November 4–5, 1998, NCSBN Archives, Chicago, IL, 6.

47.   "Advisory Committee Reviews Final Report of Phase I – Commitment to Excellence Project," *Newsletter to the Member Boards* 18, no. 20 (1998): 2.

48.   "Commitment to Public Protection Through Excellence in Nursing Regulation Project," *NCSBN Business Book* (Chicago: NCSBN, 1999): Tab 9, 1–4.

49.   Minutes, Meeting of the NCSBN Board of Directors: December 1–3, 1999, NCSBN Archives, Chicago, IL, 3.

50.   "Report of the Commitment to Public Protection Through Excellence in Nursing Regulation Advisory Group," *NCSBN Business Book* (Chicago: NCSNB, 2000): 123.

51.   Minutes, Meeting of the NCSBN Board of Directors: February 23–24, 2000, NCSBN Archives, Chicago, IL, 3.

52.   Minutes, Meeting of the NCSBN Board of Directors: June 1–2, 2000, NCSBN Archives, Chicago, IL, 2.

53.   "Report of Commitment," 2000, 123.

54.   Minutes, Meeting of the NCSBN Board of Directors: January 10–12, 2001, NCSBN Archives, Chicago, IL, 2.

55.   Minutes, Meeting of the NCSBN Board of Directors: April 4, 2001, NCSBN Archives, Chicago, IL, 2.

56.   Minutes, Meeting of the NCSBN Board of Directors: May 6–8, 2001, NCSBN Archives, Chicago, IL, 5.

57.   "Report of the Commitment to Public Protection Through Excellence in Nursing Regulation Advisory Group," *NCSBN Business Book* (Chicago: NCSBN, 2001): 195–96.

58.   Minutes, Meeting of the NCSBN Board of Directors: January 23–25, 2002, NCSBN Archives, Chicago, IL, 5.

59.   Minutes, Meeting of the NCSBN Board of Directors: April 30,–May 1, 2003, NCSBN Archives, Chicago, IL, 7.

60.   "Strengthening Nursing Education to Improve End of Life Care," *Issues* 20, no. 1 (1999): 2.

61.   Minutes, Meeting of the NCSBN Board of Directors: September 19, 2002, NCSBN Archives, Chicago, IL, 1.

62.   Minutes, Meeting of the NCSBN Board of Directors: December 2–4, 2002, NCSBN Archives, Chicago, IL, 6.

63.   Minutes, Meeting of the NCSBN Board of Directors: August 14–16, 1988, NCSBN Archives, Chicago, IL, 4–5.

64.   Minutes, Meeting of the NCSBN Board of Directors: July 6–7, 1989, NCSBN Archives, Chicago, IL, 5.

65.   Minutes, Meeting of the NCSBN Board of Directors: July 16–17, 1990, NCSBN Archives, Chicago, IL, 7.

66.   Minutes, Meeting of the NCSBN Board of Directors: February 11–13, 1991, NCSBN Archives, Chicago, IL, 3.

67. Minutes, Meeting of the NCSBN Board of Directors: June 16–19, 1991, NCSBN Archives, Chicago, IL, 6.

68. "Major Actions of the 1992 Delegate Assembly," *Issues* 13, no. 3 (1992): 3.

69. Jennifer Bosma, "Report of the Executive Director," *NCSBN Book of Reports* (Chicago: NCSBN, 1993): Tab 5, 2.

70. "Role Delineation Study Preliminary Report," *NCSBN Book of Reports* (Chicago: NCSBN, 1993): 1–48.

71. "Validation Study: Functional Abilities Essential for Nursing Practice," *NCSBN Book of Reports* (Chicago: NCSBN, 1996): Tab 9, 1–40.

72. "Supplemental Report of the Continued Competence Subcommittee," *NCSBN Book of Reports* (Chicago: NCSBN, 1996): Tab 9, 67–68.

73. Minutes, Meeting of the NCSBN Board of Directors: August 31, 2001, NCSBN Archives, Chicago, IL, 3.

74. Minutes, Meeting of the NCSBN Board of Directors: January 23–25, 2002, NCSBN Archives, Chicago, IL, 5.

75. Minutes, Meeting of the NCSBN Board of Directors: March 7, 2002, NCSBN Archives, Chicago, IL, 2.

76. "New NCSBN Research Data is Significant," *Council Connector* 2, no. 3 (2002): 1.

77. "NCSBN Staff to Present Research to International Audience," *Council Connector* 2, no. 4 (2002): 2.

78. Minutes, Meeting of the NCSBN Board of Directors: May 23–25, 1983, NCSBN Archives, Chicago, IL, 5.

79. "Report of the Board of Directors," *NCSBN Book of Reports* (Chicago: NCSBN, 1983): 61.

80. Minutes, Meeting of the NCSBN Board of Directors: August 24–25, 1984, NCSBN Archives, Chicago, IL, 6.

81. Minutes, Meeting of the NCSBN Board of Directors: May 6–8, 1985, NCSBN Archives, Chicago, IL, 4–5.

82. "First Independent Survey of NC Membership Needs Completed," *Issues* 6, no. 1 (1985): 1–4.

83. Minutes, Meeting of the NCSBN Board of Directors: February 8–10, 1988, NCSBN Archives, Chicago, IL, 5.

84. Minutes, Meeting of the NCSBN Board of Directors: March 7–9, 1994, NCSBN Archives, Chicago, IL, 5.

85. Minutes, Meeting of the NCSBN Board of Directors: June 6–8, 1994, NCSBN Archives, Chicago, IL, 4.

86. Minutes, March 7–9, 1994, 5.

87. Bosma, J. "Report of Staff Activities," *NCSBN Book of Reports* (Chicago: NCSBN, 1994): 17–91.

88. Minutes, Meeting of the NCSBN Board of Directors: October 27–28, 1994, NCSBN Archives, Chicago, IL, 3.

89. Minutes, Meeting of the NCSBN Board of Directors: January 7, 2000, NCSBN Archives, Chicago, IL, 1.

90. Minutes, Meeting of the NCSBN Board of Directors: February 23–24, 2000, NCSBN Archives, Chicago, IL, 2.

91. Minutes, Meeting of the NCSBN Board of Directors: March 9, 2000, NCSBN Archives, Chicago, IL, 1.

92. Minutes, Meeting of the NCSBN Board of Directors: January 23–25, 2002, NCSBN Archives, Chicago, IL, 5.

93. Minutes, Meeting of the NCSBN Board of Directors: August 12, 2002, NCSBN Archives, Chicago, IL, 3.

94. Minutes, Meeting of the NCSBN Board of Directors: February 19–21, 2003, NCSBN Archives, Chicago, IL, 3.

Chapter Fifteen

1.   Renatta Loquist, "President's Message," *Issues* 7, no. 2 (1988): 2.

2.   Minutes, Meeting of the National Council of State Boards of Nursing, Inc. (NCSBN) Board of Directors: March 8–10, 1982, NCSBN Archives, Chicago, IL, 4.

3.   Patricia VanBetten and Melisa Morierity, *Nursing Illuminations–A Book of Days* (St. Louis: Mosby, 2004): 134–36.

4.   Minutes, Meeting of the NCSBN Delegate Assembly: June 4–6, 1980, NCSBN Archives, Chicago, IL, 11.

5.   Minutes, Meeting of the NCSBN Board of Directors: March 8–10, 1982, NCSBN Archives, Chicago, IL, 4.

6.   Minutes, Meeting of the NCSBN Board of Directors: June 25, 1982, NCSBN Archives, Chicago, IL, 4.

7.   Minutes, Meeting of the NCSBN Board of Directors: January 24–26, 1983, NCSBN Archives, Chicago, IL, 2.

8.   Ibid., 11.

9.   Minutes, Meeting of the NCSBN Board of Directors: May 23–25, 1983, NCSBN Archives, Chicago, IL, 3.

10. Ibid.

11. Minutes, Meeting of the NCSBN Board of Directors: November 8–9, 1984, NCSBN Archives, Chicago, IL, 2.

12. Minutes, Meeting of the NCSBN Board of Directors: May 6–8, 1985, NCSBN Archives, Chicago, IL, 11.

13. "Report of Board of Directors," *NCSBN Book of Reports* (Chicago: NCSBN, 1986): 42.

14. "Ninth Annual Delegate Assembly Convention Held in Chicago," *Issues* 8, no. 5 (1987): 1–2 and 4.

15. Minutes, Meeting of the NCSBN Board of Directors: May 13–15, 1998, NCSBN Archives, Chicago, IL, 9.

16. "National Council Concludes Annual Meeting," *Issues* 19, no. 3 (1998): 4.

17. Minutes, Meeting of the NCSBN Board of Directors: February 10–12, 1987, NCSBN Archives, Chicago, IL, 9.

18. Minutes, Meeting of the NCSBN Board of Directors: April 2–4, 1991, NCSBN Archives, Chicago, IL, 5.

19. Minutes, Meeting of the NCSBN Board of Directors: March 8–10, 1993, NCSBN Archives, Chicago, IL, 6.

20. Minutes, Meeting of the NCSBN Board of Directors: June 7–9, 1993, NCSBN Archives, Chicago, IL, 3.

21. Minutes, Meeting of the NCSBN Board of Directors: November 11, 2000, NCSBN Archives, Chicago, IL, 1–2.

22. "Report of Awards Panel," *NCSBN Business Book* (Chicago: NCSBN, 2001): 185–89.

23. Minutes, Meeting of the NCSBN Board of Directors: February 14, 2001, NCSBN Archives, Chicago, IL, 1.

24. Minutes, Meeting of the NCSBN Board of Directors: January 23–25, 2002, NCSBN Archives, Chicago, IL, 8.

25. Minutes, Meeting of the NCSBN Board of Directors: May 1–3, 2002, NCSBN Archives, Chicago, IL, 2.

26. Minutes, Meeting of the NCSBN Board of Directors: June 25–27, 2002, NCSBN Archives, Chicago, IL, 2.

27. "Report of Awards Recognition Panel," *NCSBN Business Book* (Chicago: NCSBN, 2002): 229.

28. Minutes, June 25–27, 2002, 2.

29. Minutes, Meeting of the NCSBN Board of Directors: September 4–5, 2002, NCSBN Archives, Chicago, IL, 2.

30. "Report of Awards Panel," *NCSBN Business Book* (Chicago: NCSBN, 2003): 143.

31. "Awards Presented to NCSNB Leaders," *Issues* 4, no. 3 (1983): 5.

32. Minutes, Meeting of the NCSBN Delegate Assembly: June 6–8, 1979, NCSBN Archives, Chicago, IL, 8–11.

33. Minutes, Meeting of the NCSBN Delegate Assembly: June 22–25, 1982, NCSBN Archives, Chicago, IL, 12.

34. Minutes, Meeting of the NCSBN Delegate Assembly: August 27–29, 1984, NCSBN Archives, Chicago, IL, 2.

35. Ibid., 18.

36. Minutes, Meeting of the NCSBN Delegate Assembly: August 1–5, 1989, NCSBN Archives, Chicago, IL, 16.

37. "Summary of Major Actions and Activities of 1993 Annual Meeting," *Newsletter to the Member Boards* 13, no. 16 (1993) attachment.

38. Minutes, Meeting of the NCSBN Board of Directors: August 1–2, 1994, NCSBN Archives, Chicago, IL, 4.

39. Minutes, Meeting of the NCSBN Delegate Assembly: August 5–6, 1994, NCSBN Archives, Chicago, IL, 154.

40. Minutes, Meeting of the NCSBN Board of Directors: February 10–12, 1987, NCSBN Archives, Chicago, IL, 9.

41. "Report of Board of Directors," *NCSBN Book of Reports* (Chicago: NCSBN, 1988): 51.

42. "Honors bestowed during memorable awards luncheon," *Issues* 10, no. 4 (1989): 6.

43. Joyce Schowalter, "Report of the Vice President," *NCSBN Book of Reports* (Chicago: NCSBN, 1982): 17.

44. "CLEAR Honors the National Council," *Newsletter to the Member Boards* 10, no. 20 (1990): 3.

45. "National Council Receives National Leadership Award," *Newsletter to the Member Boards* 19, no. 22 (1999): 1.

46. "Award Received at National Council," *Newsletter to the Member Boards* 19, no. 2 (1999): 1.47v"Breaking the Habit Wins STTI Award," *Council Connector* 2, no. 6 (2002): 5.

48. Minutes, Meeting of the NCSBN Board of Directors: September 20–21, 1982, NCSBN Archives, Chicago, IL, 6.

49. Gertrude Malone, Shirley Fondiller and David Heidorn, *From an Idea to an Organization*, (Chicago: NCSBN, 1983).

50. "NCSBN's First Five Years Celebrated at 1983 Convention," *Issues* 4, no. 3 (1983): 1–3.

51. Minutes, Meeting of the NCSBN Board of Directors: February 8–10, 1988, NCSBN Archives, Chicago, IL, 7 and 1.

52. Shirley Fondiller, *The Promise Continues: A Decade of Progress*, (Chicago: NCSBN, 1988).

53. Renatta Loquist, "President's Message," *Issues* 9, no. 2 (1988): 3.

54. Minutes, Meeting of the NCSBN Board of Directors: July 13–15, 1992, NCSBN Archives, Chicago, IL, 10.

55. Minutes, Meeting of the NCSBN Board of Directors: February 11–13, 1998, NCSBN Archives, Chicago, IL, 4.

56. "National Council Concludes Annual Meeting," *Issues* 19, no. 3 (1998): 1 and 4–5.

57. *The Road Traveled for Twenty Years*, (Chicago: NCSBN, 1998).

58. Minutes, Meeting of the NCSBN Board of Directors: August 12, 2000, NCSBN Archives, Chicago, IL.

59. Minutes, Meeting of the NCSBN Board of Directors: October 2–3, 2001, NCSBN Archives, Chicago, IL, 3.

60. Minutes, Meeting of the NCSBN Board of Directors: January 23–25, 2002, NCSBN Archives, Chicago, IL, 3.

61. Ibid., 8–9.

62. Minutes, Meeting of the NCSBN Board of Directors: February 19–21, 2003, NCSBN Archives, Chicago, IL, 3.

63. "Report of the Twenty–Fifth Anniversary Planning Advisory Panel," *NCSBN Business Book* (Chicago: NCSBN, 2003): 165.

64. National Council of State Boards of Nursing, *1978–2003: 25 Years of the National Council of State Boards of Nursing: Honoring Our Past to Create Our Future*, (Chicago: NCSBN, 2003).

INDEX